Stanley Gibb
Commonwealth Stam

New Zealand
& Dependencies

6th edition 2016

STANLEY GIBBONS LTD
London and Ringwood

By Appointment to
Her Majesty The Queen
Philatelists
Stanley Gibbons Ltd
London

Published by Stanley Gibbons Ltd
Editorial, Publications Sales Offices
and Distribution Centre:
7 Parkside, Christchurch Road, Ringwood,
Hants BH24 3SH

© Stanley Gibbons Ltd 2016

British Library Cataloguing in
Publication Data.
A catalogue record for this book is available
from the British Library.

1st Edition - 2003
2nd Edition - 2006
3rd Edition - 2009
4th Edition - 2010
5th Edition - 2014
6th Edition - 2016

Errors and omissions excepted
the colour reproduction of stamps is only as
accurate as the printing process will allow.

ISBN-10: 0-85259-998-6
ISBN-13: 978-0-85259-998-3

Item No. R2876-16

Printed by
Park Communications, London

Contents

Stanley Gibbons Holdings Plc

Stanley Gibbons Limited, Stanley Gibbons Auctions
399 Strand, London WC2R 0LX
Tel: +44 (0)207 836 8444
Fax: +44 (0)207 836 7342
E-mail: help@stanleygibbons.com
Website: www.stanleygibbons.com
for all departments, Auction and Specialist Stamp Departments.

Open Monday–Friday 9.30 a.m. to 5 p.m.
Shop. Open Monday–Friday 9 a.m. to 5.30 p.m. and Saturday 9.30 a.m. to 5.30 p.m.

Stanley Gibbons Publications Gibbons Stamp Monthly and Philatelic Exporter
7 Parkside, Christchurch Road, Ringwood, Hampshire BH24 3SH.
Tel: +44 (0)1425 472363
Fax: +44 (0)1425 470247
E-mail: help@stanleygibbons.com
Publications Mail Order.
FREEPHONE 0800 611622

Monday–Friday 8.30 a.m. to 5 p.m.

Stanley Gibbons (Guernsey) Limited
18–20 Le Bordage, St Peter Port, Guernsey GY1 1DE.
Tel: +44 (0)1481 708270
Fax: +44 (0)1481 708279
E-mail: investment@stanleygibbons.com

Stanley Gibbons (Jersey) Limited
18 Hill Street, St Helier, Jersey, Channel Islands JE2 4UA.
Tel: +44 (0)1534 766711
Fax: +44 (0)1534 766177
E-mail: investment@stanleygibbons.com

Stanley Gibbons (Asia) Limited
Room 618, 6/F,
100 Queen's Road Central Central,
Hong Kong
Tel: +852 3180 9370
E-mail: elee@stanleygibbons.com

Stanley Gibbons Publications Overseas Representation
Stanley Gibbons Publications are represented overseas by the following

Australia *Renniks Publications PTY LTD*
Unit 3 37-39 Green Street, Banksmeadow, NSW 2019, Australia
Tel: +612 9695 7055
Website: www.renniks.com

Canada *Unitrade Associates*
99 Floral Parkway, Toronto, Ontario M6L 2C4, Canada
Tel: +1 416 242 5900
Website: www.unitradeassoc.com

Germany *Schaubek Verlag Leipzig*
Am Glaeschen 23, D-04420 Markranstaedt, Germany
Tel: +49 34 205 67823
Website: www.schaubek.de

Italy *Ernesto Marini S.R.L.*
V. Struppa, 300, Genova, 16165, Italy
Tel: +3901 0247-3530
Website: www.ernestomarini.it

Japan *Japan Philatelic*
PO Box 2, Suginami-Minami, Tokyo 168-8081, Japan
Tel: +81 3330 41641
Website: www.yushu.co.jp

Netherlands also covers Belgium Denmark, Finland & France
Uitgeverij Davo BV
PO Box 411, Ak Deventer, 7400 Netherlands
Tel: +315 7050 2700
Website: www.davo.nl

New Zealand *House of Stamps*
PO Box 12, Paraparaumu, New Zealand
Tel: +61 6364 8270
Website: www.houseofstamps.co.nz

New Zealand *Philatelic Distributors*
PO Box 863
15 Mount Edgecumbe Street
New Plymouth 4615, New Zealand
Tel: +6 46 758 65 68
Website: www.stampcollecta.com

Norway *SKANFIL A/S*
SPANAV. 52 / BOKS 2030
N-5504 HAUGESUND, Norway
Tel: +47-52703940
E-mail: magne@skanfil.no

Singapore *C S Philatelic Agency*
Peninsula Shopping Centre #04-29
3 Coleman Street, 179804, Singapore
Tel: +65 6337-1859
Website: www.cs.com.sg

South Africa *Peter Bale Philatelics*
P O Box 3719, Honeydew, 2040, South Africa
Tel: +27 11 462 2463
Tel: +27 82 330 3925
E-mail: balep@iafrica.com

Sweden *Chr Winther Sorensen AB*
Box 43, S-310 20 Knaered, Sweden
Tel: +46 43050743
Website: www.collectia.se

USA *Regency Superior Ltd*
229 North Euclid Avenue
Saint Louis, Missouri 63108, USA

PO Box 8277, St Louis,
MO 63156-8277, USA
Toll Free Tel: (800) 782-0066
Tel: (314) 361-5699
Website: www.RegencySuperior.com
Email: info@regencysuperior.com

Stanley Gibbons
Stamp Catalogues

Stamps of the World 1
the World
Simplified Catalogue · 2017 Edition
Stamps from over 730
countries Illustrated

2017 Stanley Gibbons Stamp Catalogue
COMMONWEALTH & BRITISH EMPIRE STAMPS 1840-1970
STANLEY GIBBONS

The vital reference work for Commonwealth collectors
Thousands of price increases
Hundreds of new items listed

We have catalogues to suit every aspect of stamp collecting

Our catalogues cover stamps issued from across the globe - from the Penny Black to the latest issues. Whether you're a specialist in a certain reign or a thematic collector, we should have something to suit your needs. All catalogues include the famous SG numbering system, making it as easy as possible to find the stamp you're looking for.

Commonwealth & British Empire Stamps 1840–1970 (119th edition, 2017)

Commonwealth Country Catalogues

Australia & Dependencies
(10th Edition, 2016)
Bangladesh, Pakistan & Sri Lanka
(3rd edition, 2015)
Belize, Guyana, Trinidad & Tobago
(2nd edition, 2013)
Brunei, Malaysia & Singapore
(4th edition, 2013)
Canada (6th edition, 2016)
Cyprus, Gibraltar & Malta
(4th edition, 2014)
East Africa with Egypt & Sudan
(3rd edition, 2014)
Eastern Pacific (3rd edition, 2015)
Falkland Islands (7th edition, 2016)
Hong Kong (5th edition, 2015)
India (including Convention & Feudatory States) (4th edition, 2013)
Indian Ocean (3rd edition, 2016)
Ireland (6th edition, 2015)
Leeward Islands (2nd edition, 2012)
New Zealand (6th edition, 2016)
Northern Caribbean, Bahamas & Bermuda (4th edition, 2016)
St. Helena & Dependencies
(5th edition, 2014)
Southern & Central Africa
(2nd edition, 2014)
West Africa (2nd edition, 2012)
Western Pacific (3rd edition, 2014)
Windward Islands & Barbados
(3rd edition, 2015)

Stamps of the World 2017

Volume 1 Abu Dhabi – Charkhari
Volume 2 Chile – Georgia
Volume 3 German Commands – Jasdan
Volume 4 Jersey – New Republic
Volume 5 New South Wales – Singapore
Volume 6 Sirmoor – Zululand

Great Britain Catalogues

2017 Collect British Stamps
(68th edition, 2017)

Collect Channel Islands & Isle of Man
(30th edition, 2016)
Great Britain Concise Stamp Catalogue
(31st edition, 2016)

Great Britain Specialised

Volume 1 *Queen Victoria*
(16th edition, 2012)
Volume 2 *King Edward VII to King George VI*
(14th edition, 2015)
Volume 3 *Queen Elizabeth II Pre-decimal issues*
(12th edition, 2011)
Volume 4 *Queen Elizabeth II Decimal Definitive Issues – Part 1*
(10th edition, 2008)
Queen Elizabeth II Decimal Definitive Issues – Part 2 (10th edition, 2010)

Foreign Countries

Arabia (1st edition, 2016)
Austria & Hungary (8th edition, 2014)
Balkans (5th edition, 2009)
Belgium & Luxembourg
(1st edition, 2015)
Central America (3rd edition, 2007)
Central Asia (4th edition, 2006)
China (11th edition, 2015)
Czech Republic, Slovakia & Poland
(7th edition, 2012)
France, Andorra and Monaco
(1st edition, 2015)
French Colonies (1st edition, 2016)
Germany (11th edition, 2014)
Italy & Switzerland (8th edition, 2013)
Japan & Korea (5th edition, 2008)
Portugal & Spain (6th edition, 2011)
Poland (1st edition, 2015)
Russia (7th edition, 2014)
Scandinavia (7th edition, 2013)
South America (4th edition, 2008)
South-East Asia (5th edition, 2012)
United States of America
(8th edition, 2015)

General Philatelic Information and Guidelines to the Scope of Stanley Gibbons Commonwealth Catalogues

These notes reflect current practice in compiling the Stanley Gibbons Commonwealth Catalogues.

The Stanley Gibbons Stamp Catalogue has a very long history and the vast quantity of information it contains has been carefully built up by successive generations through the work of countless individuals. Philately is never static and the Catalogue has evolved and developed over the years. These notes relate to the current criteria upon which a stamp may be listed or priced. These criteria have developed over time and may have differed somewhat in the early years of this catalogue. These notes are not intended to suggest that we plan to make wholesale changes to the listing of classic issues in order to bring them into line with today's listing policy, they are designed to inform catalogue users as to the policies currently in operation.

PRICES

The prices quoted in this Catalogue are the estimated selling prices of Stanley Gibbons Ltd at the time of publication. They are, unless it is specifically stated otherwise, for examples in fine condition for the issue concerned. Superb examples are worth more; those of a lower quality considerably less.

All prices are subject to change without prior notice and Stanley Gibbons Ltd may from time to time offer stamps below catalogue price. Individual low value stamps sold at 399 Strand are liable to an additional handling charge. Purchasers of new issues should note the prices charged for them contain an element for the service rendered and so may exceed the prices shown when the stamps are subsequently catalogued. Postage and handling charges are extra.

No guarantee is given to supply all stamps priced, since it is not possible to keep every catalogued item in stock. Commemorative issues may, at times, only be available in complete sets and not as individual values.

Quotation of prices. The prices in the left-hand column are for unused stamps and those in the right-hand column are for used.

A dagger (†) denotes that the item listed does not exist in that condition and a blank, or dash, that it exists, or may exist, but we are unable to quote a price. We welcome information concerning items which are currently unpriced; such assistance may lead to them being priced in future editions.

Prices are expressed in pounds and pence sterling. One pound comprises 100 pence (£1 = 100p).

The method of notation is as follows: pence in numerals (e.g. 10 denotes ten pence); pounds and pence, up to £100, in numerals (e.g. 4·25 denotes four pounds and twenty-five pence); prices above £100 are expressed in whole pounds with the '£' sign shown.

Unused stamps. Great Britain and Commonwealth: the prices for unused stamps of Queen Victoria to King George V are for lightly hinged examples. Unused prices for King Edward VIII, King George VI and Queen Elizabeth issues are for unmounted mint.

Some stamps from the King George VI period are often difficult to find in unmounted mint condition. In such instances we would expect that collectors would need to pay a high proportion of the price quoted to obtain mounted mint examples. Generally speaking lightly mounted mint stamps from this reign, issued before 1945, are in considerable demand.

Used stamps. The used prices are normally for stamps fine postally used, which for the vast majority of those issued since 1900 refers to cancellation with a clear circular or oval dated postmark. It may also include stamps cancelled to order, where this practice exists, or with commemorative or 'first day' postmarks.

A pen-cancellation on early issues can sometimes correctly denote postal use. Instances are individually noted in the Catalogue in explanation of the used price given.

Prices quoted for bisects on cover or large piece are for those dated during the period officially authorised.

Stamps not sold unused to the public (e.g. some official stamps) are priced used only.

The use of 'unified' designs, that is stamps inscribed for both postal and fiscal purposes, results in a number of stamps of very high face value. In some instances these may not have been primarily intended for postal purposes, but if they are so inscribed we include them. We only price such items used, however, where there is evidence of normal postal usage.

Cover prices. To assist collectors, cover prices are quoted for issues up to 1945 at the beginning of each country.

The system gives a general guide in the form of a factor by which the corresponding used price of the basic loose stamp should be multiplied when found in fine average condition on cover.

Care is needed in applying the factors and they relate to a cover which bears a single of the denomination listed; if more than one denomination is present the most highly priced attracts the multiplier and the remainder are priced at the simple figure for used singles in arriving at a total.

The cover should be of non-philatelic origin; bearing the correct postal rate for the period and distance involved and cancelled with the markings normal to the offices concerned. Purely philatelic items have a cover value only slightly greater than the catalogue value for the corresponding used stamps. This applies generally to those high-value stamps used philatelically rather than in the normal course of commerce. Low-value stamps, e.g. ¼d. and ½d., are desirable when used as a single rate on cover and merit an increase in 'multiplier' value.

First day covers in the period up to 1945 are not within the scope of the system and the multiplier should not be used. As a special category of philatelic usage, with wide variations in valuation according to scarcity, they require separate treatment.

Oversized covers, difficult to accommodate on an album page, should be reckoned as worth little more than the corresponding value of the used stamps. The condition of a cover also affects its value. Except for 'wreck covers', serious damage or soiling reduce the value where the postal markings and stamps are ordinary ones. Conversely, visual appeal adds to the value and this can include freshness of appearance, important addresses, old-fashioned but legible hand-writing, historic town-names, etc.

The multipliers are a base on which further value would be added to take account of the cover's postal historical importance in demonstrating such things as unusual, scarce or emergency cancels, interesting routes, significant postal markings, combination usage, the development of postal rates, and so on.

Minimum price. The minimum catalogue price quoted is 10p. For individual stamps prices between 10p. and 95p. are provided as a guide for catalogue users. The lowest price charged for individual stamps or sets purchased from Stanley Gibbons Ltd is £1.

Set prices. Set prices are generally for one of each value, excluding shades and varieties, but including major colour changes. Where there are alternative shades, etc., the cheapest is usually included. The number of stamps in the set is always stated for clarity. The prices for sets containing *se-tenant* pieces are based on the prices quoted for such combinations, and not on those for the individual stamps.

Varieties. Where plate or cylinder varieties are priced in used condition the price quoted is for a fine used example with the cancellation well clear of the listed flaw.

Specimen stamps. The pricing of these items is explained under that heading.

Stamp booklets. Prices are for complete assembled booklets in fine condition with those issued before 1945 showing normal wear and tear. Incomplete booklets and those which have been 'exploded' will, in general, be worth less than the figure quoted.

Repricing. Collectors will be aware that the market factors of supply and demand directly influence the prices quoted in this Catalogue. Whatever the scarcity of a particular stamp, if there is no one in the market who wishes to buy, it cannot be expected to achieve a high price. Conversely, the same item actively sought by numerous potential buyers may cause the price to rise.

All the prices in this Catalogue are examined during the preparation of each new edition by the expert staff of Stanley Gibbons and repriced as necessary. They take many factors into account, including supply and demand, and are in close touch with the international stamp market and the auction world.

Commonwealth cover prices and advice on postal history material originally provided by Edward B Proud.

GUARANTEE

All stamps are guaranteed originals in the following terms:

If not as described, and returned by the purchaser, we undertake to refund the price paid to us in the original transaction. If any stamp is certified as genuine by the Expert Committee of the Royal Philatelic Society, London, or by BPA Expertising Ltd, the purchaser shall not be entitled to make any claim against us for any error, omission or mistake in such certificate.

Consumers' statutory rights are not affected by the above guarantee.

The recognised Expert Committees in this country are those of the Royal Philatelic Society, 41 Devonshire Place, London W1G, 6JY, and BPA Expertising Ltd, PO Box 1141, Guildford, Surrey GU5 0WR. They do not undertake valuations under any circumstances and fees are payable for their services.

MARGINS ON IMPERFORATE STAMPS

Superb   Very fine   Fine   Average   Poor

GUM

Unmounted   Very lightly mounted   Lightly mounted   Mounted/ large part original gum (o.g.).   Heavily mounted small part o.g.

CENTRING

Superb   Very fine   Fine   Average   Poor

CANCELLATIONS

Superb   Very fine   Fine   Average   Poor

Superb   Very fine

Fine   Average   Poor

CONDITION GUIDE

To assist collectors in assessing the true value of items they are considering buying or in reviewing stamps already in their collections, we now offer a more detailed guide to the condition of stamps on which this catalogue's prices are based.

For a stamp to be described as 'Fine', it should be sound in all respects, without creases, bends, wrinkles, pin holes, thins or tears. If perforated, all perforation 'teeth' should be intact, it should not suffer from fading, rubbing or toning and it should be of clean, fresh appearance.

Margins on imperforate stamps: These should be even on all sides and should be at least as wide as half the distance between that stamp and the next. To have one or more margins of less than this width, would normally preclude a stamp from being described as 'Fine'. Some early stamps were positioned very close together on the printing plate and in such cases 'Fine' margins would necessarily be narrow. On the other hand, some plates were laid down to give a substantial gap between individual stamps and in such cases margins would be expected to be much wider.

An 'average' four-margin example would have a narrower margin on one or more sides and should be priced accordingly, while a stamp with wider, yet even, margins than 'Fine' would merit the description 'Very Fine' or 'Superb' and, if available, would command a price in excess of that quoted in the catalogue.

Gum: Since the prices for stamps of King Edward VIII, King George VI and Queen Elizabeth are for 'unmounted' or 'never hinged' mint, even stamps from these reigns which have been very lightly mounted should be available at a discount from catalogue price, the more obvious the hinge marks, the greater the discount.

Catalogue prices for stamps issued prior to King Edward VIII's reign are for mounted mint, so unmounted examples would be worth a premium. Hinge marks on 20th century stamps should not be too obtrusive, and should be at least in the lightly mounted category. For 19th century stamps more obvious hinging would be acceptable, but stamps should still carry a large part of their original gum—'Large part o.g.'—in order to be described as 'Fine'.

Centring: Ideally, the stamp's image should appear in the exact centre of the perforated area, giving equal margins on all sides. 'Fine' centring would be close to this ideal with any deviation having an effect on the value of the stamp. As in the case of the margins on imperforate stamps, it should be borne in mind that the space between some early stamps was very narrow, so it was very difficult to achieve accurate perforation, especially when the technology was in its infancy. Thus, poor centring would have a less damaging effect on the value of a 19th century stamp than on a 20th century example, but the premium put on a perfectly centred specimen would be greater.

Cancellations: Early cancellation devices were designed to 'obliterate' the stamp in order to prevent it being reused and this is still an important objective for today's postal administrations. Stamp collectors, on the other hand, prefer postmarks to be lightly applied, clear, and to leave as much as possible of the design visible. Dated, circular cancellations have long been 'the postmark of choice', but the definition of a 'Fine' cancellation will depend upon the types of cancellation in use at the time a stamp was current—it is clearly illogical to seek a circular datestamp on a Penny Black.

'Fine', by definition, will be superior to 'Average', so, in terms of cancellation quality, if one begins by identifying what 'Average' looks like, then one will be half way to identifying 'Fine'. The illustrations will give some guidance on mid-19th century and mid-20th century cancellations of Great Britain, but types of cancellation in general use in each country and in each period will determine the appearance of 'Fine'.

As for the factors discussed above, anything less than 'Fine' will result in a downgrading of the stamp concerned, while a very fine or superb cancellation will be worth a premium.

Combining the factors: To merit the description 'Fine', a stamp should be fine in every respect, but a small deficiency in one area might be made up for in another by a factor meriting an 'Extremely Fine' description.

Some early issues are so seldom found in what would normally be considered to be 'Fine' condition, the catalogue prices are for a slightly lower grade, with 'Fine' examples being worth a premium. In such cases a note to this effect is given in the catalogue, while elsewhere premiums are given for well-centred, lightly cancelled examples.

In the 21st century many postal administrations seem to feel that there is little need for stamps to be legibly cancelled and ink-jet markings, heavy obliterations and pen cancellations are very much the order of the day, while a large proportion of stamps are left without a postal marking of any kind. Used stamps of this type are of very little value and the prices shown in this catalogue are for clear circular operational date stamps or appropriate commemorative cancellations, although the latter are also frowned upon by many collectors.

Stamps graded at less than fine remain collectable and, in the case of more highly priced stamps, will continue to hold a value. Nevertheless, buyers should always bear condition in mind.

The Catalogue in General

Contents. The Catalogue is confined to adhesive postage stamps, including miniature sheets. For particular categories the rules are:

(a) Revenue (fiscal) stamps are listed only where they have been expressly authorised for postal duty.

(b) Stamps issued only precancelled are included, but normally issued stamps available additionally with precancel have no separate precancel listing unless the face value is changed.

(c) Stamps prepared for use but not issued, hitherto accorded full listing, are nowadays foot-noted with a price (where possible).

(d) Bisects (trisects, etc.) are only listed where such usage was officially authorised.

(e) Stamps issued only on first day covers or in presentation packs and not available separately are not listed but may be priced in a footnote.

(f) New printings are only included in this Catalogue where they show a major philatelic variety, such as a change in shade, watermark or paper. Stamps which exist with or without imprint dates are listed separately; changes in imprint dates are mentioned in footnotes.

(g) Official and unofficial reprints are dealt with by footnote.

(h) Stamps from imperforate printings of modern issues which occur perforated are covered by footnotes, but are listed where widely available for postal use.

Exclusions. The following are excluded:

(a) non-postal revenue or fiscal stamps;

(b) postage stamps used fiscally (although prices are now given for some fiscally used high values);

(c) local carriage labels and private local issues;

(d) bogus or phantom stamps;

(e) railway or airline letter fee stamps, bus or road transport company labels or the stamps of private postal companies operating under licence from the national authority;

(f) cut-outs;

(g) all types of non-postal labels and souvenirs;

(h) documentary labels for the postal service, e.g. registration, recorded delivery, air-mail etiquettes, etc.;

(i) privately applied embellishments to official issues and privately commissioned items generally;

(j) stamps for training postal officers.

Full listing. 'Full listing' confers our recognition and implies allotting a catalogue number and (wherever possible) a price quotation.

In judging status for inclusion in the catalogue broad considerations are applied to stamps. They must be issued by a legitimate postal authority, recognised by the government concerned, and must be adhesives valid for proper postal use in the class of service for which they are inscribed. Stamps, with the exception of such categories as postage dues and officials, must be available to the general public, at face value, in reasonable quantities without any artificial restrictions being imposed on their distribution.

For errors and varieties the criterion is legitimate (albeit inadvertent) sale through a postal administration in the normal course of business. Details of provenance are always important; printers' waste and deliberately manufactured material are excluded.

Certificates. In assessing unlisted items due weight is given to Certificates from recognised Expert Committees and, where appropriate, we will usually ask to see them.

Date of issue. Where local issue dates differ from dates of release by agencies, 'date of issue' is the local date. Fortuitous stray usage before the officially intended date is disregarded in listing.

Catalogue numbers. Stamps of each country are catalogued chronologically by date of issue. Subsidiary classes are placed at the end of the country, as separate lists, with a distinguishing letter prefix to the catalogue number, e.g. D for postage due, O for official and E for express delivery stamps.

The catalogue number appears in the extreme left-column. The boldface Type numbers in the next column are merely cross-references to illustrations. A catalogue number with a suffix will normally relate to the main number, so 137a will be a variant of No. 137, unless the suffix appears as part of the number in the left-hand column such as Great Britain No. 20a, in which case that should be treated as the main number. A number with multiple suffixes will relate to the first letter or letters of that suffix, so 137ab will be a variant of 137a and 137aba a variant of 137ab. The exception is an "aa" suffix, which will precede an "a" and always refers to the main number, so 137aa relates to 137, not 137a.

Once published in the Catalogue, numbers are changed as little as possible; really serious renumbering is reserved for the occasions when a complete country or an entire issue is being rewritten. The edition first affected includes cross-reference tables of old and new numbers.

Our catalogue numbers are universally recognised in specifying stamps and as a hallmark of status.

Illustrations. Stamps are illustrated at three-quarters linear size. Stamps not illustrated are the same size and format as the value shown, unless otherwise indicated. Stamps issued only as miniature sheets have the stamp alone illustrated but sheet size is also quoted. Overprints, surcharges, watermarks and postmarks are normally actual size. Illustrations of varieties are often enlarged to show the detail. Stamp booklet covers are illustrated half-size, unless otherwise indicated.

Designers. Designers' names are quoted where known, though space precludes naming every individual concerned in the production of a set. In particular, photographers supplying material are usually named only where they also make an active contribution in the design stage; posed photographs of reigning monarchs are, however, an exception to this rule.

CONTACTING THE CATALOGUE EDITOR

The editor is always interested in hearing from people who have new information which will improve or correct the Catalogue. As a general rule he must see and examine the actual stamps before they can be considered for listing; photographs or photocopies are insufficient evidence.

Submissions should be made in writing to the Catalogue Editor, Stanley Gibbons Publications at the Ringwood office. The cost of return postage for items submitted is appreciated, and this should include the registration fee if required.

Where information is solicited purely for the benefit of the enquirer, the editor cannot undertake to reply if the answer is already contained in these published notes or if return postage is omitted. Written communications are greatly preferred to enquiries by telephone or e-mail and the editor regrets that he or his staff cannot see personal callers without a prior appointment being made. Correspondence may be subject to delay during the production period of each new edition.

The editor welcomes close contact with study circles and is interested, too, in finding reliable local correspondents who will verify and supplement official information in countries where this is deficient.

We regret we do not give opinions as to the genuineness of stamps, nor do we identify stamps or number them by our Catalogue.

TECHNICAL MATTERS

The meanings of the technical terms used in the catalogue will be found in our *Philatelic Terms Illustrated*.

References below to (more specialised) listings are to be taken to indicate, as appropriate, the Stanley Gibbons *Great Britain Specialised Catalogue* in five volumes or the *Great Britain Concise Catalogue*.

1. Printing

Printing errors. Errors in printing are of major interest to the Catalogue. Authenticated items meriting consideration would include: background, centre or frame inverted or omitted; centre or subject transposed; error of colour; error or omission of value; double prints and impressions; printed both sides; and so on. Apparent "double prints" including overprints, on stamps printed by offset litho arising from movement of the rubber "blanket" involved in this process are however, outside the scope of this catalogue, although they may be included in more specialised listings. Designs *tête-bêche*, whether intentionally or by accident, are listable. *Se-tenant* arrangements of stamps are recognised in the listings or footnotes. Gutter pairs (a pair of stamps separated by blank margin) are not included in this volume. Colours only partially omitted are not listed. Stamps with embossing omitted are reserved for our more specialised listings.

Printing varieties. Listing is accorded to major changes in the printing base which lead to completely new types. In recess-printing this could be a design re-engraved; in photogravure or photolithography a screen altered in whole or in part. It can also encompass flat-bed and rotary printing if the results are readily distinguishable.

To be considered at all, varieties must be constant.

Early stamps, produced by primitive methods, were prone to numerous imperfections; the lists reflect this, recognising re-entries, retouches, broken frames, misshapen letters, and so on. Printing technology has, however, radically improved over the years, during which time photogravure and lithography have become predominant. Varieties nowadays are more in the nature of flaws and these, being too specialised for this general catalogue, are almost always outside the scope.

In no catalogue, however, do we list such items

as: dry prints, kiss prints, doctor-blade flaws, colour shifts or registration flaws (unless they lead to the complete omission of a colour from an individual stamp), lithographic ring flaws, and so on. Neither do we recognise fortuitous happenings like paper creases or confetti flaws.

"Varieties of varieties". We no longer provide individual listings for combinations of two or more varieties; thus a plate variety or overprinting error will not be listed for various watermark orientations.

Overprints (and surcharges). Overprints of different types qualify for separate listing. These include overprints in different colours; overprints from different printing processes such as litho and typo; overprints in totally different typefaces, etc. Major errors in machine-printed overprints are important and listable. They include: overprint inverted or omitted; overprint double (treble, etc.); overprint diagonal; overprint double, one inverted; pairs with one overprint omitted, e.g. from a radical shift to an adjoining stamp; error of colour; error of type fount; letters inverted or omitted, etc. If the overprint is hand-stamped, few of these would qualify and a distinction is drawn. We continue, however, to list pairs of stamps where one has a handstamped overprint and the other has not.

Albino prints or double prints, one of them being albino (i.e. showing an uninked impression of the printing plate) are listable unless they are particularly common in this form (see the note below Travancore No. 32fa, for example). We do not, however, normally list reversed albino overprints, caused by the accidental or deliberate folding of sheets prior to overprinting (British Levant Nos. 51/8).

Varieties occurring in overprints will often take the form of broken letters, slight differences in spacing, rising spaces, etc. Only the most important would be considered for listing or footnote mention.

Sheet positions. If space permits we quote sheet positions of listed varieties and authenticated data is solicited for this purpose.

De La Rue plates. The Catalogue classifies the general plates used by De La Rue for printing British Colonial stamps as follows:

VICTORIAN KEY TYPE

Die I

1. The ball of decoration on the second point of the crown appears as a dark mass of lines.

2. Dark vertical shading separates the front hair from the bun.

3. The vertical line of colour outlining the front of the throat stops at the sixth line of shading on the neck.

4. The white space in the coil of the hair above the curl is roughly the shape of a pin's head.

Die II

1. There are very few lines of colour in the ball and it appears almost white.
2. A white vertical strand of hair appears in place of the dark shading.
3. The line stops at the eighth line of shading.
4. The white space is oblong, with a line of colour partially dividing it at the left end.

Plates numbered 1 and 2 are both Die I. Plates 3 and 4 are Die II.

GEORGIAN KEY TYPE

Die I

A. The second (thick) line below the name of the country is cut slanting, conforming roughly to the shape of the crown on each side.
B. The labels of solid colour bearing the words "POSTAGE" and "& REVENUE" are square at the inner top corners.
C. There is a projecting "bud" on the outer spiral of the ornament in each of the lower corners.

Die II

A. The second line is cut vertically on each side of the crown.
B. The labels curve inwards at the top.
C. There is no "bud" in this position.

Unless otherwise stated in the lists, all stamps with watermark Multiple Crown CA (w **8**) are Die I while those with watermark Multiple Crown Script CA (w **9**) are Die II. The Georgian Die II was introduced in April 1921 and was used for Plates 10 to 22 and 26 to 28. Plates 23 to 25 were made from Die I by mistake.

2. Paper

All stamps listed are deemed to be on (ordinary) paper of the wove type and white in colour; only departures from this are normally mentioned.

Types. Where classification so requires we distinguish such other types of paper as, for example, vertically and horizontally laid; wove and laid bâtonné; card(board); carton; cartridge; glazed; granite; native; pelure; porous; quadrillé; ribbed; rice; and silk thread.

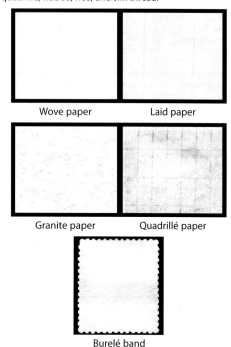

Wove paper   Laid paper

Granite paper   Quadrillé paper

Burelé band

The various makeshifts for normal paper are listed as appropriate. The varieties of double paper and joined paper are recognised. The security device of a printed burelé band on the back of a stamp, as in early Queensland, qualifies for listing.

Descriptive terms. The fact that a paper is handmade (and thus probably of uneven thickness) is mentioned where necessary. Such descriptive terms as "hard" and "soft"; "smooth" and "rough"; "thick", "medium" and "thin" are applied where there is philatelic merit in classifying papers.

Coloured, very white and toned papers. A coloured paper is one that is coloured right through (front and back of the stamp). In the Catalogue the colour of the paper is given in italics, thus:

black/*rose* = black design on rose paper.

Papers have been made specially white in recent years by, for example, a very heavy coating of chalk. We do not classify shades of whiteness of paper as distinct varieties. There does exist, however, a type of paper from early days called toned. This is off-white, often brownish or buffish, but it cannot be assigned any definite colour. A toning effect brought on by climate, incorrect storage or gum staining is disregarded here, as this was not the state of the paper when issued.

"Ordinary" and "Chalk-surfaced" papers. The availability of many postage stamps for revenue purposes made necessary some safeguard against the illegitimate re-use of stamps with removable cancellations. This was at first secured by using fugitive inks and later by printing on paper surfaced by coatings containing either chalk or china clay, both of which made it difficult to remove any form of obliteration without damaging the stamp design.

This catalogue lists these chalk-surfaced paper varieties from their introduction in 1905. Where no indication is given, the paper is "ordinary".

The "traditional" method of indentifying chalk-surfaced papers has been that, when touched with a silver wire, a black mark is left on the paper, and the listings in this catalogue are based on that test. However, the test itself is now largely discredited, for, although the mark can be removed by a soft rubber, some damage to the stamp will result from its use.

The difference between chalk-surfaced and pre-war ordinary papers is fairly clear: chalk-surfaced papers being smoother to the touch and showing a characteristic sheen when light is reflected off their surface. Under good magnification tiny bubbles or pock marks can be seen on the surface of the stamp and at the tips of the perforations the surfacing appears "broken". Traces of paper fibres are evident on the surface of ordinary paper and the ink shows a degree of absorption into it.

Initial chalk-surfaced paper printings by De La Rue had a thinner coating than subsequently became the norm. The characteristics described above are less pronounced in these printings.

During and after the Second World War, substitute papers replaced the chalk-surfaced papers, these do not react to the silver test and are therefore classed as "ordinary", although differentiating them without recourse to it is more difficult, for, although the characteristics of the chalk-surfaced paper remained the same, some of the ordinary papers appear much smoother than earlier papers and many do not show the watermark clearly. Experience is the only solution to identifying these, and comparison with stamps whose paper type is without question will be of great help.

Another type of paper, known as "thin striated" was used only for the Bahamas 1s. and 5s. (Nos. 155a, 156a, 171 and 174) and for several stamps of the Malayan states. Hitherto these have been described as "chalk-surfaced" since they gave some reaction to the silver test, but they are much thinner than usual chalk-surfaced papers, with the watermark showing clearly. Stamps on this paper show a slightly 'ribbed' effect when the stamp is held up to the light. Again, comparison with a known striated paper stamp, such as the 1941 Straits Settlements Die II 2c. orange (No. 294) will prove invaluable in separating these papers.

Glazed paper. In 1969 the Crown Agents introduced a new general-purpose paper for use in conjunction with all current printing processes. It generally has a marked glossy surface but the degree varies according to the process used, being more marked in recess-printing stamps. As it does not respond to the silver test this presents a further test where previous printings were on chalky paper. A change of paper to the glazed variety merits separate listing.

Green and yellow papers. Issues of the First World War and immediate postwar period occur on green and yellow papers and these are given separate Catalogue listing. The original coloured papers (coloured throughout) gave way to surface-coloured papers, the stamps having "white backs"; other stamps show one colour on the front and a different one at the back. Because of the numerous variations a grouping of colours is adopted as follows:

Yellow papers

(1) The original *yellow* paper (throughout), usually bright in colour. The gum is often sparse, of harsh consistency and dull-looking. Used 1912–1920.

(2) The *white-backs*. Used 1913–1914.

(3) A bright lemon paper. The colour must have a pronounced greenish tinge, different from the "yellow" in (1). As a rule, the gum on stamps using this lemon paper is plentiful, smooth and shiny, and the watermark shows distinctly. Care is needed with stamps printed in green on yellow paper (1) as it may appear that the paper is this lemon. Used 1914–1916.

(4) An experimental *orange-buff* paper. The colour must have a distinct brownish tinge. It is not to be confused with a muddy yellow (1) nor the misleading appearance (on the surface) of stamps printed in red on yellow paper where an engraved plate has been insufficiently wiped. Used 1918–1921.

(5) An experimental *buff* paper. This lacks the brownish tinge of (4) and the brightness of the yellow shades. The gum is shiny when compared with the matt type used on (4). Used 1919–1920.

(6) A *pale yellow* paper that has a creamy tone to the yellow. Used from 1920 onwards.

Green papers

(7) The original "green" paper, varying considerably through shades of blue-green and yellow-green, the front and back sometimes differing. Used 1912–1916.

(8) The *white backs*. Used 1913–1914.

(9) A paper blue-green on the surface with *pale olive* back. The back must be markedly paler than the front and this and the pronounced olive tinge to the back distinguish it from (7). Used 1916–1920.

(10) Paper with a vivid green surface, commonly called *emerald-green*; it has the olive back of (9). Used 1920.

(11) Paper with *emerald-green* both back and front. Used from 1920 onwards.

3. Perforation and Rouletting

Perforation gauge. The gauge of a perforation is the number of holes in a length of 2 cm. For correct classification the size of the holes (large or small) may need to be distinguished; in a few cases the actual number of holes on each edge of the stamp needs to be quoted.

Measurement. The Gibbons *Instanta* gauge is the standard for measuring perforations. The stamp is viewed against a dark background with the transparent gauge put on top of it. Though the gauge measures to decimal accuracy, perforations read from it are generally quoted in the Catalogue to the nearest half. For example:

Just over perf 12¾ to just under 13¼ = perf 13
Perf 13¼ exactly, rounded up = perf 13½
Just over perf 13¼ to just under 13¾ = perf 13½
Perf 13¾ exactly, rounded up = perf 14

However, where classification depends on it, actual quarter-perforations are quoted.

Notation. Where no perforation is quoted for an issue it is imperforate. Perforations are usually abbreviated (and spoken) as follows, though sometimes they may be spelled out for clarity. This notation for rectangular stamps (the majority) applies to diamond shapes if "top" is read as the edge to the top right.

P 14: perforated alike on all sides (read: "perf 14").

P 14×15: the first figure refers to top and bottom,

the second to left and right sides (read: "perf 14 by 15"). This is a compound perforation. For an upright triangular stamp the first figure refers to the two sloping sides and second to the base. In inverted triangulars the base is first and the second figure to the sloping sides.

P 14–15: perforation measuring anything between 14 and 15: the holes are irregularly spaced, thus the gauge may vary along a single line or even along a single edge of the stamp (read: "perf 14 to 15").

P 14 *irregular*: perforated 14 from a worn perforator, giving badly aligned holes irregularly spaced (read: "irregular perf 14").

P *comp(ound)* 14×15: two gauges in use but not necessarily on opposite sides of the stamp. It could be one side in one gauge and three in the other; or two adjacent sides with the same gauge. (Read: "perf compound of 14 and 15".) For three gauges or more, abbreviated as "P 12, 14½, 15 *or compound*" for example.

P 14, 14½: perforated approximately 14¼ (read: "perf 14 or 14½"). It does *not* mean two stamps, one perf 14 and the other perf 14½. This obsolescent notation is gradually being replaced in the Catalogue.

Imperf: imperforate (not perforated)

Imperf×P 14: imperforate at top ad bottom and perf 14 at sides.

P 14×*imperf*: perf 14 at top and bottom and imperforate at sides.

Such headings as "P 13×14 (*vert*) and P 14×13 (*horiz*)" indicate which perforations apply to which stamp format—vertical or horizontal.

Some stamps are additionally perforated so that a label or tab is detachable; others have been perforated for use as two halves. Listings are normally for whole stamps, unless stated otherwise.

Imperf×perf

Other terms. Perforation almost always gives circular holes; where other shapes have been used they are specified, e.g. square holes; lozenge perf. Interrupted perfs are brought about by the omission of pins at regular intervals. Perforations merely simulated by being printed as part of the design are of course ignored. With few exceptions, privately applied perforations are not listed.

In the 19th century perforations are often described as clean cut (clean, sharply incised holes), intermediate or rough (rough holes, imperfectly cut, often the result of blunt pins).

Perforation errors and varieties. Authenticated errors, where a stamp normally perforated is accidentally issued imperforate, are listed provided no traces of perforation (blind holes or indentations) remain. They must be provided as pairs, both stamps wholly imperforate, and are only priced in that form.

Note that several postal administrations and their agencies are now deliberately releasing imperforate versions of issued stamps in restricted quantities and at premium prices. These are not listable, but, where possible, thier existance will be noted.

Stamps imperforate between stamp and sheet margin are not listed in this catalogue, but such errors on Great Britain stamps will be found in the *Great Britain Specialised Catalogue*.

Pairs described as "imperforate between" have the line of perforations between the two stamps omitted.

Imperf between (horiz pair): a horizontal pair of stamps with perfs all around the edges but none between the stamps.

Imperf between (vert pair): a vertical pair of stamps with perfs all around the edges but none between the stamps.

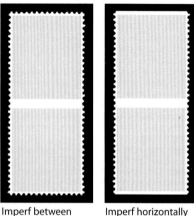

Imperf between   Imperf horizontally
(vertical pair)   (vertical pair)

Where several of the rows have escaped perforation the resulting varieties are listable. Thus:

Imperf vert (horiz pair): a horizontal pair of stamps perforated top and bottom; all three vertical directions are imperf—the two outer edges and between the stamps.

Imperf horiz (vert pair): a vertical pair perforated at left and right edges; all three horizontal directions are imperf—the top, bottom and between the stamps.

Straight edges. Large sheets cut up before issue to post offices can cause stamps with straight edges, i.e. imperf on one side or on two sides at right angles. They are not usually listable in this condition and are worth less than corresponding stamps properly perforated all round. This does not, however, apply to certain stamps, mainly from coils and booklets, where straight edges on various sides are the manufacturing norm affecting every stamp. The listings and notes make clear which sides are correctly imperf.

Malfunction. Varieties of double, misplaced or partial perforation caused by error or machine malfunction are not listable, neither are freaks, such as perforations placed diagonally from paper folds, nor missing holes caused by broken pins.

Types of perforating. Where necessary for classification, perforation types are distinguished.

These include:

Line perforation from one line of pins punching single rows of holes at a time.

Comb perforation from pins disposed across the sheet in comb formation, punching out holes at three sides of the stamp a row at a time.

Harrow perforation applied to a whole pane or sheet at one stroke.

Rotary perforation from toothed wheels operating across a sheet, then crosswise.

Sewing machine perforation. The resultant condition, clean-cut or rough, is distinguished where required.

Pin-perforation is the commonly applied term for pin-roulette in which, instead of being punched out, round holes are pricked by sharp-pointed pins and no paper is removed.

Mixed perforation occurs when stamps with defective perforations are re-perforated in a different gauge.

Punctured stamps. Perforation holes can be punched into the face of the stamp. Patterns of small holes, often in the shape of initial letters, are privately applied devices against pilferage. These (perfins) are outside the scope except for Australia, Canada, Cape of Good Hope, Papua and Sudan where they were used as official stamps by the national administration. Identification devices, when officially inspired, are listed or noted; they can be shapes, or letters or words formed from holes, sometimes converting one class of stamp into another.

Rouletting. In rouletting the paper is cut, for ease of separation, but none is removed. The gauge is measured, when needed, as for perforations. Traditional French terms descriptive of the type of cut are often used and types include:

Arc roulette (percé en arc). Cuts are minute, spaced arcs, each roughly a semicircle.

Cross roulette (percé en croix). Cuts are tiny diagonal crosses.

Line roulette (percé en ligne or *en ligne droite).* Short straight cuts parallel to the frame of the stamp. The commonest basic roulette. Where not further described, "roulette" means this type.

Rouletted in colour or coloured roulette (percé en lignes colorées or *en lignes de coleur).* Cuts with coloured edges, arising from notched rule inked simultaneously with the printing plate.

Saw-tooth roulette (percé en scie). Cuts applied zigzag fashion to resemble the teeth of a saw.

Serpentine roulette (percé en serpentin). Cuts as sharply wavy lines.

Zigzag roulette (percé en zigzags). Short straight cuts at angles in alternate directions, producing sharp points on separation. US usage favours "serrate(d) roulette" for this type.

Pin-roulette (originally *percé en points* and now *perforés trous d'epingle*) is commonly called pin-perforation in English.

4. Gum

All stamps listed are assumed to have gum of some kind; if they were issued without gum this is stated. Original gum (o.g.) means that which was present on the stamp as issued to the public. Deleterious climates and the presence of certain chemicals can cause gum to crack and, with early stamps, even make the paper deteriorate. Unscrupulous fakers are adept in removing it and regumming the stamp to meet the unreasoning demand often made for "full o.g." in cases where such a thing is virtually impossible.

The gum normally used on stamps has been gum arabic until the late 1960s when synthetic adhesives were introduced. Harrison and Sons Ltd for instance use *polyvinyl alcohol,* known to philatelists as PVA. This is almost invisible except for a slight yellowish tinge which was incorporated to make it possible to see that the stamps have been gummed. It has advantages in hot countries, as stamps do not curl and sheets are less likely to stick together. Gum arabic and PVA are not distinguished in the lists except that where a stamp exists with both forms this is indicated in footnotes. Our more specialised catalogues provide separate listing of gums for Great Britain.

Self-adhesive stamps are issued on backing paper, from which they are peeled before affixing to mail. Unused examples are priced as for backing paper intact, in which condition they are recommended to be kept. Used examples are best collected on cover or on piece.

5. Watermarks

Stamps are on unwatermarked paper except where the heading to the set says otherwise.

Detection. Watermarks are detected for Catalogue description by one of four methods: (1) holding stamps to the light; (2) laying stamps face down on a dark background; (3) adding a few drops of petroleum ether 40/60 to the stamp laid face down in a watermark tray; (4) by use of the Stanley Gibbons Detectamark Spectrum, or other equipment, which work by revealing the thinning of the paper at the watermark. (Note that petroleum ether is highly inflammable in use and can damage photogravure stamps.)

Listable types. Stamps occurring on both watermarked and unwatermarked papers are different types and both receive full listing.

Single watermarks (devices occurring once on every stamp) can be modified in size and shape as between different issues; the types are noted but not usually separately listed. Fortuitous absence of watermark from a single stamp or its gross displacement would not be listable.

To overcome registration difficulties the device may be repeated at close intervals *(a multiple watermark),* single stamps thus showing parts of several devices. Similarly, a *large sheet watermark* (or *all-over watermark)* covering numerous stamps can be used. We give informative notes and illustrations for them. The designs may be such that numbers of stamps in the sheet automatically lack watermark: this is not a listable variety. Multiple and all-over watermarks sometimes undergo modifications, but if the various types are difficult to distinguish from single stamps notes are given but not separate listings.

Papermakers' watermarks are noted where known but not listed separately, since most stamps in the sheet will lack them. Sheet watermarks which are nothing more than officially adopted papermakers' watermarks are, however, given normal listing.

Marginal watermarks, falling outside the pane of stamps, are ignored except where misplacement caused the adjoining row to be affected, in which case they may be footnoted. They usually consist of straight or angled lines and double-lined capital letters, they are particularly prevalent on some Crown CC and Crown CA watermark stamps.

Watermark errors and varieties. Watermark errors are recognised as of major importance. They comprise stamps intended to be on unwatermarked paper but issued watermarked by mistake, or stamps printed on paper with the wrong watermark. Varieties showing letters omitted from the watermark are also included, but broken or deformed bits on the dandy roll are not listed unless they represent repairs.

Watermark positions. The diagram shows how watermark position is described in the Catalogue. Paper has a side intended for printing and watermarks are usually impressed so that they read normally when looked through from that printed side. However, since philatelists customarily detect watermarks by looking at the back of the stamp the watermark diagram also makes clear what is actually seen.

Illustrations in the Catalogue are of watermarks in normal positions (from the front of the stamps) and are actual size where possible.

Differences in watermark position are collectable varieties. This Catalogue now lists inverted, sideways inverted and reversed watermark varieties on Commonwealth stamps from the 1860s onwards except where the watermark position is completely haphazard.

Great Britain inverted and sideways inverted watermarks can be found in the *Great Britain Specialised Catalogue* and the *Great Britain Concise Catalogue.*

Where a watermark comes indiscriminately in various positions our policy is to cover this by a general note: we do not give separate listings because the watermark position in these circumstances has no particular philatelic importance.

AS DESCRIBED (Read through front of stamp)		AS SEEN DURING WATERMARK DETECTION (Stamp face down and back examined
GvR	Normal	ᖉvᎮ
ᖉ∧Ꭾ	Inverted	ᅌ∧ᖉ
ᖉvᎮ	Reversed	GvR
ᅌ∧ᖉ	Reversed and Inverted	ᖉ∧Ꭾ
GvR (sideways)	Sideways	ᖉvᎮ (sideways)
GvR (sideways)	Sideways Inverted	ᖉvᎮ (sideways)

As shown in the diagram, a watermark described as "sideways" will normally show the top of the watermark (as shown in its illustration), pointing to the left of the stamp, as seen from the front and to the right as seen from the back.

For clarification, or in cases where the "normal" watermark is "sideways inverted" a note is generally provided at the foot of the relevant listing, particularly where sideways and sideways inverted varieties exist.

Standard types of watermark. Some watermarks have been used generally for various British possessions rather than exclusively for a single colony. To avoid repetition the Catalogue classifies 11 general types, as under, with references in the headings throughout the listings being given either in words or in the form ("W w 9") (meaning "watermark type w 9"). In those cases where watermark illustrations appear in the listings themselves, the respective reference reads, for example, W 153, thus indicating that the watermark will be found in the normal sequence of illustrations as (type) 153.

The general types are as follows, with an example of each quoted.

W	Description	Example
w 1	Large Star	St. Helena No. 1
w 2	Small Star	Turks Is. No. 4
w 3	Broad (pointed) Star	Grenada No. 24
w 4	Crown (over) CC, small stamp	Antigua No. 13
w 5	Crown (over) CC, large stamp	Antigua No. 31

w 6	Crown (over) CA, small stamp	Antigua No. 21
w 7	Crown CA (CA over Crown), large stamp	Sierra Leone No. 54
w 8	Multiple Crown CA	Antigua No. 41
w 9	Multiple Script CA	Seychelles No. 158
w 9a	do. Error	Seychelles No. 158a
w 9b	do. Error	Seychelles No. 158b
w 10	V over Crown	N.S.W. No. 327
w 11	Crown over A	N.S.W. No. 347

CC in these watermarks is an abbreviation for "Crown Colonies" and CA for "Crown Agents". Watermarks w 1, w 2 and w 3 are on stamps printed by Perkins, Bacon; w 4 onwards on stamps from De La Rue and other printers.

w 1
Large Star

w 2
Small Star

w 3
Broad-pointed Star

Watermark w 1, *Large Star*, measures 15 to 16 mm across the star from point to point and about 27 mm from centre to centre vertically between stars in the sheet. It was made for long stamps like Ceylon 1857 and St. Helena 1856.

Watermark w 2, *Small Star* is of similar design but measures 12 to 13½mm from point to point and 24 mm from centre to centre vertically. It was for use with ordinary-size stamps such as Grenada 1863–71.

When the Large Star watermark was used with the smaller stamps it only occasionally comes in the centre of the paper. It is frequently so misplaced as to show portions of two stars above and below and this eccentricity will very often help in determining the watermark.

Watermark w 3, *Broad-pointed Star*, resembles w 1 but the points are broader.

w 4
Crown (over) CC

w 5
Crown (over) CC

Two *Crown (over) CC* watermarks were used: w 4 was for stamps of ordinary size and w 5 for those of larger size.

w **6**	w **7**
Crown (over) CA	CA over Crown

Substituted Crown

Two watermarks of *Crown CA* type were used, w **6** being for stamps of ordinary size. The other, w **7**, is properly described as *CA over Crown*. It was specially made for paper on which it was intended to print long fiscal stamps: that some were used postally accounts for the appearance of w **7** in the Catalogue. The watermark occupies twice the space of the ordinary Crown CA watermark, w **6**. Stamps of normal size printed on paper with w **7** watermark show it *sideways*; it takes a horizontal pair of stamps to show the entire watermark.

The *Multiple Script CA* watermark, w **9**, is known with two errors, recurring among the 1950–52 printings of several territories. In the first a crown has fallen away from the dandy-roll that impresses the watermark into the paper pulp. It gives w **9a**, *Crown missing*, but this omission has been found in both "Crown only" (*illustrated*) and "Crown CA" rows. The resulting faulty paper was used for Bahamas, Johore, Seychelles and the postage due stamps of nine colonies

w **8**	w **9**
Multiple Crown CA	Multiple Script CA

w **9a**: Error, Crown missing

w **9b**: Error, St. Edward's Crown

Multiple watermarks began in 1904 with w **8**, *Multiple Crown CA*, changed from 1921 to w **9**, *Multiple Script CA*. On stamps of ordinary size portions of two or three watermarks appear and on the large-sized stamps a greater number can be observed. The change to letters in script character with w **9** was accompanied by a Crown of distinctly different shape.

It seems likely that there were at least two dandy rolls for each Crown Agents watermark in use at any one time with a reserve roll being employed when the normal one was withdrawn for maintenance or repair.

Both the Mult Crown CA and the Mult Script CA types exist with one or other of the letters omitted from individual impressions. It is possible that most of these occur from the reserve rolls as they have only been found on certain issues. The MCA watermark experienced such problems during the early 1920s and the Script over a longer period from the early 1940s until 1951.

During the 1920s damage must also have occurred on one of the Crowns as a substituted Crown has been found on certain issues. This is smaller than the normal and consists of an oval base joined to two upright ovals with a circle positioned between their upper ends. The upper line of the Crown's base is omitted, as are the left and right-hand circles at the top and also the cross over the centre circle.

When the omission was noticed a second mishap occurred, which was to insert a wrong crown in the space, giving w **9b**, St. Edward's Crown. This produced varieties in Bahamas, Perlis, St. Kitts-Nevis and Singapore and the incorrect crown likewise occurs in (Crown only) and (Crown CA) rows.

w **10**	w **11**
V over Crown	Crown over A

Resuming the general types, two watermarks found in issues of several Australian States are: w **10**, *V over Crown*, and w **11**, *Crown over A*.

w 12
Multiple St. Edward's
Crown Block CA

w 13
Multiple PTM

The *Multiple St. Edward's Crown Block CA* watermark, w **12**, was introduced in 1957 and besides the change in the Crown (from that used in Multiple Crown Script CA, w **9**) the letters reverted to block capitals. The new watermark began to appear sideways in 1966 and these stamps are generally listed as separate sets.

The watermark w **13**, *Multiple PTM*, was introduced for new Malaysian issues in November 1961.

w 14
Multiple Crown CA Diagonal

By 1974 the two dandy-rolls the "upright" and the "sideways" for w **12** were wearing out; the Crown Agents therefore discontinued using the sideways watermark one and retained the other only as a stand-by. A new dandy-roll with the pattern of w **14**, *Multiple Crown CA Diagonal*, was introduced and first saw use with some Churchill Centenary issues.

The new watermark had the design arranged in gradually spiralling rows. It is improved in design to allow smooth passage over the paper (the gaps between letters and rows had caused jolts in previous dandy-rolls) and the sharp corners and angles, where fibres used to accumulate, have been eliminated by rounding.

This watermark had no "normal" sideways position amongst the different printers using it. To avoid confusion our more specialised listings do not rely on such terms as "sideways inverted" but describe the direction in which the watermark points.

w 15
Multiple POST OFFICE

During 1981 w **15**, *Multiple POST OFFICE* was introduced for certain issues prepared by Philatelists Ltd, acting for various countries in the Indian Ocean, Pacific and West Indies.

w 16
Multiple Crown Script CA Diagonal

A new Crown Agents watermark was introduced during 1985, w **16**, *Multiple Crown Script CA Diagonal*. This was very similar to the previous w **14**, but showed "CA" in script rather than block letters. It was first used on the omnibus series of stamps commemorating the Life and Times of Queen Elizabeth the Queen Mother.

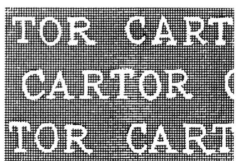

w 17
Multiple CARTOR

Watermark w **17**, *Multiple CARTOR*, was used from 1985 for issues printed by this French firm for countries which did not normally use the Crown Agents watermark.

w 18

In 2008, following the closure of the Crown Agents Stamp Bureau, a new Multiple Crowns watermark, w **18** was introduced

In recent years the use of watermarks has, to a small extent, been superseded by fluorescent security markings. These are often more visible from the reverse of the stamp (Cook Islands from 1970 onwards), but have occurred printed over the design (Hong Kong Nos. 415/30). In 1982 the Crown Agents introduced a new stock paper, without watermark, known as "C-Kurity" on which a fluorescent pattern of blue rosettes is visible on the reverse, beneath the gum. This paper was used for issues from Gambia and Norfolk Island.

6. Colours

Stamps in two or three colours have these named in order of appearance, from the centre moving outwards. Four colours or more are usually listed as multicoloured.

In compound colour names the second is the predominant one, thus:

orange-red = a red tending towards orange;
red-orange = an orange containing more red
than usual.

Standard colours used. The 200 colours most used for stamp identification are given in the Stanley Gibbons Stamp Colour Key. The Catalogue has used the Stamp Colour Key as standard for describing new issues for some years. The names are also introduced as lists are rewritten, though exceptions are made for those early issues where traditional names have become universally established.

Determining colours. When comparing actual stamps with colour samples in the Stamp Colour Key, view in a good north daylight (or its best substitute; fluorescent "colour matching" light). Sunshine is not recommended. Choose a solid portion of the stamp design; if available, marginal markings such as solid bars of colour or colour check dots are helpful. Shading lines in the design can be misleading as they appear lighter than solid colour. Postmarked portions of a stamp appear darker than normal. If more than one colour is present, mask off the extraneous ones as the eye tends to mix them.

Errors of colour. Major colour errors in stamps or overprints which qualify for listing are: wrong colours; one colour inverted in relation to the rest; albinos (colourless impressions), where these have Expert Committee certificates; colours completely omitted, but only on unused stamps (if found on used stamps the information is footnoted) and with good credentials, missing colours being frequently faked.

Colours only partially omitted are not recognised, Colour shifts, however spectacular, are not listed.

Shades. Shades in philately refer to variations in the intensity of a colour or the presence of differing amounts of other colours. They are particularly significant when they can be linked to specific printings. In general, shades need to be quite marked to fall within the scope of this Catalogue; it does not favour nowadays listing the often numerous shades of a stamp, but chooses a single applicable colour name which will indicate particular groups of outstanding shades. Furthermore, the listings refer to colours as issued; they may deteriorate into something different through the passage of time.

Modern colour printing by lithography is prone to marked differences of shade, even within a single run, and variations can occur within the same sheet. Such shades are not listed.

Aniline colours. An aniline colour meant originally one derived from coal-tar; it now refers more widely to colour of a particular brightness suffused on the surface of a stamp and showing through clearly on the back.

Colours of overprints and surcharges. All overprints and surcharges are in black unless stated otherwise in the heading or after the description of the stamp.

7. Specimen Stamps

Originally, stamps overprinted SPECIMEN were circulated to postmasters or kept in official records, but after the establishment of the Universal Postal Union supplies were sent to Berne for distribution to the postal administrations of member countries.

During the period 1884 to 1928 most of the stamps of British Crown Colonies required for this purpose were overprinted SPECIMEN in various shapes and sizes by their printers from typeset formes. Some locally produced provisionals were handstamped locally, as were sets prepared for presentation. From 1928 stamps were punched with holes forming the word SPECIMEN, each firm of printers using a different machine or machines. From 1948 the stamps supplied for UPU distribution were no longer punctured.

Stamps of some other Commonwealth territories were overprinted or handstamped locally, while stamps of Great Britain and those overprinted for use in overseas postal agencies (mostly of the higher denominations) bore SPECIMEN overprints and handstamps applied by the Inland Revenue or the Post Office.

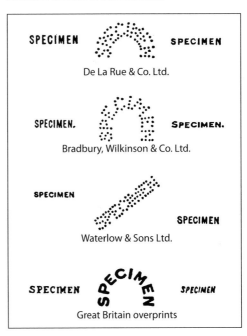

De La Rue & Co. Ltd.

Bradbury, Wilkinson & Co. Ltd.

Waterlow & Sons Ltd.

Great Britain overprints

Some of the commoner types of overprints or punctures are illustrated here. Collectors are warned that dangerous forgeries of the punctured type exist.

The *Stanley Gibbons Commonwealth Catalogues* record those Specimen overprints or perforations intended for distribution by the UPU to member countries and we are grateful to James Bendon, author and publisher of *UPU Specimen Stamps, 1878 - 1961*, a much expanded edition of which was published in 2015, for his assistance with these listings. The Specimen overprints of Australia and its dependent territories, which were sold to collectors by the Post Office, are also included.

Various Perkins Bacon issues exist obliterated with a "CANCELLED" within an oval of bars handstamp.

Perkins Bacon "CANCELLED"
Handstamp

This was applied to six examples of those issues available in 1861 which were then given to members of Sir Rowland Hill's family. 75 different stamps (including four from Chile) are recorded with this handstamp although others may possibly exist. The unauthorised gift of these "CANCELLED" stamps to the Hill family was a major factor in the loss of the Agent General for the Crown Colonies (the forerunner of the Crown Agents) contracts by Perkins Bacon in the following year. Where examples of these scarce items are known to be in private hands the catalogue provides a price.

For full details of these stamps see *CANCELLED by Perkins Bacon* by Peter Jaffé (published by Spink in 1998).

All other Specimens are outside the scope of this volume.

Specimens are not quoted in Great Britain as they are fully listed in the Stanley Gibbons *Great Britain Specialised Catalogue*.

In specifying type of specimen for individual high-value stamps, "H/S" means handstamped, "Optd" is overprinted and "Perf" is punctured. Some sets occur mixed, e.g. "Optd/ Perf". If unspecified, the type is apparent from the date or it is the same as for the lower values quoted as a set.

Prices. Prices for stamps up to £1 are quoted in sets; higher values are priced singly. Where specimens exist in more than one type the price quoted is for the cheapest. Specimen stamps have rarely survived even as pairs; these and strips of three, four or five are worth considerably more than singles.

8. Luminescence

Machines which sort mail electronically have been introduced in recent years. In consequence some countries have issued stamps on fluorescent or phosphorescent papers, while others have marked their stamps with phosphor bands.

The various papers can only be distinguished by ultraviolet lamps emitting particular wavelengths. They are separately listed only when the stamps have some other means of distinguishing them, visible without the use of these lamps. Where this is not so, the papers are recorded in footnotes or headings.

For this catalogue we do not consider it appropriate that collectors be compelled to have the use of an ultraviolet lamp before being able to identify stamps by our listings. Some experience will also be found necessary in interpreting the results given by ultraviolet. Collectors using the lamps, nevertheless, should exercise great care in their use as exposure to their light is potentially dangerous to the eyes.

Phosphor bands are listable, since they are visible to the naked eye (by holding stamps at an angle to the light and looking along them, the bands appear dark). Stamps existing with or without phosphor bands or with differing numbers of bands are given separate listings. Varieties such as double bands, bands omitted, misplaced or printed on the back are not listed.

Detailed descriptions appear at appropriate places in the listings in explanation of luminescent papers; see, for example, Australia above No. 363, Canada above Nos. 472 and 611, Cook Is. above 249, etc.

For Great Britain, where since 1959 phosphors have played a prominent and intricate part in stamp issues, the main notes above Nos. 599 and 723 should be studied, as well as the footnotes to individual listings where appropriate. In general the classification is as follows.

Stamps with phosphor bands are those where a separate cylinder applies the phosphor after the stamps are printed. Issues with "all-over" phosphor have the "band" covering the entire stamp. Parts of the stamp covered by phosphor bands, or the entire surface for "all-over" phosphor versions, appear matt. Stamps on phosphorised paper have the phosphor added to the paper coating before the stamps are printed. Issues on this paper have a completely shiny surface.

Further particularisation of phosphor – their methods of printing and the colours they exhibit under ultraviolet – is outside the scope. The more specialised listings should be consulted for this information.

9. Coil Stamps

Stamps issued only in coil form are given full listing. If stamps are issued in both sheets and coils the coil stamps are listed separately only where there is some feature (e.g. perforation or watermark sideways) by which singles can be distinguished. Coil stamps containing different stamps *se-tenant* are also listed.

Coil join pairs are too random and too easily faked to permit of listing; similarly ignored are coil stamps which have accidentally suffered an extra row of perforations from the claw mechanism in a malfunctioning vending machine.

10. Stamp Booklets

Stamp booklets are now listed in this catalogue.

Single stamps from booklets are listed if they are distinguishable in some way (such as watermark or perforation) from similar sheet stamps.

Booklet panes are listed where they contain stamps of different denominations *se-tenant*, where stamp-size labels are included, or where such panes are otherwise identifiable. Booklet panes are placed in the listing under the lowest denomination present.

Particular perforations (straight edges) are covered by appropriate notes.

The majority of stamp booklets were made up from normal sheets and panes may be bound upright or inverted and booklets may be stapled or stitched at either the left or right-hand side. Unless specifically mentioned in the listings, such variations do not command a price premium.

11. Miniature Sheets and Sheetlets

We distinguish between "miniature sheets" and "sheetlets" and this affects the catalogue numbering. An item in sheet form that is postally valid, containing a single stamp, pair, block or set of stamps, with wide, inscribed and/or decorative margins, is a miniature sheet if it is sold at post offices as an indivisible entity. As such the Catalogue allots a single **MS** number and describes what stamps make it up. The sheetlet or small sheet differs in that the individual stamps are intended to be purchased separately for postal purposes. For sheetlets, all the component postage stamps are numbered individually and the composition explained in a footnote. Note that the definitions refer to post office sale—not how items may be subsequently offered by stamp dealers.

12. Forgeries and Fakes

Forgeries. Where space permits, notes are considered if they can give a concise description that will permit unequivocal detection of a forgery. Generalised warnings, lacking detail, are not nowadays inserted, since their value to the collector is problematic.

Forged cancellations have also been applied to genuine stamps. This catalogue includes notes regarding those manufactured by 'Madame Joseph', together with the cancellation dates known to exist. It should be remembered that these dates also exist as genuine cancellations.

For full details of these see *Madame Joseph Forged Postmarks* by Derek Worboys (published by the Royal Philatelic Society London and the British Philatelic Trust in 1994) or *Madame Joseph Revisited* by Brian Cartwright (published by the Royal Philatelic Society London in 2005).

Fakes. Unwitting fakes are numerous, particularly "new shades" which are colour changelings brought about by exposure to sunlight, soaking in water contaminated with dyes from adherent paper, contact with oil and dirt from a pocketbook, and so on. Fraudulent operators, in addition, can offer to arrange: removal of hinge marks; repairs of thins on white or coloured papers; replacement of missing margins or perforations; reperforating in true or false gauges; removal of fiscal cancellations; rejoining of severed pairs, strips and blocks; and (a major hazard) regumming. Collectors can only be urged to purchase from reputable sources and to insist upon Expert Committee certification where there is any kind of doubt.

The Catalogue can consider footnotes about fakes where these are specific enough to assist in detection.

ACKNOWLEDGEMENTS

We are grateful to individual collectors, members of the philatelic trade and specialist societies and study circles for their assistance in improving and extending the Stanley Gibbons range of catalogues. The addresses of societies and study circles relevant to this volume are:

New Zealand Society of Great Britain
Membership Secretary – Mrs E. Diamond
9 Ashley Drive, Walton on Thames,
Surrey KT12 1JL

Royal Philatelic Society of New Zealand
Secretary – Mr. G Wilson
P.O. Box 1269, Wellington, New Zealand

The Fellowship of Samoa Specialists
Membership Secretary – Mr DAT Mee
23 Leo Street, Christchurch 8051, New Zealand

Abbreviations

Printers

A.B.N. Co.	American Bank Note Co, New York.
B.A.B.N.	British American Bank Note Co. Ottawa
B.D.T.	B.D.T. International Security Printing Ltd, Dublin, Ireland
B.W.	Bradbury Wilkinson & Co, Ltd.
Cartor	Cartor S.A., La Loupe, France
C.B.N.	Canadian Bank Note Co, Ottawa.
Continental	Continental Bank Note Co. B.N. Co.
Courvoisier	Imprimerie Courvoisier S.A., La-Chaux-de-Fonds, Switzerland.
D.L.R.	De La Rue & Co, Ltd, London.
Enschedé	Joh. Enschedé en Zonen, Haarlem, Netherlands.
Format	Format International Security Printers Ltd., London
Harrison	Harrison & Sons, Ltd. London
J.W.	John Waddington Security Print Ltd., Leeds
L.M.G.	Lowe Martin Group, Ottawa, Canada
P.B.	Perkins Bacon Ltd, London.
Questa	Questa Colour Security Printers Ltd, London
Walsall	Walsall Security Printers Ltd
Waterlow	Waterlow & Sons, Ltd, London.

General Abbreviations

Alph	Alphabet
Anniv	Anniversary
Comp	Compound (perforation)
Des	Designer; designed
Diag	Diagonal; diagonally
Eng	Engraver; engraved
F.C.	Fiscal Cancellation
H/S	Handstamped
Horiz	Horizontal; horizontally
Imp, Imperf	Imperforate
Inscr	Inscribed
L	Left
Litho	Lithographed
mm	Millimetres
MS	Miniature sheet
N.Y.	New York
Opt(d)	Overprint(ed)
P or P-c	Pen-cancelled
P, Pf or Perf	Perforated
Photo	Photogravure
Pl	Plate
Pr	Pair
Ptd	Printed
Ptg	Printing
R	Right

R.	Row
Recess	Recess-printed
Roto	Rotogravure
Roul	Rouletted
S	Specimen (overprint)
Surch	Surcharge(d)
T.C.	Telegraph Cancellation
T	Type
Typo	Typographed
Un	Unused
Us	Used
Vert	Vertical; vertically
W or wmk	Watermark
Wmk s	Watermark sideways

(†) = Does not exist
(–) (or blank price column) = Exists, or may exist, but no market price is known.
/ between colours means "on" and the colour following is that of the paper on which the stamp is printed.

Colours of Stamps

Bl (blue); blk (black); brn (brown); car, carm (carmine); choc (chocolate); clar (claret); emer (emerald); grn (green); ind (indigo); mag (magenta); mar (maroon); mult (multicoloured); mve (mauve); ol (olive); orge (orange); pk (pink); pur (purple); scar (scarlet); sep (sepia); turq (turquoise); ultram (ultramarine); verm (vermilion); vio (violet); yell (yellow).

Colour of Overprints and Surcharges

(B.) = blue, (Blk.) = black, (Br.) = brown, (C.) = carmine, (G.) = green, (Mag.) = magenta, (Mve.) = mauve, (Ol.) = olive, (O.) = orange, (P.) = purple, (Pk.) = pink, (R.) = red, (Sil.) = silver, (V.) = violet, (Vm.) or (Verm.) = vermilion, (W.) = white, (Y.) = yellow.

Arabic Numerals

As in the case of European figures, the details of the Arabic numerals vary in different stamp designs, but they should be readily recognised with the aid of this illustration.

Features Listing

An at-a-glance guide to what's in the Stanley Gibbons catalogues

Area	Feature	Collect British Stamps	Stamps of the World	Thematic Catalogues	Comprehensive Catalogue, Parts 1-22 (including Commonwealth and British Empire Stamps and country catalogues)	Great Britain Concise	Specialised catalogues
General	SG number	√	√	√	√	√	√
General	Specialised Catalogue number						√
General	Year of issue of first stamp in design	√	√	√	√	√	√
General	Exact date of issue of each design				√	√	√
General	Face value information	√	√	√	√	√	√
General	Historical and geographical information	√	√	√	√	√	√
General	General currency information, including dates used	√	√	√	√	√	√
General	Country name	√	√	√	√	√	√
General	Booklet panes				√	√	√
General	Coil stamps				√		
General	First Day Covers	√				√	√
General	Brief footnotes on key areas of note	√	√	√	√	√	√
General	Detailed footnotes on key areas of note				√	√	√
General	Extra background information				√	√	√
General	Miniature sheet information (including size in mm)	√	√	√	√	√	√
General	Sheetlets				√		
General	Stamp booklets				√	√	√
General	Perkins Bacon "Cancelled"				√		
General	PHQ Cards	√				√	√
General	Post Office Label Sheets	√				√	
General	Post Office Yearbooks	√				√	√
General	Presentation and Souvenir Packs	√				√	√
General	Se-tenant pairs	√			√	√	√
General	Watermark details - errors, varieties, positions				√	√	√
General	Watermark illustrations	√			√	√	√
General	Watermark types	√			√	√	√
General	Forgeries noted				√		√
General	Surcharges and overprint information	√	√	√	√	√	√
Design and Description	Colour description, simplified		√	√			
Design and Description	Colour description, extended	√			√	√	√
Design and Description	Set design summary information	√	√	√	√	√	√
Design and Description	Designer name				√	√	√
Design and Description	Short design description	√	√	√	√	√	√

Area	Feature	Collect British Stamps	Stamps of the World	Thematic Catalogues	Comprehensive Catalogue, Parts 1-22 (including Commonwealth and British Empire Stamps and country catalogues)	Great Britain Concise	Specialised catalogues
Design and Description	Shade varieties				√	√	√
Design and Description	Type number	√	√		√	√	√
Illustrations	Multiple stamps from set illustrated	√			√	√	√
Illustrations	A Stamp from each set illustrated in full colour (where possible, otherwise mono)	√	√	√	√	√	√
Price	Catalogue used price	√	√	√	√	√	√
Price	Catalogue unused price	√	√	√	√	√	√
Price	Price - booklet panes				√	√	√
Price	Price - shade varieties				√	√	√
Price	On cover and on piece price				√	√	√
Price	Detailed GB pricing breakdown	√			√	√	√
Print and Paper	Basic printing process information	√	√	√	√	√	√
Print and Paper	Detailed printing process information, e.g. Mill sheets				√		√
Print and Paper	Paper information				√		√
Print and Paper	Detailed perforation information	√			√	√	√
Print and Paper	Details of research findings relating to printing processes and history						√
Print and Paper	Paper colour	√	√		√	√	√
Print and Paper	Paper description to aid identification				√	√	√
Print and Paper	Paper type				√	√	√
Print and Paper	Ordinary or chalk-surfaced paper				√	√	√
Print and Paper	Embossing omitted note						√
Print and Paper	Essays, Die Proofs, Plate Descriptions and Proofs, Colour Trials information						√
Print and Paper	Glazed paper				√	√	√
Print and Paper	Gum details				√		√
Print and Paper	Luminescence/Phosphor bands - general coverage	√			√	√	√
Print and Paper	Luminescence/Phosphor bands - specialised coverage						√
Print and Paper	Overprints and surcharges - including colour information	√	√	√	√	√	√
Print and Paper	Perforation/Imperforate information	√	√		√	√	√
Print and Paper	Perforation errors and varieties				√	√	√
Print and Paper	Print quantities				√		√
Print and Paper	Printing errors				√	√	√
Print and Paper	Printing flaws						√
Print and Paper	Printing varieties				√	√	√
Print and Paper	Punctured stamps - where official				√		
Print and Paper	Sheet positions				√	√	√
Print and Paper	Specialised plate number information						√
Print and Paper	Specimen overprints (only for Commonwealth & GB)				√	√	√
Print and Paper	Underprints					√	√
Print and Paper	Visible Plate numbers	√			√	√	√
Print and Paper	Yellow and Green paper listings				√		√
Index	Design index	√			√	√	

International Philatelic Glossary

English	French	German	Spanish	Italian
Agate	Agate	Achat	Agata	Agata
Air stamp	Timbre de la poste aérienne	Flugpostmarke	Sello de correo aéreo	Francobollo per posta aerea
Apple Green	Vert-pomme	Apfelgrün	Verde manzana	Verde mela
Barred	Annulé par barres	Balkenentwertung	Anulado con barras	Sbarrato
Bisected	Timbre coupé	Halbiert	Partido en dos	Frazionato
Bistre	Bistre	Bister	Bistre	Bistro
Bistre-brown	Brun-bistre	Bisterbraun	Castaño bistre	Bruno-bistro
Black	Noir	Schwarz	Negro	Nero
Blackish Brown	Brun-noir	Schwärzlichbraun	Castaño negruzco	Bruno nerastro
Blackish Green	Vert foncé	Schwärzlichgrün	Verde negruzco	Verde nerastro
Blackish Olive	Olive foncé	Schwärzlicholiv	Oliva negruzco	Oliva nerastro
Block of four	Bloc de quatre	Viererblock	Bloque de cuatro	Bloco di quattro
Blue	Bleu	Blau	Azul	Azzurro
Blue-green	Vert-bleu	Blaugrün	Verde azul	Verde azzuro
Bluish Violet	Violet bleuâtre	Bläulichviolett	Violeta azulado	Violtto azzurrastro
Booklet	Carnet	Heft	Cuadernillo	Libretto
Bright Blue	Bleu vif	Lebhaftblau	Azul vivo	Azzurro vivo
Bright Green	Vert vif	Lebhaftgrün	Verde vivo	Verde vivo
Bright Purple	Mauve vif	Lebhaftpurpur	Púrpura vivo	Porpora vivo
Bronze Green	Vert-bronze	Bronzegrün	Verde bronce	Verde bronzo
Brown	Brun	Braun	Castaño	Bruno
Brown-lake	Carmin-brun	Braunlack	Laca castaño	Lacca bruno
Brown-purple	Pourpre-brun	Braunpurpur	Púrpura castaño	Porpora bruno
Brown-red	Rouge-brun	Braunrot	Rojo castaño	Rosso bruno
Buff	Chamois	Sämisch	Anteado	Camoscio
Cancellation	Oblitération	Entwertung	Cancelación	Annullamento
Cancelled	Annulé	Gestempelt	Cancelado	Annullato
Carmine	Carmin	Karmin	Carmín	Carminio
Carmine red	Rouge-carmin	Karminrot	Rojo carmín	Rosso carminio
Centred	Centré	Zentriert	Centrado	Centrato
Cerise	Rouge-cerise	Kirschrot	Color de ceresa	Color Ciliegia
Chalk-surfaced paper	Papier couché	Kreidepapier	Papel estucado	Carta gessata
Chalky Blue	Bleu terne	Kreideblau	Azul turbio	Azzurro smorto
Charity stamp	Timbre de bienfaisance	Wohltätigkeitsmarke	Sello de beneficenza	Francobollo di beneficenza
Chestnut	Marron	Kastanienbraun	Castaño rojo	Marrone
Chocolate	Chocolat	Schokolade	Chocolate	Cioccolato
Cinnamon	Cannelle	Zimtbraun	Canela	Cannella
Claret	Grenat	Weinrot	Rojo vinoso	Vinaccia
Cobalt	Cobalt	Kobalt	Cobalto	Cobalto
Colour	Couleur	Farbe	Color	Colore
Comb-perforation	Dentelure en peigne	Kammzähnung, Reihenzähnung	Dentado de peine	Dentellatura e pettine
Commemorative stamp	Timbre commémoratif	Gedenkmarke	Sello conmemorativo	Francobollo commemorativo
Crimson	Cramoisi	Karmesin	Carmesí	Cremisi
Deep Blue	Blue foncé	Dunkelblau	Azul oscuro	Azzurro scuro
Deep bluish Green	Vert-bleu foncé	Dunkelbläulichgrün	Verde azulado oscuro	Verde azzurro scuro
Design	Dessin	Markenbild	Diseño	Disegno

English	French	German	Spanish	Italian
Die	Matrice	Urstempel. Type, Platte	Cuño	Conio, Matrice
Double	Double	Doppelt	Doble	Doppio
Drab	Olive terne	Trüboliv	Oliva turbio	Oliva smorto
Dull Green	Vert terne	Trübgrün	Verde turbio	Verde smorto
Dull purple	Mauve terne	Trübpurpur	Púrpura turbio	Porpora smorto
Embossing	Impression en relief	Prägedruck	Impresión en relieve	Impressione a relievo
Emerald	Vert-eméraude	Smaragdgrün	Esmeralda	Smeraldo
Engraved	Gravé	Graviert	Grabado	Inciso
Error	Erreur	Fehler, Fehldruck	Error	Errore
Essay	Essai	Probedruck	Ensayo	Saggio
Express letter stamp	Timbre pour lettres par exprès	Eilmarke	Sello de urgencia	Francobollo per espresso
Fiscal stamp	Timbre fiscal	Stempelmarke	Sello fiscal	Francobollo fiscale
Flesh	Chair	Fleischfarben	Carne	Carnicino
Forgery	Faux, Falsification	Fälschung	Falsificación	Falso, Falsificazione
Frame	Cadre	Rahmen	Marco	Cornice
Granite paper	Papier avec fragments de fils de soie	Faserpapier	Papel con filamentos	Carto con fili di seta
Green	Vert	Grün	Verde	Verde
Greenish Blue	Bleu verdâtre	Grünlichblau	Azul verdoso	Azzurro verdastro
Greenish Yellow	Jaune-vert	Grünlichgelb	Amarillo verdoso	Giallo verdastro
Grey	Gris	Grau	Gris	Grigio
Grey-blue	Bleu-gris	Graublau	Azul gris	Azzurro grigio
Grey-green	Vert gris	Graugrün	Verde gris	Verde grigio
Gum	Gomme	Gummi	Goma	Gomma
Gutter	Interpanneau	Zwischensteg	Espacio blanco entre dos grupos	Ponte
Imperforate	Non-dentelé	Geschnitten	Sin dentar	Non dentellato
Indigo	Indigo	Indigo	Azul indigo	Indaco
Inscription	Inscription	Inschrift	Inscripción	Dicitura
Inverted	Renversé	Kopfstehend	Invertido	Capovolto
Issue	Émission	Ausgabe	Emisión	Emissione
Laid	Vergé	Gestreift	Listado	Vergato
Lake	Lie de vin	Lackfarbe	Laca	Lacca
Lake-brown	Brun-carmin	Lackbraun	Castaño laca	Bruno lacca
Lavender	Bleu-lavande	Lavendel	Color de alhucema	Lavanda
Lemon	Jaune-citron	Zitrongelb	Limón	Limone
Light Blue	Bleu clair	Hellblau	Azul claro	Azzurro chiaro
Lilac	Lilas	Lila	Lila	Lilla
Line perforation	Dentelure en lignes	Linienzähnung	Dentado en linea	Dentellatura lineare
Lithography	Lithographie	Steindruck	Litografía	Litografia
Local	Timbre de poste locale	Lokalpostmarke	Emisión local	Emissione locale
Lozenge roulette	Percé en losanges	Rautenförmiger Durchstich	Picadura en rombos	Perforazione a losanghe
Magenta	Magenta	Magentarot	Magenta	Magenta
Margin	Marge	Rand	Borde	Margine
Maroon	Marron pourpré	Dunkelrotpurpur	Púrpura rojo oscuro	Marrone rossastro
Mauve	Mauve	Malvenfarbe	Malva	Malva
Multicoloured	Polychrome	Mehrfarbig	Multicolores	Policromo
Myrtle Green	Vert myrte	Myrtengrün	Verde mirto	Verde mirto
New Blue	Bleu ciel vif	Neublau	Azul nuevo	Azzurro nuovo
Newspaper stamp	Timbre pour journaux	Zeitungsmarke	Sello para periódicos	Francobollo per giornali
Obliteration	Oblitération	Abstempelung	Matasello	Annullamento
Obsolete	Hors (de) cours	Ausser Kurs	Fuera de curso	Fuori corso
Ochre	Ocre	Ocker	Ocre	Ocra

English	French	German	Spanish	Italian
Official stamp	Timbre de service	Dienstmarke	Sello de servicio	Francobollo di
Olive-brown	Brun-olive	Olivbraun	Castaño oliva	Bruno oliva
Olive-green	Vert-olive	Olivgrün	Verde oliva	Verde oliva
Olive-grey	Gris-olive	Olivgrau	Gris oliva	Grigio oliva
Olive-yellow	Jaune-olive	Olivgelb	Amarillo oliva	Giallo oliva
Orange	Orange	Orange	Naranja	Arancio
Orange-brown	Brun-orange	Orangebraun	Castaño naranja	Bruno arancio
Orange-red	Rouge-orange	Orangerot	Rojo naranja	Rosso arancio
Orange-yellow	Jaune-orange	Orangegelb	Amarillo naranja	Giallo arancio
Overprint	Surcharge	Aufdruck	Sobrecarga	Soprastampa
Pair	Paire	Paar	Pareja	Coppia
Pale	Pâle	Blass	Pálido	Pallido
Pane	Panneau	Gruppe	Grupo	Gruppo
Paper	Papier	Papier	Papel	Carta
Parcel post stamp	Timbre pour colis postaux	Paketmarke	Sello para paquete postal	Francobollo per pacchi postali
Pen-cancelled	Oblitéré à plume	Federzugentwertung	Cancelado a pluma	Annullato a penna
Percé en arc	Percé en arc	Bogenförmiger Durchstich	Picadura en forma de arco	Perforazione ad arco
Percé en scie	Percé en scie	Bogenförmiger Durchstich	Picado en sierra	Foratura a sega
Perforated	Dentelé	Gezähnt	Dentado	Dentellato
Perforation	Dentelure	Zähnung	Dentar	Dentellatura
Photogravure	Photogravure, Heliogravure	Rastertiefdruck	Fotograbado	Rotocalco
Pin perforation	Percé en points	In Punkten durchstochen	Horadado con alfileres	Perforato a punti
Plate	Planche	Platte	Plancha	Lastra, Tavola
Plum	Prune	Pflaumenfarbe	Color de ciruela	Prugna
Postage Due stamp	Timbre-taxe	Portomarke	Sello de tasa	Segnatasse
Postage stamp	Timbre-poste	Briefmarke, Freimarke, Postmarke	Sello de correos	Francobollo postale
Postal fiscal stamp	Timbre fiscal-postal	Stempelmarke als Postmarke verwendet	Sello fiscal-postal	Fiscale postale
Postmark	Oblitération postale	Poststempel	Matasello	Bollo
Printing	Impression, Tirage	Druck	Impresión	Stampa, Tiratura
Proof	Épreuve	Druckprobe	Prueba de impresión	Prova
Provisionals	Timbres provisoires	Provisorische Marken. Provisorien	Provisionales	Provvisori
Prussian Blue	Bleu de Prusse	Preussischblau	Azul de Prusia	Azzurro di Prussia
Purple	Pourpre	Purpur	Púrpura	Porpora
Purple-brown	Brun-pourpre	Purpurbraun	Castaño púrpura	Bruno porpora
Recess-printing	Impression en taille douce	Tiefdruck	Grabado	Incisione
Red	Rouge	Rot	Rojo	Rosso
Red-brown	Brun-rouge	Rotbraun	Castaño rojizo	Bruno rosso
Reddish Lilac	Lilas rougeâtre	Rötlichlila	Lila rojizo	Lilla rossastro
Reddish Purple	Poupre-rouge	Rötlichpurpur	Púrpura rojizo	Porpora rossastro
Reddish Violet	Violet rougeâtre	Rötlichviolett	Violeta rojizo	Violetto rossastro
Red-orange	Orange rougeâtre	Rotorange	Naranja rojizo	Arancio rosso
Registration stamp	Timbre pour lettre chargée (recommandée)	Einschreibemarke	Sello de certificado lettere	Francobollo per raccomandate
Reprint	Réimpression	Neudruck	Reimpresión	Ristampa
Reversed	Retourné	Umgekehrt	Invertido	Rovesciato
Rose	Rose	Rosa	Rosa	Rosa
Rose-red	Rouge rosé	Rosarot	Rojo rosado	Rosso rosa
Rosine	Rose vif	Lebhaftrosa	Rosa vivo	Rosa vivo
Roulette	Percage	Durchstich	Picadura	Foratura
Rouletted	Percé	Durchstochen	Picado	Forato
Royal Blue	Bleu-roi	Königblau	Azul real	Azzurro reale
Sage green	Vert-sauge	Salbeigrün	Verde salvia	Verde salvia
Salmon	Saumon	Lachs	Salmón	Salmone

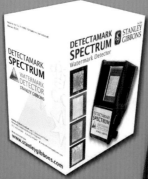

English	French	German	Spanish	Italian
Scarlet	Écarlate	Scharlach	Escarlata	Scarlatto
Sepia	Sépia	Sepia	Sepia	Seppia
Serpentine roulette	Percé en serpentin	Schlangenliniger Durchstich	Picado a serpentina	Perforazione a serpentina
Shade	Nuance	Tönung	Tono	Gradazione de colore
Sheet	Feuille	Bogen	Hoja	Foglio
Slate	Ardoise	Schiefer	Pizarra	Ardesia
Slate-blue	Bleu-ardoise	Schieferblau	Azul pizarra	Azzurro ardesia
Slate-green	Vert-ardoise	Schiefergrün	Verde pizarra	Verde ardesia
Slate-lilac	Lilas-gris	Schierferlila	Lila pizarra	Lilla ardesia
Slate-purple	Mauve-gris	Schieferpurpur	Púrpura pizarra	Porpora ardesia
Slate-violet	Violet-gris	Schierferviolett	Violeta pizarra	Violetto ardesia
Special delivery stamp	Timbre pour exprès	Eilmarke	Sello de urgencia	Francobollo per espresso
Specimen	Spécimen	Muster	Muestra	Saggio
Steel Blue	Bleu acier	Stahlblau	Azul acero	Azzurro acciaio
Strip	Bande	Streifen	Tira	Striscia
Surcharge	Surcharge	Aufdruck	Sobrecarga	Soprastampa
Tête-bêche	Tête-bêche	Kehrdruck	Tête-bêche	Tête-bêche
Tinted paper	Papier teinté	Getöntes Papier	Papel coloreado	Carta tinta
Too-late stamp	Timbre pour lettres en retard	Verspätungsmarke	Sello para cartas retardadas	Francobollo per le lettere in ritardo
Turquoise-blue	Bleu-turquoise	Türkisblau	Azul turquesa	Azzurro turchese
Turquoise-green	Vert-turquoise	Türkisgrün	Verde turquesa	Verde turchese
Typography	Typographie	Buchdruck	Tipografia	Tipografia
Ultramarine	Outremer	Ultramarin	Ultramar	Oltremare
Unused	Neuf	Ungebraucht	Nuevo	Nuovo
Used	Oblitéré, Usé	Gebraucht	Usado	Usato
Venetian Red	Rouge-brun terne	Venezianischrot	Rojo veneciano	Rosso veneziano
Vermilion	Vermillon	Zinnober	Cinabrio	Vermiglione
Violet	Violet	Violett	Violeta	Violetto
Violet-blue	Bleu-violet	Violettblau	Azul violeta	Azzurro violetto
Watermark	Filigrane	Wasserzeichen	Filigrana	Filigrana
Watermark sideways	Filigrane couché	Wasserzeichen liegend	Filigrana acostado	Filigrana coricata
Wove paper	Papier ordinaire, Papier uni	Einfaches Papier	Papel avitelado	Carta unita
Yellow	Jaune	Gelb	Amarillo	Giallo
Yellow-brown	Brun-jaune	Gelbbraun	Castaño amarillo	Bruno giallo
Yellow-green	Vert-jaune	Gelbgrün	Verde amarillo	Verde giallo
Yellow-olive	Olive-jaunâtre	Gelboliv	Oliva amarillo	Oliva giallastro
Yellow-orange	Orange jaunâtre	Gelborange	Naranja amarillo	Arancio giallastro
Zig-zag roulette	Percé en zigzag	Sägezahnartiger Durchstich	Picado en zigzag	Perforazione a zigzag

Guide to Entries

(A) Country of Issue – When a country changes its name, the catalogue listing changes to reflect the name change, for example Namibia was formerly known as South West Africa, the stamps in Southern Africa are all listed under Namibia, but split into South West Africa and then Namibia.

(B) Country Information – Brief geographical and historical details for the issuing country.

(C) Currency – Details of the currency, and dates of earliest use where applicable, on the face value of the stamps.

(D) Illustration – Generally, the first stamp in the set. Stamp illustrations are reduced to 75%, with overprints and surcharges shown actual size.

(E) Illustration or Type Number – These numbers are used to help identify stamps, either in the listing, type column, design line or footnote, usually the first value in a set. These type numbers are in a bold type face – **123**; when bracketed **(123)** an overprint or a surcharge is indicated. Some type numbers include a lower-case letter – **123a**, this indicates they have been added to an existing set.

(F) Date of issue – This is the date that the stamp/set of stamps was issued by the post office and was available for purchase. When a set of definitive stamps has been issued over several years the Year Date given is for the earliest issue. Commemorative sets are listed in chronological order. Stamps of the same design, or issue are usually grouped together, for example some of the New Zealand landscapes definitive series were first issued in 2003 but the set includes stamps issued to May 2007.

(G) Number Prefix – Stamps other than definitives and commemoratives have a prefix letter before the catalogue number.
Their use is explained in the text: some examples are A for airmail, D for postage due and O for official stamps.

(H) Footnote – Further information on background or key facts on issues.

(I) Stanley Gibbons Catalogue number – This is a unique number for each stamp to help the collector identify stamps in the listing. The Stanley Gibbons numbering system is universally recognized as definitive.
Where insufficient numbers have been left to provide for additional stamps to a listing, some stamps will have a suffix letter after the catalogue number (for example 214a). If numbers have been left for additions to a set and not used they will be left vacant.
The separate type numbers (in bold) refer to illustrations (see **E**).

(J) Colour – If a stamp is printed in three or fewer colours then the colours are listed, working from the centre of the stamp outwards (see **R**).

(K) Design line – Further details on design variations

(L) Key Type – Indicates a design type on which the stamp is based. These are the bold figures found below each illustration, for example listed in Cameroon, in the West Africa catalogue, is the Key type A and B showing the ex-Kaiser's yacht *Hohenzollern*. The type numbers are also given in bold in the second column of figures alongside the stamp description to indicate the design of each stamp. Where an issue comprises stamps of similar design, the corresponding type number should be taken as indicating the general design. Where there are blanks in the type number column it means that the type of the corresponding stamp

is that shown by the number in the type column of the same issue. A dash (–) in the type column means that the stamp is not illustrated. Where type numbers refer to stamps of another country, e.g. where stamps of one country are overprinted for use in another, this is always made clear in the text.

(M) Coloured Papers – Stamps printed on coloured paper are shown – e.g. "brown/*yellow*" indicates brown printed on yellow paper.

(N) Surcharges and Overprints – Usually described in the headings. Any actual wordings are shown in bold type. Descriptions clarify words and figures used in the overprint. Stamps with the same overprints in different colours are not listed separately. Numbers in brackets after the descriptions are the catalogue numbers of the non-overprinted stamps. The words "inscribed" or "inscription" refer to the wording incorporated in the design of a stamp and not surcharges or overprints.

(O) Face value – This refers to the value of each stamp and is the price it was sold for at the Post Office when issued. Some modern stamps do not have their values in figures but instead it is shown as a letter, for example Great Britain use 1st or 2nd on their stamps as opposed to the actual value.

(P) Catalogue Value – Mint/Unused. Prices quoted for Queen Victoria to King George V stamps are for lightly hinged examples.

(Q) Catalogue Value – Used. Prices generally refer to fine postally used examples. For certain issues they are for cancelled-to-order.

Prices
Prices are given in pence and pounds. Stamps worth £100 and over are shown in whole pounds:

Shown in Catalogue as	Explanation
10	10 pence
1·75	£1·75
15.00	£15
£150	£150
£2300	£2300

Prices assume stamps are in 'fine condition'; we may ask more for superb and less for those of lower quality. The minimum catalogue price quoted is 10p and is intended as a guide for catalogue users. The lowest price for individual stamps purchased from Stanley Gibbons is £1.
Prices quoted are for the cheapest variety of that particular stamp. Differences of watermark, perforation, or other details, often increase the value. Prices quoted for mint issues are for single examples, unless otherwise stated. Those in *se-tenant* pairs, strips, blocks or sheets may be worth more. Where no prices are listed it is either because the stamps are not known to exist (usually shown by a †) in that particular condition, or, more usually, because there is no reliable information on which to base their value.
All prices are subject to change without prior notice and we cannot guarantee to supply all stamps as priced. Prices quoted in advertisements are also subject to change without prior notice.

(R) Multicoloured – Nearly all modern stamps are multicoloured (more than three colours); this is indicated in the heading, with a description of the stamp given in the listing.

(S) Perforations – Please see page xiii for a detailed explanation of perforations.

(A) Country of issue ──────•

Bangladesh

(B) Country Information

In elections during December 1970 the Awami League party won all but two of the seats in the East Pakistan province and, in consequence, held a majority in the National Assembly. On 1 March 1971 the Federal Government postponed the sitting of the Assembly with the result that unrest spread throughout the eastern province. Pakistan army operations against the dissidents forced the leaders of the League to flee to India from where East Pakistan was proclaimed independent as Bangladesh. In early December the Indian army moved against Pakistan troops in Bangladesh and civilian government was re-established on 22 December 1971.

From 20 December 1971 various Pakistan issues were overprinted by local postmasters, mainly using handstamps. Their use was permitted until 30 April 1973. These are of philatelic interest, but are outside the scope of the catalogue.

(C) Currency ──────────•**(Currency. 100 paisa = 1 rupee)**

(D) Illustration

5c
N.Z.GOVERNMENT LIFE INSURANCE OFFICE

L **17** •

(E) Illustration or Type number

(F) Date of issue ───•**1978** (8 Mar). No. L 57 surch with Type L **16**. Chalky paper.

L63	L **14**	25c. on 2½c. ultramarine, green and buff	75	1·75

(Des A. G. Mitchell. Litho Harrison)

(G) Number prefix ───•

1981 (3 June). P 14½.

L64	L **17**	5c. multicoloured	10	10
L65		10c. multicoloured	10	10
L66		20c. multicoloured	15	15
L67		30c. multicoloured	25	25
L68		40c. multicoloured	30	30
L69		50c. multicoloured	30	45
L64/9 Set of 6			1·00	1·25

(H) Footnote ──────• Issues for the Government Life Insurance Department were withdrawn on 1 December 1989 when it became the privatised Tower Corporation.

(Des G. R. Bull and G. R. Smith. Photo Harrison)

(I) Stanley Gibbons catalogue number ──•

1959 (2 Mar). Centenary of Marlborough Province. T **198** and similar horiz designs. W **98** (sideways). P 14½×14.

772		2d. green	30	10
773		3d. deep blue	30	10
774		8d. light brown	1·25	2·25
772/4 Set of 3			1·60	2·25

(J) Colour

(K) Design line ──────• Designs:—3d. Shipping wool, Wairau Bar, 1857; 8d. Salt industry, Grassmere.

1915 (12 July). Stamps of German Kamerun. Types A and B, surch as T **1** (Nos. B1/9) or **2**. (Nos. B10/13) in black or blue.

(L) Key type column ───•

B1	A	1½d. on 3pf. (No. k7) (B.)	13·00	42·00
		a. Different fount "d"	£150	£350
340	**41**	2d. purple (1903)	£350	£325
341	**28**	3d. bistre-brown (1906)	£700	£600
342	**37**	4d. blue and chestnut/*bluish* (1904)..	£300	£350
		a. Blue and yellow-brown/*bluish*	£300	£350

(M) Coloured papers

(N) Surcharges and overprints ──•

1913 (1 Dec). Auckland Industrial Exhibition. Nos. 387aa, 389, 392 and 409 optd with T **59** by Govt Printer, Wellington.

412	**51**	½d. deep green	20·00	55·00
413	**53**	1d. carmine	25·00	48·00
		a. "Feather" flaw	£225	
414	**52**	3d. chestnut	£130	£250
415		6d. carmine	£160	£300
412/15 Set of 4			£300	£600

(P) Catalogue value – Mint

(O) Face value

(Q) Catalogue value – Used

These overprinted stamps were only available for letters in New Zealand and to Australia.

(Des Martin Bailey. Litho Southern Colour Print)

(R) Multicoloured stamp ──

2008 (2 July). Olympic Games, Beijing. T **685** and similar diamond-shaped designs. Multicoloured. Phosphorised paper. P 14½.

3056		50c. Type **685**	1·00	85

(S) Perforations

New Zealand

From 1831 mail from New Zealand was sent to Sydney, New South Wales, routed through an unofficial postmaster at Kororareka.

The first official post office opened at Kororareka in January 1840 to be followed by others at Auckland, Britannia, Coromandel Harbour, Hokianga, Port Nicholson, Russell and Waimate during the same year. New South Wales relinquished control of the postal service when New Zealand became a separate colony on 3 May 1841.

The British G.P.O. was responsible for the operation of the overseas mails from 11 October 1841 until the postal service once again passed under colonial control on 18 November 1848.

CC **1**   CC **2**

AUCKLAND
CROWNED-CIRCLE HANDSTAMPS
CC1	CC **1**	AUCKLAND NEW ZEALAND (R.) (31.10.1846)	
		.... Price on cover	£300

NELSON
CROWNED-CIRCLE HANDSTAMPS
CC2	CC **1**	NELSON NEW ZEALAND (R.) (31.10.1846)	
		.... Price on cover	£1100

NEW PLYMOUTH
CROWNED-CIRCLE HANDSTAMPS
CC3	CC **1**	NEW PLYMOUTH NEW ZEALAND (R. or	
		Black) (31.10.1846) .... Price on cover	£2750
CC3a	CC **2**	NEW PLYMOUTH NEW ZEALAND (R. or	
		Black) (1854) .... Price on cover	£3250

OTAGO
CROWNED-CIRCLE HANDSTAMPS
CC4	CC **2**	OTAGO NEW ZEALAND (R.) (1851)	
		.... Price on cover	£1900

PETRE
CROWNED-CIRCLE HANDSTAMPS
CC5	CC **1**	PETRE NEW ZEALAND (R.) (31.10.1846)	
		.... Price on cover	£1400

PORT VICTORIA
CROWNED-CIRCLE HANDSTAMPS
CC6	CC **2**	PORT VICTORIA NEW ZEALAND (R.) (1851)	
		.... Price on cover	£1200

RUSSELL
CROWNED-CIRCLE HANDSTAMPS
CC7	CC **1**	RUSSELL NEW ZEALAND (R.) (31.10.1846)	
		.... Price on cover	£7000

WELLINGTON
CROWNED-CIRCLE HANDSTAMPS
CC8	CC **1**	WELLINGTON NEW ZEALAND (R.)	
		(31.10.1846) .... Price on cover	£350

A similar mark for Christchurch as Type CC **2** is only known struck, in black, as a cancellation after the introduction of adhesive stamps.

No. CC3a is a locally-cut replacement with the office name around the circumference, but a straight "PAID AT" in the centre.

PRICES FOR STAMPS ON COVER TO 1945		
Nos.	1/125	from × 2
Nos.	126/36	from × 3
Nos.	137/9	from × 2
No.	140	—
No.	141	from × 2
No.	142	—
Nos.	143/8	from × 2
Nos.	149/51	from × 10
Nos.	152/84	from × 2
Nos.	185/6	—

PRICES FOR STAMPS ON COVER TO 1945		
Nos.	187/203	from × 3
Nos.	205/7e	—
Nos.	208/13	from × 2
Nos.	214/16j	—
Nos.	217/58	from × 3
No.	259	—
Nos.	260/9	from × 3
No.	270	—
Nos.	271/6	from × 3
Nos.	277/307	from × 2
Nos.	308/16	from × 3
No.	317	—
Nos.	318/28	from × 3
Nos.	329/48	—
No.	349	from × 5
Nos.	350/1	—
No.	352	from × 5
Nos.	353/69	—
Nos.	370/86	from × 2
No.	387	from × 4
Nos.	388/99	from × 3
Nos.	400/666	from × 2
Nos.	E1/5	from × 5
No.	E6	from × 10
Nos.	D1/8	from × 3
Nos.	D9/16	from × 5
Nos.	D17/20	from × 3
Nos.	D21/47	from × 6
Nos.	O1/34	from × 5
Nos.	O59/66	from × 4
Nos.	O67/8	—
Nos.	O69/81	from × 5
Nos.	O82/7	—
Nos.	O88/93	from × 20
Nos.	O94/9	from × 12
Nos.	O100/11	from × 5
Nos.	O112/13	—
Nos.	O115/19	from × 15
Nos.	O120/33	from × 10
Nos.	O134/51	from × 4
Nos.	P1/7	from × 8
Nos.	L1/9	from × 10
Nos.	L9a/12	—
Nos.	L13/20	from × 15
Nos.	L21/3	—
Nos.	L24/41	from × 12
No.	F1	—
No.	F2	from × 5
Nos.	F3/144	from × 3
Nos.	F145/58	—
Nos.	F159/68	—
Nos.	F169/79	from × 3
Nos.	F180/6	—
Nos.	F187/90	from × 2
Nos.	F191/203	from × 3
Nos.	F204/11	—
Nos.	F212/18	from × 2
Nos.	A1/3	from × 2

CROWN COLONY

PERKINS BACON "CANCELLED". For notes on these handstamps, showing "CANCELLED" between horizontal bars forming an oval, see Catalogue Introduction.

1   2

(Eng by Humphreys. Recess P.B.)

1855 (20 July)–**57**. Wmk Large Star, W w 1. Imperf.
1	**1**	1d. dull carmine (white paper) (H/S		
		"CANCELLED" in oval £32000)	£70000	£17000
2		2d. dull blue (blued paper) (H/S		
		"CANCELLED" in oval £32000)	£35000	£650
3		1s. pale yellow-green (blued paper)		
		(H/S "CANCELLED" in oval £26000).	£45000	£5500

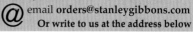

		a. Bisected (6d.) (*on cover*) (1857)	†	£42000

The 2d. and 1s. on white paper formerly listed are now known to be stamps printed on blued paper which have had the bluing washed out. Nos. 3a and 6a were used at Port Chalmers between March 1857, when the rate for ½ oz. letters to Great Britain was reduced to 6d., and August 1859. All known examples are bisected vertically.

(Printed by J. Richardson, Auckland, N.Z.)

1855 (Dec). First printing. White paper. Wmk Large Star. Imperf.

| 3*b* | **1** | 1d. orange | £32000 | |

1855 (Nov)–**58**. Blue paper. No wmk. Imperf.

4	**1**	1d. red	£13000	£2000
5		2d. blue (3.56)	£3000	£300
6		1s. green (9.57)	£40000	£3750
		a. Bisected (6d.) (*on cover*) (1858)	†	£26000

These stamps on blue paper may occasionally be found watermarked double-lined letters, being portions of the papermaker's name.

1857 (Jan). White paper similar to the issue of July 1855. Wmk Large Star.

| 7 | **1** | 1d. dull orange | † | £30000 |

This stamp is in the precise shade of the 1d. of the 1858 printing by Richardson on *no wmk* white paper. An unsevered pair is known with Dunedin cancellation on a cover front showing an Auckland arrival postmark of 19.1.1857.

The paper employed for the local printings was often too small to cover the full printing plate, a problem which was overcome by overlapping two sheets on the press. Depending on how accurately the sheets were overlapped, stamps may be found with portions of the design missing (including a unique example of the 2d. value in the Royal Philatelic Collection with the value tablet missing, formerly listed as No. 5a), or may resemble marginal copies, in spite of coming from the middle of the plate.

1857–63. Hard or soft white paper. No wmk.

(a) Imperf

8	**1**	1d. dull orange (1858)	£3500	£750
8*a*		2d. deep ultramarine (1858)	£3000	£1000
9		2d. pale blue	£1300	£180
10		2d. blue (12.57)	£1300	£180
11		2d. dull deep blue	£1800	£275
12		6d. bistre-brown (8.59)	£4000	£500
13		6d. brown	£3000	£300
14		6d. pale brown	£3000	£300
15		6d. chestnut	£4750	£600
16		1s. dull emerald-green (1858)	£20000	£1800
17		1s. blue-green	£17000	£1800

(b) Pin-roulette, about 10 at Nelson (1860)

18	**1**	1d. dull orange	†	£5500
19		2d. blue	†	£3500
20		6d. brown	†	£4250
20*a*		1s. dull emerald-green	†	£7000
21		1s. blue-green	†	£8000

(c) Serrated perf about 16 or 18 at Nelson (1862)

22	**1**	1d. dull orange	†	£5000
23		2d. blue	†	£3750
24		6d. brown	†	£3500
25		6d. chestnut	†	£7000
26		1s. blue-green	†	£6500

(d) Rouletted 7 at Auckland (April 1859)

27	**1**	1d. dull orange	£10000	£5500
28		2d. blue	£7500	£3250
29		6d. brown	£7500	£2750
		a. Imperf between (pair)	£27000	£13000
30		1s. dull emerald-green	†	£4750
31		1s. blue-green	†	£5500

(e) P 13 at Dunedin (1863)

31*a*	**1**	1d. dull orange	†	£7500
31*b*		2d. pale blue	£7500	£3500
32		6d. pale brown	†	£6500

(f) "H" roulette 16 at Nelson

| 32*a* | **1** | 2d. blue | † | £4750 |
| 32*b* | | 6d. brown | † | £5000 |

(g) "Y" roulette 18 at Nelson

32*c*	**1**	1d. dull orange	†	£6000
32*d*		2d. blue	†	£4000
32*e*		6d. brown	†	£4750
32*f*		6d. chestnut	†	£5500
32*g*		1s. blue-green	†	£8000

(h) Oblique roulette 13 at Wellington

| 32*h* | **1** | 1d. dull orange | † | £6500 |

The various separations detailed above were all applied by hand to imperforate sheets. The results were often poorly cut and badly aligned and examples showing separations on all sides are rare. Nos. 32a/b and 32c/g were produced using roulette wheels fitted with cutting edges in the shape of "H" or "Y", and cannot readily be distinguished from Nos. 22/6 unless the separations are well-preserved.

The separation type described as "Serrated perf" in these listings is technically a form of roulette.

(Printed by John Davies at the G.P.O., Auckland, N.Z.)

1862 (Feb)–**64**. Wmk Large Star.

(a) Imperf

33	**1**	1d. orange vermilion	£950	£275
34		1d. vermilion (9.62)	£750	£275
35		1d. carmine-vermilion (10.63)	£450	£300

36		2d. deep blue (Plate I)	£800	95·00
		a. Double print	—	£4000
37		2d. slate-blue (Plate I)	£2000	£200
37*a*		2d. milky blue (Plate I, worn) (1863)	—	£225
38		2d. pale blue (Plate I, worn)	£700	90·00
39		2d. blue (*to deep*) (Plate I, very worn) (1864)	£700	90·00
40		3d. brown-lilac (Jan 1863)	£600	£160
41		6d. black-brown	£1900	£130
42		6d. brown	£2000	£130
43		6d. red-brown (1863)	£1600	£110
44		1s. green	£2000	£325
45		1s. yellow-green	£1800	£350
46		1s. deep green	£2000	£375

The 2d. in a distinctive deep bright blue on white paper wmkd. Large Star is believed by experts to have been printed by Richardson in 1861 or 1862. This also exists doubly printed and with serrated perf.

No. 37 shows traces of plate wear to the right of the Queen's head. This is more pronounced on Nos. 37*a*/8 and quite extensive on No. 39.

(b) Rouletted 7 at Auckland (5.62)

47	**1**	1d. orange-vermilion	£4750	£850
48		1d. vermilion	£3500	£800
48*a*		1d. carmine-vermilion	£5000	£1000
49		2d. deep blue	£3750	£475
50		2d. slate-blue	£4500	£850
51		2d. pale blue	£3000	£600
52		3d. brown-lilac	£3750	£800
53		6d. black-brown	£3750	£475
54		6d. brown	£3750	£600
55		6d. red-brown	£3500	£475
56		1s. green	£4000	£900
57		1s. yellow-green	£4000	£900
58		1s. deep green	£5000	£1100

(c) Serrated perf 16 or 18 at Nelson (7.62)

59	**1**	1d. orange-vermilion	£10000	£2250
60		2d. deep blue	†	£1300
61		2d. slate-blue	—	
62		3d. brown-lilac	£6000	£1800
63		6d. black-brown	†	£1800
64		6d. brown	†	£2250
65		1s. yellow-green	†	£4500

(d) Pin-perf 10 at Nelson (8.62)

| 66 | **1** | 2d. deep blue | † | £3000 |
| 67 | | 6d. black-brown | † | £4000 |

(e) "H" roulette 16 at Nelson

67*a*	**1**	2d. deep blue (Plate I)	†	£2000
67*b*		6d. black-brown	†	£2250
67*c*		1s. green	†	£4250

(f) "Y" roulette 18 at Nelson (6.62)

67*d*	**1**	1d. orange-vermilion	†	£2500
67*e*		2d. deep blue (Plate I)	†	£2000
		a. Imperf between (horiz pair)	†	£7000
67*f*		2d. slate-blue (Plate I)	†	£2000
67*g*		3d. brown-lilac	†	£2500
67*h*		6d. black-brown	†	£2000
67*i*		6d. brown	†	£2000
67*j*		1s. yellow-green	†	£4250

(g) Oblique roulette 13 at Wellington

67*k*	**1**	2d. deep blue (Plate I)	†	£2500
67*l*		2d. slate-blue (Plate I)		
67*m*		3d. brown-lilac	†	£3000
67*n*		6d. brown	†	£2500

(h) Square roulette 14 at Auckland

67*o*	**1**	1d. orange-vermilion	†	£2500
67*p*		2d. deep blue (Plate I)	†	£2000
67*q*		3d. brown-lilac	†	£3000
67*r*		6d. red-brown	†	£2500

(i) Serrated perf 13 at Dunedin

67*s*	**1**	1d. orange-vermilion	†	£3000
67*t*		2d. deep blue (Plate I)	†	£2000
67*u*		3d. brown-lilac	£4250	£1800
67*v*		6d. brown	†	£2000
67*w*		1s. yellow-green	†	£4250

The dates put to the above varieties are the earliest recorded.

1862 (Dec)–**64**. Wmk Large Star. P 13 (at Dunedin).

68	**1**	1d. orange-vermilion	£3000	£350
		a. Imperf between (horiz pair)	†	£11000
69		1d. carmine-vermilion	£3000	£350
70		2d. deep blue (Plate I)	£1100	£110
71		2d. slate-blue (Plate I)	†	£750
72		2d. blue (Plate I)	£700	80·00
72*a*		2d. milky blue (Plate I)	—	£500
73		2d. pale blue (Plate I)	£700	80·00
74		3d. brown-lilac	£3000	£500
75		6d. black-brown	£2000	£225
		a. Imperf between (horiz pair)		
76		6d. brown	£1800	£160
77		6d. red-brown	£1500	£120
78		1s. dull green	£3000	£425
79		1s. deep green	£3250	£400
80		1s. yellow-green	£3000	£375

See also Nos. 110/25 and the note that follows these.

1862 (Aug)–63. Pelure paper. No wmk.

(a) Imperf

81	1	1d. orange-vermilion (1863)	£12000	£2500
82		2d. ultramarine (10.62)	£6500	£850
83		2d. pale ultramarine	£5500	£800
84		3d. lilac (1863)	£50000	†
85		6d. black-brown	£3500	£250
86		1s. deep green	£14000	£1100

The 3d. is known only unused.

(b) Rouletted 7 at Auckland

87	1	1d. orange-vermilion	†	£6500
88		6d. black-brown	£4000	£475
89		1s. deep green	£15000	£1800

(c) P 13 at Dunedin

90	1	1d. orange-vermilion	£15000	£3500
91		2d. ultramarine	£8500	£800
92		2d. pale ultramarine	£7500	£700
93		6d. black-brown	£7500	£400
94		1s. deep green	£14000	£2000

(d) Serrated perf 16 at Nelson

95	1	6d. black-brown	—	£5500

(e) Serrated perf 13 at Dunedin

95a	1	1d. orange-vermilion	†	£10000

1863 (early). Thick soft white paper. No wmk.

(a) Imperf

96	1	2d. dull deep blue (shades)	£3750	£800

(b) P 13

96a	1	2d. dull deep blue (shades)	£2000	£475

These stamps show slight beginnings of wear of the printing plate in the background to right of the Queen's ear, as one looks at the stamps. By the early part of 1864, the wear of the plate had spread, more or less, all over the background of the circle containing the head. The major portion of the stamps of this printing appears to have been consigned to Dunedin and to have been there perforated 13.

1864. Wmk "N Z", W **2**.

(a) Imperf

97	1	1d. carmine-vermilion	£950	£350
98		2d. pale blue (Plate I worn)	£1600	£275
99		6d. red-brown	£5500	£700
100		1s. green	£2000	£275

(b) Rouletted 7 at Auckland

101	1	1d. carmine-vermilion	£6000	£3000
102		2d. pale blue (Plate I worn)	£2500	£750
103		6d. red-brown	£7000	£3000
104		1s. green	£4500	£1100

(c) P 13 (line) at Dunedin

104a	1	1d. carmine-vermilion	£11000	£5500
105		2d. pale blue (Plate I worn)	£1100	£190
106		1s. green	£2500	£500
		a. Imperf between (horiz pair)	†	£40000
		aa. Perf 6½×13	†	£4250

(d) "Y" roulette 18 at Nelson

106b	1	1d. carmine-vermilion	†	£6500

(e) P 12½ (comb) at Auckland

106c	1	1d. carmine-vermilion	£11000	£4750
107		2d. pale blue (Plate I worn)	£450	75·00
108		6d. red-brown	£650	60·00
109		1s. yellow-green	£7500	£2750

The "NZ" watermark is frequently found inverted.

1864–71. Wmk Large Star. P 12½ (comb or line)* (at Auckland).

110	1	1d. carmine-vermilion (1865)	£225	42·00
111		1d. pale orange-vermilion (1866)	£275	42·00
		a. Imperf (pair)	£4500	£2750
		b. Imperf between (vert pair)	†	—
112		1d. orange (1871)	£600	90·00
113		2d. pale blue (Plate I worn)	£325	30·00
114		2d. deep blue (Plate II) (7.65)	£225	22·00
		a. Imperf vert (horiz pair)	†	£5500
115		2d. blue (Plate II)	£225	22·00
		a. Retouched (Plate II) (1867)	£350	50·00
		c. Imperf (pair) (Plate II)	£3000	£2500
		d. Retouched. Imperf (pair)	£4000	£4250
116		3d. brown-lilac	£2500	£650
117		3d. lilac (1867)	£160	35·00
		a. Imperf (pair)	£4500	£2000
		b. Imperf between (horiz pair)	†	—
118		3d. deep mauve (1867)	£800	75·00
		a. Imperf (pair)	£5000	£2000
119		4d. deep rose (1.6.65)	£3250	£250
120		4d. yellow (1866)	£250	£120
121		4d. orange (1871)	£2250	£1000
122		6d. red-brown	£325	28·00
122a		6d. brown (1867)	£350	42·00
		b. Imperf (pair)	£3000	£3000
123		1s. deep green	£1300	£350
124		1s. green	£750	£140
125		1s. yellow-green	£325	£120

The above issue is sometimes difficult to distinguish from Nos. 68/80 because the vertical perforations usually gauge 12¾ and sometimes a full 13. However, stamps of this issue invariably gauge 12½ horizontally, whereas the 1862 stamps measure a full 13.

* Until late1866 two comb perforating heads were in use. These were then converted to single-line heads, and all subsequent printings were line perforated. Some stamps (such as Nos. 110, 113, 116 and 119) only exist with the early comb perforation, while others (such as Nos. 112, 117/8, 121 and 122a) are always line perforated.

Nos. 111a, 115c/d, 117a, 118a and 122b were issued during problems with the perforation machine which occurred in 1866–67, 1869–70 and 1871–73. Imperforate sheets of the 1s. were also released, but these stamps are very similar to Nos. 44/6.

The new plate of the 2d. showed signs of deterioration during 1866 and thirty positions in rows 13 and 16 to 20 were retouched by a local engraver.

The 1d., 2d. and 6d. were officially reprinted imperforate, without gum, in 1884 for presentation purposes. They can be distinguished from the errors listed by their shades which are pale orange, dull blue and dull chocolate-brown respectively, and by the worn state of the plates from which they were printed (Prices £95 each unused).

1871 (1 Oct)–73. Wmk Large Star. New colours (except No. 129/a).

(a) P 10

126	1	1d. brown	£1000	£130

(b) P 12½×10

127	1	1d. deep brown	†	£4750

(c) P 10×12½

128	1	1d. brown	£350	55·00
		a. Perf 12½ comp 10 (1 side)	£700	£200
129		2d. deep blue (Plate II)	†	£14000
		a. Perf 10*	†	£30000
130		2d. vermilion	£300	42·00
		a. Retouched	£450	60·00
		b. Perf 12½ comp 10 (1 side)	£1800	£525
		c. Perf 10*	†	£25000
131		6d. deep blue	£3250	£900
		a. Blue	£1800	£550
		b. Imperf between (vert pair)		£500
		c. Perf 12½ comp 10 (1 side)	£1600	£450
		ca. Imperf vert (horiz pair)	†	—

(d) P 12½ (1872–73)

132	1	1d. red-brown	£250	48·00
		a. Brown (shades, worn plate) (1873)	£225	42·00
		b. Imperf horiz (vert pair)	—	£6000
133		2d. orange	£170	29·00
		a. Retouched	£275	50·00
134		2d. vermilion	£200	32·00
		a. Retouched	£300	60·00
135		6d. blue	£325	65·00
136		6d. pale blue	£225	55·00

*Only one used copy of No. 129a and two of No. 130c have been reported.

1873 (Aug–Sept). No wmk. P 12½.

137	1	1d. brown	£1200	£275
		a. Watermarked (script letters)*	£4250	£2250
		b. Watermarked (double-lined capitals)*	£2000	£600
138		2d. vermilion	£160	55·00
		a. Retouched	£275	85·00
		b. Watermarked (script letters)*	£4000	£1400
		c. Watermarked (double-lined capitals)*	£1900	£800
139		4d. orange-yellow	£200	£850
		a. Watermarked (double-lined capitals)*	£400	

*1d., 2d. and 4d. stamps were printed on paper showing sheet watermarks of either "W. T. & Co." (Wiggins Teape & Co.) in script letters or "T. H. Saunders" in double-lined capitals (the former appearing once, at the top or bottom of the sheet, and the latter occurring twice in the sheet); portions of these letters are occasionally found on stamps. A third, as yet unidentified script watermark has also been identified on the 1d. and 2d. values.

It seems likely that Nos. 137/9 were printed and issued after Nos. 140/2.

1873 (July?). Wmk "N Z", W **2**. P 12½.

140	1	1d. brown	†	£8000
141		2d. vermilion	£1400	£350
		a. Retouched	£1700	£425

The "NZ" watermark may be found inverted or inverted and reversed.

1873 (Aug). Wmk Lozenges, with "INVICTA" in double-lined capitals four times in the sheet. P 12½.

142	1	2d. vermilion	£3000	£500
		a. Retouched	£4500	£750

3    4

(Des John Davies. Die eng on wood in Melbourne. Printed from electrotypes at Govt Ptg Office, Wellington)

1873 (1 Jan).

*(a) Wmk "NZ", W F **5***

143	3	½d. pale dull rose (P 10)	£110	60·00
144		½d. pale dull rose (P 12½)	£180	85·00

145		½d. pale dull rose (P 12½×10)	£200	85·00
		a. Perf 10×12½	£350	£150

(b) No wmk

146	3	½d. pale dull rose (P 10)	£200	75·00
147		½d. pale dull rose (P 12½)	£250	£100
148		½d. pale dull rose (P 12½×10)	£275	£110
		a. Perf 10×12½	£550	£190

As the paper used for Nos. 143/5 was originally intended for fiscal stamps which were more than twice as large, about one-third of the impressions fall on portions of the sheet showing no watermark, giving rise to varieties Nos. 146/8. In later printings of No. 151 a few stamps in each sheet are without watermark. These can be distinguished from No. 147 by the shade.

1875 (Jan). Wmk Star, W **4**.

149	3	½d. pale dull rose (P 12½)	29·00	3·00
		a. Imperf horiz (vert pair)	£850	£750
		b. Imperf between (horiz pair)	†	£850
		c. Perf compound of 12½ and 10	†	—
150		½d. dull pale rose (P *nearly* 12)	70·00	13·00

1892 (May). Wmk "NZ and Star". W **12b**. P 12½.

151	3	½d. bright rose (*shades*)	14·00	2·00
		a. No wmk	25·00	16·00
		w. Wmk inverted	75·00	50·00
		x. Wmk reversed	—	£180

5 6 7

8 9 10

11 12 12a 6 mm

12b 7 mm 12c 4 mm

(T **5/10** eng De La Rue. T **11** and **12** des, eng and plates by W. R. Bock. Typo Govt Ptg Office, Wellington)

1874 (2 Jan)–**78**.

*A. White paper. W **12a***

(a) P 12½

152	5	1d. lilac	£120	17·00
		a. Imperf (pair)	—	£1800
		w. Wmk inverted	†	£100
		x. Wmk reversed	†	£450
		y. Wmk inverted and reversed	†	£1000
153	6	2d. rose	£130	8·00
154	7	3d. brown	£170	80·00
155	8	4d. maroon	£300	70·00
		w. Wmk inverted	£800	£250
156	9	6d. blue	£250	12·00
		w. Wmk inverted	—	95·00
		x. Wmk reversed	†	£425
157	10	1s. green	£600	38·00
		w. Wmk inverted	£1500	£350

(b) Perf nearly 12 (line)

158	6	2d. rose (1878)	£1200	£190

(c) Perf compound of 12½ and 10

159	5	1d. lilac	£170	45·00
		w. Wmk inverted	—	£120

160	6	2d. rose	£225	85·00
		w. Wmk inverted	—	£160
161	7	3d. brown	£200	85·00
		w. Wmk inverted	†	—
162	8	4d. maroon	£800	£160
163	9	6d. blue	£300	50·00
		w. Wmk inverted	—	£120
164	10	1s. green	£650	£140
		a. Imperf between (vert pair)	†	£7000
		bw. Wmk inverted	†	£475

(d) Perf nearly 12×12½

164c	5	1d. lilac (1875)	£1500	£375
165	6	2d. rose (1878)	£1200	£325

B. Blued paper

(a) P 12½

166	5	1d. lilac	£225	40·00
167	6	2d. rose	£225	40·00
		w. Wmk inverted	—	£120
		x. Wmk reversed	†	£225
168	7	3d. brown	£375	£110
169	8	4d. maroon	£600	£120
170	9	6d. blue	£425	55·00
171	10	1s. green	£1100	£190

(b) Perf compound of 12½ and 10

172	5	1d. lilac	£250	60·00
173	6	2d. rose	£550	£100
174	7	3d. brown	£400	£110
175	8	4d. maroon	£800	£160
176	9	6d. blue	£450	£100
177	10	1s. green	£1100	£250

1875. Wmk Large Star, W w **1**. P 12½.

178	5	1d. deep lilac	£2000	£300
179	6	2d. rose	£800	38·00

1878. W **12a**. P 12×11½ (comb).

180	5	1d. mauve-lilac	65·00	8·00
181	6	2d. rose	70·00	7·00
182	8	4d. maroon	£190	55·00
183	9	6d. blue	£130	12·00
184	10	1s. green	£200	50·00
		w. Wmk inverted	†	£450
185	11	2s. deep rose (1.07)	£375	£300
186	12	5s. grey (1.07)	£375	£300

This perforation is made by a horizontal "comb" machine, giving a gauge of 12 horizontally and about 11¾ vertically. Single examples can be found apparently gauging 11½ all round or 12 all round, but these are all from the same machine. The perforation described above as "nearly 12" was from a single-line machine.

13 14 15

16 17 18

19 20 21

22

Description of Watermarks

W **12a**. 6 mm between "NZ" and star; broad irregular star; comparatively wide "N"; "N Z" 11½ mm wide.

W **12b**. 7 mm between "N Z" and star; narrower star; narrow "N"; "N Z" 10 mm wide.

W **12c**. 4 mm between "N Z" and star; narrow star; wide "N"; "N Z" 11½ mm wide.

Description of Papers

1882–88. Smooth paper with horizontal mesh. W **12a**.
1888–98. Smooth paper with vertical mesh. W **12b**.
1890–91. Smooth paper with vertical mesh. W **12c**.
1898. Thin yellowish toned, coarse paper with clear vertical mesh. W **12b**. Perf 11 only.

In 1899–1900 stamps appeared on medium to thick white coarse paper but we do not differentiate these (except where identifiable by shade) as they are more difficult to distinguish.

PAPER MESH. This shows on the back of the stamp as a series of parallel grooves, either vertical or horizontal. It is caused by the use of a wire gauze conveyor-belt during paper-making.

Description of Dies

1d.

Die 1

Die 2

Die 3

1882. Die 1. Background shading complete and heavy.
1886. Die 2. Background lines thinner. Two lines of shading weak or missing left of Queen's forehead.
1889. Die 3. Shading on head reduced; ornament in crown left of chignon clearer, with unshaded "arrow" more prominent.

"Ellipse" flaw (Die 3, lower left pane, R. 9/2)

"Chisel" flaw (Die 3 upper left pane, R. 4/6) (a smaller break occurs in the lower right frame of this stamp)

2d.

Die 1

Die 2

Die 3

1882. Die 1. Background shading complete and heavy.
1886. Die 2. Weak line of shading left of forehead and missing shading lines below "TA".
1889. Die 3. As Die 2 but with comma-like white notch in hair below "&".

6d.

Die 1

Die 2

1882. Die 1. Shading heavy. Top of head merges into shading. Second ornament from the right on the crown shows a line in its left portion.
1892. Die 2. Background lines thinner. Shading on head more regular with clear line of demarcation between head and background shading. Second ornament from the right in the crown has small dots in its left portion. Most examples also show a break in the back line of the neck immediately above its base.

> **HIGH VALUES**. From 1882 to 1931 postal requirements for higher value stamps were met by the Queen Victoria "Stamp Duty" adhesives (F5/144).

Truebridge Miller   Sunlight Soap

STAMPS WITH ADVERTISEMENTS. During November 1891 the New Zealand Post Office invited tenders for the printing of advertisements on the reverse of the current 1d. to 1s. stamps. The contract was awarded to Messrs Miller, Truebridge & Reich and the first sheets with advertisements on the reverse appeared in February 1893. Different advertisements were applied to the backs of the individual stamps within the sheets of 240 (four panes of 60).

On the first setting those in a vertical format were inverted in relation to the stamps and each of the horizontal advertisements had its base at the left-hand side of the stamp when seen from the back. For the second and third settings the vertical advertisements were the same way up as the stamps and the bases of those in the horizontal format were at the right as seen from the back. The third setting only differs from the second in the order of the individual advertisements.

Examples of the advertisements being printed double are known, but we do not list them.

The experiment was not, however, a success and the contract was cancelled at the end of 1893.

(Des F. W. Sears (½d.), A. E. Cousins (2½d.), A. W. Jones (5d.); others adapted from 1874 issue by W. H. Norris. Dies eng A. E. Cousins (½d., 2½d., 5d.), W. R. Bock (others). Typo Govt Ptg Office)

1882–1900. Inscr "POSTAGE & REVENUE".

A. Paper with horiz mesh (1.4.82–86). W **12a**

(a) P 12×11½

187	**14**	1d. rose *to* rose-red (Die 1)	50·00	7·00
		a. Imperf (pair)	£1100	
		b. Imperf between (vert pair)	£1200	
		cw. Wmk inverted		
		d. Die 2. *Pale rose to carmine-rose* (1886)	65·00	8·00
		dw. Wmk inverted	†	£100
		dx. Wmk reversed	£170	80·00
188	**15**	2d. lilac *to* lilac-purple (Die 1)	60·00	4·00
		a. Imperf (pair)	£1100	
		b. Imperf between (vert pair)	£1200	
		cw. Wmk inverted	£160	75·00
		d. Die 2. *Lilac* (1886)	70·00	15·00
189	**17**	3d. yellow	80·00	19·00
190	**18**	4d. blue-green	85·00	11·00
191	**20**	6d. brown (Die 1)	£120	3·75
		w. Wmk inverted	£425	85·00
192	**21**	8d. blue (1885)	£100	65·00
193	**22**	1s. red-brown	£150	16·00

(b) P 12½ (1884?)

193*a*	**14**	1d. rose *to* rose-red (Die 1)	£500	£300

B. Paper with vert mesh (1888–95). W **12b**

(a) P 12×11½ (1888–95)

194	**13**	½d. black (1.4.95)	42·00	90·00
195	**14**	1d. rose *to* rosine (Die 2)	50·00	5·00
		aw. Wmk inverted	£225	38·00
		b. Die 3. *Rose to carmine* (1889)	50·00	4·50
		bb. Red-brown advert (1st setting) (2.93)	£250	70·00
		bc. Red advert (1st setting) (3.93)	£250	70·00
		bd. Blue advert (2nd setting) (4.93)	£500	£180
		be. Mauve advert (2nd setting) (5.93)	£250	60·00
		bf. Green advert (2nd setting) (6.93)	†	—
		bg. Brown-red advert (3rd setting) (9.93)	£250	55·00
		bh. "Ellipse" flaw	£140	30·00
		bi. "Chisel" flaw	£140	30·00
		bw. Wmk inverted	£140	38·00
		bx. Wmk reversed	£170	70·00
196	**15**	2d. lilac (Die 2)	60·00	5·50
		a. Die 3. *Lilac to purple* (1889)	60·00	6·50
		ab. Red advert (1st setting) (3.93)	£350	60·00
		ac. Mauve advert (2nd setting) (5.93)	£350	60·00
		ad. Sepia advert (2nd setting) (5.93)	£350	60·00
		ae. Green advert (2nd setting) (6.93)	—	£170
		af. Brown-red advert (3rd setting) (9.93)	£350	60·00
		aw. Wmk inverted	£170	38·00
197	**16**	2½d. pale blue (1891)	80·00	5·50
		a. Brown-red advert (2nd setting) (4.93)	£650	£200
		ax. Wmk reversed		£250
		b. *Ultramarine* (green advert. 2nd setting) (6.93)	£650	£200
198	**17**	3d. yellow	70·00	20·00
		a. Brown-red advert (2nd setting) (4.93)	£650	£225
		b. Sepia advert (2nd setting) (5.93)	—	£350
199	**18**	4d. green *to* bluish green	75·00	4·00
		a. Sepia advert (2nd setting) (5.93)	£375	£200
		aw. Wmk inverted	†	£300
200	**19**	5d. olive-black (1.2.91)	80·00	18·00
		a. Imperf (pair)	£1100	
		b. Brown-purple advert (3rd setting) (9.93)	£750	£180
201	**20**	6d. brown (Die 1)	£100	6·50
		a. Die 2 (1892)	£200	£150
		ab. Sepia advert (2nd setting) (5.93)	—	£750
		ac. Brown-red advert (3rd setting) (9.93)	—	£450
		ax. Wmk reversed	†	—
202	**21**	8d. blue	85·00	60·00
203	**22**	1s. red-brown	£130	6·00
		a. Black advert (2nd setting) (5.93)	—	£500
		b. Brown-purple advert (3rd setting) (9.93)	£475	75·00
		w. Wmk inverted	£550	£120

(b) P 12×12½ (1888–91)

204	**14**	1d. rose (Die 2)	£375	£500
		a. Die 3 (1889)	†	—

(c) P 12½ (1888–89)

205	**14**	1d. rose (Die 3) (1889)	£450	£300
		a. Mauve advert (3rd setting) (5.93)	†	£650
		x. Wmk reversed	†	£750
206	**15**	2d. lilac (Die 2)	£475	£475
		a. Die 3. *Deep lilac* (1889)	£475	£550
		ab. Brown-red advert (3rd setting) (9.93)	£650	£350
207	**16**	2½d. blue (1891)	£550	£350

(d) Mixed perfs 12×11½ and 12½ (1891–93)

207*a*	**14**	1d. rose (Die 3) (brown-red advert. 3rd setting)	£375	£225
207*b*	**15**	2d. lilac (Die 3)	†	£450
		ba. Brown-red advert (3rd setting) (9.93)	†	—
207*c*	**18**	4d. green	†	£325
207*d*	**19**	5d. olive-black	†	£350
207*e*	**20**	6d. brown (Die 1)	†	£225
		ea. Die 2	†	£250

C. Paper with vert mesh (1890). W **12c**

(a) P 12×11½

208	**14**	1d. rose (Die 3)	£275	32·00
		a. "Ellipse" flaw	£700	£100
		b. "Chisel" flaw	£700	£100
209	**15**	2d. purple (Die 3)	95·00	20·00
		x. Wmk reversed	†	£225
210	**16**	2½d. ultramarine (27.12)	60·00	14·00
		x. Wmk reversed	†	£225
211	**17**	3d. yellow	£110	48·00
		a. Lemon-yellow	£110	55·00
212	**20**	6d. brown (Die 1)	£170	50·00
213	**22**	1s. deep red-brown	£275	£275

(b) P 12½

214	**14**	1d. rose (Die 3)	£450	£375
215	**15**	2d. purple (Die 3)	£550	£650
216	**16**	2½d. ultramarine	£550	£450

(c) P 12×12½

216*a*	**20**	6d. brown (Die 1)	£475	£375

D. Paper with vert mesh (1891–1900). Continuation of W **12b**

(a) P 10×12½ (1891–94)

216*b*	**14**	1d. rose (Die 3)	£225	£250
		ba. Perf 12½×10	£300	£250
		bb. Red-brown advert (1st setting) (2.93)	£750	£400
		bc. Brown-red advert (2nd setting) (4.93)	£750	£400
		bd. Mauve advert (2nd setting) (5.93)	£750	£400
		be. Green advert (2nd setting) (6.93)	£750	£400
		bf. "Ellipse" flaw	£650	
		bg. "Chisel" flaw	£650	
216*c*	**15**	2d. lilac (Die 3)	£450	£300
216*d*	**16**	2½d. blue (1893)	£350	£275
		da. Perf 12½×10	£650	£450
		dab. Mauve advert (2nd setting)	†	£400
216*e*	**17**	3d. yellow	£500	£600
		ea. Perf 12½×10		
216*f*	**18**	4d. green	£500	£450
		fa. Perf 12½×10, brown-purple advert (3rd setting)	†	£1200
216*g*	**19**	5d. olive-black (1894)	£300	£275
		ga. Perf 12½×10	£375	£300
216*h*	**20**	6d. brown (Die 1)	£550	£600
		i. Die 2 (1892)	£475	£475
		ia. Brown-purple advert (3rd setting) (9.93)		
216*j*	**22**	1s. red-brown	£250	£275
		ja. Perf 12½×10	£425	£350

(b) P 10 (1891–95)

217	**13**	½d. black (1895)	9·00	2·25
218	**14**	1d. rose (Die 3)	14·00	1·00
		a. Carmine	14·00	1·50
		b. Imperf (pair)	£1000	£1000
		c. Imperf between (pair)	£1100	
		d. Imperf horiz (vert pair)	£1000	
		e. Mixed perfs 10 and 12½ (2.93)	£300	£250
		f. Red-brown advert (1st setting) (2.93)	50·00	7·00
		g. Red advert (1st setting) (3.93)	50·00	9·00
		h. Brown-red advert (2nd and 3rd settings) (4.93)	42·00	4·00
		i. Blue advert (2nd setting) (4.93)	£130	48·00
		j. Mauve advert (2nd setting) (5.93)	42·00	6·00
		k. Green advert (2nd setting) (6.93)	£100	30·00
		l. Brown-purple advert (3rd setting) (9.93)	42·00	5·50
		m. "Ellipse" flaw	45·00	11·00
		n. "Chisel" flaw	45·00	11·00
		w. Wmk inverted	£170	85·00
		x. Wmk reversed	£275	£100
219	**15**	2d. lilac (Die 3)	22·00	1·75
		a. Purple	22·00	1·75
		b. Imperf between (pair)	£1200	
		c. Mixed perfs 10 and 12½	£750	£500
		d. Red-brown advert (1st setting) (2.93)	55·00	12·00
		e. Red advert (1st setting) (3.93)	55·00	9·00
		f. Brown-red advert (2nd and 3rd settings) (4.93)	55·00	4·50
		g. Sepia advert (2nd setting) (5.93)	55·00	6·00
		h. Green advert (2nd setting) (6.93)	80·00	15·00
		i. Brown-purple advert (3rd setting) (9.93)	55·00	4·50
		x. Wmk reversed	£170	70·00
220	**16**	2½d. blue (1892)	65·00	3·50

		a. Ultramarine	65·00	4·00
		b. Mixed perfs 10 and 12½	£425	£225
		c. Mauve advert (2nd setting) (5.93) ..	£200	16·00
		d. Green advert (2nd setting) (6.93)....	£225	23·00
		e. Brown-purple advert (3rd setting) (9.93)	£200	16·00
		ex. Wmk reversed	£300	£110
221	17	3d. pale orange-yellow	65·00	19·00
		a. Orange	65·00	24·00
		b. *Lemon-yellow*	65·00	25·00
		c. Mixed perfs 10 and 12½	£750	£650
		d. Brown-red advert (2nd and 3rd settings) (4.93)	£160	30·00
		e. Sepia advert (2nd setting) (5.93)	£170	50·00
		f. Brown-purple advert (3rd setting) (9.93)	£160	28·00
222	18	4d. green (1892)	65·00	8·50
		a. Blue-green.	65·00	8·50
		b. Mixed perfs 10 and 12½	£300	£200
		c. Brown-red advert (2nd setting) (4.93)	£180	13·00
		d. Brown-purple advert (3rd setting) (9.93)	£180	13·00
223	19	5d. olive-black (1893)	65·00	30·00
		a. Brown-purple advert (3rd setting) (9.93)	£190	50·00
		ab. Mixed perfs 10 and 12½	£450	£325
224	20	6d. brown (Die 1)	£160	45·00
		a. Mixed perfs 10 and 12½		
		b. Die 2 (1892)	80·00	9·00
		ba. Black-brown	80·00	9·00
		bb. Imperf (pair)	£1200	
		bc. Mixed perfs 10 and 12½	£375	£200
		bd. Sepia advert (2nd setting) (4.93)	£400	20·00
		be. Brown-red advert (3rd setting) (9.93)	£400	20·00
		bf. Brown-purple advert (3rd setting) (9.93)	£400	20·00
		bx. Wmk reversed (with brown-purple advert)	†	£140
225	21	8d. blue (brown-purple advert. 3rd setting) (9.93)	90·00	70·00
226	22	1s. red-brown	£120	16·00
		a. Imperf between (pair)	£2000	
		b. Mixed perfs 10 and 12½	£425	£225
		c. Sepia advert (2nd setting) (5.93)	£375	55·00
		d. Black advert (2nd setting) (5.93)	£400	£150
		e. Brown-red advert (3rd setting) (9.93)	£375	55·00
		f. Brown-purple advert (3rd setting) (9.93)	£375	55·00

(c) P 10×11 (1895–97)

227	13	½d. black (1896)	4·75	60
		a. Mixed perfs 10 and 11	£170	£120
		b. Perf 11×10 (11.95)	42·00	18·00
228	14	1d. rose (Die 3)	12·00	15
		a. Mixed perfs 10 and 11	£180	£100
		b. Perf 11×10 (10.95)	75·00	13·00
		c. "Ellipse" flaw	45·00	12·00
		d. "Chisel" flaw	45·00	12·00
		x. Wmk reversed	£110	80·00
229	15	2d. purple (Die 3)	23·00	30
		a. Mixed perfs 10 and 11	£100	75·00
230	16	2½d. blue (1896)	65·00	3·75
		a. Ultramarine	65·00	4·50
		b. Mixed perfs 10 and 11	—	£150
231	17	3d. lemon-yellow (1896)	75·00	21·00
232	18	4d. pale green (1896)	95·00	12·00
		a. Mixed perfs 10 and 11	—	£180
233	19	5d. olive-black (1897)	70·00	15·00
234	20	6d. deep brown (Die 2) (1896)	90·00	18·00
		a. Mixed perfs 10 and 11	†	£325
		b. Perf 11×10	£250	£200
235	22	1s. red-brown (1896)	£100	10·00
		a. Mixed perfs 10 and 11	£300	£150

(d) P 11 (1895–1900)

236	13	½d. black (1897)	9·50	15
		aw. Wmk inverted	75·00	32·00
		ax. Wmk reversed	£170	85·00
		b. Thin coarse toned paper (1898)		6·00
		ba. Wmk sideways	†	£2000
237	14	1d. rose (Die 3) (6.95)	6·00	10
		a. Deep carmine	6·00	1·50
		b. Imperf between (pair)	£1000	
		c. *Deep carmine/thin coarse toned* (1898)		3·25
		ca. Wmk sideways	†	£2000
		d. "Ellipse" flaw	35·00	10·00
		e. "Chisel" flaw	35·00	10·00
		w. Wmk inverted	75·00	45·00
		x. Wmk reversed	85·00	55·00
		y. Wmk inverted and reversed	£150	85·00

238	15	2d. mauve (Die 3)	17·00	1·00
		a. Purple	17·00	1·00
		b. *Deep purple/thin coarse toned* (1898)	23·00	6·00
		ba. Wmk sideways	†	£2000
		w. Wmk inverted	85·00	38·00
		x. Wmk reversed	£180	60·00
239	16	2½d. blue (1897)	55·00	4·00
		a. Thin coarse toned paper (1898)	£110	27·00
240	17	3d. pale yellow (1897)	55·00	8·50
		a. *Pale dull yellow/thin coarse toned* (1898)	£110	26·00
		b. *Orange* (1899)	55·00	14·00
		c. *Dull orange-yellow* (1900)	50·00	28·00
241	18	4d. yellowish green (7.96)	60·00	5·00
		a. Bluish green (1897)	55·00	5·00
		w. Wmk inverted	£200	£100
242	19	5d. olive-black/*thin coarse toned* (1899)	70·00	40·00
243	20	6d. brown (Die 2) (1897)	70·00	6·00
		a. *Black-brown*	80·00	5·00
		b. *Brown/thin coarse toned* (1898)	£150	16·00
		x. Wmk reversed	†	£110
244	21	8d. blue (1898)	80·00	60·00
245	22	1s. red-brown (1897)	£100	7·00
		a. Imperf between (vert pair)	£2000	

Only the more prominent shades have been included.
Stamps perf compound of 10×11 and 12½ and 11 and 12½ exist.
For the ½d. and 2d. with double-lined watermark, see Nos. 271/2.

23 Mount Cook or Aorangi

24 Lake Taupo and Mount Ruapehu

25 Pembroke Peak, Milford Sound

26 Lake Wakatipu and Mount Earnslaw, inscribed "WAKITIPU"

27 Lake Wakatipu and Mount Earnslaw, inscribed "WAKATIPU"

28 Huia

29 White Terrace, Rotomahana

30 Otira Gorge and Mount Ruapehu

31 Brown Kiwi

32 Maori War Canoe

33 Pink Terrace, Rotomahana

34 Kea and Kaka

35 Milford Sound   **36** Mount Cook

(Des H. Young (½d.), J. Gaut (1d.), W. Bock (2d., 3d., 9d., 1s.), E. Howard (4d., 6d., 8d.), E. Luke (others). Eng A. Hill (2½d., 1s.), J. A. C. Harrison (5d.), Rapkin (others). Recess Waterlow)

1898 (5 Apr). No wmk. P 12 to 16.

246	**23**	½d. purple-brown	8·50	1·50
		a. Imperf between (pair)	£1700	£1400
		b. Purple-slate	8·50	1·50
		c. Purple-black	8·50	2·75
247	**24**	1d. blue and yellow-brown	6·00	60
		a. Imperf between (horiz pair)	£1300	£1300
		b. Imperf vert (horiz pair)	£900	£1000
		c. Imperf horiz (vert pair)	£900	£1000
		d. Blue and brown	6·50	80
		da. Imperf between (vert pair)	£1300	£1300
248	**25**	2d. lake	38·00	25
		a. Imperf vert (horiz pair)	£600	£1000
		b. Rosy lake	38·00	25
		ba. Imperf between (vert pair)	£1400	
		bb. Imperf vert (horiz pair)	£600	
249	**26**	2½d. sky-blue (inscr "WAKITIPU")	11·00	50·00
		a. Blue	11·00	50·00
250	**27**	2½d. blue (inscr "WAKATIPU")	50·00	8·50
		a. Deep blue	50·00	8·50
251	**28**	3d. yellow-brown	27·00	7·50
252	**29**	4d. bright rose	18·00	19·00
		a. Lake-rose	18·00	23·00
		b. Dull rose	16·00	19·00
253	**30**	5d. sepia	85·00	£200
		a. Purple-brown	55·00	22·00
254	**31**	6d. green (to deep green)	65·00	45·00
		a. Grass-green	£200	£225
255	**32**	8d. indigo	75·00	50·00
		a. Prussian blue	75·00	50·00
256	**33**	9d. purple	75·00	45·00
257	**34**	1s. vermilion	80·00	29·00
		a. Dull red	80·00	29·00
		ab. Imperf between (pair)	£5500	
258	**35**	2s. grey-green	£160	£140
		a. Imperf between (vert pair)	£5500	£5500
259	**36**	5s. vermilion	£300	£475
246/59 *Set of 13*			£850	£800

37 Lake Taupo and Mount Ruapehu

(Recess Govt Printer, Wellington)

1899 (May)–**03**. Thick, soft ("Pirie") paper. No wmk. P 11.

260	**27**	2½d. blue (6.99)	23·00	4·50
		a. Imperf between (horiz pair)	£1500	
		b. Imperf horiz (vert pair)	£600	
		c. Deep blue	23·00	4·50
261	**28**	3d. yellow-brown (5.00)	24·00	2·25
		a. Imperf between (pair)	£1500	
		b. Imperf vert (horiz pair)	£600	
		c. Deep brown	24·00	2·25
		ca. Imperf between (horiz pair)	£1500	
262	**37**	4d. indigo and brown (8.99)	6·00	3·50
		a. Bright blue and chestnut	6·00	3·50
		b. Deep blue and bistre-brown	6·00	3·50
263	**30**	5d. purple-brown (6.99)	48·00	5·50
		a. Deep purple-brown	48·00	5·50
		ab. Imperf between (pair)	£3250	
264	**31**	6d. deep green	70·00	75·00
		a. Yellow-green	£100	£130
265		6d. pale rose (5.5.00)	50·00	8·50
		a. Imperf vert (horiz pair)	£550	
		b. Imperf between (horiz pair)	£1200	
		c. Rose-red	50·00	8·50
		ca. Printed double	£800	£850
		cb. Imperf between (vert pair)	£1600	
		cc. Imperf vert (horiz pair)	£450	
		cd. Showing part of sheet wmk (7.02)*	£100	£110
		d. Scarlet	80·00	26·00
		da. Imperf vert (horiz pair)	£750	
266	**32**	8d. indigo	55·00	20·00

		a. Prussian blue	55·00	20·00
267	**33**	9d. deep purple (8.99)	60·00	38·00
		a. Rosy purple	50·00	17·00
268	**34**	1s. red (5.00)	70·00	12·00
		a. Dull orange-red	70·00	7·00
		b. Dull brown-red	70·00	17·00
		c. Bright red	75·00	40·00
269	**35**	2s. blue-green (7.99)	£150	55·00
		a. Laid paper (1.03)	£225	£250
		b. Grey-green	£150	65·00
270	**36**	5s. vermilion (7.99)	£275	£375
		a. Carmine-red	£325	£450
260/70 *Set of 11*			£700	£500

*No. 265cd is on paper without general watermark, but showing the words "LISBON SUPERFINE" wmkd once in the sheet; the paper was obtained from Parsons Bros, an American firm with a branch at Auckland.

38

1900. Thick, soft ("Pirie") paper. Wmk double-lined "NZ" and Star, W **38** (sideways*). P 11.

271	**13**	½d. black	7·50	19·00
		x. Wmk sideways reversed	£275	£225
272	**15**	2d. bright purple	32·00	20·00
		w. Wmk sideways inverted	90·00	45·00
		y. Wmk sideways inverted and reversed	—	£225

*The normal sideways wmk on Nos. 271/2 shows the top of the star pointing to the left, *as seen from the back of the stamp.*

39 White Terrace, Rotomahana   **41**

40 Commemorative of the New Zealand Contingent in the South African War

1½d. Major re-entry (R. 2/12)

(Des J. Nairn (1½d.). Recess Govt Printer, Wellington)

1900 (Mar–Dec). Thick, soft ("Pirie") paper. W **38**. P 11.

273	**23**	½d. pale yellow-green (7.3.00)	19·00	7·00
		a. Yellow-green	10·00	2·25
		b. Green	10·00	2·00
		ba. Imperf between (pair)	£600	
		c. Deep green	10·00	2·00
		w. Wmk inverted	50·00	25·00
		y. Wmk inverted and reversed	£110	50·00

274	**39**	1d. crimson (7.3.00)	13·00	20
		a. Rose-red	13·00	20
		ab. Imperf between (pair)	£1600	£1800
		ac. Imperf vert (horiz pair)	£650	
		b. Lake	48·00	5·00
		w. Wmk inverted	†	£300
		x. Wmk reversed	†	£225
		y. Wmk inverted and reversed	†	£400
275	**40**	1½d. khaki (7.12.00)	£1200	£750
		a. Brown	60·00	50·00
		ab. Imperf vert (horiz pair)	£1200	
		ac. Imperf (pair)	£1300	
		b. Chestnut	10·00	4·00
		ba. Imperf vert (horiz pair)	£1200	
		bb. Imperf horiz (vert pair)	£1800	
		c. Pale chestnut	10·00	4·00
		ca. Imperf (pair)	£1300	
		d. Major re-entry	£180	£120
276	**41**	2d. dull violet (3.00)	20·00	65
		a. Imperf between (pair)	£1500	
		b. Mauve	23·00	1·50
		c. Purple	16·00	75
		ca. Imperf between (pair)	£1400	

The above ½d. stamps are slightly smaller than those of the previous printing. A new plate was made to print 240 stamps instead of 120 as previously, and to make these fit the watermarked paper, the border design was redrawn and contracted, the centre vignette remaining as before. The 2d. stamp is also from a new plate providing smaller designs.

42

(Des G. Bach and G. Drummond. Eng J. A. C. Harrison.
Recess Waterlow)

1901 (1 Jan). Universal Penny Postage. No wmk. P 12 to 16.

277	**42**	1d. carmine	3·50	4·50

All examples of No. 277 show a minute dot above the upper left corner of the value tablet which is not present on later printings.

(Recess Govt Printer, Wellington)

1901 (Feb–Dec). Thick, soft ("Pirie") paper with vertical mesh. W **38**.

(a) P 11

278	**42**	1d. carmine	6·00	25
		a. Imperf vert (horiz pair)	£400	
		b. Deep carmine	6·00	25
		ba. Imperf vert (horiz pair)	£400	
		c. Carmine-lake	24·00	11·00
		x. Wmk reversed	†	80·00
		y. Wmk inverted and reversed	—	£120

(b) P 14

279	**23**	½d. green (11.01)	23·00	7·50
280	**42**	1d. carmine	65·00	23·00
		a. Imperf vert (horiz pair)	£325	
		y. Wmk inverted and reversed	£170	80·00

(c) P 14×11

281	**23**	½d. green	12·00	17·00
		a. Deep green	12·00	17·00
		b. Perf 11×14	14·00	26·00
282	**42**	1d. carmine	£275	£110
		a. Perf 11×14	£2250	£850

(d) P 11 and 14 mixed*

283	**23**	½d. green	55·00	80·00
284	**42**	1d. carmine	£275	£110

*The term "mixed" is applied to stamps from sheets which were at first perforated 14, or 14×11, and either incompletely or defectively perforated. These sheets were patched on the back with strips of paper, and re-perforated 11 in those parts where the original perforation was defective.

Nos. 278/84 were printed from new plates supplied by Waterlow. These were subsequently used for Nos. 285/307 with later printings on Cowan paper showing considerable plate wear.

WATERMARK VARIETIES. The watermark on the Basted Mills version of the W **38** paper used for Nos. 285/92 occurs indiscriminately normal, reversed, inverted etc.

(Recess Govt Printer, Wellington)

1901 (Dec). Thin, hard ("Basted Mills") paper with vertical mesh. W **38**.

(a) P 11

285	**23**	½d. green	85·00	£110
286	**42**	1d. carmine	£150	£130

(b) P 14

287	**23**	½d. green	45·00	45·00
		a. Imperf vert (horiz pair)	£400	
288	**42**	1d. carmine	19·00	9·00
		a. Imperf vert (horiz pair)	£300	
		b. Imperf horiz (vert pair)	£300	

(c) P 14×11

289	**23**	½d. green	50·00	65·00
		a. Deep green	50·00	65·00
		b. Perf 11×14	26·00	50·00
290	**42**	1d. carmine	38·00	20·00
		a. Perf 11×14	10·00	4·50

(d) Mixed perfs

291	**23**	½d. green	65·00	95·00
292	**42**	1d. carmine	75·00	80·00

(Recess Govt Printer, Wellington)

1902 (Jan). Thin, hard ("Cowan") paper with horizontal mesh. No wmk.

(a) P 11

293	**23**	½d. green	£180	£190

(b) P 14

294	**23**	½d. green	35·00	9·00
295	**42**	1d. carmine	13·00	4·50

(c) P 14×11

296	**23**	½d. green	£130	£190
		a. Perf 11×14	£180	£325
297	**42**	1d. carmine	£110	£130
		a. Perf 11×14	£130	£180

(d) Mixed perfs

298	**23**	½d. green	£160	£225
299	**42**	1d. carmine	£120	£160

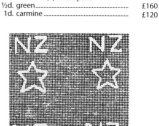

43 "Single" Wmk

SIDEWAYS WATERMARKS. In its sideways format the single NZ and Star watermark W **43**, exists indiscriminately sideways, sideways inverted, sideways reversed and sideways inverted plus reversed.

(Recess Govt Printer, Wellington)

1902 (Apr–Aug). Thin, hard ("Cowan") paper. W **43**.

(a) P 11

300	**23**	½d. green	75·00	£110
301	**42**	1d. carmine	£800	£750

(b) P 14

302	**23**	½d. green	10·00	1·50
		a. Imperf vert (horiz pair)	£300	
		b. Deep green	9·00	1·50
		ba. Imperf vert (horiz pair)	£300	
		c. Yellow green	12·00	1·50
		d. Pale yellow-green	22·00	4·25
		w. Wmk inverted	50·00	22·00
		x. Wmk reversed	55·00	30·00
		y. Wmk inverted and reversed	85·00	42·00
303	**42**	1d. carmine	3·00	10
		a. Imperf horiz (vert pair)	£200	
		b. Booklet pane of 6 (21.8.02)	£275	
		c. Pale carmine	3·00	10
		ca. Imperf horiz (vert pair)	£200	
		cb. Booklet pane of 6.	£275	
		d. Deep carmine*	32·00	4·00
		w. Wmk inverted	90·00	42·00
		x. Wmk reversed	90·00	42·00
		y. Wmk inverted and reversed	95·00	42·00

(c) P 14×11

304	**23**	½d. green	30·00	£120
		a. Deep green	35·00	£120
		b. Perf 11×14	30·00	85·00
305	**42**	1d. carmine	£100	£120
		a. Perf 11×14	£150	£140
		ab. Deep carmine*	£450	£450

(d) Mixed perfs

306	**23**	½d. green	42·00	70·00
		a. Deep green	50·00	70·00
307	**42**	1d. carmine	38·00	50·00
		a. Pale carmine	38·00	50·00
		b. Deep carmine*	£275	£300
		y. Wmk inverted and reversed		

*Nos. 303*d*, 305*ab* and 307*b* were printed from a plate made by Waterlow & Sons, known as the "Reserve" plate. The stamps do not show evidence of wearing and the area surrounding the upper part of the figure is more deeply shaded. This plate was subsequently used to produce Nos. 362, 364 and 366/9.

A special plate, made by W. R. Royle & Sons, showing a minute dot between the horizontal rows, was introduced in 1902 to print the booklet pane, No. 303b. A special characteristic of the booklet pane was that the pearl in the top left-hand corner was large. Some panes exist with the outer edges imperforate.

(Recess Govt Printer, Wellington)

1902 (28 Aug)–**07**. Thin, hard ("Cowan") paper. W **43** (sideways on 3d., 5d., 6d., 8d., 1s. and 5s.).

(a) P 11

308	27	2½d. blue (5.03)	35·00	12·00
		a. Deep blue	35·00	12·00
		w. Wmk inverted	£200	95·00
		x. Wmk reversed	£225	55·00
		y. Wmk inverted and reversed	£350	90·00
309	28	3d. yellow-brown	38·00	3·25
		a. Bistre-brown	45·00	3·25
		b. Pale bistre	50·00	5·50
310	37	4d. deep blue and deep brown/*bluish* (27.11.02)		75·00
		a. Imperf vert (horiz pair)	£650	
311	30	5d. red-brown (4.03)	55·00	10·00
		a. Deep brown	50·00	8·00
		b. Sepia	60·00	21·00
312	31	6d. rose (9.02)	40·00	7·50
		a. Rose-red	40·00	7·50
		ab. Wmk upright (?.1.03)	£2750	£2000
		b. Rose-carmine	50·00	7·50
		ba. Imperf vert (horiz pair)	£850	
		bb. Imperf horiz (vert pair)		
		c. Bright carmine-pink	60·00	8·00
		d. Scarlet	75·00	18·00
313	32	8d. blue (2.03)	55·00	11·00
		a. Steel-blue	55·00	11·00
		ab. Imperf vert (horiz pair)	£2000	
		ac. Imperf horiz (vert pair)	£2000	
314	33	9d. purple (5.03)	70·00	12·00
		w. Wmk inverted	£250	£140
		x. Wmk reversed	£275	£225
		y. Wmk inverted and reversed	£325	£275
315	34	1s. brown-red (11.02)	75·00	15·00
		a. Bright red	75·00	15·00
		b. Orange-red	75·00	8·00
		ba. Error. Wmk W **12b** (inverted)	—	£2000
		c. Orange-brown	70·00	22·00
316	35	2s. green (4.03)	£160	65·00
		a. Blue-green	£150	45·00
		x. Wmk reversed	£750	
		w. Wmk inverted	£450	£180
317	36	5s. deep red (6.03)	£300	£400
		a. Wmk upright	£325	£425
		b. Vermilion	£275	£375
		ba. Wmk upright	£325	£425
		w. Wmk inverted	£1500	£850

(b) P 14

318	40	1½d. chestnut (2.07)	25·00	60·00
		a. Major re-entry	£275	
319	41	2d. grey-purple (12.02)	5·50	2·75
		a. Purple	5·50	2·75
		ab. Imperf vert (horiz pair)	£550	£850
		ac. Imperf horiz (vert pair)	£800	
		b. Bright reddish purple	6·50	3·50
320	27	2½d. blue (1906)	27·00	5·00
		a. Deep blue	27·00	5·00
		w. Wmk inverted	£170	£130
		x. Wmk reversed	†	£300
		y. Wmk inverted and reversed	£375	£200
321	28	3d. bistre-brown (1906)	30·00	8·00
		a. Imperf vert (horiz pair)	£950	
		b. Bistre	30·00	8·00
		c. Pale yellow-bistre	65·00	20·00
322	37	4d. deep blue and deep brown/*bluish* (1903)	7·50	4·00
		a. Imperf vert (horiz pair)	£650	
		b. Imperf horiz (vert pair)	£650	
		c. Centre inverted	†	*
		d. Blue and chestnut/*bluish*	4·00	3·25
		e. Blue and ochre-brown/*bluish*	4·00	3·25
		w. Wmk inverted	60·00	30·00
		x. Wmk reversed	£140	£100
		y. Wmk inverted and reversed	£225	£180
323	30	5d. black-brown (1906)	60·00	38·00
		a. Red-brown	40·00	16·00
324	31	6d. bright carmine-pink (1906)	60·00	9·50
		a. Imperf vert (horiz pair)	£850	
		b. Rose-carmine	60·00	9·50
325	32	8d. steel-blue (1907)	50·00	11·00
326	33	9d. purple (1906)	45·00	8·50
		w. Wmk inverted	£375	£275
327	34	1s. orange-brown (1906)	80·00	8·50
		a. Orange-red	75·00	8·50
		b. Pale red	£170	65·00
328	35	2s. green (1.06)	£130	32·00
		a. Blue-green	£150	42·00
		aw. Wmk inverted	£800	£250
		ax. Wmk reversed	†	—
		ay. Wmk inverted and reversed	£800	£250
329	36	5s. deep red (1906)	£225	£300
		a. Wmk upright	£225	£375
		b. Dull red	£225	£300
		ba. Wmk upright	£225	£375

(c) Perf compound of 11 and 14

330	40	1½d. chestnut (1907)	£1600	
331	41	2d. purple (1903)	£500	£425
332	28	3d. bistre-brown (1906)	£950	£750
333	37	4d. blue and yellow-brown (1903)	£450	£500
		x. Wmk reversed	—	£850
334	30	5d. red-brown (1906)	£1700	£1400
335	31	6d. rose-carmine (1907)	£450	£450
336	32	8d. steel-blue (1907)	£1400	£1500
337	33	9d. purple (1906)	£1700	£1600
338	36	5s. deep red (wmk sideways) (1906)	£3250	£3250

(d) Mixed perfs

339	40	1½d. chestnut (1907)	£1600	
340	41	2d. purple (1903)	£450	£325
341	28	3d. bistre-brown (1906)	£900	£700
342	37	4d. blue and chestnut/*bluish* (1904)	£400	£450
		a. Blue and yellow-brown/*bluish*	£400	£450
		w. Wmk inverted	£950	£850
		x. Wmk reversed	£950	£900
343	30	5d. red-brown (1906)	£1300	£110
344	31	6d. rose-carmine (1907)	£425	£425
		a. Bright carmine-pink	£450	£450
345	32	8d. steel-blue (1907)	£1400	£1400
346	33	9d. purple (1906)	£1500	£1600
347	35	2s. blue-green (1906)	£1700	£1800
348	36	5s. vermilion (Wmk upright) (1906)	£2500	£3000
		w. Wmk inverted		

Two sizes of paper were used for the above stamps:—
(1) A sheet containing 240 wmks, with a space of 9 mm between each.
(2) A sheet containing 120 wmks, with a space of 24 mm between each vertical row.

Size (1) was used for the ½d., 1d., 2d. and 4d., and size (2) for 2½d., 5d., 9d. and 2s. The paper in each case exactly fitted the plates, and had the watermark in register, though in the case of the 4d., the plate of which contained only 80 stamps, the paper was cut up to print it. The 3d., 6d., 8d. and 1s. were printed on variety (1), but with watermark sideways: by reason of this, examples from the margins of the sheets show parts of the words "NEW ZEALAND POSTAGE" in large letters, and some have no watermark at all. For the 1½d. and 5s. stamps variety (1) was also used, but two watermarks appear on each stamp.

*The only known example of No. 322c, postmarked at Picton on 21 March 1904, was purchased for the New Zealand Post archive collection in 1998.

(Recess Govt Printer, Wellington)

1904 (Feb). Printed from new "dot" plates made by W. R. Royle & Sons. Thin, hard ("Cowan") paper. W **43**.

(a) P 14

349	42	1d. rose-carmine	11·00	50
		a. Pale carmine	11·00	50
		w. Wmk inverted	£120	38·00
		y. Wmk inverted and reversed	£120	45·00

(b) P 11×14

350	42	1d. rose-carmine	£180	£130

(c) Mixed perfs

351	42	1d. rose-carmine	42·00	55·00
		a. Pale carmine	42·00	55·00

These plates have a dot in the margins between stamps, level with the small pearls at the side of the design, but it is frequently cut out by the perforations. However, they can be further distinguished by the notes below.

In 1906 fresh printings were made from four new plates, two of which, marked in the margin "W1" and "W2", were supplied by Waterlow Bros and Layton, and the other two, marked "R1" and "R2", by W. R. Royle & Son. The intention was to note which pair of plates wore the best and produced the best results. They can be distinguished as follows:—

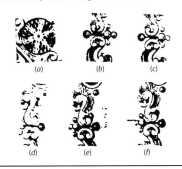

(a)	(b)	(c)
(d)	(e)	(f)

(a) Four o'clock flaw in rosette at top right corner. Occurs in all these plates but not in the original Waterlow plates.

(b) Pearl at right strong.

(c) Pearl at right weak.

(d) Dot at left and S-shaped ornament unshaded.

(e) S-shaped ornament with one line of shading within.

(f) As (e) but with line from left pearl to edge of stamp.

"Dot" plates comprise (a) and (d).

Waterlow plates comprise (a), (b) and (e).

Royle plates comprise (a), (c) and (e) and the line in (f) on many stamps but not all.

(Recess Govt Printer, Wellington)

1906. Thin, hard ("Cowan") paper. W **43**.

(a) Printed from new Waterlow plates

(i) P 14

352	**42**	1d. deep rose-carmine	55·00	3·75
		a. Imperf horiz (vert pair)	£300	
		b. Aniline carmine	50·00	3·75
		ba. Imperf vert (horiz pair)	£300	
		c. Rose-carmine	50·00	3·75
		y. Wmk inverted and reversed	—	£400

(ii) P 11

353	**42**	1d. aniline carmine	£700	£850

(iii) P 11×14

354	**42**	1d. rose-carmine	£475	£900
		a. Perf 14×11	£500	£850

(iv) Mixed perfs

355	**42**	1d. deep rose-carmine	£425	£650

(b) Printed from new Royle plates

(i) P 14

356	**42**	1d. rose-carmine	12·00	1·25
		a. Imperf horiz (vert pair)	£250	£325
		b. Bright rose-carmine	13·00	1·40
		w. Wmk inverted	†	£500
		y. Wmk inverted and reversed	—	£250

(ii) P 11

357	**42**	1d. bright rose-carmine	£110	£225

(iii) P 11×14

358	**42**	1d. rose-carmine	£100	£200
		a. Perf 14×11	£150	£200

(iv) Mixed perfs

359	**42**	1d. rose-carmine	£160	£275

(v) P 14×14½ (comb)

360	**42**	1d. bright rose-carmine	80·00	60·00
		a. Rose-carmine	80·00	60·00

Nos. 360/a are known both with and without the small dot. See also No. 386.

1905 (15 June)–**06.** Stamps supplied to penny-in-the-slot machines.

(i) "Dot" plates of 1904

(ii) Waterlow "reserve" plate of 1902

(a) Imperf top and bottom; zigzag roulette 9½ on one or both sides, two large holes at sides

361	**42**	1d. rose-carmine (i)	£200	
362		1d. deep carmine (ii)	£225	

(b) As last but rouletted 14½ (8.7.05)

363	**42**	1d. rose-carmine (i)	£200	
364		1d. deep carmine (ii)	£425	

(c) Imperf all round, two large holes each side (6.3.06)

365	**42**	1d. rose-carmine (i)	£160	
366		1d. deep carmine (ii)	£170	

(d) Imperf all round (21.6.06)

367	**42**	1d. deep carmine (ii)	£180	

(e) Imperf all round. Two small indentations on back of stamp (1.06)

368	**42**	1d. deep carmine (ii)	£225	£200

(f) Imperf all round; two small pin-holes in stamp (21.6.06)

369	**42**	1d. deep carmine (ii)	£200	£200

No. 365 only exists from strips of Nos. 361 or 363 (resulting from the use of successive coins) which have been separated by scissors. Similarly strips of Nos. 362 and 364 can produce single copies of No. 366 but this also exists in singles from a different machine.

Most used copies of Nos. 361/7 are forgeries and they should only be collected on cover.

44 Maori Canoe, *Te Arawa*

45 Maori art

46 Landing of Cook

46a Annexation of New Zealand

(Des L. J. Steele. Eng W. R. Bock. Typo Govt Printer, Wellington)

1906 (1–17 Nov). New Zealand Exhibition, Christchurch. W **43** (sideways). P 14.

370	**44**	½d. emerald-green	40·00	38·00
371	**45**	1d. vermilion	16·00	16·00
		a. Claret	£8000	£11000
372	**46**	3d. brown and blue	55·00	85·00
373	**46a**	6d. pink and olive-green (17.11)	£200	£275
370/3		Set of 4	£275	£375

The 1d. in claret was the original printing, which was considered unsatisfactory.

47 (T **28** reduced)

48 (T **31** reduced)

49 (T **34** reduced)

(New plates (except 4d.), supplied by Perkins Bacon. Recess Govt Printer, Wellington).

1907–08. Thin, hard ("Cowan") paper. W **43**.

(a) P 14 (line)

374	**23**	½d. green (1907)	42·00	16·00
		a. Imperf (pair)	£350	
		b. Yellow-green	32·00	7·50
		c. Deep yellow-green	32·00	7·50
375	**47**	3d. brown (6.07)	95·00	28·00
376	**48**	6d. carmine-pink (3.07)	48·00	12·00
		a. Red	55·00	40·00

(b) P 14×13, 13½ (comb)

377	**23**	½d. green (1907)	17·00	17·00
		a. Yellow-green	9·50	8·50
		b. Imperf three sides (top stamp of vert pair)	£500	
378	**47**	3d. brown (2.08)	55·00	50·00
		a. Yellow-brown	55·00	50·00
379	**37**	4d. blue and yellow-brown/bluish (6.08)	42·00	60·00
380	**48**	6d. pink (2.08)	£425	£170
381	**49**	1s. orange-red (12.07)	£140	65·00

(c) P 14×15 (comb)

382	**23**	½d. yellow-green (1907)	8·50	1·00
		a. Imperf three sides (top stamp of vert pair)	£450	
		y. Wmk inverted and reversed	—	£275
383	**47**	3d. brown (8.08)	50·00	15·00
		a. Yellow-brown	50·00	15·00
384	**48**	6d. carmine-pink (8.08)	50·00	11·00
385	**49**	1s. orange-red (8.08)	£110	24·00
		a. Deep orange-brown	£325	£900

The ½d. stamps of this 1907–8 issue have a minute dot in the margin between the stamps, where not removed by the perforation. (See note after No. 351a). Those perforated 14 can be distinguished from the earlier stamps, Nos. 302/d, by the absence of plate wear. This is most noticeable on the 1902 printings as a white patch at far left, level with the bottom of the "P" in "POSTAGE". Such damage is not present on the new plates used for Nos. 374/c.

Stamps of T **47**, **48** and **49** also have a small dot as described in note after No. 351a.

TYPOGRAPHY PAPERS.

1908–30. De La Rue paper is chalk-surfaced and has a smooth finish. The watermark is as illustrated. The gum is toned and strongly resistant to soaking.

Jones paper is chalk-surfaced and has a coarser texture, is poorly surfaced and the ink tends to peel. The outline of the watermark commonly shows on the surface of the stamp. The gum is colourless or only slightly toned and washes off readily.

Cowan paper is chalk-surfaced and is white and opaque. The watermark is usually smaller than in the "Jones" paper and is often barely visible.

Wiggins Teape paper is chalk-surfaced and is thin and hard. It has a vertical mesh with a narrow watermark, whereas the other papers have a horizontal mesh and a wider watermark.

50

(Typo Govt Printer, Wellington, from Perkins Bacon plate).

1908 (1 Dec). De La Rue chalk-surfaced paper. W **43**. P 14×15 (comb).
386   **50**   1d. carmine .... 23·00   3·25
       w. Wmk inverted .... —   £120

The design of Type **50** differs from Type **42** by alterations in the corner rosettes and by the lines on the globe which are diagonal instead of vertical.

51   **52**   **53**

(Eng. P.B. Typo Govt Printer, Wellington)

1909 (8 Nov)–**12**. De La Rue chalk-surfaced paper with toned gum. W **43**. P 14×15 (comb).
387   **51**   ½d. yellow-green .... 5·00   50
       aa. Deep green .... 5·00   50
       a. Imperf (pair) £225
       b. Booklet pane. 5 stamps plus label in
         position 1 (4.10) £800
       c. Ditto, but label in position 6 (4.10) ... £800
       d. Booklet pane of 6 (4.10) £250
       e. Ditto, but with coloured bars on
         selvedge (5.12) £225
       w. Wmk inverted .... †   £500

Stamps with blurred and heavy appearance are from booklets.

(Eng W. R. Royle & Son, London. Recess Govt Printer, Wellington)

1909 (8 Nov)–**16**. T **52** and similar portraits.

*(a) W **43**. P 14×14½ (comb)*
388   2d. mauve.. 9·50   6·50
       a. Deep mauve .... 18·00   6·50
       w. Wmk inverted .... †
389   3d. chestnut .... 23·00   1·25
390   4d. orange-red .... 26·00   27·00
390*a*   4d. yellow (1912) .... 6·00   9·50
       aw. Wmk inverted £475   £150
391   5d. brown (1910) .... 17·00   5·00
       a. Red-brown .... 17·00   5·00
       w. Wmk inverted .... †
392   6d. carmine (1910) .... 40·00   2·00
       a. Deep carmine (29.10.13) .... 50·00   3·50
393   8d. indigo-blue .... 13·00   3·50
       a. Deep bright blue .... 13·00   3·50
       w. Wmk inverted .... 85·00   50·00
394   1s. vermilion (1910)........................... 50·00   5·00
       w. Wmk inverted £400   £150
388/94 *Set of 8*.. £160   55·00

*(b) W **43**. P 14 (line)**
395   3d. chestnut (1910) .... 50·00   20·00
396   4d. orange (1910) .... 20·00   15·00
397   5d. brown .... 26·00   4·50
       a. Red-brown (15.9.11) .... 26·00   5·00
       w. Wmk inverted ....
398   6d. carmine .... 42·00   10·00
399   1s. vermilion...................................... 65·00   14·00
395/9 *Set of 5*.. £180   55·00

*(c) W **43** (sideways) (paper with widely spaced wmk as used for Nos. 308 and 320 – see note below No. 348). P 14 (line)**
400   8d. indigo-blue (8.16)......................... 50·00   95·00
       a. No wmk.. £120   £200

*(d) W **43**. P 14×13½ (comb)†*
401   3d. chestnut (1915)............................ 75·00   £130
       a. Vert pair. P 14×13½ and 14×14½ £250   £475
       w. Wmk inverted £400   £375
402   5d. red-brown (1916) .... 19·00   3·00
       a. Vert pair. P 14×13½ and 14×14½ .... 60·00   £170
403   6d. carmine (1915)............................. 75·00   £130
       a. Vert pair. P 14×13½ and 14×14½ £250   £600
404   8d. indigo-blue (3.16).......................... 50·00   3·00
       a. Vert pair. P 14×13½ and 14×14½ .... 70·00   £160
       b. Deep bright blue .... 55·00   3·25
       ba. Vert pair. P 14×13½ and 14×14½ .... 80·00   £170
       w. Wmk inverted .... £140   50·00
401/4 *Set of 4*.. £190   £225

*In addition to showing the usual characteristics of a line perforation, these stamps may be distinguished by their vertical perforation which measures 13.8. Nos. 388/94 generally measure vertically 14 to 14.3. An exception is 13.8 one vertical side but 14 the other.

†The 3d. and 6d. come in full sheets perf 14×13½. The 3d., 5d. and 6d. values also exist in two combinations: (*a*) five top rows perf 14×13½ with five bottom rows perf 14×14½ and (*b*) four top rows perf 14×13½ with six bottom rows perf 14×14½. The 8d. perf 14×13½ only exists from combination (*b*).

1d. "Feather" flaw (Plate 12, R. 3/1)

1d. "Globe" flaw (Plate 12, R. 5/24)

1d. "Q" flaw (Plate 13, R. 10/19)

1d. "N" flaw (Plate 12, R. 9/23, *printings from 1925*)

(Eng P.B. Typo Govt Printer, Wellington)

1909 (8 Nov)–**27**. P 14×15 (comb).

*(a) W **43**. De La Rue chalk-surfaced paper with toned gum*
405   **53**   1d. carmine .... 1·75   10
       a. Imperf (pair) £375
       b. Booklet pane of 6 (4.10) £200
       c. Ditto, but with coloured bars on
         selvedge (5.12) £160
       d. "Feather" flaw.............................. 30·00   8·50
       e. "Globe" flaw................................. 30·00   8·50
       f. "Q" flaw....................................... 60·00   25·00
       w. Wmk inverted .... 80·00   70·00
       y. Wmk inverted and reversed.............

*(b) W **43**. Jones chalk-surfaced paper with white gum*
406   **53**   1d. deep carmine (6.24)................ 19·00   9·00
       a. On unsurfaced paper. *Pale carmine* ... £400
       b. Booklet pane of 6 with bars on
         selvedge (1.12.24) £160
       c. "Feather" flaw.............................. 90·00   50·00
       d. "Globe" flaw................................. 90·00   50·00
       w. Wmk inverted .... £120   60·00

*(c) W **43**. De La Rue unsurfaced medium paper with toned gum*
407   **53**   1d. rose-carmine (4.25).................. 42·00   £140
       a. "Feather" flaw.............................. £300
       b. "Globe" flaw................................. £300

*(d) W **43** (sideways). De La Rue chalk-surfaced paper with toned gum*
408   **53**   1d. bright carmine (4.25)................ 12·00   50·00
       a. No wmk .... 24·00   80·00
       b. Imperf (pair) £160
       c. "Feather" flaw.............................. 80·00
       d. "Globe" flaw................................. 80·00

(e) No wmk, but bluish "NZ" and Star lithographed on back. Art paper

409	**53**	1d. rose-carmine (7.25)		2·00	8·00
		a. "NZ" and Star in black		24·00	
		b. "NZ" and Star colourless		24·00	
		c. "Feather" flaw		60·00	95·00
		d. "Globe" flaw		60·00	95·00

*(f) W **43**. Cowan thick, opaque, chalk-surfaced paper with white gum*

410	**53**	1d. deep carmine (8.25)		12·00	1·00
		a. Imperf (pair)		£140	£180
		b. Booklet pane of 6 with bars and adverts on selvedge		£190	
		c. "Feather" flaw		70·00	40·00
		d. "Globe" flaw		70·00	40·00
		e. "N" flaw		£120	£120
		w. Wmk inverted		65·00	42·00
		x. Wmk reversed (1926)		12·00	4·00
		xa. Booklet pane of 6 with bars and adverts on selvedge (1927)		£180	
		xc. "Feather" flaw		£120	70·00
		xd. "Globe" flaw		£120	70·00
		xe. "N" flaw		£140	£100
		y. Wmk inverted and reversed (1926)		£120	90·00

*(g) W **43**. Wiggins Teape thin, hard, chalk-surfaced paper with white gum*

411	**53**	1d. rose-carmine (6.26)		40·00	28·00
		a. "Feather" flaw		£170	70·00
		b. "Globe" flaw		£170	70·00
		c. "N" flaw		£170	90·00
		w. Wmk inverted		80·00	50·00

Examples of No. 405 with a blurred and heavy appearance are from booklets.

No. 406a comes from a sheet on which the paper coating was missing from the right-hand half.

Many stamps from the sheets of No. 408 were without watermark or showed portions of "NEW ZEALAND POSTAGE" in double-lined capitals.

**AUCKLAND
EXHIBITION,
1913.**

(59) **60**

1913 (1 Dec). Auckland Industrial Exhibition. Nos. 387*aa*, 389, 392 and 405 optd with T **59** by Govt Printer, Wellington.

412	**51**	½d. deep green		22·00	55·00
413	**53**	1d. carmine		28·00	50·00
		a. "Feather" flaw		£300	£400
		b. "Globe" flaw		£300	£400
414	**52**	3d. chestnut		£130	£250
415		6d. carmine		£160	£300
412/15 *Set of 4*				£300	£600

These overprinted stamps were only available for letters in New Zealand and to Australia.

(Des H. L. Richardson. Recess Govt Printer, Wellington, from plates made in London by P.B.)

1915 (30 July)–**30**. W **43**. P 14×13½ (comb) (see notes below).

(a) Cowan unsurfaced paper

416	**60**	1½d. grey-slate		3·25	2·50
		a. Perf 14×14½ (1915)		5·00	1·75
		aw. Wmk inverted		£500	£500
		b. Vert pair. Nos. 416/a		35·00	£100
417		2d. bright violet		12·00	65·00
		a. Perf 14×14½		7·00	50·00
		b. Vert pair. Nos. 417/a		28·00	£160
418		2d. yellow (15.1.16)		7·50	32·00
		a. Perf 14×14½		7·50	32·00
		b. Vert pair. Nos. 418/a		21·00	£250
419		2½d. blue		3·25	7·00
		a. Perf 14×14½ (1916)		9·50	32·00
		b. Vert pair. Nos. 419/a		40·00	£180
420		3d. chocolate		22·00	1·25
		aw. Wmk inverted		£225	£150
		ax. Wmk reversed			
		b. Perf 14×14½		13·00	2·00
		bw. Wmk inverted		£450	£170
		bx. Wmk reversed		£650	
		c. Vert pair. Nos. 420 and 420b		50·00	£140
		cw. Wmk inverted			
		cx. Wmk reversed			
421		4d. yellow		4·25	60·00
		a. Re-entry (Pl 20 R. 1/6)		50·00	
		b. Re-entry (Pl 20 R. 4/10)		60·00	
		c. Perf 14×14½		4·25	60·00
		d. Vert pair. Nos. 421 and 421c		27·00	£250
422		4d. bright violet (7.4.16)		11·00	50
		a. Imperf three sides (top stamp of vertical pair)		£1500	
		b. Re-entry (Pl 20 R. 1/6)		55·00	35·00
		c. Re-entry (Pl 20 R. 4/10)		65·00	40·00
		dx. Wmk reversed		—	£350

		e. Perf 14×14½	7·00	50
		ex. Wmk reversed	—	£350
		f. Vert pair. Nos. 422 and 422e	60·00	£150
		fx. Wmk reversed		
		g. Deep purple (7.26)	50·00	15·00
		h. Ditto. Perf 14×14½	7·00	50
		ha. Imperf three sides (top stamp of vertical pair)	£1500	
		hb. Vert pair. Nos. 422g/h	£2500	
		hw. Wmk inverted	†	£1900
423		4½d. deep green	18·00	28·00
		a. Perf 14×14½ (1915)	12·00	55·00
		b. Vert pair. Nos. 423/a	55·00	£170
424		5d. light blue (4.22)	7·00	1·00
		a. Imperf (pair)	£140	£180
		aa. Imperf (top stamp of vertical pair).	£850	
		bw. Wmk inverted	—	£300
		c. Perf 14×14½	12·00	38·00
		d. Pale ultramarine (5.30)	17·00	13·00
		da. Perf 14×14½	32·00	25·00
		db. Vert pair. Nos. 424d/da.	80·00	£250
425		6d. carmine	9·00	50
		a. Imperf three sides (top stamp of vert pair)	£1500	
		bw. Wmk inverted	£200	£160
		bx. Wmk reversed	—	£250
		by. Wmk inverted and reversed	†	£1900
		c. Carmine-lake (11.27)	£500	£400
		d. Perf 14×14½ (1915)	10·00	60
		dw. Wmk inverted	£190	65·00
		e. Vert pair. Nos. 425 and 425d	65·00	£140
426		7½d. red-brown	14·00	30·00
		a. Perf 14×14½ (10.20)	11·00	80·00
		b. Vert pair. Nos. 426/a	50·00	£225
427		8d. indigo-blue (19.4.21)	15·00	60·00
		a. Perf 14×14½	8·50	55·00
		b. Vert pair. Nos. 427/a	38·00	£180
428		8d. red-brown (3.22)	32·00	1·50
429		9d. sage-green	17·00	2·75
		a. Imperf (pair)	£1500	
		b. Imperf three sides (top stamp of vert pair)	£1500	
		c. Yellowish olive (12.25)	20·00	24·00
		dw. Wmk inverted	†	£1900
		e. Perf 14×14½	15·00	32·00
		f. Vert pair. Nos. 429 and 429e	75·00	£225
430		1s. vermilion	21·00	2·25
		a. Imperf (pair)	£2250	
		aa. Imperf (top stamp of vertical pair).	£2000	
		bw. Wmk inverted	£375	£350
		c. Perf 14×14½ (1915)	14·00	50
		ca. Pale orange-red (4.24)	30·00	25·00
		cb. Imperf (pair)	£325	
		cba. Imperf (top stamp of vertical pair).	£750	
		cc. Orange-brown (1.2.28)	£600	£450
		cw. Wmk inverted	£300	
		d. Vert pair. Nos. 430 and 430c.	75·00	£275
		dw. Wmk inverted		
416/30c *Set of 15*			£130	£225

*(b) W **43** (sideways on 2d., 3d. and 6d.). Thin paper with widely spaced watermark as used for Nos. 308 and 320 (see note below No. 348).*
P 14×13½ (comb) (see notes below) (1½d.) or 14 (line) (others)

431	**60**	1½d. grey-slate (3.16)		3·00	11·00
		a. No wmk		5·00	23·00
		b. Perf 14×14½		3·00	11·00
		ba. No wmk		5·00	23·00
		by. Wmk inverted and reversed		£500	£500
		c. Vert pair. Nos. 431 and 431b		26·00	£120
		ca. Vert pair. Nos. 431a and 431ba		60·00	£190
432		2d. yellow (6.16)		7·00	60·00
		a. No wmk		75·00	£160
433		3d. chocolate (6.16)		7·00	50·00
		a. No wmk		75·00	£160
434		6d. carmine (6.16)		11·00	£110
		a. No wmk		£100	£225
431/4 *Set of 4*				25·00	£200

The 1½d., 2½d., 4½d. and 7½d. have value tablets as shown in Type **60**. For the other values the tablets are shortened and the ornamental border each side of the crown correspondingly extended.

With the exception of Nos. 432/4 stamps in this issue were comb-perforated 14×13½, 14×14½ or a combination of the two.

The 1½d. (No. 416), 2½d., 4d. (both), 4½d., 5d., 6d., 7½d., 8d. red-brown, 9d. and 1s. are known to have been produced in sheets perforated 14×13½ throughout with the 4d. bright violet, 5d., 6d. and 1s. known perforated 14×14½ throughout.

On the sheets showing the two perforations combined, the top four rows are usually perforated 14×13½ and the bottom six 14×14½. Combination sheets are known to have been produced in this form for the 1½d. (Nos. 416 and 431), 2d. (both), 2½d., 3d., 4d. (both), 4½d., 6d., 7½d., 8d. indigo-blue, 9d. and 1s. On a late printing of the 4d. deep purple and 5d. pale ultramarine the arrangement is different with the top five rows perforated 14×14½ and the bottom five 14×13½.

With the exception of Nos. 432/4 any with perforations measuring 14×14 or nearly must be classed as 14×14½, this being an irregularity of the comb machine, and not a product of the 14-line machine.

4d Re-entry (Plate 20, R. 1/6)

4d Re-entry (Plate 20, R. 4/10)

During the laying-down of plate 20 for the 4d., from the roller-die which also contained dies of other values, an impression of the 4½d. value was placed on R. 1/6 and of the 2½d. on R. 4/10. These errors were subsequently corrected by re-entries of the 4d. impression, but on R. 1/6 traces of the original impression can be found in the right-hand value tablet and above the top frame line, while on R. 4/10 the foot of the "2" is visible in the left-hand value tablet with traces of "½" to its right.

61

62

WAR STAMP
(63)

Type **62** (from local plates) can be identified from Type **61** (prepared by Perkins Bacon) by the shading on the portrait. This is diagonal on Type **62** and horizontal on Type **61**.

(Die eng W. R. Bock. Typo Govt Printer, Wellington, from plates made by P.B. (T **61**) or locally (T **62**))

1915 (30 July)–**33**. W **43**. P 14×15.

		(a) De La Rue chalk-surfaced paper with toned gum		
435	**61**	½d. green	1·50	20
		a. Booklet pane of 6 with bars on selvedge	£170	
		b. *Yellow-green*	4·00	1·75
		ba. Booklet pane of 6 with bars on selvedge	£150	
		c. Very thick, hard, highly surfaced paper with white gum (12.15)	12·00	55·00
		w. Wmk inverted	£100	£140
		x. Wmk reversed	—	£180
		y. Wmk inverted and reversed	—	£225
436	**62**	1½d. grey-black (4.16)	13·00	1·75
		a. *Black*	13·00	2·00
		y. Wmk inverted and reversed	—	£350
437	**61**	1½d. slate (5.9.16)	9·00	20
		w. Wmk inverted	—	£400
438		1½d. orange-brown (9.18)	2·25	20
		w. Wmk inverted	£200	£170
		x. Wmk reversed	†	—
		y. Wmk inverted and reversed	£350	£300
439		2d. yellow (9.16)	2·25	20
		a. *Pale yellow*	6·00	1·25
		w. Wmk inverted	£150	
440		3d. chocolate (5.19)	7·00	1·25
435/40		*Set of 6*	32·00	3·50
		*(b) W **43**. Jones chalk-surfaced paper with white gum*		
441	**61**	½d. green (10.24)	10·00	14·00
		a. Booklet pane of 6 with bars on selvedge (1.12.24)	£160	
		w. Wmk inverted	£110	£110
442		2d. dull yellow (7.24)	10·00	60·00
		w. Wmk inverted	£150	
443		3d. deep chocolate (3.25)	22·00	30·00
441/3		*Set of 3*	38·00	90·00
		(c) No wmk, but bluish "NZ" and Star lithographed on back. Art paper		
444	**61**	½d. apple-green (4.25)	2·75	8·50
		a. "NZ" and Star almost colourless	5·00	
445		2d. yellow (7.25)	12·00	75·00
		*(d) W **43**. Cowan thick, opaque, chalk-surfaced paper with white gum*		
446	**61**	½d. green (8.25)	1·75	20
		a. Booklet pane of 6 with bars and adverts on selvedge	£180	
		aa. Imperf 3 sides (top stamp of vertical pair)	£1200	
		ab. Booklet pane of 6 with bars on selvedge (1928)	£425	
		bw. Wmk inverted	£110	£110
		bx. Wmk reversed (1926)	13·00	3·75
		bxa. Booklet pane of 6 with bars and adverts on selvedge (1927)	£150	
		by. Wmk inverted and reversed (1926)	£140	£110
		c. Perf 14 (1927)	2·50	35
		ca. Booklet pane of 6 with bars on selvedge (1928)	£140	
		cb. Booklet pane of 6 with bars and adverts on selvedge (1928)	£140	
		cw. Wmk inverted	£200	£110

447		1½d. orange-brown (P 14) (8.29)	8·50	40·00
		a. Perf 14×15 (7.33)	38·00	90·00
448		2d. yellow (8.25)	11·00	1·50
		ax. Wmk reversed (1927)	35·00	£130
		ay. Wmk inverted and reversed (1927)	£300	£650
		b. Perf 14 (1929)	2·75	20
		bw. Wmk inverted	£140	50·00
449		3d. chocolate (8.25)	7·50	2·00
		aw. Wmk inverted	£110	
		b. Perf 14 (1929)	7·50	4·25
446/9		*Set of 4*	18·00	40·00
		*(e) W **43**. Wiggins Teape thin, hard, chalk-surfaced paper*		
450	**61**	1½d. orange-brown (P 14) (1930)	55·00	£130
451		2d. yellow (5.26)	14·00	25·00
		aw. Wmk inverted	90·00	60·00
		b. Perf 14 (10.27)	15·00	24·00
		bw. Wmk inverted	£110	55·00

The designs of these stamps also differ as described beneath No. 434. Stamps from booklet panes often have blurred, heavy impressions. Different advertisements can be found on the listed booklet panes.

Examples of No. 446aa, which occur in booklet panes, show the stamps perforated at top.

The ½d. and 2d. (Nos. 446c and 448b) are known showing ½d. and 1d. local surcharges from 1932 applied diagonally in blue to stamps previously stuck on to envelopes or cards at Christchurch (½d.) or Wellington (1d.).

1915 (24 Sept). No. 435 optd with T **63**.

452	**61**	½d. green	2·25	50

64 "Peace" and Lion

65 "Peace" and Lion

66

67

66a

67a

(Des and typo D.L.R. from plates by P.B., Waterlow and D.L.R.)

1920 (27 Jan). Victory. De La Rue chalk-surfaced paper. W **43** (sideways on ½d., 1½d., 3d. and 1s.). P 14.

453	**64**	½d. green	3·00	2·50
		a. *Pale yellow-green*	27·00	28·00
454	**65**	1d. carmine-red	4·50	60
		a. *Bright carmine*	7·50	70
		w. Wmk inverted	32·00	20·00
		x. Wmk reversed	£110	55·00
455	**66**	1½d. brown-orange	3·00	50
456	**66a**	3d. chocolate	12·00	14·00
457	**67**	6d. violet	14·00	17·00
		a. Wmk sideways	†	£1000
		w. Wmk inverted	£650	£450
458	**67a**	1s. orange-red	24·00	24·00
453/8		*Set of 6*	55·00	75·00

The above stamps were placed on sale in London in November, 1919.

2d. **2d.**

TWOPENCE
(68)

69

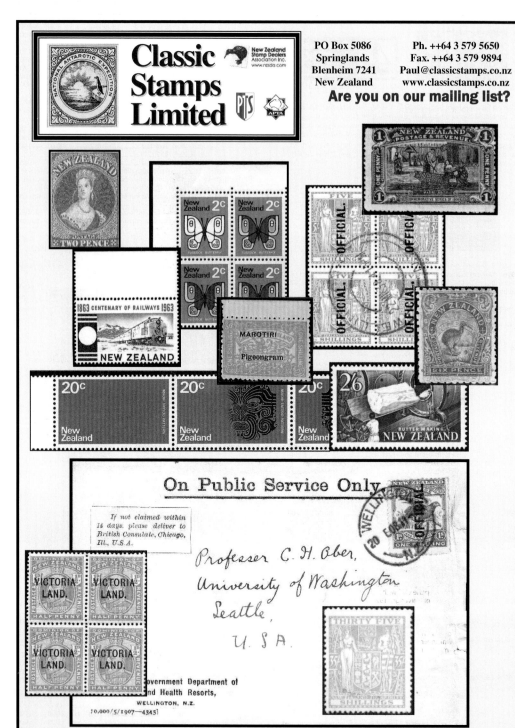

1922 (Mar.) No. 453 surch with T **68**.
459 **64** 2d. on ½d. green (R.) .... 5·50 1·40

(Des and eng W. R. Bock, Typo Govt Printer, Wellington)
1923 (1 Oct)–**25**. Restoration of Penny Postage. W **43**. P 14×15.
(a) De La Rue chalk-surfaced paper with toned gum
460 **69** 1d. carmine .... 4·75 60
(b) Jones chalk-surfaced paper with white gum
461 **69** 1d. carmine (3.24)........................ 14·00 11·00
　　　a. Wmk sideways .... † £700
　　　w. Wmk inverted .... 80·00 60·00
(c) Cowan unsurfaced paper with very shiny gum
462 **69** 1d. carmine-pink (4.25) .... 48·00 27·00
The paper used for No. 462 is similar to that of Nos. 416/30.

70 Exhibition Buildings

(Des H. L. Richardson. Eng and typo Govt Printer, Wellington)
1925 (17 Nov). Dunedin Exhibition. Cowan chalk-surfaced paper.
W **43**. P 14×15.
463 **70** ½d. yellow-green/*green*................. 3·00 16·00
　　　w. Wmk inverted £225 £180
464 　　1d. carmine/*rose*..................... 4·25 7·50
　　　w. Wmk inverted £325 £200
465 　　4d. mauve/*pale mauve* .... 30·00 75·00
　　　a. "POSTAGF" at right (R. 1/2, R. 10/1)... £100 £180
463/5 *Set of 3* .... 32·00 90·00

71 King George V　**72** King George V
as Field-Marshal　　as Admiral

(Des H. L. Richardson; plates by B.W. (1d. from sheets), P.B. (1d. from booklets), Royal Mint, London (others). Typo Govt Printer, Wellington)
1926 (12 July)–**34**. W **43**. P 14.
(a) Jones chalk-surfaced paper with white gum
466 **72** 2s. deep blue .... 80·00 70·00
　　　w. Wmk inverted .... 65·00 80·00
467 　　3s. mauve £110 £200
　　　w. Wmk inverted £130 £250
(b) Cowan thick, opaque, chalk-surfaced paper with white gum
468 **71** 1d. rose-carmine (15.11.26) 75 20
　　　a. Imperf (pair) £250
　　　b. Booklet pane of 6 with bars on
　　　　　selvedge (1928)................... £150
　　　c. Booklet pane of 6 with bars and
　　　　　adverts on selvedge (1928)........ £130
　　　dw. Wmk inverted .... £100 55·00
　　　e. Perf 14×15 (3.27).................. 65 50
　　　ea. Booklet pane of 6 with bars and
　　　　　adverts on selvedge (1934)........ £140
　　　ew. Wmk inverted .... £120 55·00
　　　ex. Wmk reversed .... 15·00
469 **72** 2s. light blue (5.27)................. 75·00 29·00
470 　　3s. pale mauve (9.27).............. £130 £190
468/70 *Set of 3*................................ £180 £200
(c) Wiggins Teape thin, hard, chalk-surfaced paper with white gum
471 **71** 1d. rose-carmine (6.30)............. 40·00 16·00
　　　w. Wmk inverted £200 £100
No. 468ex exists in a range of colours including scarlet and deep carmine to magenta but we have insufficient evidence to show that these were issued.

Following the reduction of the postage rate to ½d. on 1 June 1932 the firm of R. H. White & Co. Ltd. of Stratford returned a quantity of envelopes stamped with 1d. stamps (No. 468) to the New Plymouth post office who surcharged the stamps "HALFPENNY" in purple using a handstamp. The covers were then returned to the firm for normal use. Similar local surcharges were applied diagonally to 1d. stamps stuck onto postcards or lettercards at Dunedin, Greymouth and Invercargill in blue or at Palmerston North in purple. With the exception of the Greymouth provisional, where 40 mint examples were acquired by a stamp dealer, these local surcharges are only found unused, no gum, or used.

Nos. 472 to 543 are vacant.

73 Nurse　　　**74** Smiling Boy

(Typo Govt Printing Office, Wellington)
1929–**30**. Anti-Tuberculosis Fund. T **73** and similar design. W **43**. P 14.
(a) Inscribed "HELP STAMP OUT TUBERCULOSIS"
544 　　1d. +1d. scarlet (11.12.29) .... 11·00 19·00
　　　w. Wmk inverted £350 £250
(b) Inscribed "HELP PROMOTE HEALTH"
545 　　1d. +1d. scarlet (29.10.30) .... 20·00 45·00

HIGH VALUES. From 1931 postal requirements for higher values were met by the "Arms" "Stamp Duty" adhesives (F145 etc.).

(Des L. C. Mitchell. Dies eng and plates made Royal Mint, London (1d.), Govt Ptg Office, Wellington from W. R. Bock die (2d.). Typo Govt Ptg Office, Wellington)
1931 (31 Oct). Health Stamps. W **43** (sideways). P 14½×14.
546 **74** 1d. +1d. scarlet .... 75·00 75·00
547 　　2d. +1d. blue .... 75·00 60·00

75 New Zealand Lake Scenery

FIVE PENCE
(**76**)

(Des L. C. Mitchell. Plates, Royal Mint, London.
Typo Govt Ptg Office)
1931 (10 Nov)–**35**. Air. W **43**. P 14×14½.
548 **75** 3d. chocolate...................... 22·00 16·00
　　　a. Perf 14×15 (4.35)............... £130 £425
549 　　4d. blackish purple................ 22·00 22·00
550 　　7d. brown-orange................. 22·00 9·00
548/50 *Set of 3*............................ 60·00 42·00

1931 (18 Dec). Air. Surch with T **76**. W **43**. P 14×14½.
551 **75** 5d. on 3d. green (R.) .... 10·00 10·00

77 Hygeia,　　**78** The Path to
Goddess of Health　　Health

(Des R. E. Tripe and W. J. Cooch. Eng H. T. Peat. Recess Govt Printing Office, Wellington)
1932 (18 Nov). Health Stamp. W **43**. P 14.
552 **77** 1d. +1d. carmine...................... 25·00 32·00
　　　w. Wmk inverted £425 £225
　　　x. Wmk reversed .... † £550

(Des J. Berry. Eng H. T. Peat. Recess Govt Printing Office, Wellington)
1933 (8 Nov). Health Stamp. W **43**. P 14.
553 **78** 1d. +1d. carmine...................... 16·00 21·00
　　　w. Wmk inverted £325 £200

TRANS-TASMAN
AIR MAIL
"FAITH IN AUSTRALIA."
(**79**)　　　　　**80** Crusader

1934 (17 Jan). Air. T **75** in new colour optd with T **79**. W **43**.
P 14×14½.
554 **75** 7d. light blue (B.)........................ 35·00 50·00

(Des J. Berry. Recess D.L.R.)

1934 (25 Oct). Health Stamp. W **43** (sideways). P 14×13½.

555	**80**	1d. +1d. carmine	11·00	17·00

81 Collared Grey Fantail    **82** Brown Kiwi    **83** Maori Woman

84 Maori Carved House    **85** Mt. Cook

86 Maori Girl    **87** Mitre Peak

88 Striped Marlin    **89** Harvesting

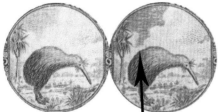

90 Tuatara Lizard    **91** Maori Panel    **92** Parson Bird

93 Capt. Cook at Poverty Bay   **94** Mt. Egmont

Die I   Die II

ALAND

CAPTAIN COQK
AT POVERTY BAY
OCTOBER 8th 1769

2s. "CAPTAIN COQK" (R. 1/4)

(Des J. Fitzgerald (½d., 4d.), C. H. and R. J. G. Collins (1d.) M. Matthews (1½d.), H. W. Young (2d.), L. C. Mitchell (2½d., 3d., 8d., 1s., 3s.), W. J. Cooch and R. E. Tripe (5d.), T. I. Archer (6d.), I. F. Calder (9d.) and I. H. Jenkins (2s.). Litho Waterlow (9d.). Recess D.L.R. (remainder))

1935 (1 May)**–36.** W **43** (sideways on. 8d.).

556	**81**	½d. bright green, P 14×13½	3·25	1·50
		w. Wmk inverted (12.35)	6·50	8·00

557	**82**	1d. scarlet (Die I), P 14×13½	3·50	1·50
		aw. Wmk inverted (2.36)	8·50	13·00
		b. Perf 13½×14 (1936)	75·00	65·00
		c. Die II. Perf 14×13½ (18.11.35)	13·00	4·75
		ca. Booklet pane of 6 with adverts on selvedge	60·00	
		cw. Wmk inverted	16·00	7·50
558	**83**	1½d. red-brown, P 14×13½	15·00	21·00
		a. Perf 13½×14 (11.35)	6·50	14·00
		ay. Wmk inverted and reversed (2.36)	20·00	42·00
559	**84**	2d. orange, P 14×13½	3·75	3·25
		w. Wmk inverted	£1200	£600
560	**85**	2½d. chocolate and slate, P 13–14×13½	14·00	40·00
		aw. Wmk inverted	40·00	95·00
		b. Perf 13½×14 (11.35)	10·00	30·00
		bx. Wmk reversed	†	£2750
561	**86**	3d. brown, P 14×13½	12·00	3·75
		w. Wmk inverted	£1100	£500
562	**87**	4d. black and sepia, P 14	4·75	3·25
		w. Wmk inverted	£850	£475
563	**88**	5d. ultramarine, P 13–14×13½	23·00	40·00
		a. Double print, one albino	†	—
		bw. Wmk inverted	†	£750
		c. Perf 13½×14	28·00	50·00
564	**89**	6d. scarlet, P 13½×14	9·00	12·00
		w. Wmk inverted	£650	£475
565	**90**	8d. chocolate, P 14×13½	13·00	20·00
		w. Wmk sideways inverted	£600	£375
566	**91**	9d. scarlet and black, P 14×14½	16·00	7·00
567	**92**	1s. deep green, P 14×13½	24·00	19·00
		w. Wmk inverted	—	£650
568	**93**	2s. olive-green, P 13–14×13½	50·00	50·00
		a. "CAPTAIN COQK"	£170	£130
		bw. Wmk inverted	£160	95·00
		c. Perf 13½×14 (1935)	65·00	60·00
		ca. "CAPTAIN COQK"	£170	£130
569	**94**	3s. chocolate and yellow-brown, P 13–14×13½	19·00	55·00
		a. Perf 13½×14 (11.35)	20·00	60·00
		aw. Wmk inverted	†	£1800
		ay. Wmk inverted and reversed (1936)	£450	£475
556/69 *Set of 14*			£170	£225

Some stamps from sheets perforated 14×13½ by De La Rue sometimes show the horizontal perforations nearer 13½.

In the 2½d., 5d., 2s. and 3s. perf 13–14×13½ the horizontal perforations of each stamp are in two sizes, one half of each horizontal side measuring 13 and the other 14.

See also Nos. 577/90 and 630/1.

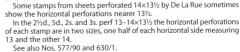

95 Bell Block Aerodrome    **96** King George V and Queen Mary

(Des J. Berry. Eng Stamp Printing Office, Melbourne. Recess Govt Printing Office, Wellington)

1935 (4 May). Air. W **43**. P 14.

570	**95**	1d. carmine	1·00	70
		w. Wmk inverted	£200	£110
571		3d. violet	4·50	3·00
		w. Wmk inverted	£250	£120
572		6d. blue	8·00	3·00
		w. Wmk inverted	£300	£130
570/2 *Set of 3*			12·00	6·00

(Frame by J. Berry. Recess B.W.)

1935 (7 May). Silver Jubilee. W **43**. P 11×11½.

573	**96**	½d. green	75	1·00
574		1d. carmine	1·00	80
575		6d. red-orange	20·00	32·00
573/5 *Set of 3*			20·00	32·00

97 "The Key to Health"   **98** "Multiple Wmk"

(Des S. Hall. Recess John Ash, Melbourne)

1935 (30 Sept). Health Stamp. W **43**. P 11.

576	**97**	1d. +1d. scarlet	2·50	3·75

WATERMARKS. In W **43** the wmk units are in vertical columns widely spaced and the sheet margins are unwatermarked or wmkd "NEW ZEALAND POSTAGE" in large letters.

In W **98** the wmk units are arranged alternately in horizontal rows closely spaced and are continued into the sheet margins.

Stamps with W **98** sideways show the top of the star pointing to the right, *as seen from the back*. Sideways inverted varieties have the top of the star to left *as seen from the back*.

(Litho Govt Ptg Office, Wellington (9d). Recess Waterlow or D.L.R. (others))

1936–42. W 98.

577	**81**	½d. bright green, P 14×13½	3·50	10
		w. Wmk inverted	5·50	9·50
578	**82**	1d. scarlet (Die II), P 14×13½ (4.36)	4·50	10
		w. Wmk inverted	10·00	8·50
579	**83**	1½d. red-brown, P 14×13½ (6.36)	20·00	7·00
580	**84**	2d. orange, P 14×13½ (3.36)	30	10
		aw. Wmk inverted	£600	£400
		b. Perf 12½† (6.41)	7·00	20
		bw. Wmk inverted		
		c. Perf 14 (6.41)	38·00	1·25
		d. Perf 14×15 (6.41)	38·00	26·00
581	**85**	2½d. chocolate and slate, P 13–14×13½	11·00	26·00
		aw. Wmk inverted	80·00	£150
		b. Perf 14 (11.36)	10·00	1·50
		bw. Wmk inverted	60·00	95·00
		c. Perf 14×13½ (11.42)	1·00	5·50
582	**86**	3d. brown, P 14×13½	35·00	1·50
		w. Wmk inverted	75·00	75·00
583	**87**	4d. black and sepia, P 14×13½	9·00	1·00
		aw. Wmk inverted	30·00	38·00
		b. Perf 12½* (8.41)	48·00	20·00
		†		—
		c. Perf 14, line (11.41)	65·00	£130
		d. Perf 14×14½ comb (7.42)	1·00	20
		dw. Wmk inverted	£600	£375
584	**88**	5d. ultramarine, P 13–14×13½ (8.36)	28·00	3·50
		aw. Wmk inverted	75·00	75·00
		b. Perf 12½*† (7.41)	13·00	10·00
		c. Perf 14×13½ (11.42)	2·00	2·25
		ca. Double print, one albino	£900	
		cw. Wmk inverted	£600	£400
585	**89**	6d. scarlet, P 13½×14 (8.36)	26·00	1·75
		aw. Wmk inverted	95·00	75·00
		b. Perf 12½* (10.41)	3·00	5·00
		c. Perf 14½×14 (6.42)	1·25	20
		cw. Wmk inverted	£800	£800
586	**90**	8d. chocolate, P 14×13½ (wmk sideways)	17·00	7·00
		aw. Wmk sideways inverted	60·00	£130
		b. Wmk upright (7.39)	4·00	7·50
		bw. Wmk inverted		
		c. Perf 12½* (wmk sideways) (7.41)	4·00	1·50
		d. Perf 14×14½ (wmk sideways) (7.42)	4·00	1·50
		dw. Wmk sideways inverted	—	£400
587	**91**	9d. red and grey, P 14×15 (wmk sideways)	50·00	4·50
		ay. Wmk sideways inverted and reversed	—	£350
		b. Wmk upright. *Red and grey-black*, P 14×14½ (1.3.38)	65·00	6·00
		bw. Wmk inverted	£225	£160
588	**92**	1s. deep green, P 14×13½	2·50	1·25
		aw. Wmk inverted	£120	£250
		b. Perf 12½* (11.41)	70·00	27·00
589	**93**	2s. olive-green, P 13–14×13½ (8.36)	50·00	11·00
		a. "CAPTAIN COQK"	95·00	42·00
		bw. Wmk inverted	£750	£600
		c. Perf 13½×14 (3.39)	£300	4·00
		ca. "CAPTAIN COQK"	£350	65·00
		d. Perf 12½*† (7.41)	19·00	9·50
		da. "CAPTAIN COQK"	80·00	38·00
		e. Perf 14×13½ (9.42)	4·25	1·50
		ea. "CAPTAIN COQK"	£180	80·00
		ew. Wmk inverted	—	£850
590	**94**	3s. chocolate and yellow-brown, P 13–14×13½	50·00	13·00
		aw. Wmk inverted	£200	£140
		b. Perf 12½* (1941)	80·00	50·00
		c. Perf 14×13½ (9.42)	3·00	3·25
577/90c		Set of 14	£120	21·00

*†Stamps indicated with an asterisk were printed and perforated by Waterlow; those having a dagger were printed by D.L.R. and perforated by Waterlow. No. 580d was printed by D.L.R. and perforated by Harrison and No. 583c was printed by Waterlow and perforated by D.L.R. These are all known as "Blitz perfs" because De La Rue were unable to maintain supplies after their works were damaged by enemy action. All the rest, except the 9d., were printed and perforated by D.L.R.

On stamps printed and perforated by De La Rue the perf 14×13½ varies in the sheet and is sometimes nearer 13½. 2d. perf 14×15 is sometimes nearer 14×14½.

2½d., 5d., 2s. and 3s. In perf 13–14×13½ one half the length of each horizontal perforation measures 13 and the other 14. In perf 14×13½ the horizontal perforation is regular.

4d. No. 583c. is line-perf measuring 14 exactly and has a blackish sepia frame. No. 583d is a comb-perf measuring 14×14.3 or 14×14.2 and the frame is a warmer shade.

2s. No. 589c is comb-perf and measures 13.5×13.75.

For 9d. typographed, see Nos. 630/1.

99 N.Z. Soldier at Anzac Cove    **100** Wool

101 Butter   **102** Sheep

103 Apples   **104** Exports

(Des L. C. Mitchell. Recess John Ash, Melbourne)

1936 (27 Apr). Charity. 21st Anniversary of "Anzac" Landing at Gallipoli. W **43**. P 11.

591	**99**	½d. +½d. green	75	1·75
592		1d. +1d. scarlet	1·25	1·40

(Des L. C. Mitchell. Recess John Ash, Melbourne)

1936 (1 Oct). Congress of British Empire Chambers of Commerce, Wellington. Industries Issue. T **100/104**. W **43** (sideways). P 11½.

593		½d. emerald-green	30	30
594		1d. scarlet	30	20
595		2½d. blue	1·50	8·00
596		4d. violet	1·25	5·50
597		6d. red-brown	4·00	6·50
593/7		Set of 5	6·50	18·00

105 Health Camp   **106** King George VI and Queen Elizabeth

(Des J. Berry. Recess John Ash, Melbourne)

1936 (2 Nov). Health Stamp. W **43** (sideways). P 11.

598	**105**	1d. +1d. scarlet	2·75	3·75

(Recess B.W.)

1937 (13 May). Coronation. W **98**. P 14×13½.

599	**106**	1d. carmine	30	10
600		2½d. Prussian blue	80	2·50
601		6d. red-orange	1·10	2·25
599/601		Set of 3	2·00	4·25

107 Rock climbing    **108** King George VI    **108a**

(Des G. Bull and J. Berry. Recess John Ash, Melbourne)

1937 (1 Oct). Health Stamp. W **43**. P 11.

602	**107**	1d. +1d. scarlet	4·00	3·75

Broken ribbon flaw (R. 6/6 of Pl 8)

(Des W. J. Cooch. Recess B.W.)

1938–44. W **98.** P 14×13½.
603	**108**	½d. green (1.3.38)	10·00	10
		w. Wmk inverted (from booklets)	27·00	5·50
604		½d. orange-brown (10.7.41)	20	40
		w. Wmk inverted	20	
605		1d. scarlet (1.7.38)	5·00	10
		a. Broken ribbon	£110	
		w. Wmk inverted (from booklets)	24·00	4·75
606		1d. green (21.7.41)	20	10
		w. Wmk inverted	£110	60·00
607	**108a**	1½d. purple-brown (26.7.38)	26·00	3·25
		w. Wmk inverted (from booklets)	40·00	12·00
608		1½d. scarlet (1.2.44)	20	80
		w. Wmk inverted	—	£170
609		3d. blue (26.9.41)	20	10
		w. Wmk inverted	—	£250
603/9 *Set of 7*			38·00	4·00

For other values see Nos. 680/9.

109 Children playing

110 Beach Ball

(Des J. Berry. Recess B.W.)

1938 (1 Oct). Health Stamp. W **98.** P 14×13½.
610	**109**	1d. +1d. scarlet	9·50	3·25

(Des S. Hall. Recess Note Printing Branch, Commonwealth Bank of Australia, Melbourne)

1939 (16 Oct). Health Stamps. Surcharged with new value. W **43.** P 11.
611	**110**	1d. on ½d. +½d. green	4·75	6·00
612		2d. on 1d. +1d. scarlet	5·50	6·00

111 Arrival of the Maoris, 1350

112 *Endeavour*, Chart of N.Z. and Capt. Cook

113 British Monarchs

114 Tasman with his ship and chart

115 Signing Treaty of Waitangi, 1840

116 Landing of immigrants, 1840

117 Road, rail, sea and air transport

118 H.M.S. *Britomart* at Akaroa, 1840

119 *Dunedin* and "frozen mutton route" to London

120 Maori council

121 Gold mining in 1861 and 1940

122 Giant Kauri tree

(Des L. C. Mitchell (½d., 3d., 4d.); J. Berry (others). Recess B.W.)

1940 (2 Jan–8 Mar). Centenary of Proclamation of British Sovereignty. T **111/122.** W **98.** P 14×13½ (2½d.), 13½×14 (5d.) or 13½ (others).
613	**111**	½d. blue-green	50	10
614	**112**	1d. chocolate and scarlet	4·00	10
615	**113**	1½d. light blue and mauve	30	60
616	**114**	2d. blue-green and chocolate	1·50	10
617	**115**	2½d. blue-green and blue	2·00	1·00
618	**116**	3d. purple and carmine	4·00	1·25
619	**117**	4d. chocolate and lake	14·00	1·50
620	**118**	5d. pale blue and brown	10·00	3·75
621	**119**	6d. emerald-green and violet	11·00	1·25
622	**120**	7d. black and red	2·00	4·00
623		8d. black and red (8.3)	11·00	6·00
624	**121**	9d. olive-green and orange	8·00	2·00
625	**122**	1s. sage-green and deep green	13·00	4·00
613/25 *Set of 13*			70·00	23·00

1940 (1 Oct). Health Stamps. As T **110**, but without extra surcharge. W **43.** P 11.
626	**110**	1d. +½d. blue-green	11·00	14·00
627		2d. +1d. brown-orange	11·00	14·00

1ᴰ	**1**ᴰ	**2**ᴰ		
■	■	■	**2**,ᴰ	**1941**
(123)	(123a)	Inserted "2"		(124)

1941. Nos. 603 and 607 surch as T **123/a.**
628	**108**	1d. on ½d. green (1.5.41)	1·75	10
629	**108a**	2d. on 1½d. purple-brown (4.41)	1·75	10
		a. Inserted "2"	£650	£450

The variety "Inserted 2" occurs on the tenth stamp, tenth row. It is identified by the presence of remnants of the damaged "2", and by the spacing of "2" and "D" which is variable and different from the normal.

(Typo Govt Printing Office, Wellington)

1941. As T **91**, but smaller (17½×20½ *mm*). Chalk-surfaced paper. P 14×15.

(a) W **43**
630	**91**	9d. scarlet and black (5.41)	95·00	32·00
		w. Wmk inverted	†	£450

(b) W **98**
631	**91**	9d. scarlet and black (29.9.41)	3·00	5·00
		w. Wmk inverted	£500	£375

1941 (4 Oct). Health Stamps. Nos. 626/7 optd with T **124.**
632	**110**	1d. +½d. blue-green	50	2·25
633		2d. +1d. brown-orange	50	2·25

125 Boy and Girl on Swing **126** Princess Margaret

127 Queen Elizabeth II as Princess

(Des S. Hall. Recess Note Printing Branch, Commonwealth Bank of Australia, Melbourne)

1942 (1 Oct). Health Stamps. W **43**. P 11.

634	**125**	1d. +½d. blue-green	30	1·25
635		2d. +1d. orange-red	30	1·25

(Des J. Berry. Recess B.W.)

1943 (1 Oct). Health Stamps. T **126/7**. W **98**. P 12.

636		1d. +½d. green	30	1·50
		a. Imperf between (vert pair)	£14000	
637		2d. +1d. red-brown	30	25
		a. Imperf between (vert pair)	£18000	£18000

The watermark is at an angle in relation to the design on single stamps.

❖ TENPENCE ❖
(128)

1944 (1 May). No. 615 surch with T **128**.

662		10d. on 1½d. light blue and mauve	15	30

129 Queen Elizabeth II as Princess and Princess Margaret **130** Statue of Peter Pan, Kensington Gardens

(Recess B.W.)

1944 (9 Oct). Health Stamps. W **98**. P 13½.

663	**129**	1d. +½d. green	30	40
664		2d. +1d. blue	30	30

(Des J. Berry. Recess B.W.)

1945 (1 Oct). Health Stamps. W **98**. P 13½.

665	**130**	1d. +½d. green and buff	15	20
		w. Wmk inverted	£110	£130
666		2d. +1d. carmine and buff	15	20
		w. Wmk inverted	£350	£170

131 Lake Matheson **132** King George VI and Parliament House, Wellington

133 St. Paul's Cathedral **134** The Royal Family

135 R.N.Z.A.F. badge and aircraft **136** Army badge, tank and plough

137 Navy badge, H.M.N.Z.S. *Achilles* (cruiser) and *Dominion Monarch* (liner) **138** N.Z. coat of arms, foundry and farm

139 "St. George" (Wellington College War Memorial Window) **140** Southern Alps and Franz Joseph Glacier

141 National Memorial Campanile **½d.** Printer's guide mark (R. 12/3)

3d. Completed rudder (R. 2/4 of Pl 42883 and R. 3/2 of Pl 42796)

5d. Trailing aerial (R. 8/1 of Pl 42794)

9d. Guide mark (R. 3/3 of Pl 42723)

(Des J. Berry. Photo Harrison (1½d. and 1s.). Recess B.W. (1d. and 2d.) and Waterlow (others))

1946 (1 Apr). Peace issue. T **131/41**. W **98** (sideways on 1½d.). P 13 (1d., 2d.), 14×14½ (1½d., 1s.), 13½ (others).

667	**131**	½d. green and brown		20	65
		a. Printer's guide mark		23·00	35·00
		w. Wmk inverted		£120	80·00
668	**132**	1d. green		10	10
		w. Wmk inverted		85·00	50·00
669	**133**	1½d. scarlet		10	50
		w. Wmk sideways inverted		10	50
670	**134**	2d. purple		15	10
671	**135**	3d. ultramarine and grey		45	15
		a. Completed rudder		19·00	22·00
		b. Ultramarine omitted		£15000	
672	**136**	4d. bronze-green and orange		50	20
		w. Wmk inverted		£200	90·00
673	**137**	5d. green and ultramarine		1·25	1·75
		a. Trailing aerial		35·00	45·00
674	**138**	6d. chocolate and vermilion		20	30
675	**139**	8d. black and carmine		20	30
676	**140**	9d. blue and black		20	30
		a. Guide mark		28·00	38·00
677	**141**	1s. grey-black		1·00	40
667/77		*Set of* 11		3·50	4·00

Only one example of No. 671b is known. It was caused by a paper fold.

142 Soldier helping Child over Stile

2d. +1d. Feathers in hat (R. 8/8 of Pl 43010)

(Des J. Berry. Recess Waterlow)

1946 (24 Oct). Health Stamps. W **98**. P 13½.

678	**142**	1d. +½d. green and orange-brown		15	15
		a. Yellow-green and orange-brown		7·00	12·00
		w. Wmk inverted		80·00	70·00
679		2d. +1d. chocolate and orange-brown		15	15
		a. Feathers in hat		35·00	35·00

144 King George VI   **145** Statue of Eros

Plate 1   Plate 2

(Des W. J. Cooch. Recess T **108a**, B.W.; T **144**, D.L.R.)

1947 (1 May)–**52**. W **98** (sideways on "shilling" values).

(a) P 14×13½

680	**108a**	2d. orange		30	10
		w. Wmk inverted		£225	£300
681		4d. bright purple		80	1·00
682		5d. slate		1·00	1·00
683		6d. carmine		1·00	10
		w. Wmk inverted		£325	£140
684		8d. violet		1·25	1·25
685		9d. purple-brown		2·00	60
		w. Wmk inverted		£100	28·00

(b) P 14

686	**144**	1s. red-brown and carmine (Plate 1)		2·00	1·50
		aw. Wmk sideways inverted		23·00	17·00
		b. Wmk upright (Plate 1)		60	80
		c. Wmk upright (Plate 2) (1950)		2·25	1·25
		cw. Wmk inverted		£180	55·00
687		1s.3d. red-brown and blue (Plate 2)		2·75	1·25
		aw. Wmk sideways inverted		22·00	10·00
		b. Wmk upright (14.1.52)		2·25	4·50
		bw. Wmk inverted		†	—
688		2s. brown-orange and green (Plate 1).		8·50	2·50
		aw. Wmk sideways inverted		38·00	26·00
		b. Wmk upright (Plate 1)		13·00	20·00
689		3s. red-brown and grey (Plate 2)		4·50	3·50
		w. Wmk sideways inverted		50·00	29·00
680/9		*Set of* 10		20·00	11·00

In head-plate 2 the diagonal lines of the background have been strengthened and result in the upper corners and sides appearing more deeply shaded.

For details of the sideways watermarks, see above No. 577.

(Des J. Berry. Recess Waterlow)

1947 (1 Oct). Health Stamps. W **98** (sideways). P 13½.

690	**145**	1d. +½d. green		15	15
		w. Wmk sideways inverted		£110	85·00
691		2d. +1d. carmine		15	15
		w. Wmk sideways inverted		£150	£130

146 Port Chalmers, 1848   **147** Cromwell, Otago

148 First Church, Dunedin

149 University of Otago

154 Christchurch Cathedral

155 Cairn on Lyttelton Hills

156 John Robert Godley

157 Canterbury University College

(Des J. Berry. Recess B.W.)

1948 (23 Feb). Centennial of Otago. T **146/9**. W **98** (sideways inverted on 3d.). P 13½.

692	**146**	1d. blue and green	25	35
		w. Wmk inverted	90·00	85·00
693	**147**	2d. green and brown	25	35
694	**148**	3d. purple	30	60
695	**149**	6d. black and rose	30	60
		w. Wmk inverted	—	£400
692/5 *Set of 4*			1·00	1·75

158 Aerial view of Timaru

(Des L. C. Mitchell (2d.), J. A. Johnstone (3d.) and J. Berry (others). Recess B.W.)

1950 (20 Nov). Centennial of Canterbury, N.Z. T **154/8**. W **98** (sideways inverted on 1d. and 3d.). P 13½.

703	**154**	1d. green and blue	50	85
704	**155**	2d. carmine and orange	50	85
705	**156**	3d. dark blue and blue	60	1·25
706	**157**	6d. brown and blue	60	1·00
707	**158**	1s. reddish purple and blue	60	1·60
703/7 *Set of 5*			2·50	5·00

150 Boy Sunbathing and Children Playing

151 Nurse and Child

(Des E. Linzell. Recess B.W.)

1948 (1 Oct). Health Stamps. W **98**. P 13½.

696	**150**	1d. +½d. blue and green	15	20
		w. Wmk inverted	£130	60·00
697		2d. +1d. purple and scarlet	15	20

1949 ROYAL VISIT ISSUE. Four stamps were prepared to commemorate this event: 2d. Treaty House, Waitangi; 3d. H.M.S. *Vanguard*; 5d. Royal portraits; 6d. Crown and sceptre. The visit did not take place and the stamps were destroyed, although a few examples of the 3d. later appeared on the market. A similar set was prepared in 1952 but was, likewise, not issued.

(Des J. Berry. Photo Harrison)

1949 (3 Oct). Health Stamps. W **98**. P 14×14½.

698	**151**	1d. +½d. green	25	20
699		2d. +1d. ultramarine	25	20
		a. No stop below "D" of "1D." (R. 1/2) ..	7·00	21·00

159 "Takapuna" class Yachts

(Des J. Berry and R. S. Phillips. Recess B.W.)

1951 (1 Nov). Health Stamps. W **98**. P 13½.

708	**159**	1½d. +½d. scarlet and yellow	50	1·00
709		2d. +1d. deep green and yellow	50	25
		w. Wmk inverted	95·00	£100

1½d.

POSTAGE

(152)

153 Queen Elizabeth II as Princess and Prince Charles

1950 (28 July). As Type F **6**, but without value, surch with T **152**. Chalk-surfaced paper. W **98** (inverted). P 14.

700	F **6**	1½d. carmine	40	30
		w. Wmk upright	5·50	6·50

(Des J. Berry and R. S. Phillips. Photo Harrison)

1950 (2 Oct). Health Stamps. W **98**. P 14×14½.

701	**153**	1d. +½d. green	25	20
		w. Wmk inverted	7·50	8·50
702		2d. +1d. plum	25	20
		w. Wmk inverted	95·00	95·00

160 Princess Anne

161 Prince Charles

3D

(162)

(From photographs by Marcus Adams. Photo Harrison)

1952 (1 Oct). Health Stamps. W **98**. P 14×14½.

710	**160**	1½d. +½d. carmine-red	15	30
711	**161**	2d. +1d. brown	15	20

1952–53. Nos. 604 and 606 surch as T **162**.

712	**108**	1d. on ½d. brown-orange (11.9.53)	50	1·00
		a. "D" omitted	†	—
713		3d. on 1d. green (12.12.52)	10	10

163 Buckingham Palace

164 Queen Elizabeth II

165 Coronation State Coach

166 Westminster Abbey

167 St. Edward's Crown and Royal Sceptre

(Des L. C. Mitchell (1s.6d.), J. Berry (others). Recess D.L.R. (2d., 4d.), Waterlow (1s.6d.) Photo Harrison (3d., 8d.))

1953 (25 May). Coronation. T **163/7**. W **98**. P 13 (2d., 4d.), 13½ (1s.6d.) or 14×14½ (3d., 8d.).

714	**163**	2d. deep bright blue	40	30
715	**164**	3d. brown	30	10
716	**165**	4d. carmine	1·40	2·50
717	**166**	8d. slate-grey	1·00	1·60
718	**167**	1s.6d. purple and ultramarine	2·75	3·25
714/18		*Set of 5*	5·00	7·00

168 Girl Guides

169 Boy Scouts

(Des J. Berry. Photo Harrison)

1953 (7 Oct). Health Stamps. W **98**. P 14×14½.

719	**168**	1½d. +½d. blue	15	10
720	**169**	2d. +1d. deep yellow-green	15	40
		a. Imperf 3 sides (block of 4)	£3500	

No. 720a shows the left-hand vertical pair imperforate at right and the right-hand pair imperforate at left, top and bottom.

170 Queen Elizabeth II

171 Queen Elizabeth II and Duke of Edinburgh

(Des L. C. Mitchell. Recess Waterlow)

1953 (9 Dec). Royal Visit. W **98**. P 13×14 (3d.) or 13½ (4d.).

721	**170**	3d. dull purple	15	10
		w. Wmk inverted	—	£170
722	**171**	4d. deep ultramarine	15	60

172

173 Queen Elizabeth II

174

Die I

Die II

(Des L. C. Mitchell (T **172/3**), J. Berry (T **174**). Recess D.L.R. (T **173**), B.W. (others))

1953 (15 Dec)–**59**. W **98**. P 14×13½ (T **172**), 14 (T **173**) or 13½ (T **174**).

723	**172**	½d. slate-black (1.3.54)	15	30
724		1d. orange (1.3.54)	15	10
		w. Wmk inverted	40	2·25
725		1½d. brown-lake	20	10
		w. Wmk inverted	†	£500
726		2d. bluish green (1.3.54)	20	10
		w. Wmk inverted	†	£500
727		3d. vermilion (1.3.54)	20	10
		w. Wmk inverted (from booklets)	40	2·25
728		4d. blue (1.3.54)	40	50
729		6d. purple (1.3.54)	70	1·60
		w. Wmk inverted	£550	£350
730		8d. carmine (1.3.54)	60	60
		w. Wmk inverted	£950	£700
731	**173**	9d. brown and bright green (1.3.54)	60	60
		w. Wmk inverted	£500	£375
732		1s. black and carmine-red (Die I) (1.3.54)	65	10
		aw. Wmk inverted	£550	£425
		b. Die II (1958)	£170	20·00
733		1s.6d. black and bright blue (1.3.54)	1·50	60
		aw. Wmk inverted	£475	£375
733*b*		1s.9d. black and red-orange (1.7.57)	5·50	1·50
		bw. Wmk inverted	£750	£450
		c. White opaque paper (2.2.59)	4·00	1·50
733*d*	**174**	2s.6d. brown (1.7.57)	13·00	5·00
734		3s. bluish green (1.3.54)	14·00	50
		w. Wmk inverted	£800	£500
735		5s. carmine (1.3.54)	30·00	3·25
736		10s. deep ultramarine (1.3.54)	50·00	17·00
723/36		*Set of 16*	£100	28·00

1s. Dies I and II. The two dies of the Queen's portrait differ in the shading on the sleeve at right. The long lines running upwards from left to right are strong in Die I and weaker in Die II. In the upper part of the shading the fine cross-hatching is visible in Die I only between the middle two of the four long lines, but in Die II it extends clearly across all four lines.

In the lower part of the shading the strength of the long lines in Die I makes the cross-hatching appear subdued, whereas in Die II the weaker long lines make the cross-hatching more prominent.

Centre plates 1A, 1B and 2B are Die I; 3A and 3B are Die II.

For stamps as T **172** but with larger figures of value see Nos. 745/51.

WHITE OPAQUE PAPER. A new white opaque paper first came into use in August 1958. It is slightly thicker than the paper previously used, but obviously different in colour (white, against cream) and opacity (the previous paper being relatively transparent).

175 Young Climber and Mts Aspiring and Everest

(Des J. Berry. Recess; vignette litho B.W.)

1954 (4 Oct). Health Stamps. W **98**. P 13½.

737	**175**	1½d. +½d. sepia and deep violet..............	15	30
738		2d. + 1d. sepia and blue-black...............	15	30

176 Maori Mail Carrier

177 Queen Elizabeth II

178 Douglas DC-3 Airliner

(Des R. M. Conly (2d.), J. Berry (3d.), A. G. Mitchell (4d.). Recess D.L.R.)

1955 (18 July). Centenary of First New Zealand Postage Stamps. W **98**. P 14 (2d.) 14×14½ (3d.) or 13 (4d.)

739	**176**	2d. sepia and deep green.........................	10	10
		w. Wmk inverted	—	£325
740	**177**	3d. brown-red	10	10
741	**178**	4d. black and bright blue	70	1·00
739/41	*Set of 3*............		80	1·00

179 Children's Health Camps Federation Emblem

180

(Des E. M. Taylor. Recess B.W.)

1955 (3 Oct). Health Stamps. W **98** (sideways). P 13½×13.

742	**179**	1½d. +½d. sepia and orange-brown	10	60
743		2d. +1d. red-brown and green..............	10	35
744		3d. +1d. sepia and deep rose-red	15	15
		a. Centre omitted..................................	£15000	
742/4	*Set of 3*		30	1·00

Only one example of No. 744a is known. It was caused by a paper fold.

1955–59. As Nos. 724/30 but larger figures of value with stars omitted from lower right corner and new colour (8d.).

745	**180**	1d. orange (12.7.56)................................	50	10
		aw. Wmk inverted	1·50	3·50
		b. White opaque paper (2.6.59).............	50	75
		bw. Wmk inverted	1·50	4·25
746		1½d. brown-lake (1.12.55)	60	60
747		2d. bluish green (19.3.56)......................	40	10
		a. White opaque paper (10.11.59).......	55	10
748		3d. vermilion (1.5.56)............................	1·50	2·50
		aw. Wmk inverted	1·50	2·50
		b. White opaque paper (20.6.59)..........	30	10
		bw. Wmk inverted	2·00	4·25
749		4d. blue (3.2.58)....................................	1·00	80
		a. White opaque paper (9.9.59)............	1·25	2·50
750		6d. purple (20.10.55)	8·00	20
751		8d. chestnut (*white opaque paper*) (1.12.59)...	3·50	4·25
745/51	*Set of 7*................		13·00	5·50

See note *re* white opaque paper after No. 736.

181 "The Whalers of Foveaux Strait"

182 "Farming"

183 Takahe

(Des E. R. Leeming (2d.), L. C. Mitchell (3d.), M. R. Smith (8d.). Recess D.L.R.)

1956 (16 Jan). Southland Centennial. T **181/3**. W **98**. P 13½×13 (8d.) or 13×12½ (others).

752	**181**	2d. deep blue-green...............................	30	15
753	**182**	3d. sepia...	10	10
		w. Wmk inverted	—	£275
754	**183**	8d. slate-violet and rose-red	1·25	1·50
752/4	*Set of 3*		1·50	1·50

184 Children picking Apples

(Des L. C. Mitchell, after photo by J. F. Louden. Recess B.W.)

1956 (24 Sept). Health Stamps. W **98**. P 13½×13½.

755	**184**	1½d. +½d. purple-brown	15	70
		a. Blackish brown	2·00	7·00
756		2d. +1d. blue-green..............................	15	55
757		3d. +1d. claret......................................	15	15
755/7	*Set of 3*		40	1·25

185 New Zealand Lamb and Map

186 Lamb, *Dunedin* and *Port Brisbane* (refrigerated freighter)

(Des M. Goaman. Photo Harrison)

1957 (15 Feb). 75th Anniversary of First Export of N.Z. Lamb. W **98** (sideways inverted on 4d.). P 14×14½ (4d.) or 14½×14 (8d.).

758	**185**	4d. blue..	50	1·00
		w. Wmk sideways	14·00	22·00
759	**186**	8d. deep orange-red	75	1·00

187 Sir Truby King

(Des M. R. Smith. Recess B.W.)

1957 (14 May). 50th Anniversary of Plunket Society. W **98**. P 13.

760	**187**	3d. bright carmine-red	10	10
		w. Wmk inverted	£150	

188 Life-savers in Action
189 Children on Seashore

(Des L. Cutten (2d.), L. C. Mitchell (3d.). Recess Waterlow.)

1957 (25 Sept). Health Stamps. W **98** (sideways). P 13½.

761	**188**	2d. +1d. black and emerald.....................	15	70
762	**189**	3d. +1d. ultramarine and rose-red..........	15	10
MS762*b*	Two sheets each 112×96 mm with Nos. 761 and 762 in blocks of 6 (2×3) ....*Per pair*		7·00	25·00
MS762*c*	As last but with wmk upright ....*Per pair*		12·00	48·00

2d

(**190**)

1958 (6 Jan–Mar). No. 746 surch as T **190**.

763	**180**	2d. on 1½d. brown-lake	70	10
		a. Smaller dot in surch	15	10
		b. Error. Surch on No. 725 (3.58)	£130	£170

Diameter of dot on No. 763 is 4¼ mm; on No. 763a 3¾ mm.
Forgeries of No. 763b are known.
Almost all examples of No. 763b have the 4¼ mm dot, but examples with the smaller dot are known.

191 Girls' Life Brigade Cadet

192 Boys' Brigade Bugler

(Des J. Berry. Photo Harrison)

1958 (20 Aug). Health Stamps. W **98**. P 14×14½.

764	**191**	2d. +1d. green	20	40
765	**192**	3d. +1d. blue	20	40
MS765a		Two sheets each 104×124 mm with Nos. 764/5 in blocks of 6 (3×2)	*Per pair*	10·00	22·00

193 Sir Charles Kingsford-Smith and Fokker F.VIIa/3m *Southern Cross*

194 Seal of Nelson

(Des J. E. Lyle. Eng F. D. Manley. Recess Commonwealth Bank of Australia Note Ptg Branch)

1958 (27 Aug). 30th Anniversary of First Air Crossing of the Tasman Sea. W **98** (sideways). P 14×14½.

766	**193**	6d. deep ultramarine	50	75

(Des M. J. Macdonald. Recess B.W.)

1958 (29 Sept). Centenary of City of Nelson. W **98**. P 13½×13.

767	**194**	3d. carmine	10	10

195 "Pania" Statue, Napier

196 Australian Gannets on Cape Kidnappers

(Des M. R. Smith (2d.), J. Berry (3d.), L. C. Mitchell (8d.). Photo Harrison)

1958 (3 Nov). Centenary of Hawke's Bay Province. T **195/6** and similar design. W **98** (sideways on 3d.). P 14½×14 (3d.) or 13½×14½ (others).

768	**195**	2d. yellow-green	10	10
769	**196**	3d. blue	30	10
770		8d. red-brown	70	1·25
768/70	*Set of 3*		1·00	1·25

Design: Vert—8d. Maori sheep-shearer.

197 "Kiwi" Jamboree Badge

198 Careening H.M.S. *Endeavour* at Ship Cove

(Des Mrs. S. M. Collins. Recess B.W.)

1959 (5 Jan). Pan-Pacific Scout Jamboree, Auckland. W **98**. P 13½×13.

771	**197**	3d. sepia and carmine	30	10

(Des G. R. Bull and G. R. Smith. Photo Harrison)

1959 (2 Mar). Centenary of Marlborough Province. T **198** and similar horiz designs. W **98** (sideways). P 14½×14.

772	**198**	2d. green	30	10
773		3d. deep blue	30	10
774		8d. light brown	1·10	1·25
772/4	*Set of 3*		1·40	1·25

Designs:—3d. Shipping wool, Wairau Bar, 1857; 8d. Salt industry, Grassmere.

201 Red Cross Flag

(Photo Harrison)

1959 (3 June). Red Cross Commemoration. W **98** (sideways). P 14½×14.

775	**201**	3d. +1d. red and ultramarine	20	10
		a. Red Cross omitted	£2250	

202 Grey Teal

203 New Zealand Stilt

(Des Display Section, G.P.O. Photo Harrison)

1959 (16 Sept). Health Stamps. W **98** (sideways). P 14×14½.

776	**202**	2d. +1d. greenish yellow, olive and rose-red	50	65
777	**203**	3d. +1d. black, pink and light blue	50	65
		a. Pink omitted	£180	
		bw. Wmk sideways inverted	18·00	28·00
MS777c		Two sheets, each 95×109 mm with Nos. 776/7 in blocks of 6 (3×2)	*Per pair*	9·00	26·00

204 "The Explorer"

205 "The Gold Digger"

(Des G. R. Bull and G. R. Smith. Photo Harrison)

1960 (16 May). Centenary of Westland Province. T **204/5** and similar vert design. W **98**. P 14×14½.

778	**204**	2d. deep dull green	20	10
779	**205**	3d. orange-red	30	10
780		8d. grey-black	90	2·25
778/80	*Set of 3*		1·25	2·25

Design:—8d. "The Pioneer Woman".

207 Manuka
(Tea Tree)

208 Karaka

209 Kowhai
Ngutu-kaka
(Kaka-Beak)

209a Titoki

210 Kowhai

211 Puarangi
(Hibiscus)

211a Matua
Tikumu
(Mountain
Daisy)

212 Pikiarero

212a Koromiko

213 Rata

214 National Flag

215 Timber Industry

216 Rainbow
Trout

217 Tiki

218 Aerial Top
Dressing

218a Aerial Top
Dressing

219 Taniwha
(Maori Rock
Drawing)

220 Butter Making

221 Tongariro National Park
and Château

221a Tongariro National Park
and Château

222 Sutherland
Falls

223 Tasman Glacier

224 Pohutu
Geyser

NEW ZFALAND

2d. "F" for "E" in "ZEALAND". (R. 3/1, black Pl. 2)

(Des Harrison (½d.), G. F. Fuller (1d., 3d., 6d.), A. G. Mitchell (2d., 4d.,
5d., 8d., 3s., 10s., £1), P.O. Public Relations Division (7d.), P.O. Publicity
Section (9d.), J. Berry (1s., 1s.6d.), R. E. Barwick (1s.3d.), J. C. Boyd
(1s.9d.), D. F. Kee (2s.), L. C. Mitchell (2s.6d., 5s.). Photo D.L.R. (½d., 1d.,
2d., 3d., 4d., 6d., 8d.) or Harrison (others))

1960 (11 July)–**66**. T **207/224**. Chalk-surfaced paper (2½d., 5d., 7d.,
1s.9d. (No. 795), 3s. (No. 799)). W **98** (sideways on 5d., 1s.3d.,
1s.6d., 2s.6d., 3s. and 10s. or sideways inverted (2½d.)). P 14×14½
(1s.3d., 1s.6d., 2s., 5s., £1) or 14½×14 (others).

781	207	½d. pale blue, green and cerise (1.9.60)	10	10
		a. Pale blue omitted	£325	£250
		b. Green omitted	£450	
782	208	1d. orange, green, lake and brown (1.9.60)	10	10
		a. Orange omitted	£650	£375
		b. Coil. Perf 14½×13. Wmk sideways (11.63)	1·40	2·75
		c. Chalk-surfaced paper (1965?)	10	2·00
783	209	2d. carmine, black, yellow and green	10	10
		a. Black omitted	£550	£400
		b. Yellow omitted	£600	
		c. "ZFALAND"	85·00	
784	209a	2½d. red, yellow, black and green (1.11.61)	1·00	10
		a. Red omitted	£850	£600
		b. Yellow omitted	£325	
		c. Green omitted	£400	
		d. Red and green omitted	£1100	
		w. Wmk sideways	£120	90·00
785	210	3d. yellow, green, yellow-brown and deep greenish blue (1.9.60)	30	10
		a. Yellow omitted	£200	£170
		b. Green omitted	£325	£225
		c. Yellow-brown omitted	£225	
		e. Coil. Perf 14½×13. Wmk sideways (3.10.63)	1·40	2·75
		f. Chalk-surfaced paper (1965?)	30	2·25
		fa. Yellow-brown omitted	£650	
786	211	4d. purple, buff, yellow-green and light blue	40	10
		a. Purple omitted	£650	£500
		b. Buff omitted	£900	
		d. Chalk-surfaced paper (1965?)	£950	18·00
787	211a	5d. yellow, deep green, black and violet (14.5.62)	1·25	10
		a. Yellow omitted	£425	
		w. Wmk sideways inverted	£170	75·00
788	212	6d. lilac, green and deep bluish green (1.9.60)	50	10
		a. No wmk	55·00	
		b. Lilac omitted	£425	
		c. Green omitted	£425	£425
		d. Chalk-surfaced paper (1966?)	65	4·50
788e	212a	7d. red, green, yellow and pale red (16.3.66)	1·00	1·10
		ew. Wmk inverted	4·50	12·00
789	213	8d. rose-red, yellow, green and grey (1.9.60)	40	10
790	214	9d. red and ultramarine (1.9.60)	40	10
		a. Red omitted	£475	
791	215	1s. brown and deep green	30	10
792	216	1s.3d. carmine, sepia and bright blue	2·50	70
		a. Carmine omitted	£850	
		b. Carmine, sepia and greyish blue	2·00	25
		w. Wmk sideways inverted	£325	£170
793	217	1s.6d. olive-green and orange-brown	75	10
794	218	1s.9d. bistre-brown	15·00	15
795	218a	1s.9d. orange-red, blue, green and yellow (4.11.63)	2·50	1·00
		a. Wmk sideways	£950	
		w. Wmk inverted	†	£750
796	219	2s. black and orange-buff	2·50	10
		a. Chalk-surfaced paper (1966)	1·00	2·75

797	**220**	2s.6d. yellow and light brown....................	1·50	1·00
		a. Yellow omitted..................................	£1400	£850
798	**221**	3s. blackish brown...................................	17·00	1·00
799	**221a**	3s. bistre, blue and green (1.4.64).......	2·00	1·75
		w. Wmk sideways inverted..................	90·00	90·00
800	**222**	5s. blackish green....................................	2·00	60
		a. Chalk-surfaced paper (1966)..........	1·50	6·00
801	**223**	10s. steel-blue..	4·00	2·75
		a. Chalk-surfaced paper (1966)..........	3·00	11·00
802	**224**	£1 deep magenta....................................	10·00	7·00
781/802	*Set of 23*..		55·00	15·00

Nos. 782b and 785e were replaced by coils with upright watermark perf 14½×14 in 1966.

Examples of the 3d., perf 14×14½ with watermark sideways inverted (top of star pointing to the left, *as seen from the back of the stamp*) are known. They are believed to come from a trial printing.

CHALKY PAPER. The chalk-surfaced paper is not only whiter but also thicker, making the watermark difficult to see. Examples of the 4d. value can be found on a thick surfaced paper. These should not be confused with the rare chalk-surfaced printing, No. 786d, which can be identified by its positive reaction to the silver test and fluoresces brightly, both front and back, under ultraviolet light.

225 Sacred Kingfisher

226 New Zealand Pigeon

(Des Display Section, G.P.O. Recess B.W.)

1960 (10 Aug). Health Stamps. W **98**. P 13½.

| 803 | **225** | 2d. +1d. sepia and turquoise-blue........ | 50 | 75 |
| 804 | **226** | 3d. +1d. deep purple-brown and orange.. | 50 | 75 |

MS804b Two sheets each 95×107 mm with Nos. 803 and 804 in blocks of 6. P 11½×11......................*Per pair* | 27·00 | 38·00 |

227 "The Adoration of the Shepherds" (Rembrandt)

(Photo Harrison)

1960 (1 Nov). Christmas. W **98**. P 12.

| 805 | **227** | 2d. red and deep brown/*cream*.............. | 15 | 10 |
| | | a. Red omitted.. | £425 | £425 |

228 Great Egret

229 New Zealand Falcon

(Des Display Section, G.P.O. Recess B.W.)

1961 (2 Aug). Health Stamps. W **98**. P 13½.

| 806 | **228** | 2d. +1d. black and purple........................ | 50 | 70 |
| 807 | **229** | 3d. +1d. deep sepia and yellow-green... | 50 | 70 |

MS807a Two sheets each 97×121 mm with Nos. 806/7 in blocks of 6 (3×2)......................................*Per pair* | 27·00 | 35·00 |

(**230**)　　　(**231**)

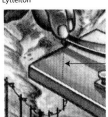

232 "Adoration of the Magi" (Dürer)

1961 (1 Sept). No. 748 surch with T **230** (wide setting).

808	**180**	2½d. on 3d. vermilion.............................	25	30
		a. Narrow setting (T **231**)........................	15	30
		b. Pair, wide and narrow..........................	16·00	35·00

The difference in the settings is in the overall width of the new value, caused by two different spacings between the "2", "½" and "d".

(Photo Harrison)

1961 (16 Oct). Christmas. W **98** (sideways). P 14½×14.

| 809 | **232** | 2½d. multicoloured.................................. | 10 | 10 |
| | | w. Wmk sideways inverted..................... | 80·00 | 48·00 |

233 Morse Key and Port Hills, Lyttelton

3d. Damage to the plate resulted in a vertical green dotted line below the fingers (R. 14/1)

(Des A. G. Mitchell (3d.) and L. C. Mitchell (8d.). Photo Harrison)

1962 (1 June). Telegraph Centenary. T **233** and similar horiz design. W **98** (sideways). P 14½×14.

810	**233**	3d. sepia and bluish green.......................	10	10
		a. Bluish green omitted............................	£3000	
		b. Dotted line flaw....................................	15·00	
811		8d. black and brown-red..........................	90	90
		a. Imperf (pair)...	£2500	
		b. Black omitted...	£2250	

Design:—8d. Modern teleprinter.

No. 811a comes from a sheet with the two top rows imperforate and the third row imperforate on three sides.

235 Red-fronted Parakeet

236 Tieke Saddleback

(Des Display Section, G.P.O. Photo D.L.R.)

1962 (3 Oct). Health Stamps. W **98**. P 15×14.

812	**235**	2½d. +1d. multicoloured.............................	50	70
		a. Orange omitted.....................................	£1600	
		b. Printed on the gummed side..........	£1300	
		w. Wmk inverted..	£160	£150
813	**236**	3d. +1d.multicoloured..............................	50	70
		a. Orange omitted.....................................	£2750	

MS813b Two sheets each 96×101 mm with Nos. 812/13 in blocks of 6 (3×2)..................................*Per pair* | 40·00 | 50·00 |

No. 812b comes from a miniature sheet.

237 "Madonna in
Prayer" (Sassoferrato)

(Photo Harrison)

1962 (15 Oct). Christmas. W **98**. P 14½×14.
814   **237**   2½d. multicoloured 10   10

238 Prince Andrew   **239**

3d.+1d. A prominent flaw
on the middle finger of the
Prince's right hand appears as
a bloodstain. Later attempts to
remove the flaw met with only
partial success (Pl. 1B, R. 3/5)

(Design after photographs by Studio Lisa, London. Recess D.L.R.)
1963 (7 Aug). Health Stamps. W **98**. P 14.
815   **238**   2½d. +1d. dull ultramarine 30   70
                a. Ultramarine 40   80
                b. Deep blue 30   40
816   **239**   3d. +1d. carmine 30   10
                a. Bloodstained finger .... 90·00   50·00
MS816*b* Two sheets each 93×100 mm with Nos. 815/16
    in blocks of 6 (3×2) ....*Per pair*   25·00   40·00
    The price for No. 816a is for the flaw in its original state, as illustrated.
Examples with the flaw partially removed are worth less.

240 "The Holy Family" (Titian)

An orange flaw over the donkey's nose
appears as a nosebag (Pl. 1B, R. 3/8)

(Photo Harrison)
1963 (14 Oct). Christmas. W **98** (sideways). P 12½.
817   **240**   2½d. multicoloured 10   10
                a. Imperf (pair) £250
                b. Yellow omitted £300
                c. Nosebag flaw .... 5·00
                w. Wmk sideways inverted 40   40

241 Steam Locomotive *Pilgrim*   **242** Diesel Express and Mt
(1863) and Class DG Diesel   Ruapehu
Locomotive

(Des Commercial Art Section, N.Z. Railways. Photo D.L.R.)
1963 (25 Nov). Railway Centenary. W **98** (sideways on 3d., sideways
    inverted on 1s.9d.). P 14.
818   **241**   3d. multicoloured 40   10
                a. Blue (sky) omitted £550
819   **242**   1s.9d. multicoloured .... 1·75   1·25
                a. Red (value) omitted £2500

243 "Commonwealth Cable"

(Des P. Morriss. Photo Note Printing Branch,
Reserve Bank of Australia)
1963 (3 Dec). Opening of COMPAC (Trans-Pacific Telephone Cable).
    No wmk. P 13½.
820   **243**   8d. red, blue and yellow 50   1·00

244 Road Map and Car   **245** Silver Gulls
Steering-wheel

3d. Flaw between "W" and "Z" of "NEW ZEALAND"
resembling an apostrophe (R. 3/2)

(Des L. C. Mitchell. Photo Harrison)
1964 (1 May). Road Safety Campaign. W **98**. P 15×14.
821   **244**   3d. black, ochre-yellow and blue 30   10
                a. "Apostrophe" flaw .... 12·00

(Des Display Section G.P.O., after Miss T. Kelly. Photo Harrison)
1964 (5 Aug). Health Stamps. T **245** and similar horiz design.
    Multicoloured. W **98**. P 14½.
822   2½d. +1d. Type **245** 40   50
                a. Red (beak and legs) omitted £350   £250
                w. Wmk inverted .... †   £475
823   3d. +1d. Little Penguin 40   50
                aw. Wmk inverted £200
MS823*b* Two sheets each 171×84 mm with Nos. 822/3
    in blocks of 8 (4×2) ....*Per pair*   48·00   65·00
                bw. Wmk inverted (No. 823 only) ....

7ᴰ

POSTAGE
(247)

246 Rev. S. Marsden taking first Christian service at Rangihoua Bay, 1814

(Des L. C. Mitchell. Photo Harrison)

1964 (12 Oct). Christmas. W **98** (sideways). P 14×13½.
824   **246**   2½d. multicoloured........................   10   10

1964 (14 Dec). As Type F **6**, but without value, surch with T **247**. W **98**. Unsurfaced paper. P 14×13½.
825   F **6**   7d. carmine-red............................   50   1·50

248 Anzac Cove

(Des R. M. Conly. Photo Harrison)

1965 (14 Apr). 50th Anniversary of Gallipoli Landing. T **248** and similar horiz design. W **98**. P 12½.
826   **248**   4d. yellow-brown..........................   10   10
827   5d. green and red..........................   10   60
   Design:—5d. Anzac Cove and poppy.

249 I.T.U. Emblem and Symbols   **250** Sir Winston Churchill

(Photo Harrison)

1965 (17 May). I.T.U. Centenary. W **98**. P 14½×14.
828   **249**   9d. blue and pale chocolate....................   55   35

(Des P. Morriss from photograph by Karsh. Photo Note Ptg Branch, Reserve Bank of Australia)

1965 (24 May). Churchill Commemoration. P 13½.
829   **250**   7d. black, pale grey and light blue........   30   50

251 Wellington Provincial Council Building

(Des from painting by L. B. Temple (1867). Photo Harrison)

1965 (26 July). Centenary of Government in Wellington. W **98** (sideways). P 14½×14.
830   **251**   4d. multicoloured.........................   10   10

252 Kaka

253 Collared Grey Fantail (after Miss T. Kelly)

(Des Display Section, G.P.O. Photo Harrison)

1965 (4 Aug). Health Stamps. W **98**. P 14×14½.
831   **252**   3d. +1d. multicoloured................   40   65
         w. Wmk inverted......................   †   £100
832   **253**   4d. +1d. multicoloured................   40   65
         a. Green ("POSTAGE HEALTH" and on leaves) omitted..................   £2250
         bw. Wmk inverted......................   80·00   £130
MS832c Two sheets each 100×109 mm with Nos. 831/2 in blocks of 6 (3×2)..........................*Per pair*   38·00   48·00
         cw. Wmk inverted (No. 831 only)...........   †   —

254 I.C.Y. Emblem   **255** "The Two Trinities" (Murillo)

(Litho D.L.R.)

1965 (28 Sept). International Co-operation Year. W **98** (sideways inverted). P 14.
833   **254**   4d. carmine-red and light yellow-olive   20   10
         w. Wmk sideways......................   4·25   4·00

(Photo Harrison)

1965 (11 Oct). Christmas. W **98**. P 13½×14.
834   **255**   3d. multicoloured.........................   10   10
         a. Gold (frame) omitted................   £1500

256 Arms of New Zealand   **259** "Progress" Arrowhead

(Des Display Section, G.P.O. Photo D.L.R.)

1965 (30 Nov). 11th Commonwealth Parliamentary Conference. T **256** and similar horiz designs. Multicoloured. P 14.
835   4d. Type **256**............................   20   10
         a. Blue (incl value) omitted..............   £1100
         b. Printed on the gummed side..........   £1000
836   9d. Parliament House, Wellington and Badge..............................   40   45
837   2s. Wellington from Mt Victoria.......   1·75   3·00
         a. Carmine omitted.....................   £1000
835/7 *Set of 3* ....   2·10   3·00

(Des Display Section, G.P.O. Photo Harrison)

1966 (5 Jan). Fourth National Scout Jamboree, Trentham. W **98**. P 14×15.
838   **259**   4d. gold and myrtle-green...............   15   10
         a. Gold (arrowhead) omitted...............   £1200   £1100

260 New Zealand Bell Bird   **262** "The Virgin with Child" (Maratta)

(Des Display Section, G.P.O. Photo Harrison)

1966 (3 Aug). Health Stamps. T **260** and similar vert design. Multicoloured. W **98** (sideways). P 14×14½.
839   3d. +1d. Type **260**........................   40   65
         w. Wmk sideways inverted..............   £120

840		4d. +1d. Weka Rail................................	40	65
		a. Deep brown (values and date) omitted...	£2500	
		w. Wmk sideways inverted.......................	£110	

MS841 Two sheets each 107×91 mm. Nos. 839/40
in blocks of 6 (3×2)..................................*Per pair* 20·00 50·00
In No. 840a besides the value, "1966" and "Weka" are also omitted and
the bird, etc. appears as light brown.

(Photo Harrison)

1966 (3 Oct). Christmas. W **98** (sideways). P 14½.

842	262	3d. multicoloured..	10	10
		a. Red omitted	£350	

263 Queen
Victoria and Queen
Elizabeth II

264 Half-sovereign
of 1867 and
Commemorative
Dollar Coin

(Des Display Section, G.P.O. Photo Harrison)

1967 (3 Feb). Centenary of New Zealand Post Office Savings Bank.
W **98** (sideways on 4d.). P 14×14½.

843	263	4d. black, gold and maroon	10	10
		w. Wmk sideways inverted.......................	85·00	29·00
844	264	9d. gold, silver, black, light blue and deep green	10	20
		w. Wmk inverted	£600	

(New Currency. 100 cents = 1 New Zealand Dollar)

265 Manuka
(Tea Tree)

266 Pohutu Geyser

1967 (10 July). Decimal Currency. Designs as 1960–66 issue, but with
values inscr in decimal currency as T **265/6**. Chalky paper. W **98**
(sideways on 8c., 10c., 20c., 50c. and $2). P 13½×14 (½c. to 3c.,
5c. and 7c.), 14½×14 (4c., 6c., 8c., 10c., 25c. and $1) or 14×14½
(15c., 20c., 50c. and $2).

845	265	½c. pale blue, yellow-green and cerise...	10	10
846	208	1c. yellow, carmine, green and light brown (as 1d.).....................................	10	10
		a. Booklet pane. Five stamps plus one printed label................................	2·25	
847	209	2c. carmine, black, yellow and green (as 2d.)..	10	10
848	210	2½c. yellow, green, yellow-brown and deep bluish green (as 3d.)...............	10	10
		a. Deep bluish green omitted*...........	£3750	
		b. Imperf (pair)†....................................	£150	
849	211	3c. purple, buff, yellow-green and light greenish blue (as 4d.).............	10	10
850	211a	4c. yellow, deep green, black and violet (as 5d.).......................................	30	10
851	212	5c. lilac, yellow-olive and bluish green (as 6d.)...	50	1·00
852	212a	6c. red, green, yellow and light pink (as 7d.)..	50	1·00
853	213	7c. rose-red, yellow, green and grey (as 8d.)..	60	1·50
		w. Wmk inverted	60	
854	214	8c. red and ultramarine	60	60
		a. Red omitted	£1200	
855	215	10c. brown and deep green (as 1s.).....	60	1·00
		w. Wmk sideways inverted......................	£650	£550
856	217	15c. olive-green and orange-brown (as 1s.6d.)...	2·50	2·25
		w. Wmk inverted	2·75	10·00
857	219	20c. black and buff......................................	1·00	20

858	220	25c. yellow and light brown...................	1·25	2·00
859	221a	30c. olive-yellow, green and greenish blue..	1·25	25
		w. Wmk inverted	£130	85·00
860	222	50c. blackish green (as 5s.).....................	1·75	50
861	223	$1 Prussian blue (as 10s.)...................	9·00	1·00
		w. Wmk inverted	£375	£200
862	266	$2 deep magenta....................................	4·00	6·00

845/62 *Set of 18*... 21·00 15·00

*This occurred on one horizontal row of ten, affecting the background
colour so that the value is also missing. In the row above and the row
below, the colour was partially omitted. The price is for a vertical strip.
The 2½c. value has been seen with the yellow omitted, but only on
a used example.

†This comes from a sheet of which the six right-hand vertical rows
were completely imperforate and the top, bottom and left-hand margins
had been removed.

The 4c., 30c. and 50c. exist with PVA gum as well as gum arabic.
For $4 to $10 in the "Arms" type, see under Postal Fiscal stamps.
For other versions of 15c., 30c. and $2 see Nos. 870/9.

268 Running with Ball

(Des L. C. Mitchell. Photo Harrison)

1967 (2 Aug). Health Stamps. Rugby Football. T **268** and similar
multicoloured design. W **98** (sideways on 2½c.). P 14½×14 (2½c.)
or 14×14½ (3c.)

867		2½c. +1c. Type **268**	15	15
868		3c. +1c. Positioning for a place-kick (*horiz*)..	15	15

MS869 Two sheets; (a) 76×130 mm (867); (b) 130×76 mm
(868). Containing blocks of 6 ....*Per pair* 20·00 38·00

270 *Kaita* (trawler) and Catch   **271** Brown Trout

272 Apples and Orchard   **273** Forest and Timber

274 Sheep and the
"Woolmark"

275 Consignments of Beef and
Herd of Cattle

276 Dairy Farm, Mt Egmont and
Butter Consignment

277 Fox Glacier,
Westland National
Park

(Des Display Section, G.P.O. (7, 8, 10, 18, 20, 25c. and 28c. from photo), R. M. Conly (7½c.). Litho B.W. (7, 8, 18, 20c.) or photo D.L.R. (7½c.) and Harrison (10, 25, 28c.) as before)

1967–70. T **270/7**. Chalky paper (except 7, 8, 18, 20c.). No wmk (7, 8, 20, 30c.) or W **98** (sideways inverted on 7½c., sideways on 10, 15, 25c, upright on 18, 28c., $2). P 13½ (7, 7½c.), 13×13½ (8, 18, 20c.), 14½×14 (10, 25, 30c.) or 14×14½ (15, 28c., $2).

870	**270**	7c. multicoloured (3.12.69)................	1·00	1·00
871	**271**	7½c. multicoloured* (29.8.67)...........	50	70
		a. Wmk upright (10.68)................	50	1·00
872	**272**	8c. multicoloured (8.7.69)................	75	70
873	**273**	10c. multicoloured (2.4.68)................	50	10
		a. Green (background) omitted........	£950	
		w. Wmk sideways inverted...............	†	£1100
874	**217**	15c. apple-green, myrtle-green and carmine (as No. 856†) (19.3.68).....	1·00	1·00
		w. Wmk sideways inverted...............	†	£170
875	**274**	18c. multicoloured (8.7.69)................	1·00	55
		a. Printed on the gummed side........	£800	
876	**275**	20c. multicoloured (8.7.69)................	1·00	20
877	**276**	25c. multicoloured (10.12.68)............	1·50	2·00
878	**277**	28c. multicoloured (30.7.68).............	60	10
		a. Yellow omitted............................	£750	
		bw. Wmk inverted............................	†	£1200
878c	**221a**	30c. olive-green, green and greenish blue (as No. 859) (2.6.70)..........	3·50	5·00
879	**266**	$2 black, ochre and pale blue (as No. 862) (10.12.68)................	13·00	13·00
870/9		Set of 11..	22·00	22·00

*No. 871 was originally issued to commemorate the introduction of the brown trout into New Zealand.
†No. 874 is slightly larger than No. 856, measuring 21×25 mm and the inscriptions and numerals differ in size.

278 "The Adoration of the Shepherds" (Poussin)

279 Mount Aspiring, Aurora Australis and Southern Cross

280 Sir James Hector (founder)

(Photo Harrison)

1967 (3 Oct). Christmas. W **98** (sideways). P 13½×14.

880	**278**	2½c. multicoloured..	10	10

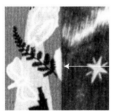

4c. A large white flaw to the right of the fern (a multipositive flaw affecting all plates, R. 1/10)

(Des J. Berry. Litho D.L.R.)

1967 (10 Oct). Centenary of the Royal Society of New Zealand. W **98** (sideways on 4c.). P 14 (4c.) or 13×14 (8c.)

881	**279**	4c. multicoloured..	25	20
		a. Fern flaw....................................	5·00	
		w. Wmk sideways inverted....................	8·00	9·00
882	**280**	8c. multicoloured..	25	80

281 Open Bible

282 Soldiers and Tank

(Des Display Section, G.P.O. Litho D.L.R.)

1968 (23 Apr). Centenary of Maori Bible. W **98**. P 13½.

883	**281**	3c. multicoloured..	10	10
		a. Gold (inscr.) omitted....................	£160	£110
		w. Wmk inverted............................	35·00	35·00

(Des L. C. Mitchell. Litho D.L.R.)

1968 (7 May). New Zealand Armed Forces. T **282** and similar horiz designs. Multicoloured. W **98** (sideways). P 14×13½.

884		4c. Type **282**............................	25	10
		w. Wmk sideways inverted...............	9·50	14·00
885		10c. Airmen, Fairey Firefly and English Electric Canberra aircraft................	40	50
886		28c. Sailors and H.M.N.Z.S. Achilles, 1939, and H.M.N.Z.S. Waikato, 1968............	70	1·60
		w. Wmk sideways inverted...............	2·00	6·00
884/6		Set of 3..	1·25	2·00

285 Boy breasting Tape, and Olympic Rings

287 Placing Votes in Ballot Box

(Des L. C. Mitchell. Photo Harrison)

1968 (7 Aug). Health Stamps. T **285** and similar horiz design. Multicoloured. P 14½×14.

887		2½c. +1c. Type **285**....................	20	15
888		3c. +1c. Girl swimming and Olympic rings..	20	15
		a. Red (ring) omitted......................	£3500	
		b. Blue (ring) omitted.....................	£2250	
MS889		Two sheets each 145×95 mm. Nos. 887/8 in blocks of six....................... Per pair	16·00	45·00

No. 888a occurred in one miniature sheet. Six examples are known, one being used. No. 888b occurred from a second miniature sheet.

(Des J. Berry. Photo Japanese Govt Ptg Bureau, Tokyo)

1968 (19 Sept). 75th Anniversary of Universal Suffrage in New Zealand. P 13.

890	**287**	3c. ochre, olive-green and light blue ...	10	10

288 Human Rights Emblem

289 "Adoration of the Holy Child" (G. van Honthorst)

(Photo Japanese Govt Ptg Bureau, Tokyo)

1968 (19 Sept). Human Rights Year. P 13.

891	**288**	10c. scarlet, yellow and deep green........	10	30

(Photo Harrison)

1968 (1 Oct). Christmas. W **98** (sideways). P 14×14½.

892	**289**	2½c. multicoloured........................	10	10

290 I.L.O. Emblem

(Photo Harrison)

1969 (11 Feb). 50th Anniversary of International Labour Organization. W **98** (sideways inverted). P 14½×14.

893	**290**	7c. black and carmine-red................	15	30

291 Supreme Court Building, Auckland

292 Law Society's Coat of Arms

(Des R. M. Conly. Litho B.W.)

1969 (8 Apr). Centenary of New Zealand Law Society. T **291/2** and similar design. P 13½×13 (3c.) or 13×13½ (others).

894	**291**	3c. multicoloured (shades)................	10	10

895	**292**	10c. multicoloured	20	35
896		18c. multicoloured (*shades*)	30	95
894/6	*Set of 3*		55	1·25

Design: Vert—18c. "Justice" (from Memorial Window in University of Canterbury, Christchurch).

295 Student being conferred with Degree

(Des R. M. Conly. Litho B.W.)

1969 (3 June). Centenary of Otago University. T **295** and similar multicoloured design. P 13×13½ (3c.) or 13½×13 (10c.)

897		3c. Otago University (*vert*)	15	10
898		10c. Type **295**	30	25

296 Boys playing Cricket

298 Dr. Elizabeth Gunn (founder of First Children's Health Camp)

(Des R. M. Conly (4c.); L. C. Mitchell (others). Litho B.W.)

1969 (6 Aug). Health Stamps. T **296** and similar horiz design and T **298**. P 12½×13 (No. 901) or 13×12½ (others).

899	**296**	2½c. +1c. multicoloured	40	65
900	—	3c. +1c. multicoloured	40	65
901	**298**	4c. +1c. brown and ultramarine	40	2·00
899/901	*Set of 3*		1·10	3·00
MS902	Two sheets each 144×84 mm. Nos. 899/900 in blocks of six ....*Per pair*		16·00	50·00

Design:—3c. Girls playing cricket.

299 Oldest existing House in New Zealand, and Old Stone Mission Store, Kerikeri

(Litho D.L.R.)

1969 (18 Aug). Early European Settlement in New Zealand, and 150th Anniversary of Kerikeri. T **299** and similar horiz design. Multicoloured. W **98** (sideways inverted). P 13×13½.

903		4c. Type **299**	20	25
904		6c. View of Bay of Islands	30	1·75

301 "The Nativity" (Federico Fiori (Barocci))

302 Captain Cook, Transit of Venus and "Octant"

(Photo Harrison)

1969 (1 Oct). Christmas. W **98**. P 13×14.

905	**301**	2½c. multicoloured	10	10
		a. No wmk	10	15

(Des Eileen Mayo. Photo; portraits embossed Harrison)

1969 (9 Oct). Bicentenary of Captain Cook's Landing in New Zealand. T **302** and similar horiz designs. P 14½×14.

906		4c. black, cerise and blue	30	15
		a. Imperf (pair)	£425	
907		6c. slate-green, purple-brown and black	40	1·00
908		18c. purple-brown, slate-green and black	60	40

909		28c. cerise, black and blue	1·00	1·25
906/9	*Set of 4*		2·10	2·50
MS910	109×90 mm. Nos. 906/9		14·00	25·00

Designs:—6c. Sir Joseph Banks (naturalist) and outline of H.M.S. *Endeavour*; 18c. Dr. Daniel Solander (botanist) and his plant; 28c. Queen Elizabeth II and Cook's chart 1769.

The miniature sheet exists additionally inscribed on the selvedge at bottom. "A SOUVENIR FROM NEW ZEALAND STAMP EXHIBITION, NEW PLYMOUTH 6TH–11TH OCTOBER. 1969". These were not sold from Post Offices.

306 Girl, Wheat Field and C.O.R.S.O. Emblem

307 Mother feeding her Child, Dairy Herd and C.O.R.S.O. Emblem

(Des L. C. Mitchell. Photo Japanese Govt Printing Bureau, Tokyo)

1969 (18 Nov). 25th Anniversary of C.O.R.S.O. (Council of Organizations for Relief Services Overseas). P 13.

911	**306**	7c. multicoloured	35	85
912	**307**	8c. multicoloured	35	90

308 "Cardigan Bay" (champion trotter)

(Des L. C. Mitchell. Photo Courvoisier)

1970 (28 Jan). Return of "Cardigan Bay" to New Zealand. P 11½.

913	**308**	10c. multicoloured	30	30

309 *Vanessa gonerilla* (butterfly)

310 Queen Elizabeth II and New Zealand Coat of Arms

(Des Enid Hunter (½c., 1c., 2c., 18c., 20c.), Eileen Mayo (2½c. to 7c.), D. B. Stevenson (7½c., 8c.), M. Cleverley (10, 15, 25, 30c., $1, $2), M. V. Askew (23, 50c.). Photo Harrison (½c. to 20c.), Enschedé (23, 50c.), Courvoisier ($1, $2) or Litho B.W. (25, 30c.))

1970 (12 Mar)–**76**. Various designs as T **309/10**. W **98** (sideways on 10c., or sideways inverted on 15, 20c.) or No wmk (23c. to $2).

*(a) Size as T **309**. P 13½×13*

914		½c. multicoloured (2.9.70)	10	20
		w. Wmk inverted	—	£200
915		1c. multicoloured (2.9.70)	10	10
		aw. Wmk inverted	50·00	35·00
		b. Wmk sideways inverted (booklets) (6.7.71)	80	2·50
		ba. Booklet pane. No. 915b×3 with three se-tenant printed labels	2·25	
		bb. Red omitted	£275	
		bc. Blue omitted (booklets)	£250	£200
		bw. Wmk sideways	£120	
916		2c. multicoloured (2.9.70)	10	10
		a. Black (inscr, etc) omitted	£400	
		w. Wmk inverted	4·00	1·50
917		2½c. multicoloured (2.9.70)	30	20
918		3c. black, brown and orange (2.9.70)	15	10
		aw. Wmk inverted	2·50	2·75
		b. Wmk sideways inverted (booklets) (6.7.71) ...	55	1·50
		bw. Wmk sideways	32·00	32·00
919		4c. multicoloured (2.9.70)	15	10
		aw. Wmk inverted	3·00	1·75
		b. Wmk sideways inverted (booklets) (6.7.71)...	55	1·75
		ba. Bright green (wing veins) omitted	£250	£110
		bw. Wmk sideways	85·00	75·00
		c. Bright green (wing veins) omitted		£250
920		5c. multicoloured (4.11.70)	30	10
		w. Wmk inverted	†	—
921		6c. blackish green, yellow-green and carmine (4.11.70)	30	1·00

922	7c. multicoloured (4.11.70)		50	1·00
	w. Wmk inverted		—	£300
923	7½c. multicoloured (4.11.70)		75	2·00
	w. Wmk inverted		†	—
924	8c. multicoloured (4.11.70)		50	1·00

(b) Size as T 310. Various perfs

925	10c. multicoloured (P 14½×14)		50	15
	w. Wmk sideways inverted		8·00	3·75
926	15c. black, flesh and pale brown (P 13½×13) (20.1.71)		75	50
	a. Pale brown omitted		£700	
	w. Wmk sideways		50·00	45·00
927	18c. chestnut, black and apple-green (P 13×13½) (20.1.71)		75	50
	w. Wmk inverted		55·00	45·00
928	20c. black and yellow-brown (P 13½×13) (20.1.71)		75	15
929	23c. multicoloured (P 13½×12½) (1.12.71)		60	30
930	25c. multicoloured (P 13×13½) (1.9.71)		1·00	50
	a. Printed on the gummed side		£750	
	b. Perf 14 (11.76?)		50	75
931	30c. multicoloured (P 13×13½) (1.9.71)		50	15
	a. Perf 14 (9.76?)		1·00	1·75
932	50c. multicoloured (P 13½×12½) (1.9.71)		50	20
	a. Apple green (hill on right) omitted		28·00	
	b. Buff (shore) omitted		55·00	
	c. Dark green (hill on left) omitted		£350	
933	$1 multicoloured (P 11½) (14.4.71)		1·00	1·00
934	$2 multicoloured (P 11½) (14.4.71)		2·50	1·00
914/34	*Set of 21*		10·00	9·00

Designs: Vert—½c. *Lycaena salustius* (butterfly); 2c. *Argyrophenga antipodum* (butterfly); 2½c. *Nyctemera annulata* (moth); 3c. *Detunda egregia* (moth); 4c. *Charagia virescens* (moth); 5c. Scarlet Wrasse ("Scarlet Parrot Fish"); 6c. Big-bellied Sea Horses; 7c. Leather jacket (fish); 7½c. Intermediate Halfbeak ("Garfish"); 8c. John Dory (fish); 18c. Maori club; 25c. Hauraki Gulf Maritime Park; 30c. Mt Cook National Park. Horiz—10c. Type **310**: 15c. Maori fish hook; 20c. Maori tattoo Pattern, 23c. Egmont National Park; 50c. Abel Tasman National Park; $1 Geothermal Power; $2 Agricultural Technology.

Although issued as a definitive No. 925 was put on sale on the occasion of the Royal Visit to New Zealand.

Used examples of No. 931 are known showing the sky in light blue instead of the normal stone colour. It was suggested by the printer involved that this was caused by a residue of ink used for another stamp remaining in the ink ducts when a printing of the 30c. commenced. Most authorities, however, agree that the "blue sky" stamps are colour changelings.

The 1c., 2c., 3c. to 7c. and 8c. to 20c. values were re-issued between 1973 and 1976 on unwatermarked paper.

311 Geyser Restaurant

312 U.N. H.Q. Building

(Des M. Cleverley. Photo Japanese Govt Printing Bureau, Tokyo)

1970 (8 Apr). World Fair, Osaka. T **311** and similar horiz designs. Multicoloured. P 13.

935	7c. Type **311**		20	55
936	8c. New Zealand Pavilion		20	55
937	18c. Bush Walk		40	55
935/7	*Set of 3*		70	1·50

(Des R. M. Conly (3c.), L. C. Mitchell (10c.). Litho D.L.R.)

1970 (24 June). 25th Anniversary of United Nations. T **312** and similar vert design. P 13½.

938	3c. multicoloured		10	10
939	10c. scarlet and yellow		20	20

Design:—10c. Tractor on horizon.

313 Soccer

(Des L. C. Mitchell. Litho D.L.R.)

1970 (5 Aug). Health Stamps. T **313** and similar multicoloured design. P 13½.

940	2½c. +1c. Netball (*vert*)		25	70
941	3c. +1c.Type **313**		25	70
MS942	Two sheets: (a) 102×125 mm (940); (b) 125×102 mm (941), containing blocks of 6	*Per pair*	16·00	50·00

314 "The Virgin adoring the Child" (Correggio)

315 "The Holy Family" (stained glass window, Invercargill Presbyterian Church)

(Litho D.L.R.)

1970 (1 Oct). Christmas. T **314/15** and similar design. P 12½.

943	**314**	2½c. multicoloured	10	10
944	**315**	3c. multicoloured	10	10
		a. Green (inscr and value) omitted	£300	
945		10c. black, orange and silver	30	75
943/5	*Set of 3*		35	75

Design: Horiz—10c. Tower of Roman Catholic Church, Sockburn.

No. 943 exists as an imperforate proof with the country inscription and face value omitted.

316 Chatham Islands Lily

(Des Eileen Mayo. Photo Japanese Govt Printing Bureau, Tokyo)

1970 (2 Dec). Chatham Islands. T **316** and similar horiz design. Multicoloured. P 13.

946	1c. Type **316**		10	35
947	2c. Shy Albatross		30	40

317 Country Women's Institute Emblem

(Des L. C. Mitchell. Photo Japanese Govt Ptg Bureau, Tokyo)

1971 (10 Feb). 50th Anniversaries of Country Women's Institutes and Rotary International in New Zealand. T **317** and similar horiz design. Multicoloured. P 13.

948	4c. Type **317**		10	10
949	10c. Rotary emblem and map of New Zealand		20	60

318 *Rainbow II* (yacht)

(Des J. Berry (5c.), G. F. Fuller (8c.). Litho B.W.)

1971 (3 Mar). One Ton Cup Racing Trophy. T **318** and similar horiz design. Multicoloured. P 13½×13.

950	5c. Type **318**		25	25
951	8c. One Ton Cup		25	1·50

319 Civic Arms of Palmerston North

(Des R. M. Conly. Photo Japanese Govt Ptg Bureau, Tokyo)

1971 (12 May). City Centenaries. T **319** and similar horiz designs. Multicoloured. P 13.

952	3c. Type **319**		15	10
953	4c. Arms of Auckland		15	15
954	5c. Arms of Invercargill		15	1·10
952/4	*Set of 3*		40	1·25

320 Antarctica on Globe

321 Child on Swing

(Des Eileen Mayo. Photo Japanese Govt Ptg Bureau, Tokyo)

1971 (9 June). Tenth Anniv of Antarctic Treaty. P 13.
955　　**320**　　6c. multicoloured .... 1·00　1·75

(Des Eileen Mayo. Photo Japanese Govt Ptg Bureau, Tokyo)

1971 (9 June). 25th Anniv of U.N.I.C.E.F. P 13.
956　　**321**　　7c. multicoloured .... 50　1·25

4c　　　**4c**　　　**4c**

　(322)　　　(322a)　　　(322b)

T **322**. Photo, showing screening dots; thin bars, wide apart. T **322a**. Typo, without screening dots; thick bars, closer together. T **322b**. Typo; bars similar to T **322**.

1971–73. No. 917 surcharged.
　　　　　　　(a) In photogravure, by Harrison (23.6.71)*
957　　**322**　　4c. on 2½c. multicoloured .... 15　10
　　　　　　a. Red omitted £1500
　　　　　　b. Pair, one without surcharge £350

　　　　　　　(b) Typographically, by Harrison (13.7.72)*
957*c*　　**322a**　　4c. on 2½c. multicoloured .... 45　10
　　　　　　ca. Albino surch £120
　　　　　　cb. Surch double, one albino .... 30·00
　　　　　　cc. Pair, one without surch £350
　　　　　　cd. Red omitted £1500

　　　　　　　(c) Typographically, locally (18.6.73)*
957*d*　　**322b**　　4c. on 2½c. multicoloured .... 15　10
*Earliest known postmarks.

323 Satellite-tracking Aerial

(Des M. Cleverley. Photo Courvoisier)

1971 (14 July). Opening of Satellite Earth Station. T **323** and similar horiz design. P 11½.
958　　　8c. black, drab-grey and vermilion .... 50　1·50
959　　　10c. black, turquoise-green and pale bluish
　　　　　　violet .... 50　1·00
Design:—10c. Satellite.

324 Girls playing Hockey

(Des L. C. Mitchell. Litho Harrison)

1971 (4 Aug). Health Stamps. T **324** and similar horiz designs. Multicoloured. W **98** (sideways on 5c.). P 13½×13.
960　　　3c.+1c. Type **324** .... 40　65
961　　　4c.+1c. Boys playing hockey .... 40　65
962　　　5c.+1c. Dental Health .... 60　2·00
960/2 *Set of 3* .... 1·25　3·00
MS963 Two sheets each 122×96 mm. Nos. 960/1
　in blocks of six ....*Per pair*　16·00　45·00

325 *Madonna bending over the Crib* (Maratta)

326 "Tiffany" Rose

(Des Enid Hunter (10c.), D. A. Hatcher (others). Photo Harrison)

1971 (6 Oct). Christmas. T **325** and similar vert designs. Multicoloured. P 13×13½.
964　　　3c. Type **325** .... 10　10
965　　　4c. "The Annunciation" (stained-glass window)
　　　　　　(21½×38 mm) .... 10　10
966　　　10c. *The Three Kings* (21½×38 mm) .... 50　1·25
964/6 *Set of 3* .... 60　1·25

(Des A. G. Mitchell. Photo Courvoisier)

1971 (3 Nov). First World Rose Convention, Hamilton. T **326** and similar vert designs showing roses. Multicoloured. P 11½.
967　　　2c. Type **326** .... 15　90
968　　　5c. "Peace" .... 35　25
969　　　8c. "Chrysler Imperial" .... 60　1·10
967/9 *Set of 3* .... 1·00　2·00

327 Lord Rutherford and Alpha Particles

(Des M. Cleverley. Litho B.W.)

1971 (1 Dec). Birth Centenary of Lord Rutherford (scientist). T **327** and similar horiz design. Multicoloured. P 13½×13.
970　　　1c. Type **327** .... 20　50
971　　　7c. Lord Rutherford and formula .... 55　1·75

328 Benz (1895)

(Des A. G. Mitchell. Litho B.W.)

1972 (2 Feb). International Vintage Car Rally. T **328** and similar horiz designs. Multicoloured. P 14.
972　　　3c. Type **328** .... 20　10
973　　　4c. Oldsmobile (1904) .... 20　10
974　　　5c. Ford "Model T" (1914) .... 20　10
975　　　6c. Cadillac Service car (1915) .... 20　45
976　　　8c. Chrysler (1924) .... 30　1·50
977　　　10c. Austin "7" (1923) .... 30　1·25
972/7 *Set of 6* .... 1·25　3·00

329 Coat of Arms of Wanganui

330 Black Scree Cotula

(Des M. Cleverley. Litho Harrison)

1972 (5 Apr). Anniversaries. T **329** and similar designs. P 13×13½ (3, 5 and 8c.) or 13½×13 (others).
978　　　3c. multicoloured .... 10　10
979　　　4c. red-orange, brown-bistre and black .... 15　10

980	5c. multicoloured	25	10
981	8c. multicoloured	30	1·25
982	10c. multicoloured	30	1·25
978/82	Set of 5	1·00	2·50

Designs and Events: Vert—3c. Type **329** (centenary of Wanganui Council govt); 5c. de Havilland DH.89 Dragon Rapide and Boeing 737 (25th anniv of National Airways Corp); 8c. French frigate and Maori palisade (bicent of landing by Marion du Fresne). Horiz—4c. Postal Union symbol (tenth anniv of Asian-Oceanic Postal Union); 10c. Stone cairn (150th anniv of New Zealand Methodist Church).

(Des Eileen Mayo. Litho Harrison)

1972 (7 June). Alpine Plants. T **330** and similar vert designs. Multicoloured. P 13½.

983	4c. Type **330**	20	10
984	6c. North Island Edelweiss	25	35
985	8c. Haast's Buttercup	35	70
986	10c. Brown Mountain Daisy	45	1·20
983/6	Set of 4	1·10	2·00

331 Boy playing Tennis

332 Madonna with Child (Murillo)

(Des L. C. Mitchell. Litho Harrison)

1972 (2 Aug). Health Stamps. T **331** and similar vert design. P 13×13½.

987	3c.+1c. light grey and chestnut	30	65
988	4c.+1c. light red-brown, grey and lemon	30	65
MS989	Two sheets each 107×123 mm. Nos. 987/8 in blocks of six.............................Per pair	15·00	40·00

Design:—No. 988, Girl playing tennis.

(Des D. A. Hatcher. Photo Courvoisier)

1972 (4 Oct). Christmas. T **332** and similar vert designs. Multicoloured. P 11½.

990	3c. Type **332**	10	10
991	5c. "The Last Supper" (stained-glass window, St. John's Church, Levin)	15	10
992	10c. Pohutukawa flower	35	70
990/2	Set of 3	50	70

333 Lake Waikaremoana

334 Old Pollen Street

(Des D. A. Hatcher. Photo Courvoisier)

1972 (6 Dec). Lake Scenes. T **333** and similar vert designs. Multicoloured. P 11½.

993	6c. Type **333**	50	1·00
994	8c. Lake Hayes	60	1·00
995	18c. Lake Wakatipu	80	1·50
996	23c. Lake Rotomahana	90	2·00
993/6	Set of 4	2·50	5·00

No. 995 is inscribed "Lake Wakatipu", but actually shows Kawarau River, which flows out of the Lake.

(Des Miss V. Jepsen (3c.), B. Langford (others). Litho Harrison)

1973 (7 Feb). Commemorations. T **334** and similar horiz designs. Multicoloured (except 8c.). P 13½×13.

997	3c. Type **334**	10	10
998	4c. Coal-mining and pasture	15	10
999	5c. Cloister	10	15
1000	6c. Forest, birds and lake	35	50
1001	8c. Rowers (light grey, indigo and gold)	15	50
1002	10c. Graph and people	35	50
997/1002	Set of 6	1·00	1·90

Events:—3c. Centennial of Thames Borough; 4c. Centennial of Westport Borough; 5c. Centennial of Canterbury University; 6c. 50th Anniv of Royal Forest and Bird Protection Society; 8c. Success of N.Z. Rowers in 1972 Olympics; 10c. 25th Anniv of E.C.A.F.E.

335 Class W Locomotive

336 Maori Woman and Child

(Des R. M. Conly. Litho Harrison)

1973 (4 Apr). New Zealand Steam Locomotives. T **335** and similar horiz designs. Multicoloured. P 14×14½.

1003	3c. Type **335**	20	10
1004	4c. Class X	20	10
1005	5c. Class Ab	20	10
1006	10c. Class Ja No. 1274	75	1·40
1003/6	Set of 4	1·25	1·50

1973–76. As Nos. 915 etc., but no wmk.

1008	1c. multicoloured (7.9.73)	60	1·25
	a. Booklet pane. No. 1008×3 with three se-tenant printed labels (8.74)	2·40	
	b. Red (wing markings) omitted	£250	
	c. Blue (spots on wings) omitted	£160	
1009	2c. multicoloured (6.73?)	30	10
	a. Purple and yellow omitted	£8500	
	b. Black (inscr, etc) omitted	£400	
1010	3c. black, light brown and orange (1974)	1·75	2·00
	a. Orange omitted	£450	
1011	4c. multicoloured (7.9.73)	45	10
	a. Bright green (wing veins) inverted	£1000	
	b. Purple-brown omitted	£250	
	c. Orange-yellow omitted	£325	
	d. Greenish blue (background) omitted	£325	
	e. Bright green (wing veins) omitted	6·00	
	f. Apple green (wings) omitted	£300	
	g. Orange-yellow, bright green and apple-green omitted	£6000	
1012	5c. multicoloured (1973)	2·75	2·00
1013	6c. blackish green, yellow-green and rose-carmine (7.9.73)	60	1·00
	a. Yellow-grn (part of sea horse) omitted	£250	
	b. Rose-carmine omitted	£1200	
1014	7c. multicoloured (1974)	6·50	3·50
	a. Black omitted	£425	
1015	8c. multicoloured (1974)	6·50	2·50
	a. Blue-green (background) omitted	£425	
1017	10c. multicoloured, P 13½×13 (6.73?)	1·25	10
	a. Silver (Arms) omitted	£200	
	b. Imperf (pair)	£275	
	c. Deep blue (Queen's head, face value etc.) omitted	£350	
	d. Red (hair ribbon) omitted	35·00	
	e. Blue (country name) omitted	£425	
1018	15c. black, flesh and pale brown, P 13½×13 (2.8.76)	1·25	20
1019	18c. chestnut, black and apple-green (1974)	1·25	1·50
	a. Black (inscr, etc) omitted	£400	
1020	20c. black and yellow-brown (1974)	80	60
	a. Black omitted	£1500	
1008/20	Set of 12	22·00	13·00

Nos. 1009a and 1011g both result from paper folds.

(Des and photo Courvoisier)

1973 (6 June). Paintings by Frances Hodgkins. T **336** and similar vert designs. Multicoloured. P 11½.

1027	5c. Type **336**	20	15
1028	8c. Hilltop	30	80
1029	10c. Barn in Picardy	30	65
1030	18c. Self Portrait Still Life	70	1·75
1027/30	Set of 4	1·40	3·00

337 Prince Edward

338 Tempi Madonna (Raphael)

(Des and litho Harrison)

1973 (1 Aug). Health Stamps. P 13×13½.

1031	**337**	3c.+1c. dull yellowish green and reddish brown	30	50
1032		4c.+1c. rose-red and blackish brown	30	50

MS1033 Two sheets each 96×121 mm with Nos. 1031/2 in blocks of 6 (3×2) ....*Per pair* 14·00 40·00

(Des A. G. Mitchell. Photo Enschedé)

1973 (3 Oct). Christmas. T **338** and similar vert designs. Multicoloured. P 12½×13½.

1034	3c. Type **338**		10	10
1035	5c. "Three Kings" (stained-glass window, St. Therese's Church, Auckland)		10	10
1036	10c. Family entering church		25	50
1034/6 *Set of 3*			40	50

339 Mitre Peak

340 Hurdling

(Des D. A. Hatcher. Photo Enschedé)

1973 (5 Dec). Mountain Scenery. T **339** and similar multicoloured designs. P 13×13½ (6, 8c.) or 13½×13 (others).

1037	6c. Type **339**		30	70
1038	8c. Mt Ngauruhoe		40	1·00
1039	18c. Mt Sefton (*horiz*)		60	1·75
1040	23c. Burnett Range (*horiz*)		70	2·25
1037/40 *Set of 4*			1·75	5·00

(Des M. Cleverley. Litho Harrison)

1974 (9 Jan). Tenth British Commonwealth Games, Christchurch. T **340** and similar vert designs. 5c. black and violet-blue, others multicoloured. P 13×14.

1041	4c. Type **340**		10	10
1042	5c. Ball-player		10	10
1043	10c. Cycling		60	15
1044	18c. Rifle-shooting		15	50
1045	23c. Bowls		20	80
1041/5 *Set of 5*			1·00	1·50

No. 1042 does not show the Games emblem, and commemorates the Fourth Paraplegic Games, held at Dunedin.

341 Queen Elizabeth II

342 "Spirit of Napier" Fountain

(Des D. A. Hatcher and A. G. Mitchell. Litho Harrison)

1974 (5 Feb). New Zealand Day. Sheet 131×74 mm. containing T **341** and similar horiz designs, size 37×20 mm. Multicoloured. P 13.

MS1046 4c.×5 Treaty House, Waitangi; Signing Waitangi Treaty; Type **341**; Parliament Buildings Extensions; Children in Class .... 70 2·50

(Des Miss V. Jepsen. Photo Courvoisier)

1974 (3 Apr). Centenaries of Napier and U.P.U. T **342** and similar vert designs. Multicoloured. P 11½.

1047	4c. Type **342**		10	10
1048	5c. Clock Tower, Berne		20	30
1049	8c. U.P.U. Monument, Berne		55	1·60
1047/9 *Set of 3*			75	1·75

343 Boeing Seaplane, 1919

344 Children, Cat and Dog

(Des R. M. Conly. Litho Harrison)

1974 (5 June). History of New Zealand Airmail Transport. T **343** and similar horiz designs. Multicoloured. P 14×13.

1050	3c. Type **343**		20	10
1051	4c. Lockheed 10 Electra *Kauha*, 1937		20	10
1052	5c. Bristol Type 170 Freighter Mk 31, 1958 ..		20	30
1053	23c. Short S.30 modified "G" Class flying boat *Aotearoa*, 1940		80	2·00
1050/3 *Set of 4*			1·25	2·25

(Des B. Langford. Litho Harrison)

1974 (7 Aug). Health Stamps. P 13×13½.

1054	**344**	3c.+1c. multicoloured	20	50
1055		4c.+1c. multicoloured	25	50
1056		5c.+1c. multicoloured	70	1·50
1054/6 *Set of 3*			1·00	2·25

MS1057 145×123 mm. No. 1055 in block of ten .... 14·00 40·00

Nos. 1055/6 are as T **344**, showing children and pets.

345 *The Adoration of the Magi* (Konrad Witz)

346 Great Barrier Island

(Des Eileen Mayo. Photo Courvoisier)

1974 (2 Oct). Christmas. T **345** and similar horiz designs. Multicoloured. P 11½.

1058	3c. Type **345**		10	10
1059	5c. "The Angel Window" (stained-glass window, Old St. Pauls Church, Wellington)		10	10
1060	10c. Madonna Lily		30	90
1058/60 *Set of 3*			40	1·00

(Des D. A. Hatcher. Photo Enschedé)

1974 (4 Dec). Off-shore Islands. T **346** and similar horiz designs. Multicoloured. P 13½×13.

1061	6c. Type **346**		20	30
1062	8c. Stewart Island		30	80
1063	18c. White Island		40	1·00
1064	23c. The Brothers		50	1·25
1061/4 *Set of 4*			1·25	3·00

347 Crippled Child

(Des Miss V. Jepsen (3c., 5c.), A. G. Mitchell (10c., 18c.). Litho Harrison)

1975 (5 Feb). Anniversaries and Events. T **347** and similar horiz designs. Multicoloured. P 13½.

1065	3c. Type **347**		10	10
1066	5c. Farming family		10	10
1067	10c. I.W.Y. symbols		15	60
1068	18c. Medical School Building, Otago University		40	1·25
1065/8 *Set of 4*			65	1·75

Commemorations:—3c. 40th Anniv of N.Z. Crippled Children Society; 5c. 50th Anniv of Women's Division, Federated Farmers of N.Z.; 10c. International Women's Year; 18c. Centenary of Otago Medical School.

348 Scow *Lake Erie*

(Des R. M. Conly. Litho Harrison)

1975 (2 Apr). Historic Sailing Ships. T **348** and similar horiz designs. P 13½×13.

1069	4c. black and red	25	10
1070	5c. black and turquoise-blue	25	10
1071	8c. black and yellow	30	50
1072	10c. black and olive-yellow	30	50
1073	18c. black and light brown	40	1·75
1074	23c. black and slate-lilac	50	1·75
1069/74	*Set of 6*	1·75	4·25

Ships:—5c. Schooner *Herald*; 8c. Brigantine *New Zealander*; 10c. Topsail schooner *Jessie Kelly*; 18c. Barque *Tory*; 23c. Full rigged clipper *Ranqitiki*.

349 Lake Sumner Forest Park

(Des and photo Enschedé)

1975 (4 June). Forest Park Scenes. T **349** and similar horiz designs. Multicoloured. P 13.

1075	6c. Type **349**	25	40
1076	8c. North-west Nelson	30	70
1077	18c. Kaweka	50	1·25
	a. Blue omitted	£225	
1078	23c. Coromandel	70	1·40
1075/8	*Set of 4*	1·60	3·25

350 Girl feeding Lamb

351 *Virgin and Child*
(Zanobi Machiavelli)

(Des Margaret Chapman. Litho Harrison)

1975 (6 Aug). Health Stamps. T **350** and similar horiz designs. Multicoloured. P 13½×13.

1079	3c.+1c. Type **350**	15	30
1080	4c.+1c. Boy with hen and chicks	15	30
1081	5c.+1c. Boy with duck and duckling	40	1·50
1079/81	*Set of 3*	65	1·90
MS1082	123×146 mm. No. 1080×10	9·00	40·00

(Des Enid Hunter. Photo Harrison)

1975 (1 Oct). Christmas. T **351** and similar horiz designs. Multicoloured. P 13×13½ (3c.) or 13½×13 (others).

1083	3c. Type **351**	10	10
	a. Red omitted*	£800	
	b. Black omitted	£1400	
1084	5c. "Cross in Landscape" (stained-glass window, Greendale Church)	10	10
	a. Brown (face value) omitted	£170	
1085	10c. *I saw three ships. . .* (carol)	35	65
1083/5	*Set of 3*	45	65

*This occurred in the last two vertical rows of the sheet with the red partially omitted on the previous row.

Used copies of No. 1083 have been seen with the orange ("Christmas 1975") omitted.

352 "Sterling Silver"

353 Queen Elizabeth II (photograph by W. Harrison)

353a Maripi (knife)

353b Rainbow Abalone or Paua

353c "Beehive" (section of Parliamentary Buildings, Wellington)

(Des A. G. Mitchell (1 to 14c.), I. Hulse (20c. to $2), R. Conly ($5). Photo Harrison (1 to 10c.), Courvoisier (11 to 14c.), Heraclio Fournier (20c. to $5))

1975 (26 Nov)–**81**.

*(a) Vert designs as T **352** showing garden roses. Multicoloured.*
P 14½ (6 to 8c.) or 14½×14 (others)

1086	1c. Type. **352**	10	10
1087	2c. "Lilli Marlene"	10	20
1088	3c. "Queen Elizabeth"	60	10
	a. Perf 14½ (8.79)	1·00	10
1089	4c. "Super Star"	10	60
1090	5c. "Diamond Jubilee"	10	10
1091	6c. "Cresset"	40	1·00
	a. Perf 14½×14 (8.76)	40	1·00
1092	7c. "Michele Meilland"	85	1·40
	a. Perf 14½×14 (5.76)	40	10
1093	8c. "Josephine Bruce"	85	1·25
	a. Perf 14½×14 (8.76)	30	10
1094	9c. "Iceberg"	40	60

*(b) Type **353**. P 14½×14 (7.12.77)*

1094a	10c. multicoloured	45	20
	ab. Perf 14½ (1.79)	30	10

*(c) Vert designs as T **353a** showing Maori artefacts. Granite paper.*
P 11½ (24.11.76)

1095	11c. reddish brown, lemon and blackish brown	30	80
1096	12c. reddish brown, lemon and blackish brown	30	50
1097	13c. reddish brown, greenish blue and blackish brown	40	1·00
1098	14c. reddish brown, lemon and blackish brown	30	20

Designs:—12c. Putorino (flute); 13c. Wahaika (club); 14c. Kotiate (club).

*(d) Horiz designs as T **353b** showing sea shells. Multicoloured. P 13*

1099	20c. Type **353b** (29.11.78)	15	20
1100	30c. Toheroa Clam (29.11.78)	25	50
1101	40c. Old Woman or Coarse Dosinia (29.11.78)	30	45
1102	50c. New Zealand or Spiny Murex (29.11.78)	40	45
1103	$1 New Zealand Scallop (29.11.79)	70	1·00
	a. Imperf between (vert pair)	£500	
1104	$2 Circular Saw (26.11.79)	1·00	1·75

*(e) Type **353c**. P 13 (2.12.81)*

1105	$5 multicoloured	1·75	1·50
	a. Imperf (vert pair)	£950	
1086/105	*Set of 20*	7·50	10·00

Faked "missing colour errors" exist of No. 1094a, involving parts of the portrait.

Used examples of No. 1099 exist with the black colour omitted so that the body of the shell appears in blue instead of green.

No. 1103a occurs on the top two rows of the sheet; the lower stamp being imperforate on three edges except for two perforation holes at the foot of each vertical side.

354 Family and League of Mothers Badge

(Des A. P. Derrick. Litho J.W.)

1976 (4 Feb). Anniversaries and Metrication. T **354** and similar horiz designs. Multicoloured. P 13½×14.

1110	6c. Type 354	10	10
1111	7c. Weight, temperature, linear measure and capacity	10	10
1112	8c. *William Bryan* (immigrant ship), mountain and New Plymouth	15	10
1113	10c. Two women shaking hands and Y.W.C.A. badge	15	60
1114	25c. Map of the world showing cable links	30	1·25
1110/14 *Set of 5*		70	1·90

Anniversaries:—6c. League of Mothers, 50th Anniv; 7c. Metrication; 8c. Centenary of New Plymouth; 10c. 50th Anniv of New Zealand Y.W.C.A.; 25c. Centenary of link with International Telecommunications Network.

355 Gig

356 Purakaunui Falls

(Des G. F. Fuller. Litho Harrison)

1976 (7 Apr). Vintage Farm Transport. T **355** and similar horiz designs. Multicoloured. P 13½×13.

1115	6c. Type 355	15	40
1116	7c. Thornycroft lorry	15	10
1117	8c. Scandi wagon	20	15
1118	9c. Traction engine	15	30
1119	10c. Wool wagon	15	30
1120	25c. Cart	40	1·75
1115/20 *Set of 6*		1·10	2·75

(Des and photo Courvoisier)

1976 (2 June). Waterfalls. T **356** and similar vert designs. Multicoloured. P 11½.

1121	10c. Type 356	25	10
1122	14c. Marakopa Falls	40	95
1123	15c. Bridal Veil Falls	45	1·10
1124	16c. Papakorito Falls	55	1·25
1121/4 *Set of 4*		1·50	3·00

357 Boy and Pony

358 "Nativity" (Spanish carving)

(Des Margaret Chapman. Litho Harrison)

1976 (4 Aug). Health Stamps. T **357** and similar vert designs. Multicoloured. P 13×13½.

1125	7c.+1c. Type 357	20	40
1126	8c.+1c. Girl and calf	20	40
1127	10c.+1c. Girls and bird	40	1·00
1125/7 *Set of 3*		70	1·60
MS1128 96×121 mm. Nos. 1125/7×2		2·50	6·00

(Des Margaret Chapman (18c.), D. A. Hatcher (others). Photo Harrison)

1976 (6 Oct). Christmas. T **358** and similar horiz designs. Multicoloured. P 14×14½ (7c.) or 14½×14 (others).

1129	7c. Type 358	15	10
1130	11c. "Resurrection" (stained-glass window, St. Joseph's Catholic Church, Grey Lynn)	25	30
1131	18c. Angels	40	1·00
1129/31 *Set of 3*		70	1·25

8c 1877 1977

359 Arms of Hamilton

360 Queen Elizabeth II

(Des P. L. Blackie. Litho Harrison)

1977 (19 Jan). Anniversaries. T **359** and similar vert designs. Multicoloured. P 13×13½.

1132	8c. Type 359	15	35
	a. Horiz strip of 3, Nos. 1132/4	40	1·00
1133	8c. Arms of Gisborne	15	35
1134	8c. Arms of Masterton	15	35
1135	10c. A.A. emblem	15	50
	a. Horiz pair. Nos. 1135/6	30	1·00
1136	10c. Arms of the College of Surgeons	15	50
1132/6 *Set of 5*		70	1·75

Events:—Nos. 1132/4, City Centenaries; 1135, 75th Anniv of the Automobile Association in New Zealand; 1136, 50th Anniv of Royal Australasian College of Surgeons.

Designs of each value were printed in the same sheet horizontally *se-tenant*.

(Des and photo Harrison from photographs by Warren Harrison)

1977 (23 Feb). Silver Jubilee. Sheet 178×82 mm containing T **360** and similar vert designs showing different portraits. P 14×14½.

MS1137 8c.×5 multicoloured		65	1·60
	a. Imperf	£1800	
	ab. Imperf and silver omitted	£5000	
	b. Silver omitted	£1700	
	c. Indian red omitted	£650	

361 Physical Education and Maori Culture

(362)

(Des A. G. Mitchell. Litho Harrison)

1977 (6 Apr). Education. T **361** and similar vert designs. Multicoloured. P 13×13½.

1138	8c. Type 361	25	50
	a. Horiz strip of 5, Nos. 1138/42	1·10	2·25
1139	8c. Geography, science and woodwork	25	50
1140	8c. Teaching the deaf, kindergarten and woodwork	25	50
1141	8c. Tertiary and language classes	25	50
1142	8c. Home science, correspondence school and teacher training	25	50
1138/42 *Set of 5*		1·10	2·25

Nos. 1138/42 were printed horizontally *se-tenant* throughout the sheet.

1977 (Apr). Coil stamps for use in stamp-fixing machines. Nos. 1010/11 surch as T **362** by Govt Printer, Wellington.

1143	7c. on 3c. *Detunda egregia* (moth) (18.4)	40	70
1144	8c. on 4c. *Charagia virescens* (moth) (20.4)	40	70
	a. Bright green (wing veins) omitted	£350	£250

Forged "7c." surcharges, similar to No. 1143, but in smaller type, are known applied to Nos. 918 and 1010.

363 Karitane Beach

364 Girl with Pigeon

(Des D. A. Hatcher. Photo Heraclio Fournier)

1977 (1 June). Seascapes. T **363** and similar horiz designs. Multicoloured. P 14½.

1145	10c. Type **363**	15	10
1146	16c. Ocean Beach, Mount Maunganui	30	30
1147	18c. Piha Beach	30	30
1148	30c. Kaikoura Coast	35	40
1145/8	Set of 4	1·00	1·00

(Des A. P. Derrick, Litho Harrison)

1977 (3 Aug). Health Stamps. T **364** and similar vert designs. Multicoloured. P 13×13½.

1149	7c.+2c. Type **364**	20	50
1150	8c.+2c. Boy with frog	20	55
1151	10c.+2c. Girl with butterfly	40	1·00
1149/51	Set of 3	70	1·90
MS1152	97×120 mm. Nos. 1149/51×2	1·10	5·50

Stamps from the miniature sheet are without white border and together form a composite design.

365 The Holy Family (Correggio)

(Des Margaret Chapman (23c.), graphics for all values produced by printer. Photo Courvoisier)

1977 (5 Oct). Christmas. T **365** and similar vert designs. Multicoloured. P 11½.

1153	7c. Type **365**	15	10
1154	16c. "Madonna and Child" (stained-glass window, St. Michael's and All Angels, Dunedin)	25	25
1155	23c. "Partridge in a Pear Tree"	40	1·25
1153/5	Set of 3	70	1·40

366 Merryweather Manual Pump, 1860

(Des R. M. Conly. Litho Harrison)

1977 (7 Dec). Fire Fighting Appliances. T **366** and similar horiz designs. Multicoloured. P 14×13.

1156	10c. Type **366**	15	10
1157	11c. 2-wheel hose, reel and ladder, 1880	15	25
1158	12c. Shand Mason steam fire engine, 1873	20	30
1159	23c. Chemical fire engine, 1888	30	90
1156/9	Set of 4	70	1·40

367 Town Clock and Coat of Arms, Ashburton

(Des P. L. Blackie (No. 1162), Harrison (No. 1163), P. J. Durrant (others), Litho Harrison)

1978 (8 Mar). Centenaries. T **367** and similar multicoloured designs. P 14.

1160	10c. Type **367**	15	25
	a. Horiz pair. Nos. 1160/1	30	50
1161	10c. Stratford and Mt Egmont	15	25
1162	12c. Early telephone	15	15
1163	20c. Bay of Islands (horiz)	20	30
1160/3	Set of 4	60	85

Centenaries commemorated are those of the towns of Ashburton and Stratford, of the telephone in New Zealand, and of the Bay of Islands County.

The 10c. values were printed together, se-tenant, in horizontal pairs throughout the sheet.

368 Students and Ivey Hall, Lincoln College

369

370 Maui Gas Drilling Platform

(Des A. P. Derrick. Litho Harrison)

1978 (26 Apr). Land Resources and Centenary of Lincoln College of Agriculture. T **368** and similar vert designs. Multicoloured. P 14½.

1164	10c. Type **368**	15	10
1165	12c. Sheep grazing	15	30
1166	15c. Fertiliser ground spreading	15	30
1167	16c. Agricultural Field Days	15	40
1168	20c. Harvesting grain	20	40
1169	30c. Dairy farming	30	90
1164/9	Set of 6	1·00	2·25

(Photo Harrison)

1978 (3 May–13 June). Coil Stamps. P 14½×14 (10c.) or 14×13 (others).

1170	**369** 1c. bright purple (13.6)	10	65
1171	2c. bright orange (13.6)	10	65
1172	5c. red-brown (13.6)	10	65
1173	10c. bright blue	30	80
1170/3	Set of 4	45	2·50

(Des R. M. Conly. Litho Harrison)

1978 (7 June). Resources of the Sea. T **370** and similar vert designs. Multicoloured. P 13×14.

1174	12c. Type **370**	15	15
1175	15c. Trawler	15	20
1176	20c. Map of 200 mile fishing limit	20	30
1177	23c. Humpback Whale and Bottle-nosed Dolphins	25	35
1178	35c. Kingfish, snapper, grouper and squid	40	60
1174/8	Set of 5	1·00	1·40

371 First Health Charity Stamp

372 The Holy Family (El Greco)

373 Sir Julius Vogel

(Des A. G. Mitchell. Litho Harrison)

1978 (2 Aug). Health Stamps. Health Services Commemorations. T **371** and similar vert design. P 13×14.

1179	10c.+2c. black, red and gold	20	35
1180	12c.+2c. multicoloured	20	40
	a. Chestnut omitted		
MS1181	97×124 mm. Nos. 1179/80×3	1·00	4·00
	a. Imprint centred	2·00	8·00

Designs and commemorations:—10c. Type **371** (50th anniversary of health charity stamps); 12c. Heart operation (National Heart Foundation). No. 1180a omits the shadow on the surgeons' faces and hands.

On **MS**1181 the printer's imprint falls below the two left-hand stamps. On **MS**1181a the imprint is 8 mm to the right, resulting in the second "N" of "LONDON" falling below the right-hand stamp.

(Des R. M. Conly. Photo Courvoisier)

1978 (4 Oct). Christmas. T **372** and similar multicoloured designs. P 11½.

1182	7c. Type **372**	10	10
1183	16c. All Saints' Church, Howick (horiz)	25	35
1184	23c. Beach scene (horiz)	30	50
1182/4	Set of 3	60	85

(Des A. G. Mitchell. Litho J.W.)

1979 (7 Feb). Statesmen. T **373** and similar vert designs in sepia and drab. P 13×13½.

1185	10c. Type **373**	25	50
	a. Horiz strip of 3, Nos. 1185/7	65	1·40

1186	10c. Sir George Grey	25	50
1187	10c. Richard John Seddon	25	50
1185/7	Set of 3	65	1·40

Nos. 1185/7 were printed together, *se-tenant*, in horizontal strips of three throughout the sheet.

Nos. 1185/7 have matt, almost invisible, gum.

374 Riverlands Cottage, Blenheim   **375** Whangaroa Harbour

(Des P. Leitch. Litho Enschedé)

1979 (4 Apr). Architecture (1st series). T **374** and similar horiz designs. P 13½×13.

1188	10c. black, new blue and deep blue	10	10
1189	12c. black, pale green and bottle green	15	40
1190	15c. black and grey	20	45
1191	20c. black, yellow-brown and sepia	25	45
1188/91	Set of 4	65	1·25

Designs:—12c. The Mission House, Waimate North; 15c. "The Elms", Tauranga; 20c. Provincial Council Buildings, Christchurch.

See also Nos. 1217/20 and 1262/5.

(Photo Heraclio Fournier)

1979 (6 June). Small Harbours. T **375** and similar multicoloured designs. P 13.

1192	15c. Type **375**	15	10
1193	20c. Kawau Island	20	40
1194	23c. Akaroa Harbour (*vert*)	20	65
1195	35c. Picton Harbour (*vert*)	30	85
1192/5	Set of 4	75	1·75

376 Children with Building Bricks

(Des W. Kelsall. Litho J.W.)

1979 (6 June). International Year of the Child. P 14.

1196	**376** 10c. multicoloured	15	10

377 Two-spotted Chromis   (**378**)

(Des P. Blackie (12c.), G. Fuller (others). Litho Harrison)

1979 (25 July). Health Stamps. Marine Life. T **377** and similar multicoloured designs. P 13×13½ (12c.) or 13½×13 (others).

1197	10c. +2c. Type **377**	20	50
	a. Horiz pair. Nos. 1197/8	40	1·00
1198	10c. +2c. Sea Urchin	20	50
1199	12c. +2c. Red Goatfish and underwater cameraman (*vert*)	20	50
1197/9	Set of 3	55	1·40

MS1200 144×72 mm. Nos. 1197/8, each×3. P 14×14½ (12c.) or 14½×14 (others) .... 1·00 2·75

Nos. 1197/8 were printed together, *se-tenant*, in horizontal pairs throughout the sheet.

1979 (31 Aug)–**80**. Nos. 1091a, 1092a, 1093a and 1094ab surch as T **378** by Govt Printer, Wellington.

1201	4c. on 8c. "Josephine Bruce" (24.9.79)	10	50
	a. Surch double	45·00	
	b. Black omitted	£1300	
1202	14c. on 10c. Type 353	20	10
	a. Surch double, one albino	£150	
	b. Surch inverted	£400	
	c. Pair, one without surch	£300	
1203	17c. on 6c. "Cresset" (8.10.79)	25	1·00
	a. Surch double, one albino	£150	
1203*b*	20c. on 7c. "Michele Meilland" (29.9.80)	25	10
1201/3*b*	Set of 4	65	1·40

Neither of the impressions of the surcharge on No. 1201a is properly inked.

379 *Madonna and Child* (sculpture by Ghiberti)   **380** Chamber, House of Representatives

(Des D. Hatcher. Photo Courvoisier)

1979 (3 Oct). Christmas. T **379** and similar vert designs. Multicoloured. P 11½.

1204	10c. Type **379**	15	10
1205	25c. Christ Church, Russell	30	50
1206	35c. Pohutukawa (tree)	40	70
1204/6	Set of 3	75	1·10

(Des D. Hatcher. Litho J.W.)

1979 (26 Nov). 25th Commonwealth Parliamentary Conference, Wellington. T **380** and similar vert designs. Multicoloured. P 13½.

1207	14c. Type **380**	15	10
1208	20c. Mace and Black Rod	20	30
1209	30c. Wall hanging from the "Beehive"	30	75
1207/9	Set of 3	60	1·00

381 1855 1d. Stamp

(Des D. Hatcher (14c. (all designs)), R. M. Conly (others). Litho Harrison)

1980 (7 Feb). Anniversaries and Events. T **381** and similar designs. P 13½×13 (14c. (*all designs*)) or 14 (others).

1210	14c. black, brown-red and yellow	20	30
	a. Horiz strip of 3. Nos. 1210/12	55	80
	ab. Black (inscription) omitted (*strip of* 3)	£375	
1211	14c. black, deep turquoise-blue and yellow	20	30
1212	14c. black, dull yellowish green and yellow	20	30
1213	17c. multicoloured	20	30
1214	25c. multicoloured	25	35
1215	30c. multicoloured	25	40
1210/15	Set of 6	1·10	1·75

MS1216 146×96 mm. Nos. 1210/12 (as horiz strip). P 14½×14 (*sold at* 52c.) .... 1·00 4·00

Designs and commemorations; (38×22 *mm*)—No. 1210, Type **381**; 1211, 1855 2d. stamp; 1212, 1855 1s. stamp (125th anniversary of New Zealand stamps). (40×23 *mm*)—No. 1213, Geyser, wood-carving and building (centenary of Rotorua (town)); 1214, *Earina autumnalis* and *thelymitra venosa* (International Orchid Conference, Auckland); 1215, Ploughing and Golden Plough Trophy (World Ploughing Championships, Christchurch).

The premium on No. **MS**1216 was used to help finance the "Zeapex 80" International Stamp Exhibition, Auckland.

Nos. 1210/12 were printed together, *se-tenant*, in horizontal strips of three throughout the sheet.

382 Ewelme Cottage, Parnell   **383** Auckland Harbour

(Des P. Leitch. Litho Enschedé)

1980 (2 Apr). Architecture (2nd series). T **382** and similar horiz designs. Multicoloured. P 13½×12½.

1217	14c. Type **382**	15	10
1218	17c. Broadgreen, Nelson	15	25
1219	25c. Courthouse, Oamaru	20	35
1220	30c. Government Buildings, Wellington	25	40
1217/20	Set of 4	65	1·00

(Des D. Hatcher. Photo Heraclio Fournier)

1980 (4 June). Large Harbours. T **383** and similar horiz designs. Multicoloured. P 13.

1221	25c. Type **383**	20	20

1222	30c. Wellington Harbour	25	30
1223	35c. Lyttelton Harbour	25	35
1224	50c. Port Chalmers	40	1·10
1221/4	Set of 4	1·00	1·90

384 Surf-fishing

385 Madonna and Child with Cherubim (sculpture by Andrea della Robbia)

(Des Margaret Chapman. Litho Enschedé)

1980 (6 Aug). Health Stamps. Fishing. T **384** and similar horiz designs. Multicoloured. P 13×12½.

1225	14c. +2c. Type **384**	20	65
	a. Horiz pair. Nos. 1225/6	40	1·25
1226	14c. +2c. Wharf-fishing	20	65
1227	17c. +2c. Spear-fishing	20	50
1225/7	Set of 3	55	1·60
MS1228 148×75 mm. Nos. 1225/7 each×2. P 13½×13		1·00	3·00

Nos. 1225/6 were printed together, *se-tenant*, in horizontal pairs throughout the sheet.

(Des P. Durrant. Photo Courvoisier)

1980 (1 Oct). Christmas. T **385** and similar vert designs. Multicoloured. P 11½.

1229	10c. Type **385**	15	10
1230	25c. St. Mary's Church, New Plymouth	25	25
1231	35c. Picnic scene	40	1·00
1229/31	Set of 3	70	1·25

386 Te Heu Heu (chief)

387 Lt.-Col. the Hon W. H. A. Feilding and Borough of Feilding Crest

(Des R. M. Conly. Litho Heraclio Fournier)

1980 (26 Nov). Maori Personalities. Vert designs as T **386**. Multicoloured. P 12½×13.

1232	15c. Type **386**	15	10
1233	25c. Te Hau (chief)	15	20
1234	35c. Te Puea (princess)	20	10
1235	45c. Ngata (politician)	30	30
1236	60c. Te Ata-O-Tu (warrior)	30	50
1232/6	Set of 5	1·00	1·00

(Des R. M. Conly. Litho Harrison)

1981 (4 Feb). Commemorations. T **387** and similar horiz design. P 14½.

| 1237 | 20c. multicoloured | 20 | 20 |
| 1238 | 25c. black and brown-ochre | 25 | 25 |

Designs and Commemorations:—20c. Type **387** (Centenary of Feilding town); 25c. I.Y.D. emblem and cupped hands (International Year of the Disabled).

388 The Family at Play

389 Kaiauai River

(Des A. Derrick. Litho J.W.)

1981 (1 Apr). "Family Life". T **388** and similar vert designs. Multicoloured. P 13½×13.

1239	20c. Type **388**	15	10
1240	25c. The family, young and old	20	20
1241	30c. The family at home	20	35
1242	35c. The family at church	25	45
1239/42	Set of 4	70	1·00

(Des D. Hatcher. Photo Heraclio Fournier)

1981 (3 June). River Scenes. T **389** and similar multicoloured designs. P 13½×13 (30, 35c.) or 13×13½ (others).

1243	30c. Type **389**	20	25
1244	35c. Mangahao	20	30
1245	40c. Shotover (*horiz*)	25	40
1246	60c. Cleddau (*horiz*)	45	65
1243/6	Set of 4	1·00	1·40

390 St. Paul's Cathedral

391 Girl with Starfish

(Des and litho Harrison)

1981 (29 July). Royal Wedding. T **390** and similar horiz design. Multicoloured. P 14½.

1247	20c. Type **390**	30	30
	a. Pair. Nos. 1247/8	60	60
	ab. Deep grey (inscriptions and date) omitted	£900	
1248	20c. Prince Charles and Lady Diana Spencer.	30	30

Nos. 1247/8 were printed together, *se-tenant*, in horizontal and vertical pairs throughout the sheet.

(Des P.O. Litho Harrison)

1981 (5 Aug). Health Stamps. Children playing by the Sea. T **391** and similar vert designs. Multicoloured. P 14½.

1249	20c. +2c. Type **391**	20	65
	a. Horiz pair. Nos. 1249/50	40	1·25
1250	20c. +2c. Boy fishing	20	65
1251	25c. +2c. Children exploring rock pool	20	35
1249/51	Set of 3	55	1·50
MS1252 100×125 mm. Nos. 1249/51, each×2		1·00	3·00

The 20c. values were printed together, *se-tenant*, in horizontal pairs throughout the sheet, forming a composite design.

The stamps from No. **MS**1252 were printed together, *se-tenant*, in two horizontal strips of three, each forming a composite design.

392 Madonna Suckling the Child (d'Oggiono)

393 Tauranga Mission House

(Des Margaret Chapman. Photo Courvoisier)

1981 (7 Oct). Christmas. T **392** and similar vert designs. Multicoloured. P 11½.

1253	14c. Type **392**	15	10
1254	30c. St. John's Church, Wakefield	20	25
1255	40c. Golden Tainui (flower)	35	35
1253/5	Set of 3	65	60

(Des A. Derrick. Litho Walsall)

1982 (3 Feb). Commemorations. T **393** and similar vert designs. Multicoloured. P 14½.

1256	20c. Type **393**	20	10
	a. Horiz pair. Nos. 1256/7	40	60
1257	20c. Water tower, Hawera	20	10
1258	25c. Cat	25	35
1259	30c. *Dunedin* (refrigerated sailing ship)	25	40
1260	35c. Scientific research equipment	25	45
1256/60	Set of 5	1·00	1·60

Commemorations:—No. 1256, Centenary of Tauranga (town); 1257, Centenary of Hawera (town); 1258, Centenary of S.P.C.A. (Society for the Prevention of Cruelty to Animals in New Zealand); 1259, Centenary of Frozen Meat Exports; 1260, International Year of Science.

The 20c. values were printed together, *se-tenant*, in horizontal pairs throughout the sheet.

394 Map of New Zealand

395 Alberton, Auckland

(Des A. G. Mitchell. Litho Leigh-Mardon Ltd, Melbourne)

1982 (1 Apr–13 Dec). P 12½.

1261	**394**	24c. pale yellowish green and ultram		30	10
		a. Perf 14½×14 (13.12.82)		35	20

(Des P. Leitch. Litho Walsall)

1982 (7 Apr). Architecture (3rd series). T **395** and similar horiz designs. Multicoloured. P 14×14½.

1262	20c. Type **395**		15	20
1263	25c. Caccia Birch, Palmerston North		15	30
1264	30c. Railway station, Dunedin		40	40
1265	35c. Post Office, Ophir		25	45
1262/5 *Set of 4*			85	1·25

396 Kaiteriteri Beach, Nelson (Summer)

397 Labrador

(Des D. Hatcher. Photo Heraclio Fournier)

1982 (2 June). "The Four Seasons". New Zealand Scenes. T **396** and similar horiz designs. Multicoloured. P 13×13½.

1266	35c. Type **396**		20	30
1267	40c. St. Omer Park, Queenstown (Autumn)....		25	35
1268	45c. Mt Ngauruhoe, Tongariro National Park (Winter)		25	40
1269	70c. Wairarapa farm (Spring)..........................		40	60
1266/9 *Set of 4*			1·00	1·50

(Des R. M. Conly. Litho Enschedé)

1982 (4 Aug). Health Stamps. Dogs. T **397** and similar vert designs. Multicoloured. P 13×13½.

1270	24c. +2c. Type **397**		65	1·00
	a. Horiz pair. Nos. 1270/1		1·25	2·00
1271	24c. +2c. Border Collie		65	1·00
1272	30c. +2c. Cocker Spaniel		65	1·00
1270/2 *Set of 3*			1·75	2·75
MS1273 98×125 mm. Nos. 1270/2, each×2. P 14×13½ .			3·25	6·50

The 24c. values were printed together, *se-tenant*, in horizontal pairs throughout the sheet.

398 Madonna with Child and Two Angels (Piero di Cosimo)

(Des Margaret Chapman. Photo Heraclio Fournier)

1982 (6 Oct). Christmas. T **398** and similar vert designs. Multicoloured. P 14×13½.

1274	18c. Type **398**		15	10
1275	35c. Rangiatea Maori Church, Otaki.................		25	30

1276	45c. Surf life-saving		40	40
1274/6 *Set of 3*..			70	65

399 Nephrite

399a Grapes

399b Kokako

(Des P. Durrant (Nos. 1277/82), D. Little (Nos. 1283/7), Janet Marshall (Nos. 1288/97). Litho Leigh-Mardon Ltd. Melbourne)

1982 (1 Dec)–**89**. Multicoloured. P 14½×14 (Nos. 1277/87) or 14½ (Nos. 1288/97).

(a) Minerals. T **399** and similar vert designs.

1277	1c. Type **399**		10	10
	a. Perf 12½		45	20
1278	2c. Agate		10	10
	a. Perf 12½		1·00	2·00
1279	3c. Iron Pyrites		10	10
1280	4c. Amethyst		15	10
1281	5c. Carnelian		15	10
1282	9c. Native Sulphur		20	10

(b) Fruits. T **399a** and similar vert designs

1283	10c. Type **399a** (7.12.83)		50	10
1284	20c. Citrus Fruit (7.12.83)		35	10
1285	30c. Nectarines (7.12.83)		35	10
1286	40c. Apples (7.12.83)		35	10
1287	50c. Kiwifruit (7.12.83)		40	10

(c) Native Birds. T **399b**, *and similar vert designs. Phosphorised paper ($1, $2)*

1288	30c. Kakapo (1.5.86)		60	25
1289	40c. Mountain ("Blue") Duck (2.2.87)		60	35
1290	45c. New Zealand Falcon (1.5.86)		1·25	35
1291	60c. New Zealand Teal (2.2.87)		2·25	2·00
1292	$1 Type **399b**, (24.4.85)		1·00	30
1293	$2 Chatham Island Robin (24.4.85)		1·00	50
1294	$3 Stitchbird (23.4.86)		1·25	1·40
1295	$4 Saddleback (23.4.86)		1·50	1·50
1296	$5 Takahe (20.4.88)		3·75	3·25
1297	$10 Little Spotted Kiwi (19.4.89)		4·00	5·00
1277/97 *Set of 21*			18·00	13·50
1292/7 Optd "Specimen" *Set of 6*			7·50	

Nos. 1292/7 overprinted "Specimen" come from a special "NEW ZEALAND 1990" Presentation Pack issued on 19 April 1989.

A miniature sheet containing No. 1293 was only available from the New Zealand stand at "PHILEXFRANCE '89" International Stamp Exhibition or the Philatelic Bureau at Wanganui.

Versions of the $3 with narrow face value and of the $4 in horizontal format were prepared, but not issued for postal purposes.

For No. 1297 in a miniature sheet for "POST X 95" Postal History Exhibition see No. **MS**1854.

400 Old Arts Building, Auckland University

401 Queen Elizabeth II

(Des G. Emery (35c.), P. Durrant (others). Litho Cambec Press, Melbourne (35c.), J.W. (others))

1983 (2 Feb). Commemorations. T **400** and similar vert designs. Multicoloured. P 13×13½ (35c.) or 14×13½ (others).

1303	24c. Salvation Army Centenary logo................		20	10

1304	30c. Type **400**	20	40
1305	35c. Stylized Kangaroo and Kiwi	20	40
1306	40c. Rainbow Trout	25	55
1307	45c. Satellite over Earth	25	55
1303/7	Set of 5	1·00	1·75

Commemorations: 24c. Centenary of Salvation Army; 30c. Centenary of Auckland University; 35c. Closer Economic Relationship agreement with Australia; 40c. Centenary of introduction of Rainbow Trout into New Zealand; 45c. World Communications Year.

(Des P. Durrant. Litho Harrison)

1983 (14 Mar). Commonwealth Day. T **401** and similar horiz designs. Multicoloured. P 13½.

1308	24c. Type **401**	20	10
1309	35c. Maori rock drawing	30	50
1310	40c. Woolmark and wool-scouring symbols	30	80
1311	45c. Coat of arms	30	80
1308/11	Set of 4	1·00	2·00

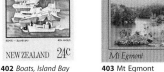

402 *Boats, Island Bay* (Rita Angus)   **403** Mt Egmont

(Des D. Hatcher. Litho Leigh-Mardon Ltd, Melbourne)

1983 (6 Apr). Paintings by Rita Angus. T **402** and similar vert designs. Multicoloured. P 14½.

1312	24c. Type **402**	20	10
1313	30c. *Central Otago Landscape*	25	45
1314	35c. *Wanaka Landscape*	30	50
1315	45c. *Tree*	35	70
1312/15	Set of 4	1·00	1·60

(Des P. Durrant. Photo Heraclio Fournier)

1983 (1 June). Beautiful New Zealand. T **403** and similar multicoloured designs. P 13.

1316	35c. Type **403**	20	35
1317	40c. Cooks Bay	25	40
1318	45c. Lake Matheson (*horiz*)	25	45
1319	70c. Lake Alexandrina (*horiz*)	40	70
1316/19	Set of 4	1·00	1·75

404 Tabby   **405** *The Family of the Holy Oak Tree* (Raphael)

(Des R. M. Conly. Litho Harrison)

1983 (3 Aug). Health Stamps. Cats. T **404** and similar vert designs. Multicoloured. P 14.

1320	24c. +2c. Type **404**	25	70
	a. Horiz pair. Nos. 1320/1	50	1·40
1321	24c. +2c. Siamese	25	70
1322	30c. +2c. Persian	40	80
1320/2	Set of 3	80	2·00
MS1323	100×126 mm. Nos. 1320/2, each×2	1·40	3·00

The 24c. values were printed together, *se-tenant*, in horizontal pairs throughout the sheet.

(Des R. M. Conly (45c.), M. Wyatt (others). Photo Courvoisier)

1983 (5 Oct). Christmas. T **405** and similar vert designs. Multicoloured. P 12×11½.

1324	18c. Type **405**	15	10
1325	35c. St. Patrick's Church, Greymouth	30	45
1326	45c. "The Glory of Christmas" (star and flowers)	35	80
1324/6	Set of 3	70	1·25

406 Geology

(Des R. M. Conly. Litho Cambec Press, Melbourne)

1984 (1 Feb). Antarctic Research. T **406** and similar horiz designs. Multicoloured. P 13½×13.

1327	24c. Type **406**	25	10
1328	40c. Biology	30	40
1329	58c. Glaciology	40	1·60
1330	70c. Meteorology	45	90
1327/30	Set of 4	1·25	2·75
MS1331	126×110 mm. Nos. 1327/30	1·25	3·50

407 *Mountaineer*, Lake Wakatipu   **408** Mount Hutt

(Des M. Wyatt. Litho Cambec Press, Melbourne)

1984 (4 Apr). New Zealand Ferry Boats. T **407** and similar horiz designs. Multicoloured. P 13½×13.

1332	24c. Type **407**	20	10
1333	40c. *Waikana*, Otago	25	45
1334	58c. *Britannia*, Waitemata	30	1·60
1335	70c. *Wakatere*, Firth of Thames	45	85
1332/5	Set of 4	1·10	2·75

(Des D. Little. Litho Cambec Press, Melbourne)

1984 (6 June). Ski-slope Scenery. T **408** and similar designs. Multicoloured. P 13½×13.

1336	35c. Type **408**	20	25
1337	40c. Coronet Park	25	30
1338	45c. Turoa	25	30
1339	70c. Whakapapa	40	50
1336/9	Set of 4	1·00	1·25

409 Hamilton's Frog

(Des A. G. Mitchell. Litho Cambec Press, Melbourne)

1984 (11 July). Amphibians and Reptiles. T **409** and similar horiz designs. Multicoloured. P 13½.

1340	24c. Type **409**	20	45
	a. Horiz pair. Nos. 1340/1	40	90
1341	24c. Great Barrier Skink	20	45
1342	30c. Harlequin Gecko	20	35
1343	58c. Otago Skink	30	80
1344	70c. Gold-striped Gecko	40	75
1340/4	Set of 5	1·10	2·50

Nos. 1340/1 were printed together, *se-tenant*, in horizontal pairs throughout the sheet.

410 Clydesdales ploughing Field

(Des Margaret Chapman. Litho Harrison)

1984 (1 Aug). Health Stamps. Horses. T **410** and similar horiz designs. Multicoloured. P 14½.

1345	24c. +2c. Type **410**	40	70
	a. Horiz pair. Nos. 1345/6	80	1·40
1346	24c. +2c. Shetland ponies	40	70

1347	30c. +2c. Thoroughbreds	40	70
1345/7	Set of 3	1·10	1·90
MS1348	148×75 mm. Nos. 1345/7, each×2	1·75	3·25

Nos. 1345/6 were printed together, *se-tenant*, in horizontal pairs throughout the sheet.

411 *Adoration of the Shepherds*
(Lorenzo di Credi)

(Des R. M. Conly (45c.), P. Durrant (others). Photo Heraclio Fournier)

1984 (26 Sept). Christmas. T **411** and similar multicoloured designs. P 13½×14 (18c.) or 14×13½ (others).

1349	18c. Type **411**	15	10
1350	35c. Old St. Paul's, Wellington (*vert*)	20	30
1351	45c. "The Joy of Christmas" (*vert*)	30	70
1349/51	Set of 3	60	1·00

412 Mounted Riflemen,
South Africa, 1901

(Des R. M. Conly. Litho Harrison)

1984 (7 Nov). New Zealand Military History. T **412** and similar horiz designs. Multicoloured. P 15×14.

1352	24c. Type **412**	20	10
1353	40c. Engineers, France, 1917	30	45
1354	58c. Tanks of 2nd N.Z. Divisional Cavalry, North Africa, 1942	40	1·50
1355	70c. Infantryman in jungle kit, and 25-pounder gun, Korea and South-East Asia, 1950–72	45	90
1352/5	Set of 4	1·25	2·75
MS1356	122×106 mm. Nos. 1352/5	1·00	2·25

413 St. John Ambulance Badge

(Des Lindy Fisher. Litho J.W.)

1985 (16 Jan). Centenary of St. John Ambulance in New Zealand. P 14.

1357	**413** 24c. black, gold and bright rosine	20	15
1358	30c. black, silver and bright ultram	25	45
1359	40c. black and grey	30	1·10
1357/9	Set of 3	65	1·50

The colours of the badge depicted are those for Bailiffs and Dames Grand Cross (24c.), Knights and Dames of Grace (30c.) and Officer Brothers and Sisters (40c.).

414 Nelson Horse Tram, 1862   **415** Shotover Bridge

(Des R. M. Conly. Litho Cambec Press, Melbourne)

1985 (6 Mar). Vintage Trams. T **414** and similar horiz designs. Multicoloured. P 13½.

1360	24c. Type **414**	20	10
1361	30c. Graham's Town steam tram, 1871	25	50
1362	35c. Dunedin cable car, 1881	25	55
1363	40c. Auckland electric tram, 1902	25	55
1364	45c. Wellington electric tram, 1904	25	65
1365	58c. Christchurch electric tram, 1905	35	1·75
1360/5	Set of 6	1·50	3·50

TARAPEX '86. To support this National Philatelic Exhibition the New Zealand Post Office co-operated with the organisers in the production of a set of "postage imprint labels". Five of the designs showed drawings of Maoris, taken from originals by Arthur Herbert Messenger and the sixth the Exhibition logo.

The sheetlets of six gummed and perforated labels were released by the Exhibition organisers on 3 April 1985. Although such labels were valid for postage, and could be so used by the general public, the sheetlets were not available from any New Zealand post office or from the Philatelic Bureau.

(Des R. Freeman. Photo Courvoisier)

1985 (12 June). Bridges of New Zealand. T **415** and similar multicoloured designs. Granite paper. P 11½.

1366	35c. Type **415**	25	45
1367	40c. Alexandra Bridge	25	45
1368	45c. South Rangitikei Railway Bridge (*vert*)	30	1·00
1369	70c. Twin Bridges (*vert*)	40	1·00
1366/9	Set of 4	1·10	2·50

416 Queen
Elizabeth II (from
photo by Camera
Press)

417 Princess of Wales
and Prince William

(Des B. Clinton. Litho Leigh-Mardon Ltd, Melbourne)

1985 (1 July). Multicoloured, background colours given. P 14½×14.

1370	**416** 25c. rosine	35	10
1371	35c. new blue	65	10

Examples of the 25c. value exist with the orders on the sash omitted. These are believed to originate from unissued sheets sent for destruction in March 1986.

(Des D. Little. Litho Cambec Press, Melbourne)

1985 (31 July). Health Stamps. T **417** and similar vert designs showing photographs by Lord Snowdon. Multicoloured. P 13½.

1372	25c. +2c. Type **417**	90	1·25
	a. Horiz pair. Nos. 1372/3	1·75	2·50
1373	25c. +2c. Princess of Wales and Prince Henry	90	1·25
1374	35c. +2c. Prince and Princess of Wales with Princes William and Henry	90	1·25
1372/4	Set of 3	2·50	3·25
MS1375	118×84 mm. Nos. 1372/4, each×2	4·25	5·50

Nos. 1372/3 were printed together, *se-tenant*, in horizontal pairs throughout the sheet.

418 The Holy Family in
the Stable

419 H.M.N.Z.S. *Philomel*
(1914–47)

(Des Eileen Mayo. Photo Enschedé)

1985 (18 Sept). Christmas. T **418** and similar vert designs. Multicoloured. P 13½×12½.

1376	18c. Type **418**	20	10
1377	40c. The shepherds	45	85
1378	50c. The angels	45	1·00
1376/8	Set of 3	1·00	1·75

Examples of the 18c. and 50c. stamps exist showing the spelling error "CRISTMAS". These are believed to originate from unissued sheets sent for destruction in March 1986. The New Zealand Post Office has stated that no such stamps were issued and that existing examples "were removed unlawfully during the destruction process".

(Des P. Durrant. Litho Cambec Press, Melbourne)

1985 (6 Nov). New Zealand Naval History. T **419** and similar horiz designs. Multicoloured. P 13½.

1379	25c. Type **419**	40	15
1380	45c. H.M.N.Z.S. *Achilles* (1936–46)	55	1·40
1381	60c. H.M.N.Z.S. *Rotoiti* (1949–65)	70	1·75
1382	75c. H.M.N.Z.S. *Canterbury* (from 1971)	85	1·75
1379/82	Set of 4	2·25	4·50
MS1383	124×108 mm. Nos. 1379/82	2·75	4·50

420 Police Computer Operator

421 Indian "Power Plus" 1000cc Motor Cycle (1920)

(Des A. Mitchell. Litho Leigh-Mardon Ltd, Melbourne)

1986 (15 Jan). Centenary of New Zealand Police. T **420** and similar vert designs, each showing historical aspects above modern police activities. Multicoloured. P 14½×14.

1384	25c. Type **420**	35	55
	a. Horiz strip of 5. Nos. 1384/8	1·60	2·50
1385	25c. Detective and mobile control room	35	55
1386	25c. Policewoman and badge	35	55
1387	25c. Forensic scientist, patrol car and policeman with child	35	55
1388	25c. Police College, Porirua, Patrol boat *Lady Elizabeth II* and dog handler	35	55
1384/8 *Set of 5*		1·60	2·50

Nos. 1384/8 were printed together, *se-tenant*, in horizontal strips of five throughout the sheet.

(Des M. Wyatt. Litho J.W.)

1986 (5 Mar). Vintage Motor Cycles. T **421** and similar horiz designs. Multicoloured. P 13×12½.

1389	35c. Type **421**	25	35
1390	45c. Norton "CS1" 500cc (1927)	25	50
1391	60c. B.S.A. "Sloper" 500cc (1930)	30	1·50
1392	75c. Triumph "Model H" 550cc (1915)	40	1·60
1389/92 *Set of 4*		1·10	3·50

422 Tree of Life

423 Knights Point

(Des Margaret Clarkson. Litho J.W.)

1986 (5 Mar). International Peace Year. T **422** and similar horiz design. Multicoloured. P 13×12½.

1393	25c. Type **422**	30	30
	a. Horiz pair. Nos. 1393/4	60	60
1394	25c. Peace dove	30	30

Nos. 1393/4 were printed together, *se-tenant*, in horizontal pairs throughout the sheet.

(Des P. Durrant. Photo Heraclio Fournier)

1986 (11 June). Coastal Scenery. T **423** and similar horiz designs. Multicoloured. P 14.

1395	55c. Type **423**	35	55
1396	60c. Reeks Bay	35	70
1397	65c. Doubtless Bay	40	1·00
1398	80c. Wainui Bay	50	1·00
1395/8 *Set of 4*		1·75	3·00
MS1399 124×99 mm. No. 1398 (*sold at* $1.20)		1·00	1·25

The 40c. premium on No. **MS**1399 was to support "New Zealand 1990" International Stamp Exhibition, Auckland.

No. **MS**1399 exists overprinted for "Stockholmia". Such miniature sheets were only available at this International Stamp Exhibition in Stockholm and were not placed on sale in New Zealand.

424 *Football* (Kylie Epapara)

425 "A Partridge in a Pear Tree"

(Litho Leigh-Mardon Ltd, Melbourne)

1986 (30 July). Health Stamps. Children's Paintings (1st series). T **424** and similar multicoloured designs. P 14½×14 (30c.) or 14×14½ (45c.).

1400	30c. +3c. Type **424**	40	75
	a. Horiz pair. Nos. 1400/1	80	1·50
1401	30c. +3c. *Children at Play* (Philip Kata)	40	75
1402	45c.+3c. *Children Skipping* (Mia Flannery) (*horiz*)	50	75
1400/2 *Set of 3*		1·10	1·75
MS1403 144×81 mm. Nos. 1400/2, each×2		2·00	2·00

Nos. 1400/1 were printed together, *se-tenant*, in horizontal pairs throughout the sheet.

No. **MS**1403 exists overprinted for "Stockholmia". Such miniature sheets were only available at this International Stamp Exhibition in Stockholm and were not placed on sale in New Zealand.

See also Nos. 1433/**MS**1436.

(Des Margaret Halcrow-Cross. Photo Heraclio Fournier)

1986 (17 Sept). Christmas. *The Twelve Days of Christmas* (carol). T **425** and similar vert designs. Multicoloured. P 14½.

1404	25c. Type **425**	20	10
1405	55c. "Two turtle doves"	45	55
1406	65c. "Three French hens"	50	1·00
1404/6 *Set of 3*		1·00	1·50

426 Conductor and Orchestra

427 Jetboating

(Des R. Freeman. Litho Leigh-Mardon Ltd, Melbourne)

1986 (5 Nov). Music in New Zealand. T **426** and similar vert designs. P 14½×14.

1407	30c. multicoloured	15	10
	a. Imperf (pair)	£275	
1408	60c. black, new blue and yellow-orange	25	60
1409	80c. multicoloured	35	1·50
1410	$1 multicoloured	45	1·00
1407/10 *Set of 4*		1·10	2·75

Designs:—60c. Cornet and brass band; 80c. Piper and Highland pipe band; $1 Guitar and country music group.

(Des M. Wyatt. Litho Leigh-Mardon Ltd, Melbourne)

1987 (14 Jan). Tourism. T **427** and similar vert designs. Multicoloured. P 14½×14.

1411	60c. Type **427**	50	50
1412	70c. Sightseeing flights	60	75
1413	80c. Camping	70	75
1414	85c. Windsurfing	70	1·00
1415	$1.05 Mountaineering	90	1·40
1416	$1.30 River rafting	1·10	1·50
1411/16 *Set of 6*		4·00	5·50

428 Southern Cross Cup

(Des R. Proud. Litho Leigh-Mardon Ltd, Melbourne)

1987 (2 Feb). Yachting Events. T **428** and similar horiz designs showing yachts. Multicoloured. P 14×14½.

1417	40c. Type **428**	15	15
1418	80c. Admiral's Cup	25	60
1419	$1.05 Kenwood Cup	35	1·00
1420	$1.30 America's Cup	40	1·00
1417/20 *Set of 4*		1·00	2·50

429 Hand writing Letter and Postal Transport

(Des Communication Arts Ltd. Litho C.P.E. Australia Ltd, Melbourne)

1987 (1 Apr). New Zealand Post Ltd Vesting Day. T **429** and similar horiz design. Multicoloured. P 13½.

1421	40c. Type **429**	1·00	1·50
	a. Horiz pair. Nos. 1421/2	2·00	3·00
1422	40c. Posting letter, train and mailbox	1·00	1·50

Nos. 1421/2 were printed together, se-tenant, in horizontal pairs throughout the sheet.

430 Avro Type 626 and Wigram Airfield, 1937

431 Urewera National Park and Fern Leaf

(Des P. Leitch. Litho Leigh-Mardon Ltd, Melbourne)

1987 (15 Apr). 50th Anniv of Royal New Zealand Air Force. T **430** and similar horiz designs. Multicoloured. P 14×14½.

1423	40c. Type **430**	55	15
1424	70c. Curtiss P-40E Kittyhawk I over World War II Pacific airstrip	80	1·75
1425	80c. Short S.25 Sunderland flying boat and Pacific lagoon	90	1·75
1426	85c. Douglas A-4F Skyhawk and Mt Ruapehu	90	1·60
1423/6	Set of 4	2·75	4·75
MS1427	115×105 mm. Nos. 1423/6	5·50	6·50

No. **MS**1427 overprinted on the selvedge with the "CAPEX" logo was only available from the New Zealand stand at this International Philatelic Exhibition in Toronto.

(Des Tracey Purkis. Litho Leigh-Mardon Ltd, Melbourne)

1987 (17 June). Centenary of National Parks Movement. T **431** and similar vert designs. Multicoloured. P 14½.

1428	70c. Type **431**	30	45
1429	80c. Mt Cook and buttercup	30	45
1430	85c. Fiordland and pineapple shrub	30	55
1431	$1.30 Tongariro and tussock	50	80
1428/31	Set of 4	1·25	2·00
MS1432	123×99 mm. No. 1431 (sold at $1.70)	1·00	1·75

The 40c. premium on No. **MS**1432 was to support "New Zealand 1990" International Stamp Exhibition, Auckland.

No. **MS**1432 overprinted on the selvedge with the "CAPEX" logo was only available from the New Zealand stand at this International Philatelic Exhibition in Toronto.

432 Kite Flying (Lauren Baldwin)

433 Hark the Herald Angels Sing

(Adapted D. Little. Litho Leigh-Mardon Ltd, Melbourne)

1987 (29 July). Health Stamps. Children's Paintings (2nd series). T **432** and similar multicoloured designs. P 14½.

1433	40c. +3c. Type **432**	80	1·50
	a. Horiz pair. Nos. 1433/4	1·60	3·00
1434	40c. +3c. Swimming (Ineke Schoneveld)	80	1·50
1435	60c. +3c. Horse Riding (Aaron Tylee) (vert)	1·25	1·50
1433/5	Set of 3	2·50	4·00
MS1436	100×117 mm. Nos. 1433/5, each×2	4·25	7·00

Nos. 1433/4 were printed together, se-tenant, in horizontal pairs throughout the sheet.

(Des Ellen Giggenbach. Litho Leigh-Mardon Ltd, Melbourne)

1987 (16 Sept). Christmas. T **433** and similar vert designs. Multicoloured. P 14½.

1437	35c. Type **433**	30	10
1438	70c. Away in a Manger	65	70
1439	85c. We Three Kings of Orient Are	80	85
1437/9	Set of 3	1·60	1·50

434 Knot ("Pona")

435 "Geothermal"

(Des Nga Puna Waihanga. Litho Security Printers (M), Malaysia)

1987 (4 Nov). Maori Fibre-work. T **434** and similar vert designs. Multicoloured. W **138** of Malaysia. P 12.

1440	40c. Type **434**	20	10
1441	60c. Binding ("Herehere")	30	50
1442	80c. Plait ("Whiri")	40	1·25
1443	85c. Cloak weaving ("Korowai") with flax fibre ("Whitau")	40	1·25
1440/3	Set of 4	1·10	2·75

(Des Fay McAlpine. Litho Leigh-Mardon Ltd, Melbourne)

1988 (13 Jan). Centenary of Electricity. T **435** and similar horiz designs, each showing radiating concentric circles representing energy generation. P 14×14½.

1444	40c. multicoloured	20	10
1445	60c. black, rosine and brownish black	30	45
1446	70c. multicoloured	30	75
1447	80c. multicoloured	30	65
1444/7	Set of 4	1·00	1·75

Designs:—60c. "Thermal"; 70c. "Gas"; 80c. "Hydro".

436 Queen Elizabeth II and 1882 Queen Victoria 1d. Stamp

437 Mangopare

(Des A. G. Mitchell (40c.), R. M. Conly and M. Stanley ($1). Litho Leigh-Mardon Ltd, Melbourne)

1988 (13 Jan). Centenary of Royal Philatelic Society of New Zealand. T **436** and similar multicoloured designs. P 14×14½.

1448	40c. Type **436**	35	75
	a. Horiz pair. Nos. 1448/9	70	1·50
1449	40c. As Type **436**, but 1882 Queen Victoria 2d.	35	75
MS1450	107×160 mm. $1 Queen Victoria (Chalon) (vert). P 14½×14	3·00	3·50

Nos. 1448/9 were printed together, se-tenant, in horizontal pairs throughout the sheet.

No. **MS**1450 overprinted on the selvedge with the "SYDPEX" logo was only available from the New Zealand stand at this International Philatelic Exhibition in Sydney and from the Philatelic Bureau at Wanganui.

(Des S. Adsett. Litho Leigh-Mardon Ltd, Melbourne)

1988 (2 Mar). Maori Rafter Paintings. T **437** and similar vert designs. Multicoloured. P 14½.

1451	40c. Type **437**	25	45
1452	40c. Koru	25	45
1453	40c. Raupunga	25	45
1454	60c. Koiri	35	75
1451/4	Set of 4	1·00	1·90

438 "Good Luck"

439 Paradise Shelduck

(Des Communication Arts Ltd. Litho CPE Australia Ltd, Melbourne)

1988 (18 May). Greetings Stamps. T **438** and similar multicoloured designs. P 13½.

1455	40c. Type **438**	70	1·00
	a. Booklet pane. Nos. 1455/9	3·25	4·50
1456	40c. "Keeping in touch"	70	1·00
1457	40c. "Happy birthday"	70	1·00
1458	40c. "Congratulations" (41×27 mm)	70	1·00

1459	40c. "Get well soon" (41×27 *mm*)		70	1·00
1455/9	Set of 5		3·25	4·50

Nos. 1455/9 were only issued in $2 stamp booklets.

(Des Pauline Morse. Litho Southern Colour Print, Dunedin (Nos. 1467ab/ac) or Leigh-Mardon Ltd, Melbourne (others))

1988 (7 June)–95. Native Birds. T **439** and similar vert designs. Multicoloured. Phosphorised paper (5c., 45c.). P 14½×14.

1459a	5c. Sooty Crake (1.7.91)		15	65
1460	10c. Double-banded Plover ("Banded Dotterel") (2.11.88)		20	40
1461	20c. Yellowhead (2.11.88)		30	40
	a. Perf 13½ (22.9.95)		2·00	1·50
1462	30c. Grey-backed White Eye ("Silvereye") (2.11.88)		40	30
1463	40c. Brown Kiwi (2.11.88)		45	20
	a. Perf 13½×13 (8.11.89)		1·25	2·25
	ab. Pack pane. No. 1463a×10 with margins all round		12·00	
1463b	45c. Rock Wren (1.7.91)		50	60
	ba. Booklet pane. No. 1463b×10 with horiz sides of pane imperf (1.10.91)		4·00	
1464	50c. Sacred Kingfisher (2.11.88)		60	70
1465	60c. Spotted Cormorant ("Spotted Shag") (2.11.88)		60	80
	a. Perf 13½ (22.9.95)		3·00	3·50
1466	70c. Type **439**		1·00	1·50
1467	80c. Victoria Penguin ("Fiordland Crested Penguin") (2.11.88)		1·00	1·50
1467a	80c. New Zealand Falcon (31.3.93)		2·00	2·00
	ab. Perf 12 (7.94)		1·50	2·00
	ac. Booklet pane. No. 1467ab×10		13·00	
1468	90c. New Zealand Robin (2.11.88)		1·25	1·50
1459a/68	Set of 12		7·00	9·50

No. 1463a was only issued in panes of ten with margins on all four sides. These panes were initially included in "Stamp Pads" of 50 such panes, but subsequently appeared in $4 stamp packs.

A miniature sheet containing No. 1466 was only available from the New Zealand stand at "WORLD STAMP EXPO '89" International Stamp Exhibition or the Philatelic Bureau, Wanganui. It was subsequently overprinted with the "New Zealand 1990" emblem.

No. 1467a was originally issued in $8 booklets on 31 March 1993, but appeared in sheets on 18 February 1994.

No. 1467ab was only issued in $8 stamp booklets and shows the vertical edges of the pane imperforate.

For 40c. and 45c. stamps in similar designs, but self-adhesive, see Nos. 1589/a.

For Nos. 1459a/65 in miniature sheet for the "Philakorea '94" International Stamp Exhibition see No. **MS**1830.

440 Milford Track

441 Kiwi and Koala at Campfire

(Des H. Thompson. Litho Leigh-Mardon Ltd, Melbourne)

1988 (8 June). Scenic Walking Trails. T **440** and similar vert designs. Multicoloured. P 14½.

1469	70c. Type **440**		25	50
1470	80c. Heaphy Track		30	55
1471	85c. Copland Track		30	65
1472	$1.30 Routeburn Track		50	1·00
1469/72	Set of 4		1·25	2·40
MS1473	124×99 mm. No. 1472 (sold at $1.70)		1·25	2·50

The 40c. premium on No. **MS**1473 was to support "New Zealand 1990" International Stamp Exhibition, Auckland.

(Des R. Harvey. Litho Leigh-Mardon Ltd, Melbourne)

1988 (21 June). Bicentenary of Australian Settlement. P 14½.

1474	**441** 40c. multicoloured		40	60

A stamp in a similar design was also issued by Australia.

442 Swimming

443 O Come All Ye Faithful

(Des R. Proud. Litho Leigh-Mardon Ltd, Melbourne)

1988 (27 July). Health Stamps. Olympic Games, Seoul. T **442** and similar horiz designs. Multicoloured. P 14½.

1475	40c. +3c. Type **442**		40	75
1476	60c. +3c. Athletics		60	1·25
1477	70c. +3c. Canoeing		70	1·25
1478	80c. +3c. Show-jumping		90	1·40
1475/8	Set of 4		2·40	3·75
MS1479	120×90 mm. Nos. 1475/8		3·25	4·25

(Des Fay McAlpine. Litho Leigh-Mardon Ltd, Melbourne)

1988 (14 Sept). Christmas. Carols. T **443** and similar vert designs, each showing illuminated verses. Multicoloured. P 14½.

1480	35c. Type **443**		30	15
1481	70c. Hark the Herald Angels Sing		50	65
1482	80c. Ding Dong Merrily on High		50	90
1483	85c. The First Nowell		55	1·10
1480/3	Set of 4		1·75	2·50

444 Lake Pukaki (John Gully)

445 Brown Kiwi

(Litho Leigh-Mardon Ltd, Melbourne)

1988 (5 Oct). New Zealand Heritage (1st issue). The Land. T **444** and similar horiz designs showing 19th-century paintings. Multicoloured. P 14×14½.

1484	40c. Type **444**		20	10
1485	60c. On the Grass Plain below Lake Arthur (William Fox)		30	35
1486	70c. View of Auckland (John Hoyte)		35	65
1487	80c. Mt. Egmont from the Southward (Charles Heaphy)		40	65
1488	$1.05 Anakiwa, Queen Charlotte Sound (John Kinder)		50	1·75
1489	$1.30 White Terraces, Lake Rotoma-hana (Charles Barraud)		50	1·40
1484/9	Set of 6		2·00	4·25

See also Nos. 1505/10, 1524/9, 1541/6, 1548/53 and 1562/7.

(Des A. Mitchell. Eng. G. Prosser of B.A.B.N. Recess Leigh Mardon Ltd, Melbourne)

1988 (19 Oct)–93. Phosphorised paper (No. 1490b). P 14½ (and 13 around design).

1490	**445** $1 bronze-green		2·00	3·75
	a. Booklet pane. No. 1490×6		11·00	
1490b	$1 bright scarlet (17.4.91)		2·25	3·25
1490c	$1 blue (9.6.93)		1·50	2·50
1490/c	Set of 3		5·25	8·75

Nos. 1490/c were each printed within a square margin, perforated vertically for No. 1490 and on all four sides for Nos. 1490b/c, and with a further circular perforation around the design.

No. 1490 was only issued in $6 stamp booklets with the horizontal edges of the booklet pane imperforate.

Nos. 1490b/c were printed in sheets of 24 (6×4).

For miniature sheets containing similar stamps, some printed in lithography, see Nos. **MS**1745, **MS**1786 and **MS**2342.

For $1 violet, $1.10 and $1.50 see Nos. 2090/b.

See also Nos. 3308/10.

446 Humpback Whale and Calf

447 Clover

(Des Lindy Fisher. Litho Govt Ptg Office, Wellington)

1988 (2 Nov). Whales. T **446** and similar horiz designs. Multicoloured. P 13½.

1491	55c. Type **446**		55	70
1492	70c. Killer Whales		60	90
1493	80c. Southern Right Whale		60	1·00
1494	85c. Blue Whale		65	1·50
1495	$1.05 Southern Bottlenose Whale and calf		80	2·00
1496	$1.30 Sperm Whale		90	2·00
1491/6	Set of 6		3·50	7·25

Although inscribed "ROSS DEPENDENCY" Nos. 1491/6 were available from post offices throughout New Zealand.

(Des Heather Arnold. Litho Leigh-Mardon Ltd, Melbourne)

1989 (18 Jan). Wild Flowers. T **447** and similar horiz designs. Multicoloured. P 14½.

1497	40c. Type **447**	30	20
1498	60c. Lotus	40	65
1499	70c. Montbretia	45	1·25
1500	80c. Wild Ginger	55	1·25
1497/1500 *Set of 4*		1·50	3·00

448 Katherine Mansfield   **449** Moriori Man and Map of Chatham Islands

(Des A. G. Mitchell. Litho Harrison)

1989 (1 Mar). New Zealand Authors. T **448** and similar vert designs. Multicoloured. P 12½.

1501	40c. Type **448**	20	15
1502	60c. James K. Baxter	30	40
1503	70c. Bruce Mason	30	60
1504	80c. Ngaio Marsh	30	65
1501/4 *Set of 4*		1·00	1·60

(Des D. Gunson. Litho Leigh-Mardon Ltd, Melbourne)

1989 (17 May). New Zealand Heritage (2nd issue). The People. T **449** and similar horiz designs. P 14×14½.

1505	40c. multicoloured	75	15
1506	60c. orange-brown, brownish grey and reddish brown	1·25	75
1507	70c. yellow-grn, brownish grey and dp olive ...	60	1·10
1508	80c. bright greenish blue, brownish grey and deep dull blue	1·50	90
1509	$1.05 grey, brownish grey and grey-black	55	1·75
1510	$1.30 bright rose-red, brownish grey and lake-brown	70	1·75
1505/10 *Set of 6*		4·75	5·75

Designs:—60c. Gold prospector; 70c. Settler ploughing; 80c. Whaling; $1.05 Missionary preaching to Maoris; $1.30 Maori village.

450 White Pine (Kahikatea)   **451** Duke and Duchess of York with Princess Beatrice

(Des D. Gunson. Litho Questa)

1989 (7 June). Native Trees. T **450** and similar vert designs. Multicoloured. P 14×14½.

1511	80c. Type **450**	30	45
1512	85c. Red Pine (Rimu)	30	45
1513	$1.05 Totara	40	80
1514	$1.30 Kauri	40	80
1511/14 *Set of 4*		1·25	2·25
MS1515 102×125 mm. No. 1514 (*sold at $1.80*)		1·50	1·75

The 50c. premium on No. **MS**1515 was to support "New Zealand 1990" International Stamp Exhibition, Auckland.

(Des and litho Leigh-Mardon Ltd, Melbourne)

1989 (26 July). Health Stamps. T **451** and similar vert designs. Multicoloured. P 14½.

1516	40c. +3c. Type **451**	80	1·50
	a. Horiz pair. Nos. 1516/17	1·60	3·00
1517	40c. +3c. Duchess of York with Princess Beatrice	80	1·50
1518	80c. +3c. Princess Beatrice	1·40	1·75
1516/18 *Set of 3*		2·75	4·25
MS1519 120×89 mm. Nos. 1516/18, each×2		4·50	7·00

Nos. 1516/17 were printed together, *se-tenant*, in horizontal pairs throughout the sheet.

No. **MS**1519 overprinted on the selvedge with the "WORLD STAMP EXPO '89" logo was only available from the New Zealand stand at this International Stamp Exhibition and from the Philatelic Bureau at Wanganui.

452 One Tree Hill, Auckland, through Bedroom Window   **453** Windsurfing

(Des H. Chapman. Litho Leigh-Mardon Ltd, Melbourne)

1989 (13 Sept). Christmas. T **452** and similar vert designs showing Star of Bethlehem. Multicoloured. P 14½.

1520	35c. Type **452**	20	10
1521	65c. Shepherd and dog in mountain valley...	50	50
1522	80c. Star over harbour	55	65
1523	$1 Star over globe	75	1·00
1520/3 *Set of 4*		1·75	2·00

(Des M. Bailey. Litho Leigh-Mardon Ltd, Melbourne)

1989 (11 Oct). New Zealand Heritage (3rd issue). The Sea. T **453** and similar horiz designs. Multicoloured. P 14×14½.

1524	40c. Type **453**	50	15
1525	60c. Fish of many species	85	90
1526	65c. Striped Marlin and game fishing launch	90	1·00
1527	80c. Rowing boat and yachts in harbour	1·00	1·00
1528	$1 Coastal scene	1·25	1·10
1529	$1.50 *Rotoiti* (container ship) and tug	1·90	3·25
1524/9 *Set of 6*		5·75	6·75

454 Games Logo

(Des Heather Arnold. Litho Leigh-Mardon Ltd, Melbourne)

1989 (8 Nov)–**90**. 14th Commonwealth Games. Auckland. T **454** and similar horiz designs. Multicoloured. P 14½.

1530	40c. Type **454**	20	30
1531	40c. Goldie (games kiwi mascot)	20	30
1532	40c. Gymnastics	20	30
1533	50c. Weightlifting	25	30
1534	65c. Swimming	30	45
1535	80c. Cycling	70	60
1536	$1 Lawn bowling	50	60
1537	$1.80 Hurdling	70	1·25
1530/7 *Set of 8*		2·75	3·50
MS1538 Two sheets, each 105×92 mm. with different margin designs. (a) Nos. 1530/1 (*horiz pair*). (b) Nos. 1530/1 (*vert pair*) (24.1.90)	*Set of 2 sheets*	3·75	4·50

455 Short S.30 Modified "G" Class Flying Boat *Aotearoa* and Boeing 747-200   **456** Chief Kawiti signing Treaty

(Des R. Proud. Litho Enschedé)

1990 (17 Jan). 50th Anniv of Air New Zealand. P 13×14½.

1539	**455**	80c. multicoloured	1·40	1·10

(Des A. G. Mitchell from painting by L. C. Mitchell. Litho Enschedé)

1990 (17 Jan). 150th Anniv of Treaty of Waitangi. Sheet 80×118 mm, containing T **456** and similar multicoloured design. P 13½.

MS1540 40c. Type **456**; 40c. Chief Hone Heke (first signatory) and Lieut-Governor Hobson (*horiz*) ... 1·50   3·00

457 Maori Voyaging Canoe   **458** *Thelymitra pulchella*

(Des G. Fuller. Litho Leigh-Mardon Ltd, Melbourne)

1990 (7 Mar). New Zealand Heritage (4th issue). The Ships. T **457** and similar horiz designs. Multicoloured. P 14×14½.

1541	40c. Type **457**	60	15
1542	50c. H.M.S. *Endeavour* (Cook), 1769	1·00	80
1543	60c. *Tory* (barque), 1839	1·00	1·00
1544	80c. *Crusader* (full-rigged immigrant ship), 1871	1·50	1·50
1545	$1 *Edwin Fox* (full-rigged immigrant ship), 1873	1·75	1·50
1546	$1.50 *Arawa* (steamer), 1884	2·00	3·25
1541/6 *Set of 6*		7·00	7·50

A miniature sheet containing No. 1542 was only available from the New Zealand stand at "Stamp World London '90" International Stamp Exhibition or from the Philatelic Bureau, Wanganui.

(Des Lindy Fisher. Litho Leigh-Mardon Ltd, Melbourne)

1990 (18 Apr). New Zealand 1990 International Stamp Exhibition, Auckland. Native Orchids. Sheet 179×80 mm, containing T **458** and similar vert designs. Multicoloured. P 14½.

MS1547 40c. Type **458**; 40c. *Corybas macranthus*; 40c. *Dendrobium cunninghamii*; 40c. *Pterostylis banksii*; 80c. *Aporostylis bifolia* (sold at $4.90)	3·00	4·50

The stamps in No. **MS**1547 form a composite design.
The $2.50 premium on No. **MS**1547 was used to support the Exhibition. Miniature sheets as No. **MS**1547, but imperforate, are from a limited printing distributed to those purchasing season tickets for the exhibition.

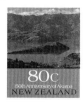

459 Grace Neill (social reformer)   **460** Akaroa
and Maternity Hospital, Wellington

(Des Elspeth Williamson. Litho Leigh-Mardon Ltd, Melbourne)

1990 (16 May). New Zealand Heritage (5th issue). Famous New Zealanders. T **459** and similar horiz designs. Multicoloured. P 14×14½.

1548	40c. Type **459**	45	10
1549	50c. Jean Batten (pilot) and Percival P.3 Gull Six aircraft	65	85
1550	60c. Katherine Sheppard (suffragette) and 19th-century women	50	1·00
1551	80c. Richard Pearse (inventor) and early flying machine	75	1·25
1552	$1 Lt.-Gen. Freyberg and tank	80	1·25
1553	$1.50 Peter Buck (politician) and Maori pattern	70	2·25
1548/53 *Set of 6*		3·25	6·00

(Des Lindy Fisher. Litho Leigh-Mardon Ltd, Melbourne)

1990 (13 June). 150th Anniversary of European Settlements. T **460** and similar vert designs. Multicoloured. P 14½.

1554	80c. Type **460**	45	70
1555	$1 Wanganui	55	75
1556	$1.50 Wellington	80	2·25
1557	$1.80 Takapuna Beach, Auckland	1·00	1·50
1554/7 *Set of 4*		2·50	4·75
MS1558 125×100 mm. No. 1557 (sold at $2.30)		2·75	3·50

The 50c. premium on No. **MS**1558 was to support "New Zealand 1990" International Stamp Exhibition, Auckland.

461 Jack Lovelock (athlete)   **462** Creation Legend of Rangi
and Race   and Papa

(Des T. Crilley. Litho Questa)

1990 (25 July). Health Stamps. Sportsmen (1st series). T **461** and similar horiz design. Multicoloured. P 14½×13½.

1559	40c. +5c. Type **461**	70	1·00
1560	80c. +5c. George Nepia (rugby player) and match	90	1·75
MS1561 115×96 mm. Nos. 1559/60, each×2		2·25	4·50

See also Nos. 1687/**MS**1689.

(Des K. Hall. Litho Leigh-Mardon Ltd, Melbourne)

1990 (24 Aug). New Zealand Heritage (6th issue). The Maori. T **462** and similar horiz designs. Multicoloured. P 14×14½.

1562	40c. Type **462**	20	10
	a. Violet-blue (face value) omitted	£300	£225
1563	50c. Pattern from Maori feather cloak	25	55
1564	60c. Maori women's choir	30	60
1565	80c. Maori facial tattoos	35	80
1566	$1 War canoe prow (detail)	40	1·00
1567	$1.50 Maori haka	60	2·25
1562/7 *Set of 6*		1·90	4·75

463 Queen Victoria   **464** Angel

(Des A. G. Mitchell. Recess Leigh-Mardon Ltd, Melbourne)

1990 (29 Aug). 150th Anniv of the Penny Black. Sheet 169×70 mm containing T **463** and similar vert designs. P 14½×14.

MS1568 40c.×6 indigo (Type **463**, King Edward VII, King George V, King Edward VIII, King George VI, Queen Elizabeth II)	4·50	6·00

(Des Sally Simons. Litho Leigh-Mardon Ltd, Melbourne)

1990 (12 Sept). Christmas. T **464** and similar vert designs showing angels. P 14½.

1569	40c. purple, deep greenish blue and deep yellow-brown	20	10
1570	$1 purple, blue-green and deep yellow-brown	45	30
1571	$1.50 purple, bright crimson and deep yellow-brown	70	2·25
1572	$1.80 purple, red and deep yellow-brown	80	1·50
1569/72 *Set of 4*		1·90	3·50

465 Antarctic Petrel   **466** Coopworth Ewe
and Lambs

(Des Janet Luxton. Litho Heraclio Fournier)

1990 (7 Nov). Antarctic Birds. T **465** and similar vert designs. Multicoloured. P 13½×13.

1573	40c. Type **465**	70	30
1574	50c. Wilson's Petrel	80	75
1575	60c. Snow Petrel	90	1·25
1576	80c. Southern Fulmar	1·00	1·25
1577	$1 Bearded Penguin ("Chinstrap Penguin")	1·10	1·25
1578	$1.50 Emperor Penguin	1·25	4·00
1573/8 *Set of 6*		5·25	8·00

Although inscribed "Ross Dependency" Nos. 1573/8 were available from post offices throughout New Zealand.

(Des Lindy Fisher. Litho Leigh-Mardon Ltd, Melbourne)

1991 (23 Jan). New Zealand Farming and Agriculture. Sheep Breeds. T **466** and similar vert designs. Multicoloured. P 14½×14.

1579	40c. Type **466**	30	20
1580	60c. Perendale	40	60
1581	80c. Corriedale	50	70
1582	$1 Drysdale	60	75
1583	$1.50 South Suffolk	80	2·75
1584	$1.80 Romney	1·00	2·25
1579/84 *Set of 6*		3·25	6·50

467 Moriori, Royal Albatross, Nikau Palm and Artefacts

468 Goal and Footballers

(Des K. Hall. Litho Southern Colour Print Ltd, Dunedin)

1991 (6 Mar). Bicentenary of Discovery of Chatham Islands. T **467** and similar vert design. Multicoloured. P 13½.

1585	40c. Type **467**	75	50
1586	80c. Carvings, H.M.S. *Chatham*, Moriori house of 1870, and Tommy Solomon	1·25	2·00

(Des T. Crilley. Litho Southern Colour Print Ltd, Dunedin)

1991 (6 Mar). Centenary of New Zealand Football Association. T **468** and similar horiz design. Multicoloured. P 13½.

1587	80c. Type **468**	60	1·60
	a. Horiz pair. Nos. 1587/8	1·10	3·25
1588	80c. Five footballers and referee	60	1·60

Nos. 1587/8 were printed together, *se-tenant*, in horizontal pairs throughout the sheet, each pair forming a composite design.

(Des Pauline Morse. Litho Printset-Cambec Pty Ltd, Melbourne (40c., 45c. (No. 1589a)) or Leigh-Mardon Ltd, Melbourne (45c. (No. 1589ab))

1991 (17 Apr–Dec). As Nos. 1463/b, but self-adhesive. Phosphorised paper. P 11½.

1589	40c. Brown Kiwi	1·25	1·40
1589a	45c. Rock Wren (1.07)	50	1·00
	ab. Perf 11 (12.91)	50	70

Nos. 1589/a were only available in coils of 100, each stamp, with die-cut perforations, being separate on the imperforate backing paper. Initially the 45c. showed the surplus surface paper removed, but from December 1991 supplies No. 1589ab had the stamps surrounded by white selvedge. The format was changed again in March 1992 when the coils again appeared without the white selvedge. Part of the March 1992 printing, and all subsequent supplies, had the stamps interlocked with no backing paper visible between them.

A limited quantity of the 45c. (No. 1589a) in sheets of 200 (8×25) was produced for use on official first day covers. It is reported that a small number of such sheets were subsequently sold by a few post offices.

469 Tuatara on Rocks

470 Clown

(Des Pauline Morse. Litho Leigh-Mardon Ltd, Melbourne)

1991 (17 Apr). Endangered Species. The Tuatara. T **469** and similar horiz designs. Multicoloured. P 14½.

1590	40c. Type **469**	35	60
1591	40c. Tuatara in crevice	35	60
1592	40c. Tuatara with foliage	35	60
1593	40c. Tuatara in dead leaves	35	60
1590/3	*Set of 4*	1·25	2·25

(Des Helen Crawford. Litho Leigh-Mardon Ltd, Melbourne)

1991 (15 May–1 July). "Happy Birthday". T **470** and similar multicoloured designs. P 13½.

1594	40c. Type **470**	75	85
	a. Booklet pane. Nos. 1594/8	3·25	3·75
1595	40c. Balloons	75	85
1596	40c. Party hat	75	85
1597	40c. Birthday present (41×27 *mm*)	75	85
1598	40c. Birthday cake (41×27 *mm*)	75	85
1599	45c. Type **470** (1.07)	75	85
	a. Booklet pane. Nos. 1599/1603	3·25	3·75
1600	45c. As No. 1595 (1.07)	75	85
1601	45c. As No. 1596 (1.07)	75	85
1602	45c. As No. 1597 (1.07)	75	85
1603	45c. As No. 1598 (1.07)	75	85
1594/1603	*Set of 10*	6·50	7·50

The above were only issued in $2 (Nos. 1594/8) or $2.25 (Nos. 1599/1603) stamp booklets, SB54 and SB57.

471 Cat at Window

472 Punakaiki Rocks

(Des Jennifer Lautusi. Litho Leigh-Mardon Ltd, Melbourne)

1991 (15 May–1 July). "Thinking of You". T **471** and similar multicoloured designs. P 13½.

1604	40c. Type **471**	75	95
	a. Booklet pane. Nos. 1604/8	3·25	4·25
1605	40c. Cat playing with slippers	75	95
1606	40c. Cat with alarm clock	75	95
1607	40c. Cat in window (41×27 *mm*)	75	95
1608	40c. Cat at door (41×27 *mm*)	75	95
1609	45c. Type **471** (1.07)	75	85
	a. Booklet pane. Nos. 1609/13	3·25	3·75
1610	45c. As No. 1605 (1.07)	75	85
1611	45c. As No. 1606 (1.07)	75	85
1612	45c. As No. 1607 (1.07)	75	85
1613	45c. As No. 1608 (1.07)	75	85
1604/13	*Set of 10*	6·50	8·00

The above were only issued in $2 (Nos. 1604/8) or $2.25 (Nos. 1609/13) stamp booklets, SB55 and SB58.

(Des H. Thompson. Litho Leigh-Mardon Ltd, Melbourne)

1991 (12 June). Scenic Landmarks. T **472** and similar horiz designs. Multicoloured. P 14½.

1614	40c. Type **472**	30	10
1615	50c. Moeraki Boulders	35	35
1616	80c. Organ Pipes	55	80
1617	$1 Castle Hill	60	70
1618	$1.50 Te Kaukau Point	1·00	1·60
1619	$1.80 Ahuriri River Clay Cliffs	1·25	1·50
1614/19	*Set of 6*	3·50	4·50

473 Dolphins Underwater

474 Children's Rugby

(Des Heather Arnold. Litho Leigh-Mardon Ltd, Melbourne)

1991 (24 July). Health Stamps. Hector's Dolphin. T **473** and similar horiz design. Multicoloured. P 14½.

1620	45c. +5c. Type **473**	90	1·25
1621	80c. +5c. Dolphins leaping	1·25	2·00
MS1622	115×100 mm. Nos. 1620/1, each×2	4·50	6·50

(Des A. G. Mitchell. Litho Leigh-Mardon Ltd, Melbourne)

1991 (21 Aug). World Cup Rugby Championship. T **474** and similar vert designs. Multicoloured. P 14½×14.

1623	80c. Type **474**	45	80
1624	$1 Women's rugby	50	60
1625	$1.50 Senior rugby	80	2·25
1626	$1.80 "All Blacks" (national team)	90	2·00
1623/6	*Set of 4*	2·40	5·00
MS1627	113×90 mm. No. 1626 (*sold at* $2.40)	2·25	4·25

No. **MS**1627 additionally inscribed "PHILA NIPPON '91" was available, at $1.80, from the New Zealand stand at this International Stamp Exhibition in Tokyo and from the Philatelic Bureau at Wanganui.

475 Three Shepherds

476 *Dodonidia helmsii*

(Des Designworks Communications. Litho Southern Colour Print, Dunedin)

1991 (18 Sept). Christmas. T **475** and similar vert designs. Multicoloured. P 13½.

1628	45c. Type **475**	40	80
	a. Block of four. Nos 1628/31	1·40	3·50
1629	45c. Two Kings on camels	40	80
1630	45c. Mary and Baby Jesus	40	80
1631	45c. King with gift	40	80
1632	65c. Star of Bethlehem	50	60
1633	$1 Crown	60	80
1634	$1.50 Angel	80	2·00
1628/34 *Set of 7*		3·25	6·00

Nos. 1628/31 were printed together, *se-tenant*, in blocks of four throughout the sheet.

(Des Pauline Morse)

1991 (6 Nov)–**2008**. Butterflies. T **476** and similar vert designs. Multicoloured.

(a) Litho Leigh-Mardon Ltd, Melbourne. Phosphorised paper ($4, $5). P 14½

1635	$1 Type **476**	1·00	60
1636	$2 *Zizina otis oxleyi*	2·75	1·50
1637	$3 *Vanessa itea*	5·00	2·50
1638	$4 *Lycaena salustius* (25.1.95)	4·00	4·50
1639	$5 *Bassaris gonerilla* (25.1.95)	4·75	5·50
1635/9 *Set of 5*		16·00	13·00

(b) Litho Southern Colour Print (No. 1643a) or Questa (others). P 13½×14

1640	$1 As Type **476** (6.11.96)	1·75	1·50
1641	$2 As No. 1636 (6.11.96)	2·50	3·25
1642	$3 As No. 1637 (8.96)	3·25	4·50
	a. Grey (inscrs) and apple-green (frame) omitted	£600	
1643	$4 As No. 1638 (10.97)	2·50	4·00
	a. Perf 14 (3.4.08)	7·50	6·50
1644	$5 As No. 1639 (9.10.96)	7·50	6·50
1640/4 *Set of 5*		16·00	18·00

(c) Booklet stamps. Litho Southern Colour Print, Dunedin. P 14×14½

1645	$1 Type **476** (1.9.95)	4·50	6·50
	a. Booklet pane. No. 1645×5 and five "air POST" labels	21·00	

Nos. 1640/2 are from the three kiwi printings, Nos. 1643/4 from the one kiwi and No. 1643a from the two kiwi. The designs of Nos. 1640/1 and 1643a are redrawn.

No. 1645 only exists imperforate at foot and was issued in $5 stamp booklets in which the airmail labels were vertically *se-tenant* with the stamps (No. SB74).

A miniature sheet containing No. 1637 was only available from the New Zealand stand at "PHILA NIPPON '91" International Stamp Exhibition, Tokyo, or the Philatelic Bureau, Wanganui.

PRINTINGS: The initial printings of this and subsequent definitive sets had no Kiwi symbols in the sheet margins. Later printings had one, two, three or four Kiwis in the margin, to represent the first, second, third and fourth reprints.

479 Yacht *Kiwi Magic*, 1987

480 *Heemskerk*

(Des R. Proud. Litho Leigh-Mardon Ltd, Melbourne)

1992 (22 Jan). New Zealand Challenge for America's Cup. T **479** and similar horiz designs. Multicoloured. P 14.

1655	45c. Type **479**	30	10
1656	80c. Yacht *New Zealand*, 1988	50	70
1657	$1 Yacht *America*, 1851	60	85
1658	$1.50 "America's Cup" Class yacht, 1992	90	1·75
1655/8 *Set of 4*		2·10	3·00

(Des G. Fuller. Litho Enschedé)

1992 (12 Mar). Great Voyages of Discovery. T **480** and similar horiz designs. Multicoloured. P 13×14.

1659	45c. Type **480**	55	25
1660	80c. *Zeehan*	90	1·10
1661	$1 *Santa Maria*	1·25	1·10
1662	$1.50 *Pinta* and *Nina*	1·50	2·50
1659/62 *Set of 4*		3·75	4·50

Nos. 1659/60 commemorate the 350th anniversary of Tasman's discovery of New Zealand and Nos. 1661/2 the 500th anniversary of discovery of America by Columbus.

A miniature sheet containing stamps as Nos. 1661/2, but perforated 14, was only available from the New Zealand stand at "World Columbian Stamp Expo '92", Chicago, and from the Philatelic Bureau at Wanganui.

481 Sprinters

482 Weddell Seal and Pup

(Des Sheryl McCammon. Litho Southern Colour Print, Dunedin)

1992 (3 Apr). Olympic Games, Barcelona (1st issue). P 13½.

1663	**481**	45c. multicoloured	50	50

See also Nos. 1670/**MS**1674.

(Des Lindy Fisher. Litho Southern Colour Print, Dunedin)

1992 (8 Apr). Antarctic Seals. T **482** and similar horiz designs. Multicoloured. P 13½.

1664	45c. Type **482**	60	15
1665	50c. Crabeater Seals swimming	70	60
1666	65c. Leopard Seal and Adelie Penguins	90	1·50
1667	80c. Ross Seal	1·00	1·25
1668	$1 Southern Elephant Seal and harem	1·10	1·25
1669	$1.80 Hooker's Sea Lion and pup	1·75	4·25
1664/9 *Set of 6*		5·50	8·00

Although inscribed "ROSS DEPENDENCY" Nos. 1664/9 were available from post offices throughout New Zealand.

483 Cycling

484 Ice Pinnacles, Franz Josef Glacier

(Des M. Bailey. Litho Southern Colour Print, Dunedin)

1992 (13 May). Olympic Games, Barcelona (2nd issue). T **483** and similar horiz designs. P 13½.

1670	45c. Type **483**	65	20
1671	80c. Archery	60	70
1672	$1 Equestrian three-day eventing	65	85
1673	$1.50 Sailboarding	80	1·60
1670/3 *Set of 4*		2·40	3·00
MS1674 125×100 mm. Nos. 1670/3. P 14×14½		4·00	5·00

No. **MS**1674 exists overprinted with the emblem of the "World Columbian, Stamp Expo '92" and was only available from the New Zealand stand at this International Stamp Exhibition in Chicago and from the Philatelic Bureau at Wanganui.

(Des A. Hollows. Litho Southern Colour Print, Dunedin)

1992 (12 June). Glaciers. T **484** and similar horiz designs. Multicoloured. P 13½.

1675	45c. Type **484**	30	10
1676	50c. Tasman Glacier	40	35
1677	80c. Snowball Glacier, Marion Plateau	50	70
1678	$1 Brewster Glacier	60	85
1679	$1.50 Fox Glacier	85	1·60
1680	$1.80 Franz Josef Glacier	95	1·60
1675/80 *Set of 6*		3·25	4·75

485 "Grand Finale" Camellia

486 Tree and Hills

(Des Patricia Altman. Litho Leigh-Mardon Ltd, Melbourne)

1992 (8 July). Camellias. T **485** and similar vert designs. Multicoloured. P 14½.

1681	45c. Type **485**	35	10
1682	50c. "Shows-No-Sakae"	40	40
1683	80c. "Sugar Dream"	55	60
1684	$1 "Night Rider"	60	70
1685	$1.50 "E.G. Waterhouse"	85	2·75
1686	$1.80 "Dr. Clifford Parks"	95	2·50
1681/6 *Set of 6*		3·25	6·25

(Des T. Crilley. Litho Southern Colour Print, Dunedin)

1992 (12 Aug). Health Stamps. Sportsmen (2nd series). Horiz designs as T **461**. Multicoloured. P 13½.

1687	45c. +5c. Anthony Wilding (tennis player) and match	1·00	1·25

1688	80c. +5c. Stewie Dempster (cricketer) and batsman	1·25	1·75
MS1689	115×96 mm. Nos. 1687/8, each×2. P 14	5·00	6·50

(Des Van de Roer Design. Litho Leigh-Mardon Ltd, Melbourne)

1992 (1 Sept). Landscapes. T **486** and similar horiz designs. Multicoloured. P 14×14½.

1690	45c. Type **486**	60	65
	a. Booklet pane. Nos. 1690/9	5·50	6·00
1691	45c. River and hills	60	65
1692	45c. Hills and mountain	60	65
1693	45c. Glacier	60	65
1694	45c. Hills and waterfall	60	65
1695	45c. Tree and beach	60	65
1696	45c. Estuary and cliffs	60	65
1697	45c. Fjord	60	65
1698	45c. River delta	60	65
1699	45c. Ferns and beach	60	65
1690/9	Set of 10	5·50	6·00

Nos. 1690/9 were only issued in $4.50 stamp booklets with the pane forming a composite design.

487 Reindeer over Houses   **488** 1920s Fashions

(Des K. Hall. Litho Leigh-Mardon Ltd, Melbourne)

1992 (16 Sept). Christmas. T **487** and similar vert designs. Multicoloured. P 14½.

1700	45c. Type **487**	90	1·25
	a. Block of 4. Nos. 1700/3	3·25	4·50
1701	45c. Santa Claus on sleigh over houses	90	1·25
1702	45c. Christmas tree in window	90	1·25
1703	45c. Christmas wreath and children at window	90	1·25
1704	65c. Candles and fireplace	1·10	90
1705	$1 Family going to church	1·40	1·00
1706	$1.50 Picnic under Pohutakawa tree	2·00	3·50
1700/6	Set of 7	7·25	9·25

Nos. 1700/3 were printed together, se-tenant, in blocks of four throughout the sheet.

(Des T. Crilley. Litho Southern Colour Print, Dunedin)

1992 (4 Nov). New Zealand in the 1920s. T **488** and similar vert designs. Multicoloured. P 13½.

1707	45c. Type **488**	50	15
1708	50c. Dr. Robert Jack and early radio announcer	55	65
1709	80c. "All Blacks" rugby player, 1924	85	1·00
1710	$1 Swaggie and dog	95	1·00
1711	$1.50 Ford "Model A" car and young couple	1·75	2·25
1712	$1.80 Amateur aviators and biplane	2·00	2·75
1707/12	Set of 6	6·00	7·00

489 "Old Charley" Toby Jug   **490** Women's Fashions of the 1930s

(Des Brand New Ltd. Litho Leigh-Mardon Ltd, Melbourne)

1993 (20 Jan). Royal Doulton Ceramics Exhibition, New Zealand. T **489** and similar vert designs. Multicoloured. P 13.

1713	45c. Type **489**	25	10
1714	50c. "Bunnykins" nursery plate	30	35
1715	80c. "Maori Art" tea set	45	60
1716	$1 "Ophelia" handpainted plate	55	75
1717	$1.50 "St. George" figurine	80	2·25
1718	$1.80 "Lambeth" saltglazed stoneware vase	90	2·25
1713/18	Set of 6	3·00	5·50
MS1719	125×100 mm. No. 1718	1·25	2·25

(Des R. Jones. Litho Leigh-Mardon Ltd, Melbourne)

1993 (17 Feb). New Zealand in the 1930s. T **490** and similar vert designs. Multicoloured. P 14½×14.

1720	45c. Type **490**	40	10
1721	50c. Unemployed protest march	45	40
1722	80c. "Phar Lap" (racehorse)	85	70
1723	$1 State housing project	65	65
1724	$1.50 Boys drinking free school milk	1·25	3·00
1725	$1.80 Cinema queue	1·25	2·50
1720/5	Set of 6	4·25	6·50

491 Women signing Petition   **492** Champagne Pool

(Des Lindy Fisher. Litho Southern Colour Print, Dunedin)

1993 (31 Mar). Centenary of Women's Suffrage. T **491** and similar vert designs. Multicoloured. P 13½.

1726	45c. Type **491**	25	10
1727	80c. Aircraft propeller and woman on tractor	45	75
1728	$1 Housewife with children	50	75
1729	$1.50 Modern women	75	2·00
1726/9	Set of 4	1·75	3·25

(Des A. Hollows. Litho Southern Colour Print, Dunedin)

1993 (5 May). Thermal Wonders, Rotorua. T **492** and similar square designs. Multicoloured. P 12.

1730	45c. Type **492**	50	10
1731	50c. Boiling mud	50	40
1732	80c. Emerald Pool	65	70
1733	$1 Hakereteke Falls	70	80
1734	$1.50 Warbrick Terrace	1·25	1·75
1735	$1.80 Pohutu Geyser	1·25	1·75
1730/5	Set of 6	4·25	5·00

For miniature sheet containing $1.80 see No. **MS**1770.

493 Yellow-eyed Penguin, Hector's Dolphin and New Zealand Fur Seal   **494** Boy with Puppy

(Des Donna McKenna. Litho Southern Colour Print, Dunedin (No. 1740) or Leigh-Mardon Ltd, Melbourne (others))

1993 (9 June). Endangered Species Conservation. T **493** and similar horiz designs. Multicoloured. P 13½ (No. 1740) or 14×14½ (others).

1736	45c. Type **493**	85	1·25
	a. Block of 4. Nos. 1736/9	3·00	4·50
1737	45c. Taiko (bird), Mount Cook Lily and Mountain Duck ("Blue Duck")	85	1·25
1738	45c. Giant Snail, Rock Wren and Hamilton's Frog	85	1·25
1739	45c. Kaka (bird), New Zealand Pigeon and Giant Weta	85	1·25
1740	45c. Tusked Weta (23×28 mm)	85	1·00
1736/40	Set of 5	3·75	5·50

Nos. 1736/9 were issued either in sheets of one design or in sheets containing se-tenant blocks of four, as No. 1736a, each forming a composite design.

No. 1740 was only issued in $4.50 stamp booklets, SB74.

(Des Karen Odiam. Litho Southern Colour Print, Dunedin)

1993 (21 July). Health Stamps. Children's Pets. T **494** and similar vert design. Multicoloured. P 13½.

1741	45c. +5c. Type **494**	60	90
1742	80c. +5c. Girl with kitten	90	1·50
MS1743	115×96 mm. Nos. 1741/2, each×2. P 14½	3·00	4·50

No. **MS**1743 exists surcharged "STAMPEX '93 NATIONAL YOUTH PHILATELIC EXHIBITION CHRISTCHURCH 19TH–21ST AUGUST 1993 $6-00" in ultramarine. Such miniature sheets were prepared by the organisers and sold at the Exhibition P.O. philatelic counter.

(Recess and litho Leigh-Mardon Ltd, Melbourne (No. **MS**1745))

1993 (14 Aug). Taipei '93 Asian International Stamp Exhibition, Taiwan.

*(a) No.***MS**1743 *optd* "TAIPEI '93" *and emblem on sheet margin*
MS1744 Nos. 1741/2, each×2.................................... 18·00   22·00

(b) Sheet 125×100 mm containing No. 1490c (recess) and two similar
designs as Nos. 1490/b, but litho. P 13 *(around design)*
MS1745 **445** $1 deep green, $1 blue, $1 rosine.......... 6·50   8·50
Unlike previous miniature sheets produced by New Zealand Post for international stamp exhibitions overseas Nos. **MS**1744/5, and all subsequent issues of this type, were supplied to collectors in New Zealand and abroad by standing order.

495 Christmas Decorations (value at left)

496 Rainbow Abalone or Paua

(Des Kristine Cotton. Litho Southern Colour Print, Dunedin (Nos. 1746b/9a) or Leigh-Mardon Ltd, Melbourne (others))

1993 (1 Sept–3 Nov). Christmas. T **495** and similar vert designs. Multicoloured. P 14½×14.

1746	45c. Type **495**..	45	85
	a. Block of 4. Nos. 1746/9....................	1·60	4·00
	b. Perf 12 (3.11).....................................	1·40	1·60
	ba. Booklet pane. Nos. 1746b/7a, each×3, and 1748a/9a, each×2.......................	12·00	
1747	45c. Christmas decorations (value at right)....	45	85
	a. Perf 12 (3.11).....................................	1·40	1·60
1748	45c. Sailboards, gifts and Christmas pudding (value at left).........................	45	85
	a. Perf 12 (3.11).....................................	1·40	1·60
1749	45c. Sailboards, gifts and Christmas pudding (value at right).......................	45	85
	a. Perf 12 (3.11).....................................	1·40	1·60
1750	$1 Sailboards, baubles and Christmas cracker..	75	1·00
1751	$1.50 Sailboards, present and wreath...............	1·25	3·00
1746/51 *Set of 6*		3·50	6·75

Nos. 1746/9 were printed together, *se-tenant*, in blocks of four throughout the sheet.
Booklet pane No. 1746ba contains two *se-tenant* blocks of four and a horizontal pair.

(Des R. Youmans. Litho Southern Colour Print, Dunedin)

1993 (1 Sept). Marine Life. T **496** and similar horiz designs. Multicoloured. P 13½.

1752	45c. Type **498**..	1·25	1·25
	a. Booklet pane. Nos. 1752/61 and two stamp-size labels..................................	11·00	11·00
1753	45c. Green Mussels	1·25	1·25
1754	45c. Tarakihi	1·25	1·25
1755	45c. Salmon	1·25	1·25
1756	45c. Southern Blue-finned Tuna, Yellow finned Tuna and Kahawai	1·25	1·25
1757	45c. Rock Lobster.....................................	1·25	1·25
1758	45c. Snapper..	1·25	1·25
1759	45c. Grouper..	1·25	1·25
1760	45c. Orange Roughy................................	1·25	1·25
1761	45c. Squid, Hoki and Black Oreo..............	1·25	1·25
1752/61 *Set of 10*..		11·00	11·00

Nos. 1752/61 were only issued in $4.50 stamp booklets with the *se-tenant* pane, which includes two inscribed labels at left, forming a composite design.

497 Sauropod

498 Soldiers, National Flag and Pyramids

(Des G. Cox. Litho Southern Colour Print, Dunedin)

1993 (1 Oct). Prehistoric Animals. T **497** and similar multicoloured designs.

(a) P 14

1762	45c. Type **497**..	50	15
1763	80c. Pterosaur	75	85
1764	$1 Ankylosaur	80	95
1765	$1.20 Mauisaurus	1·10	2·50
1766	$1.50 Carnosaur	1·25	2·50
1762/6 *Set of 5*..		4·00	6·25
MS1768 125×100 mm. $1.50, As No. 1766. P 14½×14...		2·00	2·00

*(b) Smaller Design,*30×25 *mm.* P 12

1767	45c. Carnosaur and Sauropod	75	90
	a. Booklet pane of 10 and two labels	6·50	

No. 1767 was only issued in $4.50 stamp booklets, SB66.
A used example of No. 1762 is known with the yellow omitted.

(Des A. Hollows (No. **MS**1770). Litho Southern Colour Print, Dunedin)

1993 (1 Oct). Bangkok '93 International Stamp Exhibition, Thailand.

(a) No. **MS**1768 *optd* "BANGKOK '93" *and emblem on sheet margin*
MS1769 $1.50 As No. 1767... 1·60   2·00

(b) Sheet 115×100 mm, containing No. 1735
MS1770 $1.80 multicoloured.. 2·25   3·25

(Des P. Andrews. Litho Questa)

1993 (3 Nov). New Zealand in the 1940s. T **498** and similar vert designs. Multicoloured. P 14.

1771	45c. Type **498**..	80	25
1772	50c. Aerial crop spraying	85	60
1773	80c. Hydro-electric scheme	1·10	80
1774	$1 Marching majorettes	1·40	90
1775	$1.50 American troops	1·90	2·75
1776	$1.80 Crowd celebrating victory	2·00	2·75
1771/6 *Set of 6*..		7·25	7·25

499 Bungy Jumping

(Des G. Taylor. Litho Southern Colour Print, Dunedin)

1994 (19 Jan). Tourism. T **499** and similar multicoloured designs. P 12.

(a) As T **499**

1777	45c. Type **499**..	30	10
1778	80c. Trout fishing....................................	50	70
1779	$1 Jet boating *(horiz)*..........................	60	80
1780	$1.50 Tramping	1·00	2·00
1781	$1.80 Heli-skiing	1·25	2·00
1777/81 *Set of 5*...		3·25	5·00

(b) Smaller design, 25×25 mm.

1782	45c. White water rafting	40	55
	a. Booklet pane of 10 plus 4 half stamp-size greetings labels.................................	4·00	5·00

No. 1782 was only issued in $4.50 stamp booklets, SB68.
For miniature sheet containing the $1.80 see No. **MS**1785.

500 *New Zealand Endeavour* (yacht)

(Des B. Hall. Litho Leigh-Mardon Ltd, Melbourne)

1994 (19 Jan). Round the World Yacht Race. P 14½ (and 13 around design).

1783	**500**	$1 multicoloured......................................	1·00	1·75

No. 1783 was printed in sheets of 24 (6×4) with each stamp within a square perforated margin and with a further circular perforation around the design.

501 Mt Cook and New Zealand Symbols

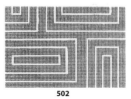

502

(Des Heather Arnold. Engraved C. Slania. Recess and die-stamped (gold) Leigh-Mardon Ltd, Melbourne)

1994 (18 Feb). W **502**. Phosphorised paper. P 14½×15.
1784 **501** $20 deep violet-blue and gold............... 13·00 16·00
No. 1784 shows a fluorescent security pattern of "New Zealand Post" printed beneath the design.

(Des G. Taylor (No. **MS**1785), Karen Odiam (No. **MS**1786). Litho Southern Colour Print, Dunedin (No. **MS**1785) or Leigh-Mardon Ltd, Melbourne (No. **MS**1786))

1994 (18 Feb). Hong Kong '94 International Stamp Exhibition. P 12 (No. **MS**1785) or 13 (No. **MS**1786).
MS1785 95×115 mm. $1.80, mult (No. 1781).................... 3·50 3·50
MS1786 100×125 mm. $1 deep green, $1 rosine, $1 blue (As Nos. 1490/c, but all printed litho)............................. 5·00 6·00

503 Rock and Roll Dancers

504 Mt Cook and Mt Cook Lily ("Winter")

(Des Karen Odiam. Litho Leigh-Mardon Ltd, Melbourne)

1994 (23 Mar). New Zealand in the 1950s. T **503** and similar vert designs. Multicoloured. P 14½×14.
1787 45c. Type **503**... 35 10
1788 80c. Sir Edmund Hillary on Mt Everest........... 75 55
1789 $1 Aunt Daisy (radio personality)................. 65 65
1790 $1.20 Queen Elizabeth II during 1953 royal visit .... 1·25 1·25
1791 $1.50 Children playing with Opo the dolphin . 1·25 1·75
1792 $1.80 Auckland Harbour Bridge .... 1·40 1·75
1787/92 *Set of 6* .... 5·00 5·50

(Des R. Youmans. Litho Southern Colour Print, Dunedin)

1994 (27 Apr). The Four Seasons. T **504** and similar horiz designs. Multicoloured. P 12.
1793 45c. Type **504**... 30 10
      a. Horiz strip of 4. Nos. 1793/6........... 2·75 4·25
1794 70c. Lake Hawea and Kowhai ("Spring")......... 45 45
1795 $1.50 Opononi Beach and Pohutukawa ("Summer") .... 80 1·00
1796 $1.80 Lake Pukaki and Puriri ("Autumn") .... 1·10 1·25
1793/6 *Set of 4* .... 2·40 2·50
In addition to separate sheets of 100 (10×10) Nos. 1793/6 were also printed together, *se-tenant*, in horizontal strips of four throughout sheets of 80 (8×10).

505 Rainbow Abalone or Paua Shell

506 Maui pulls up Te Ika

(Des D. Gunson. Litho Southern Colour Print, Dunedin)

1994 (27 Apr). New Zealand Life (1st series). T **505** and similar multicoloured designs. P 12.
1797 45c. Type **505** (25×20 mm)......................... 30 45
      a. Booklet pane. Nos. 1797/1806.......... 2·75 4·00
1798 45c. Pavlova dessert (35×20 mm)................... 30 45
1799 45c. Hokey pokey ice cream (25×20 mm)....... 30 45
1800 45c. Fish and chips (35×20 mm).................... 30 45
1801 45c. Jandals (30×20 mm)............................. 30 45
1802 45c. Bush shirt (25×30½ mm)....................... 30 45
1803 45c. Buzzy Bee (toy) (35×30½ mm)................ 30 45
1804 45c. Gumboots and black singlet (25×30½ mm)... 30 45
1805 45c. Rugby boots and ball (35×30½ mm)....... 30 45
1806 45c. Kiwifruit (30×30½ mm) 30 45
1797/1806 *Set of 10* .... 2·75 4·00
Nos. 1797/1806 were only issued in $4.50 stamp booklets, SB69.
See also Nos. 2318/27.

(Des Manu Kopere Society. Litho Leigh-Mardon Ltd, Melbourne)

1994 (8 June). Maori Myths. T **506** and similar vert designs. Multicoloured. P 13.
1807 45c. Type **506**... 25 10
1808 80c. Rona snatched up by Marama................. 40 40
1809 $1 Maui attacking Tuna............................... 45 50
1810 $1.20 Tane separating Rangi and Papa........... 60 1·50
1811 $1.50 Matakauri slaying the Giant of Wakatipu... 70 1·50
1812 $1.80 Panenehu showing crayfish to Tangaroa... 80 1·50
1807/12 *Set of 6* .... 3·00 5·00

507 1939 2d. on 1d.+1d. Health Stamp and Children playing with Ball

(Des D. Gunson. Litho Leigh-Mardon Ltd, Melbourne)

1994 (20 July). Health Stamps. 75th Anniv of Children's Health Camps. T **507** and similar vert designs. Multicoloured. P 14½.
1813 45c.+5c. Type **507**..................................... 40 80
1814 45c.+5c. 1949 1d.+½d. stamp and nurse holding child....................................... 40 80
1815 45c.+5c. 1969 4c.+1c. stamp and children reading... 40 80
1816 80c.+5c. 1931 2d.+1d. stamp and child in cap.... 60 1·00
1813/16 *Set of 4* .... 1·60 3·00
MS1817 130×90 mm. Nos. 1813/16........................... 1·60 3·25

508 Astronaut on Moon (hologram)

(Des Brand New Ltd, Wellington. Litho Southern Colour Print, Dunedin (hologram by Woodmansterne. Ltd, Watford))

1994 (20 July). 25th Anniv of First Moon Landing. P 12.
1818 **508** $1.50 multicoloured............................. 2·25 2·75

509 "people reaching people"

510 African Elephants

Two types of Type **509**:

Type I: "w" of "new" partly in blue. "i" of "reaching" without dot.
Type II: "w" of "new" all in magenta. "i" of "reaching" with dot.

(Des Van de Roer Designs. Litho Leigh-Mardon Ltd, Melbourne (Nos. 1818a, 1819) or SNP Cambec (Nos. 1818ab, 1819a))

1994 (20 July)–**95**. Self-adhesive. Phosphorised paper (Nos. 1818ab, 1819a). P 11.

1818a	**509**	40c. multicoloured (I) (2.10.95)	1·50	1·50
		ab. Perf 11½. Type II (11.95)	75	55
1819		45c. multicoloured (I)	1·00	65
		a. Perf 11½. Type II (8.95)	1·50	1·25

Nos. 1818a/19a were each available in coils of 100. On Nos. 1818a and 1819 the vertical die-cut perforations interlock, but on Nos. 1818ab and 1819a the stamps are separate on the backing paper.

(Des Denise Durkin. Litho Leigh-Mardon Ltd, Melbourne)

1994 (16 Aug). Stamp Month. Wild Animals. T **510** and similar horiz designs. Multicoloured. P 14×14½.

1820	45c. Type **510**	90	1·10
	a. Block of 10. Nos. 1820/9	8·00	10·00
1821	45c. White Rhinoceros	90	1·10
1822	45c. Lions	90	1·10
1823	45c. Common Zebras	90	1·10
1824	45c. Giraffe and calf	90	1·10
1825	45c. Siberian Tiger	90	1·10
1826	45c. Hippopotami	90	1·10
1827	45c. Spider Monkey	90	1·10
1828	45c. Giant Panda	90	1·10
1829	45c. Polar Bear and cub	90	1·10
1820/9 Set of 10		8·00	10·00

Nos. 1820/9 were printed together, se-tenant, in sheets of 100 so arranged as to provide horizontal or vertical strips of ten or blocks of ten (5×2) showing all the designs.

(Des Pauline Morse (No. **MS**1830), Denise Durkin (No. **MS**1831). Litho Leigh-Mardon Ltd, Melbourne)

1994 (16 Aug). Philakorea '94 International Stamp Exhibition, Seoul. Multicoloured. P 14½×14 (No. **MS**1830) or 14×14½ (No. **MS**1831).

MS1830 125×100 mm. Nos. 1459a/65	6·50	6·00
MS1831 125×100 mm. Nos. 1820, 1822, 1824/5 and 1828/9	3·25	4·50

511 Children with Crib

512 Batsman

(Des Karen Odiam. Litho Southern Colour Print, Dunedin (No. 1832) or Leigh-Mardon Ltd, Melbourne (others))

1994 (21 Sept). Christmas. T **511** and similar horiz designs. Multicoloured. P 12 (No. 1832) or 14½ (others).

1832	45c. Father Christmas and children (30×25 mm)	40	40
1833	45c. Type **511**	30	10
1834	70c. Men and toddler with crib	40	60
1835	80c. Three carol singers	45	65
1836	$1 Five carol singers	50	65
1837	$1.50 Children and candles	75	2·25
1838	$1.80 Parents with child	90	1·75
1832/8 Set of 7		3·25	5·75
MS1839 125×100 mm. Nos. 1833/6		2·00	2·75

No. 1832 was only issued in $4.50 stamp booklets, SB70.

(Des M. Bailey (Nos. 1840/9), P. Andrews (others). Litho Southern Colour Print, Dunedin)

1994 (2 Nov). Centenary of New Zealand Cricket Council.

(a) Horiz designs, each 30×25 mm. Multicoloured. P 12

1840	45c. Bathers catching balls	75	90
	a. Booklet pane of 10. Nos. 1840/9	6·50	8·00
1841	45c. Child on surf board at top	75	90
1842	45c. Young child with rubber ring at top	75	90
1843	45c. Man with beach ball at top	75	90
1844	45c. Woman with cricket bat at right	75	90
1845	45c. Boy in green cap with bat	75	90
1846	45c. Man in spotted shirt running	75	90
1847	45c. Woman in striped shorts with bat	75	90
1848	45c. Boy in wct suit with surf board at right	75	90
1849	45c. Sunbather with newspaper at right	75	90

*(b) T **512** and similar vert designs. Multicoloured.* P 13½

1850	45c. Type **512**	85	40
1851	80c. Bowler	1·50	1·00
1852	$1 Wicket keeper	1·75	1·00
1853	$1.80 Fielder	2·75	3·00
1840/53 Set of 14		13·00	13·00

Nos. 1840/9 were only issued in $4.50 stamp booklets, SB71.

(Litho Leigh-Mardon Ltd, Melbourne)

1995 (3 Feb). "POST X '95" Postal History Exhibition, Auckland. Sheet 130×90 mm, containing No. 1297 and a reproduction of No. 557 optd "SPECIMEN". P 14½.

MS1854 $10 multicoloured	18·00	19·00

513 Auckland

514 The 15th Hole, Waitangi

(Des Red Cactus Design. Litho Southern Colour Print, Dunedin)

1995 (22 Feb). New Zealand by Night. T **513** and similar horiz designs. Multicoloured. P 12.

1855	45c. Type **513**	35	10
1856	80c. Wellington	60	45
1857	$1 Christchurch	70	65
1858	$1.20 Dunedin	80	1·50
1859	$1.50 Rotorua	90	1·90
1860	$1.80 Queenstown	1·10	1·90
1855/60 Set of 6		4·00	5·75

See also No. **MS**1915.

(Des R. Jones. Litho Leigh-Mardon Ltd, Melbourne)

1995 (22 Mar). New Zealand Golf Courses. T **514** and similar vert designs. Multicoloured. P 14½×14.

1861	45c. Type **514**	65	30
1862	80c. The 6th hole, New Plymouth	1·00	90
1863	$1.20 The 9th hole, Rotorua	1·50	2·50
1864	$1.80 The 5th hole, Queenstown	2·40	3·00
1861/4 Set of 4		5·00	6·00

515 New Zealand Pigeon and Nest

516 Teacher with Guitar and Children

(Des Niki Hill. Litho Southern Colour Print, Dunedin)

1995 (22 Mar). Environment. T **515** and similar horiz designs. Multicoloured. P 12.

1865	45c. Type **515**	65	65
	a. Booklet pane. Nos. 1865/74	6·00	6·00
1866	45c. Planting sapling	65	65
1867	45c. Dolphins and Whales	65	65
1868	45c. Thunderstorm	65	65
1869	45c. Backpackers	65	65
1870	45c. Animal pests	65	65
1871	45c. Noxious plants	65	65
1872	45c. Undersized fish and shellfish	65	65
1873	45c. Pollution from factories	65	65
1874	45c. Family at picnic site	65	65
1865/74 Set of 10		6·00	6·00

Nos. 1865/74 were only issued in $4.50 stamp booklets, SB72, with the vertical edges of the pane imperforate. Each vertical pair forms a composite design.

(Des M. Kopere. Litho Southern Colour Print, Dunedin)

1995 (3 May). Maori Language Year. T **516** and similar vert designs. Multicoloured. P 13½.

1875	45c. Type **516**	25	10
1876	70c. Singing group	40	55
1877	80c. Mother and baby	45	60
1878	$1 Women performing traditional welcome	55	75
1879	$1.50 Grandfather reciting family genealogy ..	80	2·00
1880	$1.80 Tribal orator	90	2·00
1875/80 *Set of 6*		3·00	5·50

In addition to sheets containing stamps of one value Nos. 1875/80 also exist in sheetlets of 24 containing four of each value *se-tenant*. These sheetlets were only available from Limited Edition Collectors Packs costing NZ$135.

517 Map of Australasia and Asia   **518** *Black Magic* (yacht)

(Des Cue Design. Litho Southern Colour Print, Dunedin)

1995 (3 May). Meetings of Asian Development Bank Board of Governors and International Pacific Basin Economic Council, Auckland. T **517** and similar horiz design. Multicoloured. P 13½.

1881	$1 Type **517**	1·00	1·00
1882	$1.50 Map of Australasia and Pacific	1·50	2·75

(Des A. Hollows. Litho Southern Colour Print, Dunedin)

1995 (16 May). New Zealand's Victory in 1995 America's Cup. P 12.

1883	**518**	45c. multicoloured	55	55

No. 1883 was issued in small sheets of ten with a seascape printed on the margins. This sheetlet also exists numbered and overprinted in gold foil from a Limited Edition Collectors Pack costing NZ$25.

519 Boy on Skateboard   **520** Lion Red Cup and Players

(Des P. Martinson. Litho Leigh-Mardon Ltd, Melbourne)

1995 (21 June). Health Stamps. Children's Sports. T **519** and similar triangular design. Multicoloured. P 14½.

1884	45c. +5c. Type **519**	75	1·50
	a. *Tête-bêche* (pair)	1·50	3·00
1885	80c. +5c. Girl on bicycle	1·75	2·00
	a. *Tête-bêche* (pair)	3·50	4·00
MS1886 130×90 mm. Nos. 1884/5, each×2		5·00	6·50

Nos. 1884/5 were each printed in sheets with the horizontal rows made up of *tête-bêche* pairs.

1995 (1 July). "Stampex '95" National Stamp Exhibition, Wellington. No. **MS**1886 additionally inscr with "Stampex '95" and emblem on sheet margin.

MS1887 130×90 mm. Nos. 1884/5, each×2		6·00	7·00

(Des Heather Arnold. Litho Southern Colour Print, Dunedin (No. 1888) or Schédé (others))

1995 (26 July). Centenary of Rugby League. T **520** and similar horiz designs. Multicoloured.

(a) As T **520**. P 14×14½

1888	45c. Type **520**	35	10
1889	$1 Children's rugby and mascot	60	1·10
1890	$1.50 George Smith, Albert Baskerville and early match	1·10	2·50
1891	$1.80 Courtney Goodwill Trophy and match against Great Britain	1·25	2·25
1888/91 *Set of 4*		3·00	5·50
MS1893 125×100 mm. No. 1892		2·00	2·50

(b) Smaller design, 30×25 mm. P 12.

1892	45c. Trans Tasman test match	50	60
	a. Booklet pane. No. 1892×10	5·00	5·50

No. 1892 was only issued in $4.50 stamp booklets, SB73, and has the vertical edges of the pane imperforate.

No. **MS**1893 imperforate comes from a Limited Edition Collectors Pack costing NZ$135.

521 Sheep and Lamb   **522** Archangel Gabriel

(Des Joanne Kreyl. Litho Southern Colour Print, Dunedin)

1995 (1 Sept–2 Oct). Farmyard Animals. T **521** and similar horiz designs. P 14×14½.

1894	40c. Type **521** (2.10)	75	75
	a. Booklet pane. Nos. 1894/1903	7·00	7·00
1895	40c. Deer (2.10)	75	75
1896	40c. Mare and foal (2.10)	75	75
1897	40c. Cow with calf (2.10)	75	75
1898	40c. Goats and kid (2.10)	75	75
1899	40c. Common Turkey (2.10)	75	75
1900	40c. Ducks (2.10)	75	75
1901	40c. Red Junglefowl (2.10)	75	75
1902	40c. Sow with piglets (2.10)	75	75
1903	40c. Border Collie (2.10)	75	75
1904	45c. Type **521**	75	75
	a. Booklet pane. Nos. 1904/13	7·00	7·00
1905	45c. As No. 1895	75	75
1906	45c. As No. 1896	75	75
1907	45c. As No. 1897	75	75
1908	45c. As No. 1898	75	75
1909	45c. As No. 1899	75	75
1910	45c. As No. 1900	75	75
1911	45c. As No. 1901	75	75
1912	45c. As No. 1902	75	75
1913	45c. As No. 1903	75	75
1894/1913 *Set of 20*		14·00	14·00

Nos. 1894/1903 and 1904/13 were each only issued in $4 (Nos. 1894/1903) and $4.50 (Nos. 1904/13) stamp booklets in which the horizontal edges of the booklet panes are imperforate, SB75 and SB76.

(Des Joanne Kreyl (No. **MS**1914), Red Cactus Design (No. **MS**1915). Litho Southern Colour Print, Dunedin)

1995 (1 Sept). "Singapore '95" International Stamp Exhibition. P 12.

MS1914 170×70 mm. Nos. 1909/13		3·25	4·00
MS1915 148×210 mm. Nos. 1855/60		11·00	16·00

No. **MS**1915 also includes the "JAKARTA '95" logo.

(Des K. Hall. Litho Southern Colour Print, Dunedin)

1995 (1 Sept–9 Nov). Christmas. Stained Glass Windows from St. Mary's Anglican Church, Merivale (Nos. 1916/18), The Lady Chapel of St. Luke's Anglican Church, Christchurch (Nos. 1919/22) or St. John the Evangelist Church, Cheviot (No. 1923). Multicoloured. P 12.

(a) As T **522**

1916	40c. Type **522** (2.10)	70	25
1917	45c. Type **522**	70	25
1918	70c. Virgin Mary	1·00	90
1919	80c. Shepherds	1·10	1·10
1920	$1 Virgin and Child	1·40	1·10
1921	$1.50 Two Wise Men	2·25	2·75
1922	$1.80 Wise Man kneeling	2·50	2·75
1916/22 *Set of 7*		8·50	8·00

(b) Smaller design, 25×30 mm. P 14½×14

1923	40c. Angel with Trumpet (9.11)	50	50
	a. Booklet pane. No. 1923×10	5·00	

No. 1923 was only issued in $4 stamp booklets which show the outer edges of the pane imperforate, SB77.

Nos. 1916 and 1918/22 also exist as a miniature sheet, only available as part of a joint Phone Card and Stamp Collectors Pack produced in a limited quantity and costing NZ$115.

A used imperf pair of No. 1923 has been reported.

523 Face and Nuclear   **524** Mount Cook
Disarmament Symbol

(Des C. Martin. Litho Southern Colour Print, Dunedin)

1995 (1 Sept). Nuclear Disarmament. P 13½.

1924	**523**	$1 multicoloured	1·00	1·25

(Des Comm Arts Design (90c.), S. Fuller ($1.30, $2), Red Cactus Design (others). Litho Enschedé ($10) or Southern Colour Print, Dunedin (others))

1995 (2 Oct)–**2002**. New Zealand Scenery. T **524** and similar multicoloured designs. Ordinary or phosphorised paper (5c., $2), phosphorised paper (others). P 13½×14 ($10) or 13½ (others).

1925	5c. Type **524** (27.3.96)	10	50
1926	10c. Champagne Pool (27.3.96)	10	20
1927	20c. Cape Reinga (27.3.96)	15	50
1928	30c. Mackenzie Country (27.3.96)	20	25
1929	40c. Mitre Peak (*vert*)	30	35
	a. Yellow foliage frame and pink clouds (5.02)	1·00	35
	b. Olive-brown foliage frame..........................	1·00	35
1930	50c. Mount Ngauruhoe (27.3.96)......................	35	40
1931	60c. Lake Wanaka (*vert*) (27.3.96)	45	50
1932	70c. Giant Kauri tree (*vert*) (27.3.96)	50	55
1933	80c. Doubtful Sound (*vert*) (27.3.96)	60	65
1934	90c. Waitomo Limestone Cave (*vert*) (27.3.96)...	65	70
1934*a*	90c. Rangitoto Island (27×22 *mm*) (11.10.00)	3·50	70
1934*b*	$1 Taiaroa Head (27×22 *mm*) (6.3.00)...........	1·00	80
1934*c*	$1.10 Kaikoura Coast (27×22 *mm*) (6.3.00).....	1·00	85
1934*d*	$1.30 Lake Camp, South Canterbury (27×22 *mm*) (11.10.00)..	5·50	2·50
1934*e*	$2 Great Barrier Island (27×22 *mm*) (6.3.00)..	1·50	1·60
1934*f*	$3 Cape Kidnappers (27×22 *mm*) (6.3.00) ...	2·25	2·40
1935	$10 Mt Ruapehu (38×32 *mm*) (12.2.97)...........	6·50	7·75
1925/35 Set of 17..		22·00	19·00

No. 1929*a* is from the two kiwi printing. On No. 1929 the foliage frame is predominantly green and the clouds white.

For miniature sheets containing some of these designs see Nos. **MS**1978, **MS**1998, **MS**2005, **MS**2328 and **MS**2401.

For similar self-adhesive designs see Nos. 1983*a*/91*b*.

525 Dame Kiri te Kanawa (opera singer) **526** National Flags, Peace Dove and "50"

(Des Karen Odium. Litho Southern Colour Print, Dunedin)

1995 (4 Oct). Famous New Zealanders. T **525** and similar horiz designs. Multicoloured. P 12.

1936	40c. Type **525**...	1·00	50
1937	80c. Charles Upham, V.C. (war hero)	1·00	1·25
1938	$1 Barry Crump (author)...................................	1·25	1·00
1939	$1.20 Sir Brian Barratt-Boyes (surgeon)	1·75	1·75
1940	$1.50 Dame Whina Cooper (Maori leader)	1·75	2·25
1941	$1.80 Sir Richard Hadlee (cricketer)	3·00	2·25
1936/41 Set of 6..		8·75	8·00

Nos. 1936/41 were issued in sheets with each stamp *se-tenant* horizontally with a 10×30 mm label inscribed "STAMP MONTH October 1995".

(Des S. Fuller. Litho Leigh-Mardon Ltd, Melbourne)

1995 (4 Oct). 50th Anniv of United Nations. P 15.

1942	**526**	$1.80 multicoloured.......................................	2·25	3·00

527 Fern and Globe

(Des Red Cactus Design. Litho Leigh-Mardon Ltd, Melbourne)

1995 (9 Nov). Commonwealth Heads of Government Meeting, Auckland. T **527** and similar horiz design. Multicoloured. P 14.

1943	40c. Type **527**...	50	25
1944	$1.80 Fern and New Zealand flag	2·50	3·00

528 "Kiwi" **529** Kete (basket)

(Des Communication Arts Ltd. Litho Enschedé)

1996 (24 Jan). Famous Racehorses. T **528** and similar horiz designs. Multicoloured. P 14×14½.

1945	40c. Type **528**...	55	10
1946	80c. "Rough Habit"...	85	55
1947	$1 "Blossom Lady"..	1·00	65
1948	$1.20 "Il Vicolo"...	1·40	1·60
1949	$1.50 "Horlicks"..	1·50	2·00
1950	$1.80 "Bonecrusher".......................................	2·00	2·50
1945/50 Set of 6...		6·50	6·75

MS1951 Seven sheets, each 162×110 mm. (a) No. 1945. (b) No. 1946. (c) No. 1947. (d) No. 1948. (e) No. 1949. (f) No. 1950. (g) Nos. 1945/50.................*Set of 7 sheets* ... 16·00 ... 19·00

Nos. **MS**1951*a*/*g* were only available from $13.70 stamp booklets, with each miniature sheet showing a line of roulettes at left, SB78.

An overprinted and numbered miniature sheet containing Nos. 1945/50 comes from a Limited Edition Collectors Pack costing NZ$135.

(Des G. Hubbard. Litho Enschedé)

1996 (21 Feb). Maori Crafts. T **529** and similar vert designs. Multicoloured. P 14×13½.

1952	40c. Type **529**...	20	10
1953	80c. Head of Taiaha (spear)...............................	40	40
1954	$1 Taniko (embroidery)...................................	50	50
1955	$1.20 Pounamu (greenstone)	60	1·00
1956	$1.50 Hue (gourd)...	65	1·50
1957	$1.80 Korowai (feather cloak)	80	1·50
1952/7 Set of 6...		2·75	4·50

For miniature sheet containing some of these designs see No **MS**2049.

530 Black-backed Gulls **531** Fire and Ambulance Services

(Des Sue Wickison)

1996 (21 Feb–7 Aug). Seaside Environment. T **530** and similar horiz designs. Multicoloured.

(a) Litho Southern Colour Print, Dunedin. P 14×14½

1958	40c. Type **530**...	70	80
	a. Booklet pane of 10. Nos. 1958/67............	6·25	7·00
1959	40c. Children, Sea Cucumber and Spiny Starfish	70	80
1960	40c. Yacht, gull and Common Shrimps............	70	80
1961	40c. Gaudy Nudibranch	70	80
1962	40c. Large Rock Crab and Clingfish..................	70	80
1963	40c. Snake Skin Chiton and Red Rock Crab ...	70	80
1964	40c. Estuarine Triplefin and Cat's-eye shell......	70	80
1965	40c. Cushion Star and Sea Horses....................	70	80
1966	40c. Blue-eyed Triplefin and Yaldwyn's Triplefin	70	80
1967	40c. Common Octopus	70	80
1958/67 Set of 10...		6·25	7·00

Nos. 1958/67 were only issued in $4 stamp booklets in which the horizontal edges of the pane are imperforate.

(b) Litho SNP Cambec, Australia. Self-adhesive. Phosphor frame. P 11½ (7 Aug)

1968	40c. Type **530**...	55	60
	a. Booklet pane of 10. Nos. 1968/77............	5·00	5·50
1969	40c. Children, Sea Cucumber and Spiny Starfish	55	60
1970	40c. Yacht, gull and Common Shrimps............	55	60
1971	40c. Gaudy Nudibranch	55	60

1972	40c. Large Rock Crab and Clingfish.....................	55	60
1973	40c. Snake Skin Chiton and Red Rock Crab ...	55	60
1974	40c. Estuarine Triplefin and Cat's-eye shell.....	55	60
1975	40c. Cushion Star and Sea Horses	55	60
1976	40c. Blue-eyed Triplefin and Yaldwyn's Triplefin	55	60
1977	40c. Common Octopus	55	60
1968/77	*Set of 10*..	5·00	5·50

Nos. 1968/77 were only issued in $4 self-adhesive stamp booklets, containing No. 1968a on which the surplus self-adhesive paper around each stamp was retained, SB80.

The phosphor, which shows pink under U.V. light, forms an irregular frame on two sides of each design.

(Litho Southern Colour Print, Dunedin)

1996 (15 Mar). "SOUTHPEX '96" Stamp Show, Invercargill. Sheet 100×215 mm, containing No. 1929×10. P 12.

MS1978	40c.×10 multicoloured..	6·50	7·50

(Des Dave Clark Design Associates. Litho Southern Colour Print, Dunedin)

1996 (27 Mar). Rescue Services. T **531** and similar vert designs. Multicoloured. P 14½×15.

1979	40c. Type **531**	50	20
1980	80c. Civil Defence	90	90
1981	$1 Air-sea rescue	1·10	1·10
1982	$1.50 Air ambulance and rescue helicopter	1·60	2·75
	a. Yellow value and background.........................		
1983	$1.80 Mountain rescue and Red Cross..............	2·25	2·50
1979/83	*Set of 5*	5·75	6·75

No. 1982a shows the value and background in yellow instead of green.

532 Mt Egmont, Taranaki   **533** Yellow-eyed Penguin

(Des Comm Arts Design (90c.), S. Fuller ($1.10) or Red Cactus Design (others). Litho Southern Colour Print, Dunedin (Nos. 1983a, 1984b/9, 1990b and 1991b) or SNP Cambec, Australia (others))

1996 (1 May)–2004. New Zealand Scenery. Self-adhesive. T **532** and similar multicoloured designs. Phosphor frame. P 10 (10c., 90c., $1.10) or 11½ (others).

1983a	10c. Champagne Pool (28.1.04)	1·00	1·25
	ab. Booklet pane. Nos. 1983a×4 and 1986b×10...	6·00	
1984	40c. Type **532**..	55	55
	a. Sheetlet of 10. Nos. 1984/9 (one each of two designs and two each of the remainder)	20·00	
	b. Perf 10 (14.1.98)..	35	40
	ba. Booklet pane. Nos. 1984b×2, 1985b, 1986b×2, 1987b and 1988b/9b, each×2	3·25	
	bab. Booklet pane. Printed on the backing paper...	60·00	
	bb. On phosphorised paper (4.2000)...............	1·00	1·50
1985	40c. Piercy Island, Bay of Islands......................	55	55
	b. Perf 10 (14.1.98)..	75	1·00
	bb. On phosphorised paper (4.2000)...............	1·00	1·50
1986	40c. Tory Channel, Marlborough Sounds.......	55	55
	b. Perf 10 (14.1.98)..	35	40
	ba. "Marlborough Sounds" inscr omitted.......	40·00	
	bb. On phosphorised paper (4.2000)...............	1·00	1·50
1987	40c. *Earnslaw* (ferry), Lake Wakatipu.............	55	55
	b. Perf 10 (14.1.98)..	75	1·00
	bb. On phosphorised paper (4.2000)...............	1·00	1·50
1988	40c. Lake Matheson..	55	55
	b. Perf 10 (14.1.98)..	35	40
	bb. On phosphorised paper (4.2000)...............	1·00	1·50
1989	40c. Fox Glacier..	55	55
	b. Perf 10 (14.1.98)..	35	40
	bb. On phosphorised paper (4.2000)...............	1·00	1·50
1990	80c. Doubtful Sound (as No. 1933) (*vert*) (13.11.96)..	90	90
	a. Booklet pane. No. 1990b×10........................	8·00	
1990b	90c. Rangitoto Island (5.4.04).........................	90	1·00
	ba. Booklet pane. No. 1990b×10......................	8·00	
1991	$1 Pohutukawa tree (33×22 *mm*) (7.8.96) ...	1·00	1·00
	a. Booklet pane. No. 1991b×5.........................	4·50	
1991b	$1.10 Kaikoura Coast (3.4.2000).......................	1·00	1·50
	ba. Booklet pane. No. 1991b×5 plus 5 airmail labels..	4·50	
1983a/91b	*Set of 11*..	6·50	7·50

The phosphor, which shows pink under U.V. light, appears as an irregular frame on the initial printing of Nos. 1984/9, but further supplies released in November 1997 showed a regular phosphor frame as do Nos. 1983a, 1984b/9b and 1990/1b.

Nos. 1984/9 and 1984bb/9bb occur in rolls of 100, with the surplus self-adhesive paper around each stamp removed.

No. 1984a comes from the residue of special sheet stock used to prepare first day covers and subsequently sold as $4 "hang-sell" sheetlets.

Nos. 1984b/9b come from $4 stamp booklets, containing No. 1984ba, on which the surplus self-adhesive paper was retained, SB89.

No. 1984bab occurred when the self-adhesive paper "sandwich" became reversed so that the designs were printed on what should have been the back of the booklet. This results in the gum being attached to the backing paper instead of the stamps. Normal versions of the booklet show the paper around the stamps, outside the phosphor frames, as white with a strong fluorescent content. On the error this paper is off-white and non-fluorescent.

No. 1986ba occurs on one of the examples of this design in 2% of the original printing of booklet pane No. 1984ba.

Nos. 1983a, 1990 and 1991/b all come from separate stamp booklets on which the surplus self-adhesive paper around each stamp was retained.

No. 1990b was issued in sheets of 50 and in $4.50 booklets, both with the surplus paper retained.

(Des Sea Sky Design. Litho Southern Colour Print, Dunedin)

1996 (1 May). Marine Wildlife. T **533** and similar multicoloured designs. P 14.

1992	40c. Type **533**..	35	25
	a. Block of 6. Nos. 1992/7..............................	3·75	6·25
1993	80c. Royal Albatross (*horiz*)	70	60
1994	$1 White Herons (*horiz*)	75	70
1995	$1.20 Flukes of Sperm Whale (*horiz*)	75	1·25
1996	$1.50 Fur Seals...	80	1·50
1997	$1.80 Bottlenose Dolphin	90	1·50
1992/7	*Set of 6*...	3·75	5·25

In addition to separate sheets of 100 Nos. 1992/7 were also issued in *se-tenant* blocks of six which also contained two irregular-shaped labels. For miniature sheets containing these designs see Nos. **MS**1999 and **MS**2037.

(Des Diane Prosser (No. **MS**1998), Sea Sky Design (No. **MS**1999). Litho Southern Colour Print, Dunedin)

1996 (18 May). CHINA '96 Ninth International Stamp Exhibition, Peking. Multicoloured. P 13½ (No. **MS**1998) or 14 (No. **MS**1999).

MS1998	180×80 mm. Nos. 1926/8 and 1930................	1·50	2·00
MS1999	140×90 mm. Nos. 1994 and 1996...................	2·25	3·00
	a. $1.50 value imperf at foot..........................		

No. **MS**1999 also shows designs as Nos. 1992/3, 1995 and 1997, but without face values.

NEW ZEALAND

534 Baby in Car Seat

(Des Helen Casey)

1996 (5 June). Health Stamps. Child Safety. T **534** and similar vert design. Multicoloured.

(a) Litho Southern Colour Print, Dunedin (No. 2000), Enschedé (Nos. 2000a, 2001) or SNP Cambec (No. MS2002). P 13½

2000	40c. +5c. Type **534**.......................................	40	75
	a. As Type **534**, but teddy bear at top right and face value at bottom left...............	£800	£900
2001	80c. +5c. Child and adult on zebra crossing..	60	1·50
MS2002	130×90 mm. Nos. 2000/1, each×2. P 14×14½.	2·25	2·75

(b) Litho SNP Cambec. Self-adhesive. Phosphor frame on three sides. P 11½

2003	40c. +5c. Type **534**.......................................	50	75
	a. As Type **534**, but teddy bear at top right and face value at bottom left...............	£1300	£1300

The original versions (Nos. 2000a and 2003a) of the 40c.+5c. showed a teddy bear at top right and the face value above the inscription at bottom left. As depicted the design breached New Zealand safety guidelines and both versions were redrawn and replaced by Type **534**. All the original versions should have been withdrawn from post office stocks before the release date, but examples were sold from at least two New Zealand Post outlets at Royal Oak (Auckland) and Te Ngae (Rotorua) and used for postal purposes.

Two examples of the miniature sheet, one with the "CAPEX '96" overprint, including the teddy bear, were sold in the Netherlands during 1997. There is no evidence to link these two miniature sheets with New Zealand.

Stamps from No. **MS**2002 are slightly larger with "NEW ZEALAND" and the face values redrawn.

No. 2003 is smaller, 21½×38 mm, and occurs in rolls of 100 with the surplus self-adhesive paper around each stamp removed. The phosphor shows pink under U.V. light.

(Des Diane Prosser (No. **MS**2005). Litho SNP Cambec (No. **MS**2004) or Southern Colour Print, Dunedin (No. **MS**2005))

1996 (8 June). CAPEX '96 International Stamp Exhibition, Toronto.

(a) No. **MS**2002 *optd* "CAPEX '96" *and emblem on sheet margin*
MS2004 Nos. 2000/1, each×2................................ 2·75   2·75

(b) Sheet 180×80 mm, containing Nos. 1931/4. P 13½
MS2005 $3 multicoloured.. 2·75   3·25

535 Violin

(Des M. Bailey. Litho and gold die-stamped Southern Colour Print, Dunedin)

1996 (10 July). 50th Anniv of New Zealand Symphony Orchestra. T **535** and similar horiz design. Multicoloured. P 15×14½.
2006   40c. Type **535**................................. 30   50
2007   80c. French horn............................. 80   1·50

536 Swimming   **537** *Hinemoa*

(Des S. Fuller. Litho Southern Colour Print, Dunedin)

1996 (10 July). Centennial Olympic Games, Atlanta. T **536** and similar circular designs. Multicoloured. P 14½ (and 14 around design).
2008   40c. Type **536**............................. 30   15
2009   80c. Cycling................................... 1·25   80
2010 $1 Running.................................... 60   80
2011 $1.50 Rowing 80   2·00
2012 $1.80 Dinghy sailing..................... 80   2·00
2008/12 *Set of 5*....................................... 3·25   5·25
MS2013 120×80 mm. Nos. 2008/12........ 3·25   5·25
     A miniature sheet containing Nos. 2008/12 both perforated and imperforate comes from a Limited Edition Collectors Pack costing NZ$135.

(Des Eyework Design and Production. Litho Southern Colour Print, Dunedin (prize labels printed by Sabre Print))

1996 (7 Aug). Centenary of New Zealand Cinema. T **537** and similar vert designs. Multicoloured. P 14½.
2014   40c. Type **537**............................. 25   15
2015   80c. *Broken Barrier*..................... 50   60
2016 $1.50 *Goodbye Pork Pie*.............. 80   2·25
2017 $1.80 *Once Were Warriors* 90   2·25
2014/17 *Set of 4*....................................... 2·25   4·75
     Nos. 2014/17 were printed in sheets of 25, each stamp being *se-tenant* with a "Scratch and Win" stamp-size label.

538 Danyon Loader   **539** Beehive Ballot Box
(swimmer) and Blyth Tait
(horseman)

(Des Red Cactus Design. Litho Southern Colour Print, Dunedin)

1996 (28 Aug). New Zealand Olympic Gold Medal Winners, Atlanta. P 14½ (and 14 around design).
2018   **538**   40c. multicoloured........................... 50   50

No. 2018 was printed in sheets of 36 (6×6) with each stamp within a square perforated margin showing a pattern of Olympic rings and fern leaves.

(Des Gatehaus Design. Litho Southern Colour Print, Dunedin)

1996 (4 Sept). New Zealand's First Mixed Member Proportional Representation Election. P 12.
2019   **539**   40c. black, scarlet and pale yellow 30   40
     No. 2019 was printed in sheets of ten (2×5) with decorated margins.

540 King following Star   **541** Adzebill

(Des Lindy Fisher)

1996 (4 Sept). Christmas. T **540** and similar horiz designs. Multicoloured.

(a) Litho Questa. Designs 35×35 mm. P 14
2020   40c. Type **540**............................. 30   10
2021   70c. Shepherd and Baby Jesus...... 50   40
2022   80c. Angel and shepherd 50   40
2023 $1 Mary, Joseph and Baby Jesus ... 65   50
2024 $1.50 Mary and Joseph with donkey.......... 1·00   2·75
2025 $1.80 The Annunciation................ 1·00   2·50
2020/5 *Set of 6*... 3·50   6·00

(b) Litho SNP Cambec, Australia. Smaller designs, 30×24 mm. Self-adhesive. Phosphor frame. P 11½
2026   40c. Angels with trumpets............. 50   75
2027   40c. King with gift....................... 50   50
     a. Booklet pane. No. 2027×10........... 4·25   4·25
     No. 2026 comes from rolls of 100, on which the surplus self-adhesive paper around each stamp was removed, and No. 2027 from $4 booklets, containing No. 2027a on which the surplus paper was retained, SB82.
     The phosphor, which shows pink under U.V. light, appears as a three-sided frame on stamps from both rolls and booklets.

(Des G. Cox)

1996 (2 Oct). Extinct Birds. T **541** and similar horiz designs. Multicoloured.

(a) Litho Southern Colour Print, Dunedin. Designs 40×28 mm. P 13½
2028   40c. Type **541**............................. 60   40
2029   80c. South Island Whekau ("Laughing Owl"). 1·25   1·25
2030 $1 Piopio...................................... 1·25   1·40
2031 $1.20 Huia.................................... 1·50   2·00
2032 $1.50 Giant Eagle......................... 1·75   2·75
2033 $1.80 Giant Moa........................... 2·00   2·50
2028/33 *Set of 6*....................................... 7·50   9·25
MS2034 105×92 mm. No. 2033. P 14....... 2·00   2·00

(b) Litho SNP Cambec, Australia. Smaller design, 30×24 mm. Self-adhesive. P 11½
2035   40c. Stout-legged Wren 60   60
     a. Booklet pane. No. 2035×10........... 4·75   4·75
     No. 2035 comes from $4 booklets, containing No. 2035a on which the surplus self-adhesive paper was retained, SB83.
     The phosphor, which shows orange under U.V. light, appears as a vertical band at the right of the stamp.

(Des G. Cox (No. **MS**2036), Sea Sky Design (No. **MS**2037). Litho Southern Colour Print, Dunedin)

1996 (21 Oct). TAIPEI '96 Tenth Asian International Stamp Exhibition, Taiwan.

(a) No. **MS**2034 *overprinted with* "TAIPEI '96" *logo on sheet margin*
MS2036 105×92 mm. No. 2033 .... 2·25   2·75

(b) Sheet 140×90 mm containing Nos. 1993 and 1997. Phosphor frame. Multicoloured. P 14
MS2037 Nos. 1993 and 1997...................... 2·25   2·75
     No. **MS**2037 also shows designs as Nos. 1992 and 1994/6, but without face values.

542 Seymour Square,   **543** Holstein Friesian
Blenheim   Cattle

(Des H. Thompson. Litho Walsall)

1996 (13 Nov). Scenic Gardens. T **542** and similar vert designs. Multicoloured. P 13½.

2038	40c. Type **542**	30	10
2039	80c. Pukekura Park, New Plymouth	60	60
2040	$1 Wintergarden, Auckland	70	70
2041	$1.50 Botanic Garden, Christchurch	1·10	2·50
2042	$1.80 Marine Parade Gardens, Napier	1·25	2·50
2038/42 *Set of 5*		3·50	5·75

"BEST OF '96". Sets of three miniature sheets with this inscription and containing Nos. 1950, 1957, 1983, 1997, 2012, 2017, 2025, 2033 and 2042 were distributed by the Philatelic Bureau to customers who had purchased a certain amount of philatelic material from them during the year. These miniature sheets were printed in lithography by Southern Colour Print, Dunedin, and a number of the stamps they contain show different perforations from the examples in normal sheets. They could not be purchased by the general public at post offices.

(Des Lindy Fisher. Litho Questa)

1997 (15 Jan). Cattle Breeds. T **543** and similar vert designs. Multicoloured. P 14×14½.

2043	40c. Type **543**	40	10
2044	80c. Jersey	80	70
2045	$1 Simmental	1·00	75
2046	$1.20 Ayrshire	1·10	1·60
2047	$1.50 Angus	1·25	2·25
2048	$1.80 Hereford	1·50	2·00
2043/8 *Set of 6*		5·50	6·75

(Des Red Cactus Design (No. **MS**2049), Lindy Fisher (No. **MS**2050) Litho Southern Colour Print, Dunedin (**MS**2049) or Questa (**MS**2050))

1997 (12 Feb). HONG KONG '97 International Stamp Exhibition. P 13 (No. **MS**2049) or 14×14½ (No. **MS**2050).

MS2049 130×110 mm. Nos. 1952/3 and 1956		2·00	2·50
MS2050 101×134 mm. Nos. 2044/5 and 2047		2·25	2·75

No. **MS**2050 is also inscribed for the Chinese New Year (Year of the Ox).

544 James Cook and Sextant

(Des Red Cactus Design. Litho Southern Colour Print, Dunedin)

1997 (12 Feb). Millennium Series (1st issue). Discoverers of New Zealand. T **544** and similar multicoloured designs. P 14½×14 ($1, $1.20) or 14×14½ (others).

2051	40c. Type **544**	80	45
2052	80c. Kupe and ocean-going canoe	1·00	90
2053	$1 Carved panel depicting Maui (*vert*)	1·25	1·00
2054	$1.20 Anchor and Jean de Surville's *St. Jean Baptiste* (*vert*)	1·75	1·60
2055	$1.50 Dumont d'Urville, crab and *L'Astrolabe*	2·00	2·00
2056	$1.80 Abel Tasman and illustration from journal	2·00	2·00
2051/6 *Set of 6*		8·00	7·25

A miniature sheet containing Nos. 2051/6 comes from a Limited Edition Millennium Collection costing NZ$129.

See also Nos. 2140/5, 2216/21, 2239/44, 2304/9 and 2310.

545 Rippon Vineyard, Central Otago **546** Cottage Letterbox

(Des Dianne Prosser from paintings by Nancy Tichborne. Litho Southern Colour Print, Dunedin)

1997 (19 Mar). New Zealand Vineyards. T **545** and similar horiz designs. Multicoloured. P 14.

2057	40c. Type **545**	25	10
2058	80c. Te Mata Estate, Hawke's Bay	50	60
2059	$1 Cloudy Bay Vineyard, Marlborough	60	70
2060	$1.20 Pegasus Bay Vineyard, Waipara	75	1·75
2061	$1.50 Milton Vineyard, Gisborne	1·00	2·50
2062	$1.80 Goldwater Estate, Waiheke Island	1·10	2·25
2057/62 *Set of 6*		3·75	7·00
MS2063 Seven sheets, each 150×110 mm. (a) No. 2057; (b) No. 2058; (c) No. 2059; (d) No. 2060; (e) No. 2061; (f) No. 2062; (g) Nos. 2057/62 *Set of 7 sheets*		11·00	16·00

Nos. **MS**2063a/g were only available from $13.40 stamp booklets with each miniature sheet showing a line of roulettes at left, SB85.

An overprinted and numbered miniature sheet containing Nos. 2057/62 comes from a Limited Edition Collectors Pack costing NZ$135.

For a further miniature sheet containing Nos. 2057, 2059 and 2061 see No. **MS**2081.

(Des Communication Arts. Litho SNP Cambec, Australia)

1997 (19 Mar). Curious Letterboxes. T **546** and similar vert designs. Multicoloured. Self-adhesive. Phosphor frame. P 11½.

2064	40c. Type **546**	50	50
	a. Booklet pane of 10. Nos. 2064/73	4·50	4·50
	b. Sheetlet of 10. Nos. 2064/73	11·00	
2065	40c. Owl letterbox	50	50
2066	40c. Blue Whale letterbox	50	50
2067	40c. "Kilroy is Back" letterbox	50	50
2068	40c. Nesting box letterbox	50	50
2069	40c. Piper letterbox	50	50
2070	40c. Diver's helmet letterbox	50	50
2071	40c. Aircraft letterbox	50	50
2072	40c. Water tap letterbox	50	50
2073	40c. Indian palace letterbox	50	50
2064/73 *Set of 10*		4·50	4·50

The phosphor, which shows orange under U.V. light, appears as a frame on two adjacent sides of each design.

Nos. 2064/73 were only issued in $4 stamp booklets in which the booklet pane, No. 2064a, shows the surplus self-adhesive paper around each stamp retained, SB86.

No. 2064b comes from the residue of special sheet stock used to prepare first day covers and subsequently sold as $4 "hang-sell" sheetlets. The stamps are on plain backing paper with the surplus self-adhesive paper around each stamp removed.

547 *The Promised Land*, 1948 (Colin McCahon)

(Des H. Thompson. Litho Southern Colour Print, Dunedin)

1997 (7 May). Contemporary Paintings by Colin McCahon. T **547** and similar horiz designs. Multicoloured. P 14.

2074	40c. Type **547**	25	10
2075	$1 *Six Days in Nelson and Canterbury*, 1950.	55	60
2076	$1.50 *Northland Panels* (detail), 1958	80	1·75
2077	$1.80 *Moby Dick is sighted off Muriwai Beach*, 1972.	90	1·60
2074/7 *Set of 4*		2·25	3·50

548 Carrier Pigeon (based on 1899 "Pigeon-gram" local stamp)

(Des S. Fuller. Litho Southern Colour Print, Dunedin)

1997 (7 May). Centenary of Great Barrier Island Pigeon Post. P 14×13½.

2078	**548**	40c. scarlet	50	1·00
		a. Tête-bêche pair	1·00	2·00
2079		80c. deep dull blue	90	1·50
		a. Tête-bêche pair	1·75	3·00

Nos. 2078/9 were each issued in sheets of 50 on which the stamps were arranged both horizontally and vertically *tête bêche*.

For these stamps in miniature sheets see Nos. **MS**2080 and **MS**2122.

(Des S. Fuller (No. **MS**2080), Dianne Prosser (No. **MS**2081). Litho Southern Colour Print, Dunedin)

1997 (29 May). Pacific '97 International Stamp Exhibition, San Francisco. P 14×13½ (No. **MS**2080) or 14 (No. **MS**2081).

MS2080 137×120 mm. Nos. 2078/9, each×2		2·50	2·50
MS2081 140×100 mm. Nos. 2057, 2059 and 2061		2·50	3·00

No. **MS**2080 is in a triangular format.

549 Rainbow Trout and Red
Setter Fly

(Des Joanne Kreyl. Litho Southern Colour Print, Dunedin)

1997 (18 June). Fly Fishing. T **549** and similar horiz designs.
Multicoloured. P 13.

2082	40c. Type **549**..	25	10
2083	$1 Sea-run Brown Trout and Grey Ghost fly	55	60
2084	$1.50 Brook Charr and Twilight Beauty fly	80	2·00
2085	$1.80 Brown Trout and Hare and Cooper fly	90	2·00
2082/5	*Set of 4*..	2·25	4·25

For miniature sheet containing Nos. 2082 and 2085 see No. **MS**2172.

550 *Beach Scene* (Fern Petrie)

(Adapted Communication Arts Ltd. Litho Southern Colour Print,
Dunedin)

1997 (18 June). Children's Health. T **550** and similar multicoloured
designs showing children's paintings.

(a) P 14

2086	40c. +5c. Type **550**	45	75
2087	80c. +5c. *Horse-riding on the Water-front* (Georgia Dumergue)	80	1·50
MS2088	130×90 mm. Nos. 2086/7 and 40c.+5c. As No. 2089 (25×36 mm). P 14½	1·75	1·75

(b) Self-adhesive. P 10×10½

2089	40c. +5c. *Picking Fruit* (Anita Pitcher)	70	60
2086/9	*Set of 3*	1·75	2·40

No. 2089 comes from rolls of 100 on which the surplus self-adhesive
paper around each stamp was removed. This design with traditional gum
was only available as part of No. **MS**2088.

(Des A. Mitchell. Litho Southern Colour Print, Dunedin)

1997 (6 Aug)–**2002**. P 14½ (and 14 around design).

2090	**445**	$1 violet	1·00	1·25
2090*a*		$1.10 gold (6.3.00)	1·00	2·25
2090*b*		$1.50 purple-brown (5.6.02)	1·10	1·75

Nos. 2090/*b* were printed in sheets of 36 with each stamp within a
square margin perforated on all four sides and with a further circular
perforation around the design.

On Nos. 2090*a/b* the border pattern continues around the top of the
stamp, in place of the "ONE DOLLAR" inscription in Type **445**.

Sheets of No. 2090 were re-issued on 31 December 1999 with a pattern
of gold suns overprinted on the margins around each stamp to mark
the Millennium.

For miniature sheet containing Nos. 2090/*a* see No. **MS**2342.

See aslo Nos. 3308/10.

551 The "Overlander" at Paremata,
Wellington

552 Samuel Marsden's
Active, Bay of Islands

(Des R. Jones. Litho Southern Colour Print, Dunedin)

1997 (6 Aug). Scenic Railway Services. T **551** and similar horiz
designs. Multicoloured. P 14×14½.

2091	40c. Type **551**..	50	20
2092	80c. The "Tranz Alpine" in the Southern Alps	90	80
2093	$1 The "Southerner" at Canterbury	1·00	90
2094	$1.20 The "Coastal Pacific" on the Kaikoura Coast	1·40	2·00

2095	$1.50 The "Bay Express" at Central Hawke's Bay	1·60	2·50
2096	$1.80 The "Kaimai Express" at Tauranga Harbour	1·75	2·25
2091/6	*Set of 6*..	6·50	7·75

For miniature sheet containing Nos. 2092/3 and 2095 see No. **MS**2173.
A miniature sheet containing Nos. 2091/6 comes from a Limited Edition
Collectors Pack costing NZ$135.

(Des Fifi Colston. Litho Southern Colour Print, Dunedin)

1997 (3 Sept). Christmas. T **552** and similar vert designs.
Multicoloured.

(a) P 14

2097	40c. Type **552**..	30	10
	a. Block of 6. Nos. 2097/2102	4·25	5·00
2098	70c. Revd. Marsden preaching	50	50
2099	80c. Marsden and Maori chiefs	60	50
2100	$1 Maori family	70	70
2101	$1.50 Handshake and cross	1·00	1·75
2102	$1.80 Pohutukawa (flower) and Rangihoua Bay	1·10	1·75

(b) Self-adhesive. Smaller design, 29×24 mm. P 10

2103	40c. Memorial cross, Pohutukawa and Bay of Islands	40	40
	a. Booklet pane of 10	4·00	4·00
2097/103	*Set of 7*...	4·25	5·00

In addition to separate sheets Nos. 2097/2102 were also issued as
se-tenant blocks of six.

No. 2103 comes from either rolls of 100, on which the surplus adhesive
paper was removed, or from $4 booklets on which the surplus paper
was retained, SB87.

553 Huhu Beetle

(Des D. Gunson. Litho SNP Cambec, Australia)

1997 (1 Oct). Insects. T **553** and similar horiz designs. Multicoloured.
Self-adhesive. Two phosphor bands. P 11½.

2104	40c. Type **553**..	50	50
	a. Booklet pane. Nos. 2104/13	4·50	4·50
	b. Sheetlet of 10. Nos. 2104/13	8·00	
2105	40c. Giant Land Snail	50	50
2106	40c. Giant Weta	50	50
2107	40c. Giant Dragonfly	50	50
2108	40c. Peripatus...	50	50
2109	40c. Cicada...	50	50
2110	40c. Puriri Moth	50	50
2111	40c. Veined Slug...	50	50
2112	40c. Katipo...	50	50
2113	40c. Flax Weevil	50	50
2104/13	*Set of 10*	4·50	4·50

The phosphor, which shows pink under U.V. light, appears as horizontal
bands across the top and bottom of each design.

Nos. 2104/13 were only issued in $4 stamp booklets in which the
booklet pane, No. 2104a, shows the surplus self-adhesive paper around
each stamp retained, SB88.

No. 2104b comes from the residue of special sheet stock used to prepare
first day covers and subsequently sold as $4 "hang-sell" sheetlets. The
stamps are on plain backing paper, with the surplus self-adhesive paper
around each stamp removed.

554 *Rosa rugosa*

(Des Z. Guizheng. Litho Southern Colour Print, Dunedin)

1997 (9 Oct). New Zealand–China. Joint Issue. Roses. T **554** and
similar vert design. Multicoloured. P 14.

2114	40c. Type **554**..	50	50
	a. Horiz pair. Nos. 2114/15	1·00	1·00
2115	40c. Aotearoa	50	50
MS2116	115×95 mm. 80c. Nos. 2114/15	1·00	1·00

Nos. 2114/15 were printed together, *se-tenant*, in horizontal pairs
throughout the sheet.

Stamps in similar designs were also issued by China.

555 Queen Elizabeth II
and Prince Philip

(Des Red Cactus Design. Litho Southern Colour Print, Dunedin)

1997 (12 Nov). Golden Wedding of Queen Elizabeth and Prince Philip.
P 12.

2117	**555**	40c. multicoloured	50	75

No. 2117 was printed in sheets of ten (2×5) with decorated margins.

556 Cartoon Kiwi on Busy-bee

(Des G. Tremain (40c.), J. Hubbard ($1), E. Heath ($1.50); B. Silver
($1.80). Litho Southern Colour Print, Dunedin)

1997 (12 Nov). New Zealand Cartoons. "Kiwis taking on the
World". T **556** and similar horiz designs. Multicoloured. P 14.

2118		40c. Type **556**	30	10
2119		$1 "Let's have 'em for Breakfast"	55	55
2120		$1.50 Kiwi dinghy winning race	80	1·25
2121		$1.80 "CND" emblem cut in forest	90	1·25
2118/21 *Set of 4*			2·25	2·75

(Des S. Fuller. Litho Southern Colour Print, Dunedin)

1997 (13 Nov). Aupex '97 National Stamp Exhibition, Auckland. Sheet
140×120 mm. P 14×13½.

MS2122 Nos. 2078/9, each×2		2·10	2·10

No. **MS**2122 is in a triangular format.

1997 (19 Nov). International Stamp and Coin Exhibition, 1997,
Shanghai. Sheet as No. **MS**2116 but redrawn to include "Issued
by New Zealand Post to commemorate the International Stamp
and Coin Expo. Shanghai, China. 19-23: November 1997" inscr in
English and Chinese with additional die-stamped gold frame and
logo.

MS2123 115×95 mm. Nos. 2114/15	1·00	1·00

"BEST OF '97". A further set of three miniature sheets, as described below
No. 2042, was distributed by the Philatelic Bureau in 1997 to customers
purchasing a certain amount of philatelic material. The stamps shown for
1997 were Nos. 2048, 2056, 2062, 2077, 2085, 2090, 2096, 2102 and 2121.

557 Modern Dancer

(Des N. Childs. Litho Southern Colour Print, Dunedin)

1998 (14 Jan). Performing Arts. T **557** and similar vert designs.
Multicoloured. P 13½.

2124		40c. Type **557**	25	10
2125		80c. Trombone player	55	55
	a.	Perf 14	1·75	2·50
2126		$1 Opera singer	1·25	75
2127		$1.20 Actor	80	1·25
2128		$1.50 Singer	1·00	2·00
2129		$1.80 Ballet dancer	1·25	2·00
	a.	Perf 14	4·00	6·00
2124/9 *Set of 6*			4·50	6·00

MS2130 Seven sheets, each 150×110 mm. (a) No. 2124;
(b) No. 2125; (c) No. 2126; (d) No. 2127; (e) No. 2128;
(f) No. 2129; (g) Nos. 2124/9. P 12 (Nos. **MS**2130c,

MS2130g) or 13½ (others) *Set of 7 sheets*	10·00	15·00

Nos. 2130a/g were only available from $13.40 stamp booklets, with each
miniature sheet showing a line of roulettes at left, SB90.

558 Museum of New Zealand

(Des Joanne Kreyl. Litho Southern Colour Print, Dunedin)

1998 (11 Feb). Opening of Museum of New Zealand, Wellington. T **558**
and similar diamond-shaped design. Multicoloured. P 14½.

2131	40c. Type **558**	30	35
2132	$1.80 Museum and Spotted Cormorant and Silver Gull	1·40	1·40

559 Domestic Cat   **560** Maoris and Canoe

(Des Julie Grieg. Litho Southern Colour Print, Dunedin)

1998 (11 Feb). Cats. T **559** and similar vert designs. Multicoloured.
P 13½.

2133		40c. Type **559**	30	10
2134		80c. Burmese	60	60
2135		$1 Birman	65	65
2136		$1.20 British Blue	70	1·25
2137		$1.50 Persian	90	2·25
2138		$1.80 Siamese	1·10	2·00
2133/8 *Set of 6*			3·75	6·00

(Des Julie Grieg. Litho Southern Colour Print, Dunedin)

1998 (11 Feb). Chinese New Year (Year of the Tiger). P 13½.

MS2139 100×135 mm. Nos. 2133, 2135 and 2138	2·00	3·00

(Des T. Crilley. Litho Southern Colour Print, Dunedin)

1998 (18 Mar). Millennium Series (2nd issue). Immigrants. T **560** and
similar vert designs. Multicoloured. P 14½×14.

2140		40c. Type **560**	35	15
2141		80c. 19th-century European settlers and immigrant ship	75	65
2142		$1 Gold miners and mine	1·00	80
2143		$1.20 Post 1945 European migrants and liner.	1·25	1·10
2144		$1.50 Pacific islanders and church	1·40	1·75
2145		$1.80 Asian migrant and jumbo jet	1·60	1·60
2140/5 *Set of 6*			5·75	5·50

Miniature sheets containing Nos. 2140/5 come from a Limited Edition
Collectors Pack costing NZ$135 or a Limited Edition Millennium Collection
costing NZ$129.

561 "With Great   **562** Mother and Son
Respect to the   hugging
Mehmetcik" Statue,
Gallipoli

(Des Dianne Prosser. Litho Southern Colour Print, Dunedin)

1998 (18 Mar). Joint Issue New Zealand–Turkey. Memorial Statues. T **561** and similar vert design. Multicoloured. P 13½.

2146	40c. Type **561**	30	35
2147	$1.80 "Mother with Children", National War Memorial, Wellington	1·10	1·40

(Des Colenso Communications Ltd. Litho Southern Colour Print, Dunedin)

1998 (15 Apr). "Stay in Touch" Greetings Stamps. T **562** and similar multicoloured designs. Self-adhesive. Phosphorised paper. P 10½×10 (horiz) or 10×10½ (vert).

2148	40c. Type **562**	35	35
	a. Booklet pane. Nos. 2148/57	3·25	3·25
	b. Sheetlet of 4. Nos. 2148/51	2·50	4·25
2149	40c. Couple on beach	35	35
2150	40c. Boys striking hands	35	35
2151	40c. Grandmother and grandson	35	35
2152	40c. Young boys in pool (horiz)	35	35
	b. Sheetlet of 6. Nos. 2152/7	3·75	6·50
2153	40c. "I'LL MISS YOU... PLEASE WRITE" (horiz)	35	35
2154	40c. Symbolic couple and clouds (horiz)	35	35
2155	40c. Young couple kissing (horiz)	35	35
2156	40c. Couple sat on sofa (horiz)	35	35
2157	40c. Maoris rubbing noses (horiz)	35	35
2148/57 Set of 10		3·25	3·25

Nos. 2148/57 were only available from $4 stamp booklets, containing No. 2148a on which the surplus self-adhesive paper was retained, SB91.

Nos. 2148b and 2152b come from the residue of special sheet stock used to prepare first day covers and subsequently sold as $4 "hang-sell" packs containing the two sheetlets. The stamps are on plain backing paper, with the surplus self-adhesive paper around each stamp removed.

563 Mount Cook or Aorangi

564 Wounded at Cassino

(Adapted R. Jones. Litho Southern Colour Print, Dunedin)

1998 (20 May). Centenary of 1898 Pictorial Stamps. Designs as T **23/36** with modern face values as T **563**. P 14×14½ (Nos. 2158/65) or P 14½ (others).

2158	**563**	40c. purple-brown	25	50
2159	**24**	40c. deep blue and orange-brown	25	50
2160	**25**	40c. lake-brown	25	50
2161	**28**	40c. chestnut	25	50
2162	**29**	40c. deep rose-red	25	50
2163	**31**	40c. deep green	25	50
2164	**32**	40c. indigo	25	50
2165	**34**	40c. red-orange	25	50
2166	**26**	80c. steel-blue (inscr "LAKE WAKITIPU") (35×23 mm)	50	75
2167	**27**	80c. steel-blue (inscr "LAKE WAKIPU") (35×23 mm)	50	75
2168	**30**	$1 reddish brown (23×35 mm)	60	85
2169	**33**	$1.20 purple-brown (35×23 mm)	85	1·60
2170	**35**	$1.50 deep blue-green (35×23 mm)	1·00	1·75
2171	**36**	$1.80 dull vermilion (23×35 mm)	1·25	1·75
2158/71 Set of 14			6·00	10·50

For miniature sheets containing Nos. 2166/7 and 2170 see Nos. **MS**2188 and **MS**2214.

Sheets of Nos. 2158/71 numbered and with the margins decorated in gold come from special Centenary Collections.

(Des Joanne Kreyl (No. **MS**2172), R. Jones (No. **MS**2173). Litho Southern Colour Print, Dunedin)

1998 (20 May). "Israel '98" World Stamp Exhibition, Tel Aviv. P 13 (No. **MS**2172) or 14×14½ (No. **MS**2173).

MS2172 112×90 mm. Nos. 2082 and 2085		2·50	2·75
MS2173 125×100 mm. Nos. 2092/3 and 2095		4·00	4·50

(Des H. Thompson. Litho Southern Colour Print, Dunedin)

1998 (24 June). Paintings by Peter McIntyre. T **564** and similar horiz designs. Multicoloured. P 13½.

2174	40c. Type **564**	20	10
2175	$1 The Cliffs of Rangitikei	60	55
2176	$1.50 Maori Children, King Country	80	1·10
2177	$1.80 The Anglican Church, Kakahi	1·00	1·10
2174/7 Set of 4		2·40	2·50

For Nos. 2176/7 in miniature sheet for "Italia '98" see No. **MS**2215. A similar miniature sheet, but with the exhibition logo replaced by the Limited Edition symbol at bottom right, comes from Limited Edition Collectors Packs costing NZS135.

565 Girl wearing Lifejacket

(Des Sea Sky Design)

1998 (24 June). Children's Health. Water Safety. T **565** and similar vert design. Multicoloured.

(a) Litho Southern Colour Print, Dunedin. P 13½

2178	40c. +5c. Type **565**	40	75
2179	80c. +5c. Boy learning to swim	60	1·25
MS2180 125×90 mm. Nos. 2178/9, each×2. P 14½×14		2·00	2·00

(b) Litho SNP Cambec. Smaller design, 25×37 mm. Self-adhesive. Phosphor on inscr panel and background. P 11½

2181	40c. +5c. Type **565**	30	50

No. 2181, on which the phosphor shows pink under U.V. light, comes from rolls of 100 on which the surplus self-adhesive paper around each stamp was removed. Examples without printer's imprint on the reverse come from $4.35 "hang-sell" packs containing Nos. 2178/81.

566 Sunrise near Cambridge

(Des Cato Design. Litho Southern Colour Print, Dunedin)

1998 (29 July). Scenic Skies. T **566** and similar horiz designs. Multicoloured. P 15×14½.

2182	40c. Type **566**	30	10
2183	80c. Clouds over Lake Wanaka	60	50
2184	$1 Sunset over Mount Maunganui	70	55
2185	$1.20 Rain clouds over South Bay, Kaikoura	80	1·10
2186	$1.50 Sunset near Statue of Wairaka, Whakatane Harbour	1·10	1·25
2187	$1.80 Cloud formation above Lindis Pass	1·25	1·50
2182/7 Set of 6		4·25	4·50

For Nos. 2182 and 2187 in miniature sheet for "Australia '99" see No. **MS**2245.

(Des R. Jones. Litho Southern Colour Print, Dunedin)

1998 (7 Aug). "TARAPEX '98" National Stamp Exhibition, New Plymouth. P 14½.

MS2188 90×80 mm. Nos. 2166/7		1·25	1·75

567 Virgin Mary and Christ Child

568 Lemon and Mineral Water Bottle, Paeroa

(Des Sally Simons)

1998 (2 Sept). Christmas. T **567** and similar vert designs. Multicoloured.

(a) Litho Southern Colour Print, Dunedin. P 13½

2189	40c. Type **567**	20	10
2190	70c. Shepherds approaching the stable	35	30
2191	80c. Virgin Mary, Joseph and Christ Child	40	35
2192	$1 Magi with gift of gold	50	40
2193	$1.50 Three magi	80	1·50
2194	$1.80 Angel and shepherds	90	1·50
2189/94 Set of 6		2·75	3·50

(b) Litho SNP Cambec, Australia. Smaller design, 24×29 mm. Self-adhesive. Phosphor frame. P 11½

2195	40c. Type **567**		35	30
	a. Booklet pane of 10		3·50	3·50

No. 2195, which shows a broad band of pink phosphor over both the right-hand part of the centre design and "NEW ZEALAND", comes from either rolls of 100, on which the surplus adhesive paper was removed, or from $4 booklets on which the surplus paper was retained, SB92.

(Des Donna McKenna. Litho SNP Cambec, Melbourne)

1998 (7 Oct). Town Icons. T **568** and similar vert designs. Multicoloured. Self-adhesive. Phosphor backgrounds. P 11 (Nos. 2202/5) or 11½ (others).

2196	40c. Type **568**		40	40
	a. Booklet pane of 10. Nos. 2196/2205		3·75	3·75
	b. Sheetlet of 10. Nos. 2196/2205		5·50	
2197	40c. Carrot, Ohakune		40	40
2198	40c. Brown Trout, Gore (25×36 mm)		40	40
2199	40c. Crayfish, Kaikoura (25×36 mm)		40	40
2200	40c. Sheep-shearer, Te Kuiti (25×36 mm)		40	40
2201	40c. "Pania of the Reef" (Maori legend), Napier (25×36 mm)		40	40
2202	40c. Paua Shell, Riverton (24×29 mm)		40	40
2203	40c. Kiwifruit, Te Puke (24×29 mm)		40	40
2204	40c. Border Collie, Lake Tekapo (24×29 mm).		40	40
2205	40c. "Big Cow", Hawera (24×29 mm)		40	40
2196/205	*Set of 10*		3·75	3·75

Nos. 2196/2205 were only issued in $4 self-adhesive stamp booklets containing No. 2196a on which the surplus self-adhesive paper was retained, SB93.

The phosphor, which shows pink under U.V. light, covers most of the background on each design.

No. 2196b comes from the residue of special sheet stock used to prepare first day covers and subsequently sold as $4 "hang-sell" sheetlets. The stamps are on plain backing paper with the surplus self-adhesive paper around each stamp removed. Similar "hang-sell" packs, selling at $9.60, were prepared containing blocks or pairs of the individual designs for sale at the towns depicted. On these blocks or pairs the surplus self-adhesive paper was retained.

569 Moonfish   **570** Wellington in 1841 and 1998

(Des G. Cox. Litho Southern Colour Print, Dunedin)

1998 (7 Oct). International Year of the Ocean. T **569** and similar vert designs. Multicoloured. P 14.

2206	40c. Type **569**		25	50
	a. Block of 4. Nos. 2206/9		1·00	2·00
2207	40c. Mako Shark		25	50
2208	40c. Yellowfin Tuna		25	50
2209	40c. Giant Squid		25	50
2210	80c. Striped Marlin		40	70
	a. Block of 4. Nos. 2210/3		1·40	2·50
2211	80c. Porcupine Fish		40	70
2212	80c. Eagle Ray		40	70
2213	80c. Sandager's Wrasse		40	70
2206/13	*Set of 8*		2·40	4·25

Nos. 2206/9 and 2210/13 were each printed together, *se-tenant*, in blocks of four, forming composite designs.

A miniature sheet containing Nos. 2206/13 comes from a Limited Edition Collectors Pack costing NZ$135.

For Nos. 2206/7 and 2210/11 in miniature sheet for "Australia '99" see No. **MS**2246 and for Nos. 2208/9 and 2212/13 in a miniature sheet for "PhilexFrance 99" see No. **MS**2277.

(Adapted R. Jones. Litho Southern Colour Print, Dunedin)

1998 (23 Oct). "Italia '98" International Philatelic Exhibition, Milan. P 14½ (No. **MS**2214) or 14 (No. **MS**2215).

MS2214	90×80 mm. Nos. 2167 and 2170	2·50	3·25
MS2215	112×90 mm. Nos. 2176/7	1·60	2·25

(Des Niki Hill. Litho Southern Colour Print, Dunedin)

1998 (11 Nov). Millennium Series (3rd issue). Urban Transformations. T **570** and similar horiz designs. Multicoloured. P 14×14½.

2216	40c. Type **570**		30	10
2217	80c. Auckland in 1852 and 1998		50	40
2218	$1 Christchurch in 1851 and 1998		55	50
2219	$1.20 Westport in 1919 and 1998		70	1·25
2220	$1.50 Tauranga in 1880 and 1998		80	1·50
2221	$1.80 Dunedin in 1862 and 1998		1·00	1·50
2216/21	*Set of 6*		3·50	4·75

A miniature sheet containing Nos. 2216/21 comes from a Limited Edition Millennium Collection costing NZ$129.

"BEST OF '98". A further set of three miniature sheets, as described below No. 2042, was distributed by the Philatelic Bureau in 1998 to customers purchasing a certain amount of philatelic material. The stamps shown for 1998 were Nos. 2129, 2132, 2138, 2147, 2171, 2177, 2187, 2194 and 2221.

571 *Fuchsia excorticata*   **572** Civic Theatre, Auckland

(Des Sue Wickison. Litho Southern Colour Print, Dunedin)

1999 (13 Jan). Flowering Trees of New Zealand. T **571** and similar vert designs. Multicoloured. P 14½×14.

2222	40c. Type **571**		20	10
2223	80c. *Solanum laciniatum*		35	35
2224	$1 *Sophora tetraptera*		40	50
2225	$1.20 *Carmichaelia stevensonii*		50	1·00
2226	$1.50 *Olearia angustifolia*		70	1·50
2227	$1.80 *Metrosideros umbellata*		80	1·50
2222/7	*Set of 6*		2·75	4·50

A miniature sheet containing Nos. 2226/7 comes from a Limited Edition Collectors Pack costing NZ$135.

For Nos. 2222/3 in miniature sheet for "China '99" see No. **MS**2286.

(Des Donna McKenna. Litho Southern Colour Print, Dunedin)

1999 (10 Feb). Art Deco Architecture. T **572** and similar vert designs. Multicoloured. P 14½×14.

2228	40c. Type **572**		30	10
2229	$1 Masonic Hotel, Napier		2·00	80
2230	$1.50 Medical and Dental Chambers, Hastings		80	1·40
2231	$1.80 Buller County Chambers, Westport		90	1·40
2228/31	*Set of 4*		3·50	3·25

573 Labrador Puppy and Netherland Dwarf Rabbit   **574** Toy Fire Engine and Marbles

(Des Lindy Fisher. Litho Southern Colour Print, Dunedin)

1999 (10 Feb). Popular Pets. T **573** and similar vert designs. Multicoloured. P 14.

2232	40c. Type **573**		40	20
2233	80c. Netherland Dwarf Rabbit		60	40
2234	$1 Tabby kitten and Netherland Dwarf Rabbit		70	50
2235	$1.20 Lamb		85	1·25
2236	$1.50 Welsh pony		1·25	1·50
2237	$1.80 Two Budgerigars		1·25	1·50
2232/7	*Set of 6*		4·50	4·75
MS2238	100×135 mm. Nos. 2232/4		1·75	1·75

No. **MS**2238 also commemorates the Chinese New Year (Year of the Rabbit).

For Nos. 2232 and 2234 in miniature sheet for "China '99" see No. **MS**2287.

(Des Siren Communications Ltd. Litho Southern Colour Print, Dunedin)

1999 (10 Mar). Millennium Series (4th issue). Nostalgia. T **574** and similar horiz designs. Multicoloured. P 14×14½.

2239	40c. Type **574**		30	10
2240	80c. Commemorative tin of biscuits and cereal packet		40	40
2241	$1 Tram, tickets and railway crockery		60	50
2242	$1.20 Radio and *Woman's Weekly* magazine		70	1·25
2243	$1.50 Coins, postcards and stamps		80	1·60
2244	$1.80 Lawn mower and seed packets		90	1·60
2239/44	*Set of 6*		3·25	4·75

A miniature sheet containing Nos. 2239/44 comes from a Limited Edition Millennium Collection costing NZ$129.

(Des Cato Design (No. **MS**2245), G. Cox (No. **MS**2246). Litho Southern Colour Print, Dunedin)

1999 (19 Mar). Australia '99 World Stamp Exhibition, Melbourne. P 15×14½ (No. **MS**2245) or 14 (No. **MS**2246).
MS2245 130×70 mm. Nos. 2182 and 2187 .... 1·90   1·90
MS2246 130×90 mm. Nos. 2206/7 and 2210/11 .... 2·00   2·00

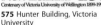

575 Hunter Building, Victoria University

576 Auckland Blue Player kicking Ball

(Litho Southern Colour Print)

1999 (7 Apr). Centenary of Victoria University, Wellington. P 14×14½.
2247   **575**   40c. multicoloured 30   30

(Des P. Martinson and Diane Prosser)

1999 (7 Apr). New Zealand U-Bix Rugby Super 12 Championship. T **576** and similar vert designs. Multicoloured.

(a) Litho Southern Colour Print. P 14½

2248	40c. Type **576**	30	40
	a. Sheetlet. Nos. 2248/57	2·75	3·50
2249	40c. Auckland Blues player being tackled	30	40
2250	40c. Chiefs player being tackled.........................	30	40
2251	40c. Chiefs lineout jump	30	40
2252	40c. Wellington Hurricanes player being tackled	30	40
2253	40c. Wellington Hurricanes player passing ball	30	40
2254	40c. Canterbury Crusaders lineout jump	30	40
2255	40c. Canterbury Crusaders player kicking ball	30	40
2256	40c. Otago Highlanders player diving for try	30	40
2257	40c. Otago Highlanders player running with ball	30	40
2248/57	*Set of 10*......................................	2·75	3·50

(b) Litho SNP Ausprint. Self-adhesive. Phosphor frame. P 11½

2258	40c. Type **576**	30	45
	a. Booklet pane. Nos. 2258/9, each×5	2·75	
2259	40c. Auckland Blues player being tackled	30	45
2260	40c. Chiefs player being tackled......................	30	45
	a. Booklet pane. Nos. 2260/1, each×5	2·75	
2261	40c. Chiefs lineout jump	30	45
2262	40c. Wellington Hurricanes player being tackled	30	45
	a. Booklet pane. Nos. 2262/3, each×5	2·75	
2263	40c. Wellington Hurricanes player passing ball	30	45
2264	40c. Canterbury Crusaders lineout jump	30	45
	a. Booklet pane. Nos. 2264/5, each×5	2·75	
2265	40c. Canterbury Crusaders player kicking ball	30	45
2266	40c. Otago Highlanders player diving for try	30	45
	a. Booklet pane. Nos. 2266/7, each×5	2·75	
2267	40c. Otago Highlanders player running with ball	30	45
2258/67	*Set of 10*......................................	2·75	4·00

Nos. 2248/57 were printed together, *se-tenant*, in sheetlets of ten (2×5).

Nos. 2258/67, on which the phosphor shows pink under U.V. light, were only issued in $4 booklets (one for each team) on which the surplus self-adhesive paper was retained, SB94/8.

Examples on plain backing paper with the surplus self-adhesive paper around each stamp removed come from the residue of special sheet stock used to prepare first day covers and subsequently sold as $4 "hang-sell" packs containing five separate panes.

577 *The Lake, Tuai*

(Des H. Thompson. Litho Southern Colour Print, Dunedin)

1999 (16 June). Paintings by Doris Lusk. T **577** and similar horiz designs. Multicoloured. P 14.
2268   40c. Type **577**..................................... 25   10

2269	$1 *The Pumping Station*......................	60	50
2270	$1.50 *Arcade Awning, St. Mark's Square, Venice (2)*	80	1·60
2271	$1.80 *Tuam St. 11*	90	1·40
2268/71	*Set of 4*..................................	2·25	3·25

For Nos. 2268 and 2271 in miniature sheet for "PhilexFrance '99" see No. **MS**2276.

578 *A lion in the Meadow* (Margaret Mahy)
579 "APEC"

(Des Ann Adams from book illustrations. Litho Southern Colour Print, Dunedin)

1999 (16 June). Children's Health. Children's Books. T **578** and similar horiz designs. Multicoloured. Phosphorised paper.

(a) P 14

2272	40c. +5c. Type **578**	55	55
2273	80c. +5c. *Greedy Cat* (Joy Cowley).......	70	70
MS2274	130×90 mm. 40c.+5c. Type **578**; 40c.+5c. As No. 2275 (37×25 mm); 80c.+5c. No. 2273	1·40	1·40

(b) Self-adhesive. P 10

2275	40c. +5c. *Hairy Maclary's Bone* (Lynley Dodd) (37×25 mm)	50	50

No. 2275 comes only in rolls of 100 on which the surplus self-adhesive paper around each stamp was removed.

(Des G. Cox (No. **MS**2276), H. Thompson (No. **MS**2277). Litho Southern Colour Print, Dunedin)

1999 (2 July). PhilexFrance '99 International Stamp Exhibition, Paris. P 14.
MS2276 112×90 mm. Nos. 2268 and 2271 .... 1·75   1·75
MS2277 130×90 mm. Nos. 2208/9 and 2212/13 .... 2·00   2·00

(Des S. Fuller. Litho Southern Colour Print, Dunedin)

1999 (21 July). 10th Asia-Pacific Economic Co-operation Meeting, New Zealand. P 14.
2278   **579**   40c. multicoloured 30   30

580 West Ruggedy Beach, Stewart Island

(Des Ocean Design. Litho Southern Colour Print, Dunedin)

1999 (28 July). Scenic Walks. T **580** and similar horiz designs. Multicoloured. P 14.

2279	40c. Type **580**....................................	30	10
2280	80c. Ice lake, Butler Valley, Westland.......	50	40
2281	$1 Tonga Bay, Abel Tasman National Park...	65	65
2282	$1.20 East Matakitaki Valley, Nelson Lakes National Park.............	75	90
2283	$1.50 Great Barrier Island.........................	90	1·60
2284	$1.80 Mt. Egmont, Taranaki	1·10	1·40
2279/84	*Set of 6*..................................	3·75	4·50
MS2285	Seven sheets, each 150×110 mm. (a) No. 2279. (b) No. 2280. (c) No. 2281. (d) No. 2282. (e) No. 2283. (f) No. 2284. (g) Nos. 2279/84.........*Set of 7 sheets*	11·00	13·00

Nos **MS**2285a/g were only available from $13.40 stamp booklets, with each miniature sheet showing a line of roulettes at left, SB99.

No. **MS**2285(g) numbered and with logo in silver comes from a Limited Edition Collectors Pack costing NZ$135.

For No. 2284 in miniature sheet for "Palmpex '99" see No. **MS**2295.

(Des Lindy Fisher (No. **MS**2286), Sue Wickison (No. **MS**2287). Litho Southern Colour Print, Dunedin)

1999 (21 Aug). China '99 International Stamp Exhibition, Peking. P 14½×14 (No. **MS**2286) or 14 (No. **MS**2287).
MS2286 112×90 mm. Nos. 2222/3 .... 1·00   1·00
MS2287 100×135 mm. Nos. 2232 and 2234..................... 1·00   1·00

581 Baby Jesus with Animals   **582** "P" Class Dinghy

(Des Lindy Fisher. Litho Southern Colour Print, Dunedin)

1999 (8 Sept–1 Nov). Christmas.

*(a) T **581** and similar square designs. Multicoloured. P 13*
2288	40c. Type **581**	20	10
2289	80c. Virgin Mary praying	40	30
2290	$1.10 Mary and Joseph on way to Bethlehem	55	50
2291	$1.20 Angel playing harp	60	80
2292	$1.50 Three shepherds	75	1·25
2293	$1.80 Three wise men with gifts	90	1·25
2288/93 *Set of 6*		3·00	3·75

*(b) Smaller multicoloured design, 23×28 mm. Self-adhesive.
Phosphor frame. P 9½*
2294	40c. Type **581**	30	30
	a. Booklet pane. No. 2294×10 (1.11)	3·00	3·00

No. 2294, on which the phosphor shows pink under U.V. light, comes from rolls of 100 on which the surplus self-adhesive paper around each stamp was removed or from booklet SB101 where the surplus paper was retained. Examples on plain backing paper come from a "hang-sell" pack.

(Des Ocean Design. Litho Southern Colour Print, Dunedin)

1999 (1 Oct). "Palmpex '99" National Stamp Exhibition, Palmerston North. Sheet 130×90 mm containing No. 2284. Multicoloured. P 14.

MS2295 $1.80, Mt Egmont, Taranaki .... 1·40   1·40

(Des BNA Design, Litho Southern Colour Print, Dunedin)

1999 (20 Oct). Yachting. T **582** and similar vert designs. Phosphorised paper. Multicoloured.

(a) Size 28×39 mm. P 14
2296	40c. Type **582**	25	10
2297	80c. Laser dinghy	45	35
2298	$1.10 18' skiff	50	60
2299	$1.20 Hobie catamaran	50	75
2300	$1.50 Racing yacht	60	1·25
2301	$1.80 Cruising yacht	80	1·25
2296/301 *Set of 6*		2·75	4·25
MS2302 125×100 mm. Nos. 2296/2301		2·75	3·75

(b) Self-adhesive. Size 23×28 mm. P 9½
2303	40c. Optimist dinghy	30	30
	a. Booklet pane. No. 2303×10	3·00	3·00

No. **MS**2302 imperforate comes from a Limited Edition Collectors Pack costing NZ$135.

No. 2303 was only issued in $4 stamp booklets, containing No. 2303a, on which the surplus self-adhesive paper was retained, SB100.

583 Group of Victorian Women
(female suffrage, 1893)

(Des Deirdre Cassell. Litho Southern Colour Print, Dunedin)

1999 (17 Nov). Millennium Series (5th issue). New Zealand Achievements. T **583** and similar horiz designs. Phosphorised paper. Multicoloured. P 14×14½.
2304	40c. Type **583**	30	15
2305	80c. Richard Pearse's aircraft (powered flight, 1903)	75	55
2306	$1.10 Lord Rutherford (splitting the atom, 1919)	80	85
2307	$1.20 Boat on lake (invention of jet boat, 1953)	80	90
2308	$1.50 Sir Edmund Hillary (conquest of Everest 1953)	1·10	1·50
2309	$1.80 Protesters and warship (nuclear free zone, 1987)	1·10	1·60
2304/9 *Set of 6*		4·25	5·00

A miniature sheet containing Nos. 2304/9 comes from a Limited Edition Millennium Collection costing NZ$129.

"BEST OF '99". A further set of three miniature sheets, as described below No. 2042, was distributed by the Philatelic Bureau to customers purchasing a certain amount of philatelic material. The stamps shown for 1999 were Nos. 2227, 2230, 2237, 2244, 2271, 2284, 2293, 2301 and 2309.

584 Sunrise and World Map   **585** Araiteuru (North Island sea guardian)

(Des Diane Prosser. Litho Southern Colour Print, Dunedin)

2000 (1 Jan). Millennium Series (6th issue). Phosphorised paper. P 14×14½.
2310	**584** 40c. multicoloured	65	30
	a. Sheetlet. No. 2310×10	6·00	
	b. New Zealand Millennium logo missing from bottom left (sheetlet R. 3/1)	3·25	

No. 2310 was printed in sheets of 50 (5×10) and in sheetlets of ten (2×5) with an enlarged right margin separated from the block of stamps by a line of roulettes. No. 2310b, which shows the map of New Zealand and rays omitted from beside the time at bottom left, occurs on R. 3/1 of the sheetlet only.

A miniature sheet containing six examples of No. 2310 comes from a Limited Edition Millennium Collection costing NZ$129.

(Des M. Smith. Litho Southern Colour Print, Dunedin)

2000 (9 Feb). Chinese New Year (Year of the Dragon). Maori Spirits and Guardians. T **585** and similar vert designs. Multicoloured. P 14.
2311	40c. Type **585**	20	10
2312	80c. Kurangaituku (giant bird woman)	35	25
2313	$1.10 Te Hoata and Te Pupu (volcanic taniwha sisters)	50	45
2314	$1.20 Patupaiarehe (mountain fairy tribe)	55	70
2315	$1.50 Te Ngarara-huarau (giant first lizard)	60	1·00
2316	$1.80 Tuhirangi (South Island sea guardian)	70	1·00
2311/16 *Set of 6*		2·50	3·00
MS2317 125×90 mm. Nos. 2315/16		2·00	2·00

A further miniature sheet, containing Nos. 2313/14, comes from a Limited Edition Collectors Pack costing NZ$135.

586 Chilly Bin (cool box)   **587** Volkswagen Beetle

(Des B. Gagnon. Litho Southern Colour Print, Dunedin)

2000 (3 Apr). New Zealand Life (2nd series). T **586** and similar vert designs each including a cartoon kiwi. Multicoloured. Phosphorised paper. Self-adhesive. P 10.
2318	40c. Type **586**	35	45
	a. Booklet pane. Nos. 2318/27	3·25	4·00
	b. Sheetlet of 10. Nos. 2318/27	12·00	
2319	40c. Pipis (seafood delicacy)	35	45
2320	40c. "Lilo"	35	45
2321	40c. Chocolate fish	35	45
2322	40c. Bach or Crib (holiday home)	35	45
2323	40c. Barbeque	35	45
2324	40c. Ug (fur-lined) boots	35	45
2325	40c. Anzac biscuits	35	45
2326	40c. Hot dog	35	45
2327	40c. Meat pie	35	45
2318/27 *Set of 10*		3·25	4·00

No. 2318/27 were normally issued in $4 stamp booklets with the surplus self-adhesive paper retained, SB102.

No. 2318b comes from the residue of special sheet stock used to prepare first day covers and subsequently sold as $4 "hang-sell" sheetlets. Philatelic Bureau customers with a standing order for stamps, rather than stamp booklets, also received this item, which has plain backing paper and the surplus self-adhesive paper removed.

(Des Red Cactus Design. Litho Southern Colour Print, Dunedin)

2000 (27 May). The Stamp Show 2000 International Stamp Exhibition, London. Sheet 110×80 mm, containing Nos. 1934b and 1934e/f. Multicoloured. Phosphorised paper. P 13½.
MS2328 $1 Taiaroa Head; $2 Great Barrier Island; $3 Cape Kidnappers .... 4·00   4·50

(Des Cato Partners. Litho Southern Colour Print, Dunedin)

2000 (1 June). "On the Road". Motor Cars. T **587** and similar square designs. Phosphorised paper. P 14.

2329	40c. red-brown and black	25	10
2330	80c. grey-blue and black	45	35
2331	$1.10 light brown and black	65	60
2332	$1.20 green and black	70	75
2333	$1.50 olive-brown and black	80	1·25
2334	$1.80 slate-lilac and black	90	1·25
2329/34 *Set of 6*		3·25	3·75

Designs:—80c., Ford Zephyr MK I; $1.10, Morris Mini Mk II; $1.20, Holden HQ Kingswood; $1.50, Honda Civic; $1.80, Toyota Corolla.

The stamps also exist in seven miniature sheets, each 150×110 mm with a line of roulettes at left. Six of the miniature sheets contain Nos. 2329/34 as single stamps and the seventh sheet contains all six designs. These miniature sheets were only available from a booklet, No. SP1, containing stamps with a face value of $13.60, but sold at $14.95.

A further miniature sheet, containing Nos. 2329/34, both perforated and imperforate, comes from a Limited Edition Collectors Pack costing NZ$135.

588 Lake Lyndon, Canterbury

(Des Donna McKenna. Litho Southern Colour Print, Dunedin)

2000 (7 July). Scenic Reflections. T **588** and similar horiz designs. Multicoloured. P 14.

2336	40c. Type **588**	40	20
2337	80c. *Lion* (cruising launch) on Lake Wakatipu	70	40
2338	$1.10 Eruption of Mount Ruapehu	80	70
2339	$1.20 Rainbow Mountain Scenic Reserve, Rotorua	80	1·90
2340	$1.50 Tairua Harbour, Coromandel Peninsula	85	1·75
2341	$1.80 Lake Alexandrina	1·00	1·60
2336/41 *Set of 6*		4·00	5·25

For miniature sheet containing Nos. 2336 and 2341 see No. **MS**2368.

(Des Donna McKenna. Litho Southern Colour Print, Dunedin)

2000 (7 July). "EXPO 2000" World Stamp Exhibition, Anaheim, U.S.A. Sheet 132×78 mm, containing circular designs as Nos. 1490, 1490*b*/*c* and 2090/*a*, but all now litho. P 14.

MS2342	$1 bright scarlet; $1 blue; $1 violet; $1 bronze-green; $1.10 gold	3·25	4·00

589 Lady Elizabeth Bowes-Lyon and Glamis Castle, 1907

(Des Comm Arts Design. Litho Southern Colour Print, Dunedin)

2000 (4 Aug). Queen Elizabeth the Queen Mother's 100th Birthday. T **589** and similar horiz designs. Multicoloured. P 14.

2343	40c. Type **589**	45	30
2344	$1.10 Fishing in Lake Wanaka, New Zealand, 1966	80	70
2345	$1.80 With racehorse and holding bunch of daisies, 1997	1·25	1·60
2343/5 *Set of 3*		2·25	2·40
MS2346	115×60 mm. Nos. 2343/5	2·25	2·75

Nos. 2343/5 with commemorative inscriptions on the sheet selvedge and No. **MS**2346 in imperforate vertical strip of three miniature sheets come from a limited edition book costing NZ$99.

590 Rowing

(Des M. Bailey. Litho Southern Colour Print, Dunedin)

2000 (4 Aug). Olympic Games, Sydney, and Other Sporting Events. T **590** and similar horiz designs. Multicoloured. P 14×14½.

2347	40c. Type **590**	30	10

	a. "New Zealand" and "40c" omitted	£275	
2348	80c. Show jumping	65	40
2349	$1.10 Cycling	1·25	80
2350	$1.20 Triathlon	75	85
2351	$1.50 Bowling	90	1·40
2352	$1.80 Netball	90	1·40
2347/52 *Set of 6*		4·25	4·25

No. 2347a occurs on the bottom row of the sheet and was caused by a perforation shift.

Nos. 2351/2 omit the Olympic logo.

591 Virgin Mary and Baby Jesus   **592** Geronimo (teddy bear)

(Des Joanne Kreyl)

2000 (6 Sept–1 Nov). Christmas.

(a) Litho Southern Colour Print, Dunedin. T591 and similar horiz designs. Multicoloured. Phosphorised paper. P 14

2353	40c. Type **591**	30	10
2354	80c. Mary and Joseph on way to Bethlehem	50	25
2355	$1.10 Baby Jesus in manger	70	60
2356	$1.20 Archangel Gabriel	80	90
2357	$1.50 Shepherd with lamb	1·00	1·90
2358	$1.80 Three Wise Men	1·10	1·75
2353/8 *Set of 6*		4·00	5·00

(b) Litho SNP Ausprint. Self-adhesive. Multicoloured design 30×25 mm. Phosphor frame. P 11

2359	40c. Type **591**	35	30
	a. Booklet pane. No. 2359×10 (1.11)	3·25	3·25

No. 2359 was issued in rolls of 100 on which the surplus self-adhesive paper around each stamp was removed, or in booklets of ten, SB105, on which the surplus paper was retained. The phosphor frame on three sides of the stamp appears pink under U.V. light.

2000 (5 Oct). Children's Health. Teddy Bears and Dolls. T **592** and similar horiz designs. Multicoloured.

(a) Litho Southern Colour Print, Dunedin. Phosphorised paper. P 14½

2360	40c. +5c. Type **592**	35	50
	a. Block of 6. Nos. 2360/5	3·00	4·00
2361	80c. +5c. Antique French doll and wooden Schoenhut doll	45	70
2362	$1.10 Chad Valley bear	50	50
2363	$1.20 Poppy (doll)	55	80
2364	$1.50 Swanni (large bear) and Dear John (small bear)	60	1·00
2365	$1.80 Lia (doll) and bear	80	1·00
2360/5 *Set of 6*		3·00	4·00
MS2366	100×60 mm. 40c.+5c. Type **592**; 80c.+5c. As No. 2361	1·00	1·00

(b) Litho SNP Ausprint. Self-adhesive. Size 29×24 mm. Phosphor on bear. P 11

2367	40c. +5c. Type **592**	35	40

Nos. 2360/5 were either printed in individual sheets of 50 or together as *se-tenant* blocks of six.

No. 2367 was issued in rolls of 100 on which the surplus self-adhesive paper was removed. The phosphor, which shows pink under U.V. light, covers the bear.

(Litho Southern Colour Print, Dunedin)

2000 (5 Oct). CANPEX 2000 National Stamp Exhibition, Christchurch. Sheet 95×80 mm, containing Nos. 2336 and 2341. Phosphorised paper. P 14.

MS2368	40c. Type **588**; $1.80 Lake Alexandrina	1·60	1·75

593 Lesser Kestrel   **594** *Sonoma* (mail ship) at Quay

(Des P. Martinson. Litho Southern Colour Print, Dunedin)

2000 (4 Nov). Threatened Birds. T **593** and similar horiz designs. Multicoloured. Phosphorised paper. P 14.

2369	40c. Type **593**	50	30
	a. Pair. Nos. 2369/70	1·00	1·00
2370	40c. Yellow-fronted Parakeet	50	30
2371	80c. New Zealand Stilt ("Black Stilt")	70	55
2372	$1.10 Fernbird ("Stewart Island Fernbird")	75	70
2373	$1.20 Kakapo	90	1·00

2374	$1.50 Weka Rail ("North Island Weka")................	1·10	1·25
2375	$1.80 Brown Kiwi ("Okarito Brown Kiwi")..........	1·25	1·25
2369/75 *Set of 7*		5·25	5·25

Nos. 2369/75 are printed in sheets of 25. The 40c. values exist either in separate sheets or with the two designs horizontally and vertically *se-tenant*. Nos. 2369 and 2375 form a joint issue with France.

For miniature sheet containing Nos. 2374/5 see No. **MS**2393.

"BEST OF 2000". A further set of three miniature sheets as described below No. 2042, was distributed by the Philatelic Bureau to customers purchasing a certain amount of philatelic material during 2000. The stamps shown for 2000 were Nos. 1934*e*, 2090*a*, 2316, 2334, 2341, 2345, 2352, 2358 and 2375.

(Des Designworks. Litho Southern Colour Print, Dunedin)

2001 (1 Jan). Moving the Mail in the 20th-Century. T **594** and similar square designs. Phosphorised paper. P 14.

2376	40c. brown-purple and scarlet	35	35
	a. Sheetlet. Nos. 2376/85	3·25	3·25
2377	40c. grey-green	35	35
2378	40c. agate	35	35
2379	40c. violet-blue	35	35
2380	40c. olive-brown	35	35
2381	40c. blackish purple..	35	35
2382	40c. black and cinnamon	35	35
2383	40c. multicoloured..	35	35
2384	40c. maroon	35	35
2385	40c. multicoloured..	35	35
2376/85 *Set of 10*..		3·25	3·25

Designs:—No. 2376, Type **594**; 2377, Stagecoach crossing river; 2378, Early postal lorry; 2379, Paddle-steamer on River Wanganui; 2380, Railway T.P.O.; 2381, Loading mail through nose door of aircraft; 2382, Postwoman with bicycle; 2383, Loading lorry by fork-lift truck; 2384, Aircraft at night; 2385, Computer mouse.

Nos. 2376/85 were printed together, *se-tenant*, in sheetlets of ten. Each design carries a description on the reverse over the gum.

For miniature sheet containing Nos. 2376/85 without inscription on reverse see No. **MS**2424.

595 Green Turtle

596 Camellia

(Des Veda Austin. Litho Southern Colour Print, Dunedin)

2001 (1 Feb). Chinese New Year (Year of the Snake). Marine Reptiles. T **595** and similar vert designs. Multicoloured. Phosphorised paper. P 14.

2386	40c. Type **595**..	30	10
2387	80c. Leathery Turtle	50	30
2388	90c. Loggerhead Turtle	55	50
2389	$1.30 Hawksbill Turtle	75	1·10
2390	$1.50 Banded Sea-snake...................................	80	1·40
2391	$2 Yellow-bellied Sea-snake...........................	1·00	1·40
2386/91 *Set of 6*		3·50	4·25
MS2392 125×90 mm. Nos. 2390/1		2·00	3·00

(Des P. Martinson. Litho Southern Colour Print, Dunedin)

2001 (1 Feb). Hong Kong 2001 Stamp Exhibition. Sheet 100×80 mm, containing Nos. 2374/5. Phosphorised paper. P 14.

MS2393 $1.50, North Island Weka; $1.80, Okarito Brown			
Kiwi		2·50	2·50

(Des Lindy Fisher. Litho Southern Colour Print, Dunedin)

2001 (16 Mar). Garden Flowers. T **596** and similar horiz designs. Multicoloured. Phosphorised paper. P 14.

2394	40c. Type **596**..	20	10
2395	80c. Siberian Iris..	40	30
2396	90c. Daffodil...	50	50
2397	$1.30 Chrysanthemum.......................................	75	1·10
2398	$1.50 Sweet Pea...	80	1·25
2399	$2 Petunia	1·00	1·25
2394/9 *Set of 6*		3·25	4·00
MS2400 95×125 mm. Nos. 2394/9		3·25	4·25

An imperforate version of No. **MS**2400 comes from a Limited Edition Collectors Pack costing NZ$135.

(Des S. Fuller. Litho Southern Colour Print, Dunedin)

2001 (16 Mar). Invercargill "Stamp Odyssey 2001" National Stamp Exhibition. Sheet 133×81 mm, containing Nos. 1934*a/d*. Phosphorised paper. P 13½.

MS2401 90c. Rangitoto Island; $1 Taiaroa Head; $1.10,			
Kaikoura Coast; $1.30, Lake Camp, South Canterbury		2·75	3·00

597 Greenstone Amulet   **598** Douglas DC-3

(Des Cato Partners. Litho Southern Colour Print, Dunedin)

2001 (4 Apr). Art from Nature. T **597** and similar square designs. Multicoloured. Phosphorised paper. P 14.

2402	40c. Type **597**..	20	10
2403	80c. Oamaru Stone sculpture	40	30
2404	90c. Paua ornament	50	50
2405	$1.30 Kauri ornament..	75	1·10
2406	$1.50 Flax basket	80	1·25
2407	$2 Silver-dipped Fern frond	1·00	1·25
2402/7 *Set of 6*		3·25	4·00

Nos. 2402/7 were each printed in sheets of 25 (5×5) in which the stamps were included in four different orientations so that four blocks of four in each sheet showed the complete work of art.

(Des R. Poulton. Litho Southern Colour Print, Dunedin)

2001 (2 May). Aircraft. T **598** and similar horiz designs. Multicoloured. P 14.

2408	40c. Type **598**..	35	15
2409	80c. Fletcher FU24 Topdresser.........................	65	35
2410	90c. de Havilland DH.82A Tiger Moth.............	70	60
2411	$1.30 Fokker FVIIb/3m *Southern Cross*	90	1·10
2412	$1.50 de Havilland DH.100 Vampire	1·00	1·40
2413	$2 Boeing & Westervelt Seaplane	1·25	1·40
2408/13 *Set of 6*		4·50	4·50

Nos. 2408/13 also exist as seven miniature sheets, each 164×110 mm containing single examples of each value or the complete set. These come from a miniature sheet booklet (No. SP2), containing stamps with a face value of $13.80, which was sold for $19.95.

599 Parcel   **600** Bungy Jumping, Queenstown

(Des Esther Bunning. Litho SNP Ausprint)

2001 (6 June). Greetings Stamps. T **599** and similar square designs. Multicoloured. P 14½×14.

2414	40c. Type **599**..	35	45
	a. Vert strip of 5. Nos. 2414/18	1·60	2·00
2415	40c. Trumpet	35	45
2416	40c. Heart and ribbon.......................................	35	45
2417	40c. Balloons	35	45
2418	40c. Flower	35	45
2419	90c. Photo frame..	65	80
	a. Vert strip of 5. Nos. 2419/23	3·00	3·50
2420	90c. Fountain pen and letter............................	65	80
2421	90c. Candles on cake...	65	80
2422	90c. Star biscuits..	65	80
2423	90c. Candle and flowers....................................	65	80
2414/23 *Set of 10*..		4·50	5·50

Nos. 2414/18 and 2419/23 were printed together, *se-tenant*, as vertical strips of five in sheets of 20, each stamp with a *se-tenant* label inscribed with the "greetings".

Examples could also be personalised by the addition of a photograph in place of the inscriptions on the label.

(Des Comm Arts Design, Wellington. Litho Southern Colour Print, Dunedin)

2001 (9 June). "Belgica 2001" International Stamp Exhibition, Brussels. Sheet 180×90 mm, containing Nos. 2376/85 but with blue border and without inscriptions on reverse. P 14.

MS2424 40c.×10, Nos. 2376/85		4·75	5·00

(Des Designworks)

2001 (4 July). Tourism Centenary. T **600** and similar horiz designs. Multicoloured.

(a) Litho Southern Colour Print, Dunedin. Designs 38×32 mm. Ordinary or phosphorised paper ($1.50), phosphorised paper (others). P 14½

2425	40c. Type **600**..	20	10
2426	80c. Maori Canoe on Lake Rotoiti	40	30

2427	90c. Sightseeing from Mount Alfred..................	45	60
2428	$1.30 Fishing on Rees river................................	60	80
2429	$1.50 Sea-kayaking in Abel Tasman National Park	75	1·25
2430	$2 Fiordland National Park	95	1·40
2425/30	Set of 6	3·00	4·00

(b) Litho SNP Ausprint (also Southern Colour Print, Dunedin 40c., 2431c/ca). Designs 27×22 mm (2431c/ca), 26×21 mm (others). Phosphor frame. Self-adhesive. P 11

2431	40c. Type **600**.......................................	45	60
	a. Horiz strip of 3. Nos. 2431/33	2·25	3·00
	b. Booklet pane. No. 2431×10........................	4·00	5·00
	c. Perf 10	1·50	2·00
	ca. Phosphorised paper..............................	45	60
2432	90c. Sightseeing from Mount Alfred..................	80	1·25
	a. Booklet pane. No. 2432×10........................	7·50	10·00
2433	$1.50 Sea-kayaking in Abel Tasman National Park	1·25	1·50
	a. Booklet pane. No. 2433×5 plus 5 "air post international" labels......................................	6·50	8·00

Nos. 2431/3 were printed by SNP Ausprint in booklets of five or ten, SB106/8, and as a strip of three. The 40c. perf 10 comes from rolls of 100 printed by Southern Colour Print. The strip of three and the roll have the surplus self-adhesive paper removed, but this is retained for the three booklet panes.

All self-adhesive stamps from booklets and the se-tenant strip have a phosphor frame which reacts pink under U.V. light. The rolls of a 100 have a similar frame which stops short of the black panel at the foot of the stamps. Some coils comprise 16 stamps (at right-hand end) with phosphor frames and 84 on phosphorised paper, the two sections being separated by a coil-join.

For miniature sheet containing Nos. 2429/30 see **MS**2434.

(Des Designworks. Litho Southern Colour Print, Dunedin)

2001 (1 Aug). Philanippon 01 International Stamp Exhibition, Tokyo. Sheet 90×82 mm, containing Nos. 2429/30. Phosphorised paper. P 14.

MS2434	$1.50 Sea-kayaking in Abel Tasman National Park; $2 Fiordland National Park	2·25	3·00

601 Family cycling

602 When Christ was born of Mary free

(Des Comm Arts Design. Litho Southern Colour Print, Dunedin)

2001 (1 Aug). Children's Health. Cycling. T **601** and similar horiz designs. Multicoloured.

(a) Size 39×29 mm. Ordinary gum. Phosphorised paper. P 14

2435	40c. +5c. Type **601**.....................................	50	35
2436	90c. +5c. Stunt bike	85	75
MS2437	circular 100 mm diameter. Nos. 2435/6............	1·25	1·10

(b) Size 29×23½. Self-adhesive. Phosphor frame. P 10

2438	40c. +5c. Boy on bike....................................	40	30

No. 2435 was issued in sheets of 50 or in small sheets of ten (2×5) with red margins.

No. 2438 was issued in rolls of 100 on which the surplus self-adhesive paper was removed. The phosphor, which appears orange under U.V. light, is a three-sided frame with no markings along the top of the stamp.

(Des Comm Arts Design and R. Jones. Litho Southern Colour Print, Dunedin)

2001 (5 Sept–7 Nov). Christmas. Carols. T **602** and similar vert designs. Multicoloured.

(a) Size 29×34 mm. Ordinary gum. Phosphorised paper. P 13×14

2439	40c. Type **602**...	25	10
2440	80c. Away in a manger	45	35
2441	90c. Joy to the world......................................	50	50
2442	$1.30 Angels we have heard on high	75	1·00
2443	$1.50 O holy night..	85	1·25
2444	$2 While shepherds watched	1·10	1·75
2439/44	Set of 6	3·50	4·50

(b) Size 21×26 mm. Self-adhesive. Phosphor frame. P 10

2445	40c. Type **602**...	40	30
	a. Phosphorised paper (7.11)	45	40
	b. Booklet pane No. 2445a×10	4·00	

No. 2445, on which the phosphor appears pink under U.V. light, was issued in rolls of 100 on which the surplus self-adhesive paper was removed. Booklet pane No 2445b, SB109, retains the surplus self-adhesive paper around each stamp.

603 Queen Elizabeth II at State Opening of Parliament, 1954

604 Rockhopper Penguins

(Des Ann Adams. Litho Southern Colour Print, Dunedin)

2001 (3 Oct). Queen Elizabeth II's 75th Birthday. T **603** and similar vert designs. Multicoloured. Phosphorised paper. P 14.

2446	40c. Type **603** (black and silver)	50	30
	a. Horiz strip of 6. Nos. 2446/51	5·75	6·25
2447	80c. Queen Elizabeth II on walkabout, 1970..	80	50
2448	90c. Queen Elizabeth II wearing Maori cloak, 1977...	90	55
2449	$1.30 Queen Elizabeth II with bouquet, 1986..	1·25	80
2450	$1.50 Queen Elizabeth II at Commonwealth Games, 1990...	1·40	90
2451	$2 Queen Elizabeth II, 1997...........................	1·60	1·25
2446/51	Set of 6	5·75	3·75

Nos. 2446/51 were printed in sheets of one value or together, se-tenant, as horizontal strips of six.

Imperforate sheets of Nos. 2446/51 and se-tenant strips of the six values were distributed by the Philatelic Bureau to customers who had purchased a certain amount of material from them during 2001.

(Des Communication Arts Ltd. Litho Southern Colour Print, Dunedin)

2001 (7 Nov). New Zealand Penguins. T **604** and similar horiz designs. Multicoloured. P 14½.

2452	40c. Type **604**...	50	30
2453	80c. Little Blue Penguin	75	50
2454	90c. Snares Crested Penguins...........................	85	60
2455	$1.30 Erect-crested Penguins	1·10	85
2456	$1.50 Fiordland Crested Penguins	1·25	1·10
2457	$2 Yellow-eyed Penguins	1·60	1·40
2452/7	Set of 6	5·50	4·25

605 Gandalf (Sir Ian McKellen) and Saruman (Christopher Lee)

606 "Christian Cullen" (harness racing)

(Des Sacha Lees. Litho Southern Colour Print, Dunedin)

2001 (4 Dec). Making of The Lord of the Rings Film Trilogy (1st issue): The Fellowship of the Ring. T **605** and similar multicoloured designs.

(a) Designs 24×50 mm. Phosphorised paper. P 14½×14 (vert designs) or 14×14½ (horiz designs)

2458	40c. Type **605**...	60	30
2459	80c. The Lady Galadriel (Cate Blanchett).........	1·10	1·00
2460	90c. Sam Gamgee (Sean Austin) and Frodo Baggins (Elijah Wood) (horiz)....................	1·10	1·00
2461	$1.30 Guardian of Rivendell	1·60	2·50
2462	$1.50 Strider (Viggo Mortensen).........................	1·75	2·50
2463	$2 Boromir (Sean Bean) (horiz)......................	2·25	3·50
2458/63	Set of 6	7·75	9·75

(b) Designs 26×37 mm or 37×26 mm. Self-adhesive. Phosphor frame. P 10½

2464	40c. T **605**..	40	50
	a. Horiz strip of 6. Nos. 2464/9......................	5·50	8·00
	b. Booklet pane. Nos. 2464×4, 2465, 2466×2 and 2467/9	7·00	
2465	80c. The Lady Galadriel (Cate Blanchett).........	60	75
2466	90c. Sam Gamgee (Sean Austin) and Frodo Baggins (Elijah Wood) (horiz)....................	75	1·00
2467	$1.30 Guardian of Rivendell	1·25	2·00
2468	$1.50 Strider (Viggo Mortensen).........................	1·50	2·25
2469	$2 Boromir (Sean Bean) (horiz)......................	1·60	2·50
2464/9	Set of 6...	5·50	8·00

Nos. 2458/63 were each printed in sheets of 25 with the 40c. also available as a sheetlet of ten (5×2). They also exist as a set of six miniature sheets, each containing a single stamp, which were only available at a premium of $3 over the face value of the stamps.

Nos. 2464/9, on which the phosphor shows pink under U.V. light, were issued as strips of six, on which the surplus self-adhesive paper around each stamp was either retained or removed, or as a $9 booklet containing pane No. 2464b on which the surplus paper was retained, SB110.

For miniature sheets containing Nos. 2458, 2461, 2463 and 2462/63, see **MS**2490 and **MS**2523.

See also Nos. 2550/61, 2652/63 and 2714/26.

"**BEST OF 2001**." The Stamp Rewards" distributed by the Philatelic Bureau to customers purchasing a certain amount of material during 2001 were inperforate sheets of Nos. 2446/51, and an imperforate se-tenant strip and imperforate se-tenant block of the same six stamps.

(Des K. Dunkley. Litho Southern Colour Print, Dunedin)

2002 (7 Feb). Chinese New Year (Year of the Horse). New Zealand Racehorses. T **606** and similar horiz designs. Phosphorised paper. Multicoloured. P 14.

2470	40c. Type **606**	30	15
2471	80c. "Lyell Creek" (harness racing)	50	25
2472	90c. "Yulestar" (harness racing)	55	50
2473	$1.30 "Sunline"	80	80
2474	$1.50 "Ethereal"	90	1·40
2475	$2 "Zabeel"	1·25	1·40
2470/5	Set of 6	3·75	4·00
MS2476	127×90 mm. Nos. 2473/4	3·75	4·25

Nos. 2470/5 were each printed in sheets of 25 containing panes of 15 (3×5) and ten (2×5) separated by a vertical gutter showing Year of the Horse symbols.

607 Hygrocybe rubrocarnosa

608 War Memorial Museum, Auckland

(Des DNA Design. Litho Southern Colour Print, Dunedin)

2002 (6 Mar). Fungi. T **607** and similar vert designs. Multicoloured. Phosphorised paper. P 14.

2477	40c. Type **607**	30	10
2478	80c. Entoloma hochstetteri	45	30
2479	90c. Aseroe rubra	55	50
2480	$1.30 Hericium coralloides	70	1·10
2481	$1.50 Thaxterogaster porphyreus	80	1·40
2482	$2 Ramaria aureorhiza	1·00	1·60
2477/82	Set of 6	3·50	4·50
MS2483	114×104 mm. Nos. 2477/82	4·50	5·50

(Des Mission Hall Design. Litho Southern Colour Print, Dunedin)

2002 (3 Apr). Architectural Heritage. T **608** and similar multicoloured designs. Phosphorised paper. P 14½×14.

2484	40c. Type **608**	25	10
	a. Block of 6. Nos. 2484/9	3·25	4·50
2485	80c. Stone Store, Kerikeri (25×30 mm)	45	40
2486	90c. Arts Centre, Christchurch (50×30 mm)	50	50
2487	$1.30 Government Buildings, Wellington (50×30 mm)	75	80
2488	$1.50 Dunedin Railway Station (25×30 mm)	80	1·00
2489	$2 Sky Tower, Auckland	1·00	1·25
2484/9	Set of 6	3·25	3·50

Nos. 2484/9 were printed in sheets of one value or together, se-tenant, as blocks of six.

Nos. 2484/9 also exist as seven miniature sheets, each 150×110 mm, containing single examples of each value or the complete set. These come from a miniature sheet booklet (No. SP3), containing stamps with a face value of $13.80, which was sold for $16.95.

(Des Sacha Lees. Litho Southern Colour Print, Dunedin)

2002 (5 Apr). "Northpex 2002" Stamp Exhibition. Sheet, 130×95 mm, containing Nos. 2458, 2461 and 2463. Phosphorised paper. P 14×14½ ($2) or comp 14½×14 (others)*.

MS2490	40c. Gandalf (Sir Ian McKellen) and Saruman
	(Christopher Lee); $1.30, Guardian of Rivendell; $2
	Boromir (Sean Bean) (horiz) .... 6·50 6·50

*The 40c. and $1.30 values in the miniature sheet are perforated 14½ at top and 14 on the other three sides.

No. **MS**2490 was sold at face value.

609 "Starfish Vessel" (wood sculpture)

610 Brodie (Anna Poland, Cardinal Priddle)

(Des Gardyne Design. Litho and recess Swedish Stamp Ptg Office (Nos. 2492, 2497) or Litho Southern Colour Print, Dunedin (others))

2002 (1 May). Artistic Crafts. Joint Issue with Sweden. T **609** and similar horiz designs. Multicoloured. Phosphorised paper. P 12½ (Nos. 2492, 2497) or 14 (others).

2491	40c. Type **609**	25	25
2492	40c. Flax basket (Willa Rogers) (37×29 mm)	25	25
2493	80c. "Catch II" (clay bowl) (Raewyn Atkinson)	40	40
2494	90c. "Vessel Form" (silver brooch) (Gavin Hitchings)	50	50
2495	$1.30 Glass towers from "Immigration" series (Emma Camden)	75	85
2496	$1.50 "Pacific Rim" (clay vessel) (Merilyn Wiseman)	80	1·40
2497	$2 Glass vase (Ola and Maria Höglund) (37×29 mm)	1·00	1·40
2491/7	Set of 7	3·50	4·50

Nos. 2492 and 2497 are additionally inscribed "JOINT ISSUE WITH SWEDEN".

(Des CommArts Design. Litho Southern Colour Print, Dunedin)

2002 (5 June). Children's Book Festival. Stamp Design Competition. T **610** and similar horiz designs illustrating books. Multicoloured. P 14.

2498	40c. Type **610**	30	35
	a. Block of 10. Nos. 2498/2507	2·75	3·25
2499	40c. The Last Whale (Hee Su Kim)	30	35
2500	40c. Scarface Claw (Jayne Bruce)	30	35
2501	40c. Which New Zealand Bird? (Teigan Stafford-Bush)	30	35
2502	40c. Which New Zealand Bird? (Hazel Gilbert)	30	35
2503	40c. The Plight of the Penguin (Gerard Mackle)	30	35
2504	40c. Scarface Claw (Maria Rodgers)	30	35
2505	40c. Knocked for Six (Paul Read)	30	35
2506	40c. Grandpa's Shorts (Jessica Hitchings, Ashleigh Bree, Malyna Sengdara and Aniva Kini)	30	35
2507	40c. Which New Zealand Bird? (Olivia Duncan)	30	35
2498/507	Set of 10	2·75	3·25
MS2508	230×90 mm. Nos. 2498/2507	4·25	4·50

Nos. 2498/2507 were printed together, se-tenant, as blocks of ten throughout the sheets of 50.

611 Queen Elizabeth the Queen Mother, 1992

612 Tongaporutu Cliffs, Taranaki

(Des Red Cactus Design. Litho Southern Colour Print, Dunedin)

2002 (5 June). Queen Elizabeth the Queen Mother Commemoration. P 14.

2509	**611**	$2 multicoloured	2·00 1·60

(Des The Bureau Interactive. Litho Pemara (2516c) or Southern Colour Print, Dunedin) (others)

2002 (3 July)–03. Coastlines. T **612** and similar horiz designs. Multicoloured.

(a) Size 38×29 mm. Ordinary gum. Phosphorised paper. P 14

2510	40c. Type **612**	25	20
2511	80c. Lottin Point, East Cape	50	55
2512	90c. Curio Bay, Catlins	60	65
2513	$1.30 Kaikoura Coast	85	1·00
2514	$1.50 Meybille Bay, West Coast	95	1·75

2515	$2 Papanui Point, Raglan	1·25	1·75
2510/15 *Set of 6*		4·00	5·50

(b) Size 28×21 mm. Self-adhesive. Phosphor frame. P 10

2516	40c. Type **612**..	35	50
	a. Horiz strip of 3. Nos. 2516/18.......	2·40	3·00
	b. Booklet pane. No. 2516×10............	3·25	
	c. Perf 11 (27.5.03)............................	35	50
	ca. Booklet pane. No. 2516×10............	3·25	
	d. Perf 12½×13....................................	30	50
2517	90c. Curio Bay, Catlins...........................	80	1·10
	b. Booklet pane. No. 2517×10............	7·00	
2518	$1.50 Meybille Bay, West Coast..............	1·50	1·75
	b. Booklet pane. No. 2518×5	6·50	

Nos. 2516/18, on which the phosphor shows pink under U.V. light with a break in the frame corresponding to the design overlap on to the margin, were either issued together as strips of three, on which the surplus self-adhesive paper around each stamp was removed, or in booklets, each containing one value, on which it was retained, SB111/3.

No. 2516 was issued in rolls of 100 with surplus self-adhesive paper around each stamp removed.

For a cancelled *se-tenant* strip comprising Nos. 2510/5 see note below No. 2561.

613 Basket of Fruit

(Des R. Jones. Litho Southern Colour Print, Dunedin)

2002 (7 Aug). Children's Health. Healthy Eating. T **613** and similar multicoloured designs. Phosphorised paper.

(a) Ordinary gum. P 14

2519	40c. +5c. Type **613**.............................	50	55
2520	90c. +5c. Selection of vegetables........	75	80
MS2521	90×75 mm. Nos. 2519/20 and as No. 2522		
	(22×26 mm)..	1·75	2·00

(b) Self-adhesive. P 10

2522	40c. +5c. Fruit and vegetables (22×26 mm)...	30	35

No. 2522 was issued in rolls of 100 on which the surplus self-adhesive paper was removed.

(Des Sacha Lees/Comm Arts Design. Litho Southern Colour Print, Dunedin)

2002 (30 Aug). Amphilex 2002, International Stamp Exhibition, Amsterdam. Sheet 130×95 mm, containing Nos. 2462/3. Phosphorised paper. P 14½×14 ($1.50) or comp 14×14½ ($2)*.

MS2523	$1.50 Strider (Viggo Mortensen); $2 Boromir		
	(Sean Bean) (*horiz*)	2·50	2·50

*The $2 value in the miniature sheet is perforated 14 at top and left and 14½ at bottom and right.

No. **MS**2523 was sold at face value.

614 St. Werenfried, Tokaanu

(Des Comm Arts Design. Litho Southern Colour Print, Dunedin)

2002 (4 Sept). Christmas. Church Interiors. T **614** and similar multicoloured designs.

(a) Size 35×35 mm. Phosphorised paper. Ordinary gum. P 14½

2524	40c. Type **614**....................................	25	10
2525	80c. St. David's, Christchurch	50	25
2526	90c. Orthodox Church of Transfiguration of		
	Our Lord, Masterton	60	50
2527	$1.30 Cathedral of the Holy Spirit, Palmerston		
	North...	85	75
2528	$1.50 St. Paul's Cathedral, Wellington	95	1·10
2529	$2 Cathedral of the Blessed Sacrament,		
	Christchurch..................................	1·25	1·60
2524/9 *Set of 6*..		4·00	3·75

(b) Size 25×30 mm. Self-adhesive. Phosphor frame. P 13½×12½

2530	40c. St. Werenfried, Tokaanu	30	30
	a. Perf 10	40	30
	ab. Booklet pane. No. 2530a×10.........	3·50	

On Nos. 2530/a the phosphor shows pink under U.V. light, No. 2530 was printed in rolls of 100 on which the surplus self-adhesive paper around each stamp was removed.

No. 2530a was only available from $4 stamp booklets with the surplus self-adhesive paper around each stamp retained, SB114.

615 *KZ 1* (racing yacht)

(Des Capiche Design. Litho Southern Colour Print, Dunedin)

2002 (2 Oct). Racing and Leisure Craft. T **615** and similar horiz designs. Multicoloured. Phosphorised paper. P 14.

2531	40c. Type **615**....................................	30	30
2532	80c. *High 5* (ocean racing yacht)........	55	55
2533	90c. *Gentle Spirit* (sports fishing and diving		
	boat)...	65	70
2534	$1.30 *North Star* (luxury motor cruiser)	90	1·00
2535	$1.50 *Ocean Runner* (powerboat)..........	1·00	1·40
2536	$2 *Salperton* (ocean-going yacht)...........	1·25	1·60
2531/6 *Set of 6*..		4·25	5·00
MS2537	140×80 mm. Nos. 2531/6	4·25	5·00

616 *Black Magic* (New Zealand) and *Luna Rossa* (Italy)

(Des CommArts Design. Litho Southern Colour Print, Dunedin)

2002 (2 Oct). America's Cup, 2003 (1st issue). T **616** and similar horiz designs showing scenes from 2000 final, between New Zealand and Italy. Multicoloured. Phosphorised paper. P 14.

2538	$1.30 Type **616**.................................	95	90
2539	$1.50 Aerial view of race	1·00	1·00
2540	$2 Yachts turning.................................	1·40	1·60
2538/40 *Set of 3*......................................		3·00	3·25
MS2541	140×80 mm. Nos. 2538/40.................	3·00	4·00

See also Nos. 2562/4.

(Litho Southern Colour Print, Dunedin)

2002 (4 Oct). Stampshow 02, International Stamp Exhibition, Melbourne. No. **MS**2541 with "Stampshow 02" emblem and inscription on the margin. Multicoloured. Phosphorised paper. P 14.

MS2542	140×80 mm. Nos. 2538/40.......................	3·00	3·25

617 Green-roofed Holiday Cottage and Paua Shell

(Des Cato Partners. Litho Southern Colour Print, Dunedin)

2002 (6 Nov). Holiday Homes. T **617** and similar horiz designs. Multicoloured. P 14.

2543	40c. Type **617**....................................	30	35
2544	40c. Red-roofed cottage and Sunflower.........	30	35
2545	40c. White-roofed cottage and life-belt	30	35
2546	40c. Cottage with orange door, boat and		
	fishing fly..	30	35
2547	40c. Blue-roofed cottage and fish..................	30	35
2548	40c. Cottage and caravan..............................	30	35
2543/8 *Set of 6*..		1·60	1·90

618 *The Nativity* (15th-cent painting in style of Di Baldese)

(Des CommArts Design. Litho Southern Colour Print, Dunedin)

2002 (21 Nov). New Zealand–Vatican City Joint Issue. Phosphorised paper. P 14.

2549	**618**	$1.50 multicoloured	1·25	1·40

No. 2549 was printed in sheets of ten.

(Des Sacha Lees. Litho Southern Colour Print, Dunedin)

2002 (4 Dec). Making of *The Lord of the Rings* Film Trilogy (2nd issue): *The Two Towers.* Multicoloured designs as T **605**.

(a) Designs 50×24 mm or 24×50 mm. Phosphorised paper. P 14×14½ (horiz) or 14½×14 (vert)

2550	40c. Aragorn (Viggo Mortensen) and Eowyn (Miranda Otto) (*horiz*)	60	20
2551	80c. Orc raider (*horiz*)	1·00	40
2552	90c. Gandalf the White (Sir Ian McKellen)	1·10	70
2553	$1.30 Easterling warriors (*horiz*)	1·40	1·25
2554	$1.50 Frodo (Elijah Wood)	1·60	2·00
2555	$2 Eowyn, Shield Maiden of Rohan (Miranda Otto) (*horiz*)	1·90	2·25
2550/5	*Set of 6*	7·00	6·00

(b) Designs 37×26 mm or 26×37 mm. Self-adhesive. Phosphor frame. P 10½

2556	40c. Aragorn (Viggo Mortensen) and Eowyn (Miranda Otto) (*horiz*)	25	50
	a. Block of 6. Nos. 2556/61	5·00	6·25
	b. Booklet pane. Nos. 2556×4, 2557, 2558×2 and 2559/61	6·50	
2557	80c. Orc raider (*horiz*)	80	70
2558	90c. Gandalf the White (Sir Ian McKellen)	70	80
2559	$1.30 Easterling warriors (*horiz*)	1·10	1·40
2560	$1.50 Frodo (Elijah Wood)	1·25	1·50
2561	$2 Eowyn, Shield Maiden of Rohan (Miranda Otto) (*horiz*)	1·40	2·00
2556/61	*Set of 6*	5·00	6·25

Nos. 2550/5 were each printed in sheets of 25. They also exist as a set of six miniature sheets, each containing a single stamp, which were only available at a premium of $3 over the face value of the stamps.

Nos. 2556/61, on which the phosphor shows pink under U.V. light, were either issued as blocks of six, or as a $9 booklet containing pane No. 2556b, SB115, with the surplus paper retained in both instances.

"**BEST OF 2002**". A Further set of miniature sheets as described below No. 2042 was distributed by the Philatelic Bureau to customers purchasing a certain amount of philatelic material during 2002. The stamps shown for 2002 were Nos. 2090b, 2475, 2482, 2489, 2496, 2515, 2520, 2529 and 2545. In addition, a cancelled *se-tenant* strip was distributed comprising Nos. 2510/5.

(Des CommArts Design. Litho Southern Colour Print, Dunedin)

2003 (8 Jan). America's Cup (2nd issue). The Defence. Horiz designs as T **616**. Multicoloured. P 14.

2562	40c. Aerial view of *Team New Zealand* yacht.	25	30
2563	80c. Two *Team New Zealand* yachts	50	55
2564	90c. *Team New Zealand* yacht tacking	60	65
2562/4	*Set of 3*	1·25	1·40
MS2565	140×80 mm. Nos. 2562/4	1·75	1·75

619 Shepherd with Flock in High Country

620 Jon Trimmer in *Carmina Burana*

(Des Denise Durkin. Litho Southern Colour Print, Dunedin)

2003 (5 Feb). Chinese New Year (Year of the Sheep). Sheep Farming. T **619** and similar horiz designs. Multicoloured. P 14.

2566	40c. Type **619**	30	15
2567	90c. Mustering the sheep	50	50
2568	$1.30 Sheep in pen with sheep dog	80	1·00
2569	$1.50 Sheep shearing	1·00	1·50
2570	$2 Sheep shearing (*different*)	1·25	1·60
2566/70	*Set of 5*	3·50	4·25
MS2571	125×85 mm. Nos. 2568 and 2570	2·25	2·50

(Des CommArts Design. Litho Southern Colour Print, Dunedin)

2003 (5 Mar). 50th Anniv of Royal New Zealand Ballet. T **620** and similar multicoloured designs showing scenes from past productions. P 14.

2572	40c. Type **620**	30	15
2573	90c. *Papillon* (*horiz*)	50	35
2574	$1.30 *Cinderella*	80	70
2575	$1.50 *FrENZy*	1·00	1·25
2576	$2 *Swan Lake* (*horiz*)	1·25	1·40
2572/6	*Set of 5*	3·50	3·50

621 Officer, Forest Rangers, 1860s

622 Ailsa Mountains

(Des R. Jones. Litho Southern Colour Print, Dunedin)

2003 (2 Apr). New Zealand Military Uniforms. T **621** and similar vert designs. Multicoloured. P 14.

2577	40c. Type **621**	45	65
	a. Sheetlet. Nos. 2577/96	8·00	11·50
2578	40c. Lieutenant, Napier Naval Artillery Volunteers, 1890s	45	65
2579	40c. Officer, 2nd Regt, North Canterbury Mounted Rifles, 1900–10	45	65
2580	40c. Mounted Trooper, New Zealand Mounted Rifles, South Africa, 1899–1902	45	65
2581	40c. Staff Officer, New Zealand Division, France, 1918	45	65
2582	40c. Petty Officer, Royal New Zealand Navy, 1914–18	45	65
2583	40c. Rifleman, New Zealand Rifle Brigade, France, 1916–18	45	65
2584	40c. Sergeant, New Zealand Engineers, 1939–45	45	65
2585	40c. Matron, Royal New Zealand Navy Hospital, 1940s	45	65
2586	40c. Private, New Zealand Women's Auxiliary Army Corps, Egypt, 1942	45	65
2587	40c. Pilot serving with R.A.F. Bomber Command, Europe, 1943	45	65
2588	40c. Fighter Pilot, No. 1 (Islands) Group, Royal New Zealand Air Force, Pacific, 1943	45	65
2589	40c. Driver, Women's Auxiliary Air Force, 1943	45	65
2590	40c. Gunner, 16th Field Regt, Royal New Zealand Artillery, Korea, 1950–53	45	65
2591	40c. Acting Petty Officer, H.M.N.Z.S. Tamaki, 1957	45	65
2592	40c. Scouts, New Zealand Special Air Service, Malaya, 1955–57	45	65
2593	40c. Canberra Pilot serving with R.A.F. Far East Command, Malaya, 1960	45	65
2594	40c. Infantrymen, 1st Bn, Royal New Zealand Infantry Regt, South Vietnam, 1960s	45	65
2595	40c. Infantryman, New Zealand Bn, UNTAET, East Timor, 2000	45	65
2596	40c. Monitor, Peace Monitoring Group, Bougainville, 2001	45	65
2577/96	*Set of 20*	8·00	11·50

Nos. 2577/96 were printed together, *se-tenant*, in sheetlets of 20 with detailed descriptions of the designs printed on the reverse.

The stamps also exist in five miniature sheets, each 150×110 mm, containing two examples each of Nos. 2577/80, 2581/4, 2585/8, 2589/92 and 2593/6. These come from a miniature sheet booklet No. SP4, containing stamps with a face value of $16, which was sold for $19.95, SP4.

Two Types of 45c.:

New Zealand   New Zealand

I   II

(Des CommArts Design. (Nos. 2600/1, 2603, 2605/7, 2610/11, 2614 or Stamps Business (others). Litho Walsall (2605), SNP Sprint, Australia (2611) or Southern Colour Print, Dunedin (others))

2003 (9 May)–**09**. New Zealand Landscapes (1st series). T **622** and similar horiz designs, each including the fern symbol after the country inscr. Multicoloured.

(a) Ordinary gum. Phosphorised paper. P 14×14½ ($1.35) or 13½ (others)

2597	5c. Geyser, Whakarewarewa, Rotorua (9.5.07)	10	40
2598	10c. Central Otago (9.5.07)	15	30
2599	20c. Rainbow Falls, Northland (9.5.07)	25	40
2600	45c. Kaikoura (I) (22.3.04)	55	50
2601	50c. Type **622**	55	60
2602	50c. Lake Coleridge, Canterbury (9.5.07)	55	50
2603	$1 Coromandel	1·00	75
2604	$1. Rangitoto Island, Auckland (9.5.07)	1·60	1·50
2605	$1.35 Church of the Good Shepherd Lake Tekapo (22.3.04)	1·75	2·00
	a. Perf 13½ (8.2006)	2·50	2·50
2606	$1.50 Arrowtown	2·00	1·00
2607	$2 Tongariro National Park	2·25	1·50
2608	$2.50 Abel Tasman National Park (9.5.07)	2·50	2·00
2609	$3 Tongaporutu, Taranaki (9.5.07)	3·00	3·00
2610	$5 Castlepoint Lighthouse	5·50	5·50
2597/610	*Set of 14*	19·00	18·00

(b) Self-adhesive. Phosphor frame. P 11½×11 (45c.) or 10 (others)

2611	45c. Kaikoura (I) (22.3.04)	55	35
	a. Booklet pane. No. 2611×10	5·50	
	b. Type II	55	55
2612	50c. As No. 2602 (9.5.07)	65	65
	a. Booklet panc. No. 2612×10	6·25	
	b. Horiz pair. Nos. 2612/13	1·90	1·90
2613	$1 As No. 2604 (6.5.07)	1·25	1·25
	a. Booklet pane. No. 2613×10	12·50	
2614	$1.50 Arrowtown	1·40	2·25
	a. Booklet pane. No. 2614×5	7·50	
	b. Booklet pane. No. 2614×5, 5 International Economy labels and 5 International Air labels (27.03.07)	10·00	
	c. Ordinary paper	2·00	2·25
	ca. Booklet pane. No. 2614×5 (2.3.09)	10·00	
	d. Booklet pane. No. 2614×5 and 2 International Air labels (18.5.09)	10·00	

Nos. 2601, 2603, 2606/7 and 2610 were sold in limited quantities (and only in complete numbered sheets), with the black fern frond overprinted in silver foil. On all values the silver matches the black, with the fern frond segmented on its underside. An initial printing of the 50c. with the larger unsegmented fern frond was distributed by the New Zealand Post, who subsequently attempted to have them recalled for replacement.

No. 2611 was issued in sheets of 100 and $4.50 stamp booklets, No. SB122, both with the surplus self-adhesive paper retained. No. 2611b was issued in rolls of 100 with the surplus self-adhesive paper around each stamp removed.

No. 2612 was issued in rolls of 100 and $5 stamp booklets, No. SB135, No. 2613 was issued in $10 booklets No. SB137. No. 2612/13 were also issued in rolls containing the two designs.

No. 2614, on which the phosphor shows pink under U.V. light, was normally only available from $7.50 stamp booklets (Nos. SB116 and SB135), but single stamps with plain backing paper could be purchased from the philatelic bureau. Both versions have the surplus self-adhesive paper around each stamp retained.

See also No. 3150/6, 3227/33b, 3363/7, 3556/61 and 3773/80.

623 Sir Edmund Hillary and Mount Everest

(Des S. Fuller. Litho Southern Colour Print, Dunedin)

2003 (29 May). 50th Anniv of Conquest of Everest. T **623** and similar horiz design. Multicoloured. Phosphorised paper. P 14.

2616	40c. Type **623**	75	1·10
	a. Pair. Nos. 2616/17	1·50	2·10
2617	40c. Climbers reaching summit and Tenzing Norgay	75	1·10

Nos. 2616/17 were printed together, *se-tenant*, in horizontal and vertical pairs and were available in sheets of 50 and in sheetlets of ten with enlarged illustrated left-hand margins.

624 Buckingham Palace   **625** New Zealand vs. South Africa Match, 1937

(Des L. C. Mitchell ($2), J. Berry (others), adapted CommArts Design, Wellington. Litho Southern Colour Print, Dunedin)

2003 (4 June). 50th Anniv of Coronation. As T **163/4** (Coronation issue of 1953) but face values in decimal currency as T **624**. Phosphorised paper. P 14×14½ (40c., $1.30, $2) or 14½×14 (90c., $1.50).

2618	40c. deep ultramarine	45	25
2619	90c. reddish brown	80	1·00
2620	$1.30 carmine-red	1·25	1·50
2621	$1.50 deep blue	1·40	1·75
2622	$2 reddish violet and dull ultramarine	1·60	2·00
2618/22 *Set of 5*		5·00	6·00

Designs: Vert (as T **164**)—90c. Queen Elizabeth II; $1.50, Westminster Abbey. Horiz (as T **624**)—$1.30, Coronation State Coach; $2 St. Edward's Crown and Royal Sceptre.

(Des DNA Design. Litho Southern Colour Print, Dunedin)

2003 (2 July). Centenary of New Zealand Test Rugby. T **625** and similar horiz designs. Multicoloured. Phosphorised paper. P 14.

2623	40c. Type **625**	30	15
2624	90c. New Zealand vs. Wales match, 1963	50	45
2625	$1.30 New Zealand vs. Australia, 1985	70	70

2626	$1.50 New Zealand vs. France, 1986	80	1·40
2627	$1.50 All Black jersey	80	1·40
2628	$2 New Zealand vs. England, 1997	1·00	1·50
2623/8 *Set of 6*		3·50	5·00
MS2629 100×180 mm. Nos. 2623/8		3·50	5·00

626 Papaaroha, Coromandel Peninsula   **627** Boy on Swing

(Des Capiche Design. Litho Southern Colour Print, Dunedin)

2003 (6 Aug). New Zealand Waterways. T **626** and similar horiz designs. Multicoloured. Phosphorised paper. P 14½.

2630	40c. Type **626**	45	25
2631	90c. Waimahana Creek, Chatham Islands	75	85
2632	$1.30 Blue Lake, Central Otago	1·25	1·40
2633	$1.50 Waikato River	1·40	1·75
2634	$2 Hooker River, Canterbury	1·60	2·25
2630/4 *Set of 5*		5·00	6·00

(Des G. Taylor. Litho Southern Colour Print, Dunedin)

2003 (6 Aug). Children's Health. Playgrounds. T **627** and similar multicoloured designs. Phosphorised paper.

(a) Size 39×29 mm. Ordinary gum. P 14

2635	40c. +5c. Type **627**	50	60
2636	90c. +5c. Girls playing hopscotch	90	1·00
MS2637 88×90 mm. Nos. 2635/6 (P 14) and 40c.+5c. Girl on climbing frame (P 14½×14)		2·00	2·00

(b) Size 24×29 mm. Self-adhesive. P 9½×10

2638	40c. +5c. Girl on climbing frame	60	40

No. 2638 was available as single stamps or in rolls of 100, both with the surplus self-adhesive paper around each stamp retained.

628 Benz Velo (1895)   **629** Christ Child in Crib

(Des S. Fuller. Litho Cartor)

2003 (3 Sept). Veteran Vehicles. T **628** and similar horiz designs. Multicoloured. Phosphorised paper. P 13×13½.

2639	40c. Type **628**	35	25
2640	90c. Oldsmobile (1903)	60	70
2641	$1.30 Wolseley (1911)	90	1·25
2642	$1.50 Talbot (1915)	1·10	1·50
2643	$2 Model T Ford (1915)	1·25	1·75
2640/3 *Set of 5*		3·75	5·00

(Des Lindy Fisher)

2003 (1 Oct). Christmas Decorations. T **629** and similar square designs. Multicoloured. Phosphorised paper.

(a) Size 30×30 mm. Ordinary gum. Litho Cartor. P 13½

2644	40c. Type **629**	35	10
2645	90c. Silver and gold bird	65	50
2646	$1.30 Silver candle	90	1·00
2647	$1.50 Bells	1·00	1·50
2648	$2 Angel	1·25	1·60
2644/8 *Set of 5*		3·75	4·25

(b) Size 21×26 mm. Self-adhesive. Litho Southern Colour Print, Dunedin. P 9½×10

2649	40c. Type **629**	45	35
	a. Black "Silver Fern" omitted	£350	£250
	b. Booklet pane. No. 2649×10	4·50	
2650	$1 Filigree metalwork decoration with baubles	1·00	1·00
	a. Booklet pane. No. 2650×8	8·00	

Nos. 2644/8 were each printed in sheets of 50 (5×10) in which the stamps were included in four different orientations to make ten blocks of four and five pairs in each sheet.

No. 2649 was issued in rolls of 100 and $4 booklets, No. SB117. No. 2649a comes from rolls.

No. 2650 was issued as self-adhesive stamps or $8 booklets, No. SB118.

(Des CommArts Designs. Litho Southern Colour Print, Dunedin)

2003 (4 Oct). Bangkok 2003 World Philatelic Exhibition. Sheet 110×80 mm containing Nos. 2572/3 and 2576. Phosphorised paper. P 14.
MS2651 40c. Type **620**; 90c. *Papillon* (horiz); $2 *Swan Lake* (horiz) .... 3·00 3·00

(Des F. Lenzen. Litho Southern Colour Print, Dunedin)

2003 (5 Nov). Making of *The Lord of the Rings* Film Trilogy (3rd issue): *The Return of the King*. Multicoloured designs as T **605**.

(a) Designs 24×49 mm or 49×24 mm. Phosphorised paper. P 14½×14 (vert designs) or 14×14½ (horiz designs)
2652	40c. Legolas	50	35
2653	80c. Frodo Baggins	85	1·00
2654	90c. Merry and Pippin (horiz)	95	1·00
2655	$1.30 Aragorn	1·25	1·50
2656	$1.50 Gandalf the White	1·50	1·75
2657	$2 Gollum (horiz)	2·00	2·75
2652/7 *Set of 6*		6·25	7·50

(b) Designs 24×35 mm or 35×24 mm. Self-adhesive. Phosphor frame. P 10×10½ (vert designs) or 10½×10 (horiz designs)
2658	40c. Legolas	50	55
	a. Horiz strip of 6. Nos. 2658/63	6·25	7·75
	b. Booklet pane. No. 2658×4, 2659, 2660×2 and 2661/3	9·50	
2659	80c. Frodo Baggins	85	1·00
2660	90c. Merry and Pippin (horiz)	95	1·00
2661	$1.30 Aragorn	1·25	1·50
2662	$1.50 Gandalf the White	1·50	1·75
2663	$2 Gollum (horiz)	2·00	2·75
2658/63 *Set of 6*		6·25	7·75

Nos. 2652/7 were each printed in sheets of 25.
They also exist as a set of six miniature sheets, each containing a single stamp, which were only available at a premium of $3 over the face value of the stamps.
Nos. 2658/63 were either issued as strips of six, or as a $9 booklet containing pane No. 2658b, SB119, with the surplus paper retained in both circumstances.

2003 (7 Nov). Welpex 2003 National Stamp Exhibition, Wellington. Sheet 120×100 mm containing Nos. 2626/8. P 14.
MS2664 $1.50 New Zealand vs. France, 1986; $1.50 All Blacks jersey; $2 New Zealand vs. England, 1997 .... 4·25 5·00

"BEST OF 2003". A further miniature sheet as described below No. 2042 was distributed by the Philatelic Bureau to customers purchasing a certain amount of material during 2003.
The sheet comprised Nos. 2570, 2576 and 2602.
Imperforate sheets of Nos. 2618/22 and a *se-tenant* strip comprising Nos. 2639/43 were also distributed.

630 Hamadryas Baboon

631 New Zealand Team

(Des Donna McKenna (Nos. 2665/9) or Lindy Fisher (MS2670))

2004 (28 Jan). New Zealand Zoo Animals. T **630** and similar vert designs. Multicoloured.

(a) Litho Cartor. Ordinary gum. Size 29×39 mm. Phosphorised paper. P 13½×13
2665	40c. Type **630**	45	25
2666	90c. Malayan Sun Bear	85	70
2667	$1.30 Red Panda	1·25	1·25
2668	$1.50 Ring-tailed Lemur	1·40	1·50
2669	$2 Spider Monkey	1·60	1·75
2665/9 *Set of 5*		5·00	5·00
MS2670 125×90 mm. Nos. 2668/9		3·00	3·00

(b) Litho Pemara (No. 2671) or SNP Sprint (No. 2671a). Self-adhesive. Size 24×29 mm. Phosphor frame. P 13½×12½
2671	40c. Type **630**	45	35
	a. Perf 11×11½	50	45
	ab. Booklet pane. No. 2671a×10	5·00	

No. MS2670 commemorates Chinese New Year, "Year of the Monkey".
No. 2671 was printed in rolls of 100 and has the surplus self-adhesive paper around each stamp removed.
No. 2671a comes from $4 booklets, No. SB120, and has the surplus self-adhesive paper around the stamps retained.

(Des CommArts Design. Litho Southern Colour Print, Dunedin)

2004 (30 Jan). Hong Kong 2004 International Stamp Exhibition. Sheet 110×80 mm containing Nos. 2627/8. Phosphorised paper. P 14.
MS2672 $1.50 All Blacks jersey; $2 New Zealand vs. England, 1997 .... 2·50 3·00

(Des CommArts Design. Litho Southern Colour Print, Dunedin)

2004 (25 Feb). Rugby Sevens. T **631** and similar horiz designs. Multicoloured. Phosphorised paper. P 14×14½.
2673	40c. Type **631**	45	25
2674	90c. Hong Kong team	85	70
2675	$1.50 Hong Kong Stadium	1·40	1·50
2676	$2 Westpac Stadium, Wellington	1·75	2·00
2673/6 *Set of 4*		4·00	4·00
MS2677 125×85 mm. Nos. 2673/6		4·00	4·00

Stamps of the same design were issued by Hong Kong.

632 Parliament Building, Auckland, 1854

(Des D. Gray. Litho Walsall)

2004 (3 Mar–5 Apr). 150th Anniv of First Official Parliament in New Zealand. T **632** and similar horiz designs. Phosphorised paper. P 14½.
2678	**632**	40c. purple and black	45	35
2679		45c. purple and black (5.4)	55	60
2680	–	90c. deep lilac and black	85	70
2681	–	$1.30 brownish grey and black	1·25	1·25
2682	–	$1.50 greenish blue and black	1·40	1·40
2683	–	$2 deep grey-green and black	1·60	1·75
2678/83 *Set of 6*			5·50	5·50
MS2684 186×65 mm. Nos. 2678 and 2680/3 ..			4·00	5·00

Designs:—90c. Parliament Buildings, Wellington, 1865; $1.30 Parliament Buildings, Wellington, 1899; $1.50 Parliament House, Wellington, 1918; $2 The Beehive, Wellington, 1977.

Nos. 2685/94. The three sets previously listed as Nos. 2685/8, "Draw it Yourself", 2689/91, Wild Food, and 2692/4, Kiwi Characters, have been deleted from this catalogue as it is now clear that they did not conform to listing criteria. *Prices (complete sets):*
"Draw it Yourself". £3.50 *unused*, £5.50 *used*
Wild Food. £4.00 *unused*, £5.50 *used*
Kiwi Characters. £4.00 *unused*, £5.50 *used*

636 Kinnard Haines Tractor   **637** "Dragon Fish"

(Des R. Jones. Litho Southern Colour Print, Dunedin)

2004 (5 Apr). Historic Farm Equipment. T **636** and similar horiz designs. Multicoloured. Phosphorised paper. P 14.
2695	45c. Type **636**	45	25
2696	90c. Fordson F tractor with plough	80	65
2697	$1.35 Burrell traction engine	1·25	1·40
2698	$1.50 Threshing mill	1·25	1·60
2699	$2 Duncan's Seed Drill	1·60	1·75
2695/9 *Set of 5*		4·75	5·00

The stamps also exist in six miniature sheets, each 148×109 mm with a line of roulettes at left. The stamps in these miniature sheets are larger than Nos. 2695/9.
Five of the miniature sheets contain Nos. 2695/9 as single stamps and the sixth sheet contains all six designs.
These miniature sheets were only available from a booklet, No. SP5, printed by Wyatt and Wilson, containing stamps with a face value of $12.40, but sold at $19.95.

(Des Cato Design. Litho Southern Colour Print, Dunedin)

2004 (5 May). Wearable Art. T **637** and similar vert designs. Multicoloured. Phosphorised paper. P 14.
2701	45c. Type **637**	30	15
2702	90c. "Persephone's Descent" (man in armour costume)	60	50
2703	$1.35 "Meridian" (woman in silk costume)	85	1·10
2704	$1.50 "Taunga Ika" (woman in net costume)....	85	1·25
2705	$2 "Cailleach Na Mara" (woman in sea witch costume)	1·25	1·50
2701/5 *Set of 5*		3·50	4·00

638 Magnolia "Vulcan"   **639**

(Des CommArts Design. Litho Southern Colour Print, Dunedin)

2004 (2 June). Garden Flowers. T **638** and similar vert designs. Multicoloured. Phosphorised paper. P 13½.

2706	45c. Type **638**	35	15
2707	90c. Helleborus (unnamed hybrid)	65	50
2708	$1.35 Nerine "Anzac"	90	1·25
2709	$1.50 Rhododendron "Charisma"	90	1·40
2710	$2 Delphinium "Sarita"	1·40	1·50
2706/10 *Set of 5*		3·75	4·25
MS2711 160×65 mm. Nos. 2706/10		3·75	4·25

The 45c. stamp in No. **MS**2711 was impregnated with the fragrance of Magnolia.

(Litho Southern Colour Print, Dunedin)

2004 (26 June). Salon du Timbre International Stamp Exhibition, Paris. Sheet, 125×95 mm, containing designs from **MS**2664 and No. 2676. P 14 ($1.50) or 14×14½ ($2).

MS2712	$1.50 New Zealand vs. France, 1986; $1.50 All Blacks jersey; $2 Westpac Stadium	2·75	3·25

2004 (29 June). Emergency 5c. Provisional Stamp. Die-cut wavy line.

2713	**639**	5c. steel-blue and scarlet-vermilion	2·00	2·00

640 Skippers Canyon
(The Ford of Bruinen)

(Des CommArts Design. Litho Southern Colour Print, Dunedin (Nos. 2714/**MS**2722) or SNP Sprint (Nos. 2723/6))

2004 (7 July). Making of *The Lord of the Rings* Film Trilogy (4th issue): *Home of Middle Earth*. T **640** and similar horiz designs. Multicoloured.

(a) Ordinary gum. Designs 40×30 mm. Phosphorised paper. P 14

2714	45c. Type **640**	35	50
	a. Vert pair. Nos. 2714/15	70	1·00
	b. Block of 8. Nos. 2714/21	6·50	9·00
2715	45c. Arwen facing Black Riders	35	50
2716	90c. Mount Olympus (South of Rivendell)	65	1·00
	a. Vert pair. Nos. 2716/17	1·25	2·00
2717	90c. Gimli and Legolas	65	1·00
2718	$1.50 Erewhon (Edoras)	1·10	1·75
	a. Vert pair. Nos. 2718/19	2·10	3·50
2719	$1.50 Gandalf the White, Legolas, Gimli and Aragorn riding to Rohan	1·10	1·75
2720	$2 Tongariro (Emyn Muil, Mordor)	1·50	2·00
	a. Vert pair. Nos. 2720/1	3·00	4·00
2721	$2 Frodo and Sam	1·50	2·00
2714/21 *Set of 8*		6·50	9·00
MS2722 100×180 mm. Nos. 2714/21		7·25	9·00

(b) Designs 29×24 mm. Self-adhesive. One side phosphor band. P 11½×11

2723	45c. Skippers Canyon (The Ford of Bruinen)	45	45
	a. Block of 4. Nos. 2723/6	2·00	2·50
	ba. Booklet pane. Nos. 2723/4 each×3 and Nos. 2725/6 each×2	5·50	
2724	45c. Arwen facing Black Riders	45	45
2725	90c. Mount Olympus (South of Rivendell)	65	1·00
2726	90c. Gimli and Legolas	65	1·00
2723/6 *Set of 4*		2·00	2·50

Nos. 2714/21 were printed together, *se-tenant*, as vertical pairs in blocks of eight or throughout sheets of 50.

They also exist as horizontal pairs in a miniature sheet (No. **MS**2722).

Nos. 2723/6, on which the phosphor shows pink under U.V. light, were printed in sheets of 100 (45c.) sheets of 50 (90c.) or as a coil of 100 (45c.).

They were also available as blocks of four and in $6.30 booklets (No. SB124) containing pane No. 2723ba with the surplus self-adhesive paper retained in both instances.

641 John Walker winning 1500 Metre Race

642 Children playing in the Sea

(Des Saatchi and Saatchi, Wellington. Litho and lenticular Xtreme Graphics USA)

2004 (2 Aug). Olympic Games, Athens. Gold Medal Winners. T **641** and similar horiz designs. Multicoloured. Self-adhesive. P 10½.

2727	45c. Type **641**	60	40
	a. Horiz strip of 4. Nos. 2727/30	4·50	4·50
2728	90c. Yvette Williams (long jump)	95	85
2729	$1.50 Ian Ferguson and Paul MacDonald (kayaking)	1·60	1·75
2730	$2 Peter Snell (800 metre race)	1·75	1·75
	a. Lenticular image inverted	£2000	
2727/30 *Set of 4*		4·50	4·25

Nos. 2727/30 were available as strips of four stamps or in sheets of 16. They were printed by lenticular process, producing 3-D animated images.

Examples of No. 2730a were sold from at least three post offices. Other values purporting to have the lenticular image inverted are considered to be forgeries.

(Litho Southern Colour Print)

2004 (28 Aug). World Stamp Exhibition, Singapore. Sheet 125×95 mm containing Nos. 2716/19. Multicoloured. Phosphorised paper. P 14.

MS2731	90c. Gimli and Legolas; 90c. Mount Olympus (South of Rivendell); $1.50 Gandalf the White, Legolas, Gimli and Aragorn riding to Rohan; $1.50 Erewhon (Edoras)	3·00	3·50

(Des CommArts Design. Litho Southern Colour Print, Dunedin)

2004 (1 Sept). Tourism (1st series). Horiz designs as T **622**, Multicoloured. Phosphorised paper. P 13½.

2732	$1.50 The Bath House, Rotorua	1·25	1·60
2733	$1.50 Pohutu Geyser, Rotorua	1·25	1·60
2734	$1.50 Hawke's Bay	1·25	1·60
2735	$1.50 Lake Wakatipu, Queenstown	1·25	1·60
2736	$1.50 Mitre Peak, Milford Sound	1·25	1·60
2737	$1.50 Kaikoura	1·25	1·60
2732/7 *Set of 6*		6·50	8·50

See also Nos. 2868/73.

(Des Chrometoaster. Litho Southern Colour Print, Dunedin)

2004 (1 Sept). Children's Health. A Day at the Beach. T **642** and similar vert designs. Multicoloured.

(a) Size 30×40 mm. Ordinary gum. Phosphorised paper. P 14

2738	45c. +5c.Type **642**	35	40
2739	90c. +5c. People in dinghy and swimmer	65	70
MS2740	102×90 mm. Nos. 2738/9 and 45c.+5c. Children fishing (25×30 *mm*). (P 14×14½)	1·40	1·50

No. 2741 was available as single stamps or in sheets of 100.

Some examples of No. 2741 showed phosphor bands of various sizes at the foot of the stamp.

(b) Size 24×29 mm. Self-adhesive. Phosphor frame. P 9½×10

2741	45c. +5c. Children fishing	35	40

643 Christmas Dinner

644 Christmas Dinner

(Des P. Hooker. Litho Southern Colour Print, Dunedin)

2004 (4 Oct). Christmas. T **643** and similar diamond-shaped designs. Multicoloured.

(a) Ordinary gum. Designs 49×49 mm. Phosphorised paper. P 14½

2742	45c. Type **643**	40	10
2743	90c. Traditional Maori meal	65	45

2744	$1.35 Barbecued prawns and salmon............	95	1·25
2745	$1.50 Pie and salad..	1·00	1·50
2746	$2 Plum pudding and pavlova........................	1·40	1·75
2742/6 Set of 5..		4·00	4·50

*(b) Vert designs as T **644**. Self-adhesive. Phosphor frame. P 10*

2747	45c. Type **644**..	45	40
	a. Booklet pane. No. 2747×10..................	4·00	
2748	90c. Traditional Maori meal........................	80	1·25
2749	$1 Christmas cake and cards........................	95	1·25
	a. Booklet pane. No. 2749×8....................	7·00	

Nos. 2742/6 and No. 2748 were each printed in sheets of 50 stamps. No. 2747 was issued in rolls of 100 and $4.50 stamp booklets, No. SB125. No. 2749 was issued in $8 booklets, No. SB126.
The surplus self-adhesive paper around each stamp in booklets Nos. SB125/6 was retained.

(Litho Southern Colour Print, Dunedin)

2004 (29 Oct). "Baypex 2004 Hawke's Bay Stamp Show". Sheet 130×70 mm, containing Nos. 1934f and 2734. Multicoloured. Phosphorised paper. P 13½.

MS2750	$1.50 Hawke's Bay, $3 Cape Kidnappers............	4·00	4·75

645 Whitewater Rafting

(Des CommArts Design. Litho Southern Colour Print, Dunedin)

2004 (1 Dec). Extreme Sports. T **645** and similar horiz designs. Multicoloured. Phosphorised paper. P 14.

2751	45c. Type **645**..	35	25
2752	90c. Snowsports...	60	65
2753	$1.35 Skydiving...	1·00	1·25
2754	$1.50 Jet boating..	1·00	1·60
2755	$2 Bungy jumping..	1·25	1·75
2751/5 Set of 5..		3·75	5·00

The stamps also exist in six miniature sheets, each 148×110 mm with a line of roulettes at left.
Five of the miniature sheets contain Nos. 2751/5 as single stamps and the sixth sheet contains all six designs.
These miniature sheets were only available from a booklet, No. SP6, containing stamps with a face value of $12.40, but sold at $14.95.

"**BEST OF 2004**." A further set of minature sheets as described below No. 2042 were distributed by the Philatelic Bureau to customers purchasing a certain amount of material during 2004. The sheets comprised; 1. Nos. 2669, 2676 and 2683; 2. Nos. 2699, 2705 and 2710; 3. Nos. 2720, 2755 and 2746. Imperforate sheets and mint and cancelled *se-tenant* strips of Nos. 2701/5 were also distributed.

646 Sheep

(Des S. Sakaria. Litho Southern Colour Print, Dunedin)

2005 (12 Jan). Farmyard Animals and Chinese New Year (Year of the Rooster). T **646** and similar vert designs. Multicoloured.

(a) Ordinary gum. Phosphorised paper. P 14

2757	45c. Type **646**..	45	40
	a. Horiz strip of 5. Nos. 2757/61............	4·75	5·50
2758	90c. Sheep dog and puppy...........................	80	90
2759	$1.35 Pigs...	1·25	1·50
2760	$1.50 Rooster..	1·25	1·40
2761	$2 Rooster perched on farm equipment......	1·60	1·75
2757/61 Set of 5..		4·75	5·50
MS2762 126×90 mm. Nos. 2760/1.............................		3·50	4·25

(b) Size 24×30 mm. Self-adhesive. Phosphor frame. P 11

2763	45c. Sheep...	45	40
	a. Booklet pane. No. 2763×10..................	4·00	

Nos. 2757/61 were available printed *se-tenant* as horizontal strips of five with the backgrounds forming a composite design and also in single stamp sheets.
No. 2763 was issued in rolls of 100 and $4.50 stamp booklets, No. SB127, both of which have the surplus self-adhesive paper retained.

647 Beneficiaries (Centenary of Rotary International)

648 1855 Full Face Queen (Chalon head), London Print (No. 1)

(Des R. Jones. Litho Southern Colour Print, Dunedin)

2005 (2 Feb). Anniversaries of Organisations. T **647** and similar horiz designs. Multicoloured. Phosphorised paper. P 14.

2764	45c. Type **647**..	45	50
2765	45c. Rural development (50th Anniv of the Lions)..	45	50
2766	45c. Canoeists (150th Anniv of YMCA)...........	45	50
2767	$1.50 Building development (Centenary of Rotary International)................................	1·25	1·50
2768	$1.50 Miniature train (50th Anniv of the Lions).	1·25	1·50
2769	$1.50 Beneficiaries jumping (150th Anniv of YMCA)..	1·25	1·50
2764/9 Set of 6..		4·50	5·25
MS2770 130×100 mm. Nos. 2764/9 and central gutter.....		4·50	5·25

(Des Totem Design. Litho Southern Colour Print, Dunedin)

2005 (2 Mar). 150th Anniv of New Zealand Stamps (1st issue). Stamps of 1855–1905. T **648** and similar vert designs. Multicoloured. Phosphorised paper. P 14.

2771	45c. Type **648**..	45	25
2772	90c. 1873 Newspaper (Nos. 143/5)................	80	90
2773	$1.35 1891 Government Life (No. L 5).............	1·25	1·60
2774	$1.50 1989 Pictorial, Mt. Cook (No. 259)........	1·40	1·75
2775	$2 1901 Universal Postage (No. 277)...........	1·60	1·75
2771/5 Set of 5..		5·00	5·50
MS2776 160×80 mm. Nos. 2771/5..............................		5·00	5·50

See also Nos. 2777/84 and 2791/**MS**2796.

(Des Totem Design. Litho SNP Sprint (2783/4) or Southern Colour Print, Dunedin (others))

2005 (6 Apr). 150th Anniv of New Zealand Stamps (2nd issue). Stamps of 1905–1955. Vert designs as T **648**. Multicoloured.

(a) Phosphorised paper. Ordinary gum. P 14

2777	45c. 1906 New Zealand Exhibition (No. 371).	45	25
2778	90c. 1931 Health (No. 546)...........................	80	90
2779	$1.35 1935 Airmail (No. 571).........................	1·25	1·60
2780	$1.50 1946 Peace (No. 676)...........................	1·40	1·75
2781	$2 1954 Queen Elizabeth II (No. 736)..........	1·60	1·75
2777/81 Set of 5..		5·00	5·50
MS2782 160×80 mm. Nos. 2777/81...........................		5·00	5·50

(b) Designs 25×30 mm. Phosphor frame. Self-adhesive. P 13

2783	45c. As No 2777..	50	65
	a. Horiz pair. Nos. 2783/4.....................	1·25	1·60
	b. Perf 11..	50	65
	ba. Booklet pane. No. 2783×10................	4·50	
2784	90c. As No 2778..	75	1·00
	b. Perf 11..	75	1·00
	ba. Booklet pane. No. 2784×10................	7·00	

Nos. 2783/4, on which the phosphor shows pink under U.V. light, were printed together, *se-tenant*, as horizontal pairs and separately in booklets of ten.
No. 2784 was also available as a coil of 100 stamps.

(Litho Southern Colour Print, Dunedin)

2005 (21 Apr). Pacific Explorer World Stamp Exhibition, Sydney. Phosphorised paper. P 14.

MS2785 109×90 mm. Nos. 2775 and 2781........................		3·25	3·50

649 Café, 1910s

650 All Blacks Jersey

(Litho Wyatt and Wilson)

2005 (4 May). Café Culture. T **649** and similar cup-shaped designs. Multicoloured. Phosphor frame. Self-adhesive. Die-cut.

2786	45c. Type **649**	45	30
	a. Horiz strip of 5. Nos. 2786/90	4·75	5·50
2787	90c. Café, 1940s	80	70
2788	$1.35 Café, 1970s	1·25	1·25
2789	$1.50 Tables outside café on pavement, 1990s	1·25	1·40
2790	$2 Internet café, 2005	1·60	1·75
2786/90 *Set of 5*		4·75	5·00

Nos. 2786/90 were printed together, *se-tenant*, in horizontal strips of five stamps, and also in separate sheets of 25.

(Des Totem Design. Litho Southern Colour Print, Dunedin)

2005 (7 June). 150th Anniv of New Zealand Stamps (3rd issue). Stamps of 1955–2005. Vert designs as T **648**. Multicoloured. Phosphorised paper. P 14.

2791	45c. 1965 50th Anniversary of the Gallipoli Landing (No. 827)	45	25
2792	90c. 1988 Round Kiwi (No. 1490)	80	90
2793	$1.35 1990 The Achievers – Katherine Sheppard (No. 1550)	1·25	1·60
2794	$1.50 1994 Maori Myths – Maui (No. 1807)	1·40	1·75
2795	$2 2003 Centenary of New Zealand Test Rugby (No. 2627)	1·60	1·75
2791/5 *Set of 5*		5·00	5·50
MS2796 160×80 mm. Nos. 2791/5		5·00	5·50

(Des Saatchi and Saatchi. Litho Southern Colour Print, Dunedin)

2005 (1 June). DHL New Zealand Lions Rugby Series. T **650** and similar jersey-shaped designs. One phosphor band at foot. Self-adhesive. Die-cut.

2797	45c. black and grey	40	65
	a. Pair. Nos. 2797/8	80	1·25
2798	45c. multicoloured	40	65
2799	$1.50 black and grey	1·00	1·25
	a. Pair. Nos. 2799/2800	2·00	2·50
2800	$1.50 multicoloured	1·00	1·25
2797/800 *Set of 4*		2·50	3·50

Designs—No. 2797, Type **650**; No. 2798, Red Lions jersey; No. 2799, As No. 2797; No. 2800, As No. 2798.

Nos. 2797/8 and 2799/2800 were each printed together, *se-tenant*, as horizontal pairs in sheets of 24 stamps.

651 Kiwi

652 Kakapo ("Relies heavily on camouflage for defence")

(Litho Southern Colour Print, Dunedin)

2005 (6 July). Personalised Stamps. T **651** and similar square designs. Multicoloured. Phosphorised paper. P 14.

2801	45c. Type **651**	45	75
	a. Sheetlet. Nos. 2801/10	7·00	9·75
2802	45c. Pohutukawa (native Christmas tree)	45	75
2803	45c. Champagne glasses	45	75
2804	45c. Balloons	45	75
2805	45c. Wedding bands	45	75
2806	45c. Gift box	45	75
2807	45c. Baby's hand	45	75
2808	$1.50 Globe	1·25	1·60
2809	$2 As Type **651**	1·60	2·00
2810	$2 Fern	1·60	2·00
2801/10 *Set of 10*		7·00	9·75

Nos. 2801/10 were each printed together, *se-tenant*, in sheetlets of ten stamps.

(Des Cue Design. Litho Southern Colour Print, Dunedin)

2005 (3 Aug). Endangered Species. Kakapo. T **652** and similar horiz designs showing the Kakapo with different facts inscribed. Multicoloured. Phosphorised paper. P 14.

2811	45c. Type **652**	80	80
	a. Strip of 4. Nos. 2811/14	3·00	3·00
2812	45c. "Night Parrot unique to New Zealand"	80	80
2813	45c. "Nocturnal bird living on the forest floor"	80	80
2814	45c. "Endangered – only 86 known surviving"	80	80
2811/14 *Set of 4*		3·00	3·00

Nos. 2811/14 were each printed together, *se-tenant*, in horizontal and vertical rows within sheets of 16 stamps.

653 Child and Horse

654 Baby Jesus

(Des Donna Cross. Litho Southern Colour Print, Dunedin)

2005 (3 Aug). Children's Health. Pets. T **653** and similar vert designs. Multicoloured.

(a) Size 30×40 mm. Ordinary gum. Phosphorised paper. P 14

2815	45c. +5c. Type **653**	55	55
2816	90c. +5c. Child holding rabbit	90	95
MS2817 100×90 mm. Nos. 2815/16 and 45c.+5c. Children and dog (25×30 *mm*) (P 14½×14)		2·50	2·50

(b) Size 25×30 mm. Self-adhesive. Phosphor frame. Die-cut perf 9½×10

2818	45c. +5c. Children and dog	50	55

No. 2818 was available as single stamps or in sheets of 100.

(Litho Southern Colour Print, Dunedin)

2005 (18 Aug). TAIPEI 2005 International Stamp Exhibition. Sheet, 110×90 mm, containing Nos. 2733 and 2737. Phosphorised paper. P 13½.

MS2819 $1.50 Kaikoura; $1.50 Pohutu Geyser, Rotorua		2·50	2·75

(Des A. Petrov. Litho Southern Colour Print, Dunedin (2820/4) or SEP Sprint, Australia (2825/6))

2005 (5 Oct–2 Nov). Christmas. T **654** and similar multicoloured designs.

(a) Ordinary gum. Designs 35×35 mm. Phosphorised paper. P 14½

2820	45c. Type **654** (2.11)	30	15
	a. Horiz strip of 5. Nos. 2820/4	3·50	6·00
2821	90c. Mary and Joseph (2.11)	55	55
2822	$1.35 Shepherd (2.11)	90	1·10
2823	$1.50 Wise Men (2.11)	1·10	1·50
2824	$2 Star (2.11)	1·25	2·00
2820/4 *Set of 5*		3·50	4·75

(b) Size 24×29 mm. Self-adhesive. Phosphor frame. Die-cut perf 11

2825	45c. Type **654** (2.11)	45	35
	a. Booklet pane. No. 2825×10	4·00	
2826	$1 Gifts on straw	85	1·00
	a. Booklet pane. No. 2826×10	7·50	

Nos. 2820/4 were printed together, *se-tenant*, in horizontal strips of five stamps and separately in sheets of 50.

No. 2825 was issued in rolls of 100 and $4.50 stamp booklets (SB130). No. 2826 was issued in $10 stamp booklets (SB131).

The surplus self-adhesive paper around in each stamp in booklets Nos. SB130/1 was retained.

655 *King Kong*

656 Lucy opening the Wardrobe

(Des Saatchi & Saatchi. Litho Southern Colour Print, Dunedin)

2005 (19 Oct). *King Kong* (film). T **655** and similar vert designs. Multicoloured. Phosphorised paper. P 14½×15.

2827	45c. Type **655**	40	35
	a. Horiz strip of 5. Nos. 2827/31	4·75	5·50
2828	90c. Carl Denham	75	70
2829	$1.35 Ann Darrow	1·25	1·50
2830	$1.50 Jack Driscoll	1·40	1·50
2831	$2 Ann Darrow and Jack Driscoll	1·60	1·75
2827/31 *Set of 5*		4·75	5·25
MS2832 180×65 mm. Nos. 2827/31		4·75	5·50

Nos. 2827/31 were printed together, *se-tenant*, in horizontal strips of five stamps and separately in sheets of 25.

(Des A. Hollows. Litho Southern Colour Print, Dunedin)

2005 (17 Nov). National Stamp Show, Auckland. Sheet, 120×90 mm, containing Nos. 2774, 2780 and 2794. Phosphorised paper. P 14.

MS2833 $1.50 1989 Pictorial, Mt Cook (No. 259); $1.50 1946 Peace (No. 676); $1.50 1994 Maori Myths – Maui (No. 1807) .... 4·25   5·00

(Des Commarts Design)

2005 (1 Dec). Making of *The Chronicles of Narnia: The Lion the Witch and the Wardrobe* (film). T **656** and similar multicoloured designs.

(a) Ordinary gum. Litho Southern Colour Print. Phosphorised paper. P 14×14½ (vert) or 14½×14 (horiz)

2834	45c. Type **656**	40	25
2835	90c. Lucy, Edmund, Peter and Susan (*horiz*) ..	75	80
2836	$1.35 The White Witch tempting Edmund (*horiz*)	1·25	1·50
2837	$1.50 Dissenters turned to stone statues	1·40	1·60
2838	$2 Lucy and body of Aslan (*horiz*)	1·60	1·75
2834/8 *Set of 5*		4·75	5·50

(b) Self-adhesive. Litho Wyatt & Wilson. Designs as Nos. 2834/8 but smaller. Phosphor frame. Die-cut perf 13×12½

MS2839 200×70 mm. 45c. Type **656** (25×35 *mm*); 90c. As No. 2835 (35×25 *mm*); $1.35 As No. 2836 (35×25 *mm*); $1.50 As No. 2837 (25×35 *mm*); $2 As No. 2838 (35×25 *mm*) .... 6·00   7·00

Nos. 2834/8 also exist as a set of five miniature sheets, each containing a single stamp, which was sold at $8.70, a premium of $2.50 over the face value.

"BEST OF 2005". A further set of miniature sheets as described below No. 2042 were distributed by the Philatelic Bureau to customers purchasing a certain amount of material during 2005. The sheets comprised: 1. Nos. 2771, 2774 and 2775; 2. Nos. 2777, 2780 and 2781; 3. Nos. 2791, 2794 and 2795. Imperforate sheets of Nos. 2791/5 and a perforated *se-tenant* strip comprising the same five stamps were also distributed.

657 Labrador Retriever Guide Dog

658 Street Scene, *c.* 1930

(Des Stephen Fuller)

2006 (4 Jan). Chinese New Year (Year of the Dog). T **657** and similar vert designs. Multicoloured.

(a) Ordinary gum. Litho Southern Colour Print. Phosphorised paper. P 14

2840	45c. Type **657**	50	25
2841	90c. German Shepherd Dog	90	70
2842	$1.35 Jack Russell Terrier	1·40	1·25
2843	$1.50 Golden Retriever	1·50	1·90
2844	$2 Huntaway (New Zealand Sheepdog)	1·75	1·60
2840/4 *Set of 5*		5·50	5·50
MS2845 124×89 mm. Nos. 2843/4		5·50	6·00

(b) Self-adhesive. Size 25×30 mm

(i) Litho Pemara, Australia. Phosphor frame on three sides. Die-cut perf 13

2846	45c. Type **657**	50	60

(ii) Litho Sprintpak, Australia. Phosphor frame. Die-cut perf 11½

2847	45c. Type **657**	50	60
	a. Booklet pane. No. 2848×10	5·00	

No. 2846 was issued in rolls of 100. No. 2847 was issued in $4.50 stamp booklets (No. SB132).

(Des CommArts Design. Litho Southern Colour Print, Dunedin)

2006 (3 Feb). 75th Anniv of Hawke's Bay Earthquake. T **658** and similar horiz designs. Multicoloured. Phosphorised paper. P 14.

2848	45c. Type **658**	60	60
	a. Sheetlet. Nos. 2848/67	11·00	11·00
2849	45c. Aerial view of devastated city of Napier	60	60
	a. Horiz pair. Nos. 2849/50	1·10	1·10
2850	45c. Aerial view with roofless church and intact Public Trust Building, Napier	60	60
2851	45c. Fire engine and crew	60	60
2852	45c. HMS *Veronica*	60	60
2853	45c. Sailors from HMS *Veronica* clearing debris	60	60
2854	45c. Red Cross nurses with hospital patient..	60	60
2855	45c. Rescue services	60	60
2856	45c. Abandoned vehicles on broken road ("Devastation")	60	60
2857	45c. Outdoor hospital ward, Botanical Gardens, Napier ("Medical services")	60	60
2858	45c. Emergency mail plane	60	60
2859	45c. Refugees on road	60	60
2860	45c. Refugee tents, Nelson Park	60	60
2861	45c. Makeshift cooking facilities, Hastings	60	60
2862	45c. Maori women ("Community spirit")	60	60
2863	45c. Refugees boarding train	60	60
2864	45c. Reconstruction work ("Building industry") ..	60	60
2865	45c. Hastings Street rebuilt in Art Deco style, 1933	60	60
2866	45c. Carnival procession ("Celebrations")	60	60
2867	45c. Entrance to National Tobacco Company building, Ahuriri, 2005	60	60
2848/67 *Set of 20*		11·00	11·00

Nos. 2848/67 were printed together, *se-tenant*, in sheetlets of 20 stamps.

Nos. 2849/50 form a composite design showing an aerial view of Napier after the earthquake.

Nos. 2848/67 also exist in seven miniature sheets, each 150×110 mm, containing two examples each of Nos. 2848/50, 2865/7, 2851/3, 2854/5, 2856, 2858 and 2863, 2857 and 2859/60 and 2861/2 and 2864.

These only came from a miniature sheet booklet, No. SP7, containing stamps with a face value of $18.80, which was sold for $19.95.

(Des CommArts Design. Litho Southern Colour Print, Dunedin)

2006 (1 Mar). Tourism (2nd series). Horiz designs as T **622**. Multicoloured. Phosphorised paper. P 13½×14.

2868	$1.50 Lake Wanaka	1·40	1·75
2869	$1.50 Mount Taranaki	1·40	1·75
2870	$1.50 Halfmoon Bay, Stewart Island	1·40	1·75
2871	$1.50 Franz Josef Glacier, West Coast	1·40	1·75
2872	$1.50 Huka Falls, Taupo	1·40	1·75
2873	$1.50 Cathedral Cove, Coromandel	1·40	1·75
2868/73 *Set of 6*		7·50	9·50

659 Queen Elizabeth II

660 Champagne Glasses

(Litho and embossed Cartor)

2006 (21 Apr). 80th Birthday of Queen Elizabeth II. P 13½.

2874	**659** $5 multicoloured	5·00	5·00
MS2875 150×100 mm. No. 1272 of Jersey; $5 Type **659** (sold at $17.50)		12·00	15·00

An identical miniature sheet was issued by Jersey on the same date.

(Des Communication Arts. Litho Southern Colour Print, Dunedin)

2006 (3 May). Personalised Stamps. T **660** and similar horiz designs. Multicoloured. Phosphorised paper. P 14.

2876	45c. Type **660**	45	65
	a. Sheetlet. Nos. 2876/85 and 5 stamp-size labels	7·00	9·00
2877	45c. Buzzy Bee (toy)	45	65
2878	45c. Silver fern	45	65
2879	45c. Pohutukawa flower	45	65
2880	45c. Christmas star decorations	45	65
2881	45c. Engagement and wedding rings	45	65
2882	45c. Red rose	45	65
2883	$1.50 As No. 2878	1·25	1·60
2884	$2 As No. 2879	1·60	2·00
2885	$2 As No. 2880	1·60	2·00
2876/85 *Set of 10*		7·00	9·00

Nos. 2876/85 were printed together, *se-tenant*, in sheetlets of ten stamps containing two horizontal strips of five stamps separated by five stamp-size labels inscribed "Personalised Stamps 2006".

2006 (27 May). Washington 2006 World Philatelic Exhibition. Sheet, 120×80 mm containing designs as Nos. 2809/10 but without imprint date. Phosphorised paper. P 14.

MS2886 $2 Fern; $2 Type **651** .... 4·50   4·50

'Maori Performing Arts' A set of five stamps (45c., 90c., $1.35, $1.50 and $2) with the above title was due to be issued on 7 June 2006. The stamps were conventionally gummed but the 45c. value was also prepared in self-adhesive coils and booklets of ten stamps.

Three days prior to issue date, New Zealand Post announced that the issue would be withdrawn, but some stamps, in each format, including first day covers, had already been sent out to Philatelic Bureau customers.

661 Wind Farm, Tararua, Palmerston North

662 "5" and Tomatoes

(Des Watermark. Litho Southern Colour Print, Dunedin)

2006 (5 July). Renewable Energy. T **661** and similar multicoloured designs. Phosphorised paper. P 14.

2887	45c. Type **661**	75	25
2888	90c. Roxburgh Dam, Central Otago (hydro)...	1·50	90
2889	$1.35 Biogas production, Waikato	1·75	1·50
2890	$1.50 Wairakei Geothermal Power Station	2·00	2·50
2891	$2 Solar-powered lighthouse, Cape Reinga (vert)	3·25	3·00
2887/91 Set of 5		8·25	7·25

(Des Cue Design. Litho Southern Colour Print, Dunedin)

2006 (2 Aug). Children's Health. "5+ A Day" Healthy Eating Campaign. T **662** and similar multicoloured designs.

(a) Ordinary gum. Phosphorised paper. P 14

2892	45c. +5c. Type **662** (30×40 mm)	85	1·00
2893	90c. +10c. "+" and oranges (30×40 mm)	1·50	2·00
2894	$1.35 "a" and garlic (30×30 mm)	1·75	2·00
2895	$1.50 "DAY" and kiwi fruit (40×30 mm)	2·25	2·75
2896	$2 Hand silhouette and red cabbage (30×40 mm)	2·50	3·00
2892/6 Set of 5		8·00	9·75
MS2897 120×90 mm. Nos. 2892/6		9·00	10·00

(b) Self-adhesive. Phosphor frame. Die-cut perf 10

2898	45c. +5c. Type **662** (25×30 mm)	1·25	1·25

663 Gold Panning, c. 1880s

664 Decorated Silver Fern (Hanna McLachlan)

(Des Cato Partners. Litho Southern Colour Print, Dunedin)

2006 (6 Sept). Gold Rush. T **663** and similar multicoloured designs. Phosphorised paper. P 14.

2899	45c. Type **663**	75	25
2900	90c. Settlement at Kurunui Creek, Thames, c. 1868 (horiz)	1·40	1·00
2901	$1.35 Chinese prospectors at Tuapeka, Otago, c. 1900s (horiz)	1·75	2·00
2902	$1.50 Last Otago gold escort at Roxburgh, 1901 (horiz)	1·90	2·50
2903	$2 Waterfront at Dunedin, c. 1900s (horiz)..	2·25	8·00
2899/2903 Set of 5		7·25	8·00
MS2904 125×90 mm. As Nos. 2899/2903 but "NEW ZEALAND" on stamp and fern symbol in gold		9·50	11·00

The bottom of the prospector's pan on Nos. 2899 and **MS**2904 is printed in thermochromic ink which fades temporarily when exposed to heat, making the gold nuggets visible.

The stamps within **MS**2904 have the country inscription "NEW ZEALAND" on stamp and fern symbol die-stamped in gold.

(Litho Southern Colour Print, Dunedin)

2006 (4 Oct). Christmas. T **664** and similar square designs showing winning entries in children's stamp design competition "What Christmas Means to Me". Multicoloured.

(a) Ordinary gum. Designs 34×34 mm. Phosphorised paper. P 14½

2905	45c. Type **664**	60	15
	a. Sheetlet. Nos. 2905/10	3·25	2·75
2906	45c. Angel appearing to shepherds and magi (Isla Hewitt)	60	60
	a. Horiz strip of 5. Nos. 2906/10	2·75	2·75
2907	45c. Extended family around Christmas tree (Caitlin Davidson)	60	60
2908	45c. Virgin Mary and baby Jesus (Maria Petersen)	60	60

2909	45c. Beach and pohutakawa tree (Deborah Yoon)	60	60
2910	45c. New Zealand wood pigeon and Christmas star (Hannah Webster)	60	60
2911	90c. Santa hat on kiwi fruit (Pierce Higginson)	1·00	1·00
2912	$1.35 Kiwiana Christmas trees (Rosa Tucker)....	1·50	1·60
2913	$1.50 Pattern of four pohutakawa flowers (Sylvie Webby)	1·75	1·75
2914	$2 Camping at Christmas (Gemma Baldock)	2·00	2·00
2905/14 Set of 10		9·00	8·50

(b) Size 24×29 mm. Self-adhesive. Phosphor frame. Die-cut perf 10

2915	45c. Type **664**	50	40
	a. Booklet pane. No. 2915×10	5·00	
2916	$1.50 As No. 2913	1·40	1·75
	a. Booklet pane. No. 2916×10	14·00	

Nos. 2905/10 were printed together, *se-tenant*, in sheetlets of six stamps. No. 2905 was also printed in ordinary sheets.

Nos. 2906/10 were printed together, *se-tenant*, in horizontal strips of five stamps in sheets of 50.

No. 2915 was issued in rolls of 100 and $4.50 stamp booklets (SB133).

No. 2916 was issued in stamp booklets (SB134) sold at $13.50, providing a discount of $1.50 off the face value of the stamps.

Nos. 2915/16 could be purchased as *se-tenant* pairs from the Philatelic Bureau.

665 Dragon Boat Festival

(Des The Church. Litho Southern Colour Print, Dunedin)

2006 (1 Nov). Summer Festivals. T **665** and similar horiz designs. Multicoloured. Phosphorised paper. P 14½.

2917	45c. Type **665**	75	40
	a. Horiz strip of 5. Nos. 2917/21	7·25	7·25
2918	90c. Race day	1·40	90
2919	$1.35 Teddy bears' picnic	1·75	1·50
2920	$1.50 Outdoor concert	1·90	2·50
2921	$2 Jazz festival	2·25	2·75
2917/21 Set of 5		7·25	7·25
MS2922 185×80 mm. Nos. 2917/21		9·00	9·00

Nos. 2917/21 were printed together, *se-tenant*, as horizontal strips of five in sheets of 25, and also in separate sheets.

2006 (2 Nov). Kiwipex 2006 International Stamp Exhibition, Christchurch. Sheet 120×90 mm. Phosphorised paper. P 14.
MS2923 As Nos. 2809/10 but without imprint date (sold at $5) .... 5·50 7·50

No. **MS**2923 was sold at $5, a premium of $1 above the face value. The premium funded the NZ National Philatelic Trust.

(Litho Southern Colour Print, Dunedin)

2006 (16 Nov). Belgica '06 International Stamp Exhibition, Brussels. Sheet 120×90 mm. Phosphorised paper. P 14.
MS2924 Nos. 2883×2 and 2884 .... 5·50 7·50

"BEST OF 2006". A further set of miniature sheets as described below No. 2042 were distributed by the Philatelic Bureau to customers purchasing a certain amount of material during 2006. The sheets comprised: 1. Nos. 2844, 2852 and 2872; 2. Nos. 2879, 2891 and 2896; 3. Nos. 2903, 2914 and 2921.

Imperforate sheets of Nos. 2899/2903 and a perforated *se-tenant* strip comprising the same five stamps were also distributed.

666 Opening Ceremony, 1957

(Litho Southern Colour Print, Dunedin)

2007 (20 Jan). 50th Anniv of Scott Base, Antarctica. T **666** and similar horiz designs. Multicoloured. Phosphorised paper. P 14.

2925	45c. Type **666**	1·50	40
2926	90c. Scott Base, 1990	2·50	1·10
2927	$1.35 Aerial view of Scott Base, 2000	3·00	2·00
2928	$1.50 "SCOTT BASE" sign	3·50	4·50
2929	$2 Scott Base, 2005	3·50	4·50
2925/9 Set of 4		12·50	11·00

Nos. 2925/9 also exist as a set of five miniature sheets, each containing a single stamp, which was sold at $8.70, a premium of $2.50 over the face value.

667 Kunekune Piglet

668 Tuatara

(Des Cue Design. Litho Sprintpak, Australia)

2007 (7 Feb). Chinese New Year (Year of the Pig). T **667** and similar horiz designs. Multicoloured. P 14½×14.

2930	45c. Type **667**	75	40
2931	90c. Kunekune Pig	1·40	1·00
2932	$1.35 Arapawa Pig	1·75	2·00
2933	$1.50 Auckland Island Pig	1·90	3·00
2934	$2 Kunekune Pig, young sow "Ruby"	2·25	3·00
2930/4 Set of 5		7·00	8·50
MS2935 125×90 mm. Nos. 2933/4		4·25	4·75

(Des P. Faulkner. Litho Southern Colour Print, Dunedin)

2007 (7 Mar). Native Wildlife. T **668** and similar circular designs. Multicoloured. Phosphorised frame. Self-adhesive. Die-cut perf 11½.

2936	45c. Type **668**	75	40
	a. Horiz strip of 5. Nos. 2936/40	8·00	10·00
2937	90c. Kiwi	1·40	90
2938	$1.35 Hamilton's Frog	1·75	1·60
2939	$1.50 Yellow-eyed Penguin	2·50	3·00
2940	$2 Hector's Dolphin	2·50	3·00
2936/40 Set of 5		8·00	8·00

The backing paper of Nos. 2936/40 is divided into squares by lines of rouletting.

Nos. 2936/40 were issued in separate sheets; No. 2936a could only be purchased from the Philatelic Bureau.

(Litho Southern Colour Print, Dunedin)

2007 (30 Mar). Northland 2007 National Stamp Exhibition, Whangarei. Sheet 119×80 mm. Phosphorised paper. P 14.

MS2941 Nos. 2884 and 2891		7·00	8·00

NEW ZEALAND 50c

669 Scouts of 1908 and Lt. Col. David Cossgrove (NZ Scouts founder)

(Des S. Fuller. Litho Southern Colour Print, Dunedin)

2007 (24 Apr). Centenaries. T **669** and similar horiz designs. Multicoloured. Phosphorised paper. P 14.

2942	50c. Type **669**	1·25	1·40
	a. Horiz strip of 4. Nos. 2942/5	4·25	4·75
	b. Block of 8. Nos. 2942/9	14·50	16·00
2943	50c. Dr. Truby King (founder of Plunket Society) and nurse with baby, 1920s	1·25	1·40
2944	50c. All Golds, first New Zealand rugby league team, 1907	1·25	1·40
2945	50c. Sister Suzanne Aubert (founder) and classroom at Home of Compassion, 1907	1·00	1·00
2946	$1 Parents with baby, 2007 (Plunket Society)	2·00	90
2947	$1.50 Elderly lady and carer, 2007 (Home of Compassion)	2·50	2·75
2948	$2 Kiwi rugby league team, 2007	3·50	4·75
	a. Horiz pair. Nos. 2948/9	7·00	9·50
2949	$2 Scouts abseiling, 2007	3·50	4·75
2942/9 Set of 8		14·50	16·00

Nos. 2942/5 were printed together, se-tenant, in horizontal strips of four stamps in sheets of 20.

Nos. 2948/9 were printed together, se-tenant, in horizontal pairs in sheets of 20.

No. 2942b could only be purchased from the Philatelic Bureau.

No. 2945 could also be purchased in sheets of 20 of the same design at $10 a sheet from the Philatelic Bureau.

Centenaries: Nos. 2942, 2949 World Scout Movement; 2943, 2946 Plunket Society; 2944, 2948 Rugby League in New Zealand; 2945, 2947 Home of Compassion.

2007 (9 May). Personalised Stamps. As Nos. 2876/82 but new values. Multicoloured. Phosphorised paper. P 14.

2950	50c. Buzzy Bee (toy)	70	70
	a. Sheetlet. Nos. 2950/6 and 8 stamp-size labels	3·75	3·75
2951	50c. Pohutukawa flower	70	70
2952	50c. Engagement and wedding rings	70	70

2953	50c. Silver fern	70	70
2954	50c. Type **660**	70	70
2955	50c. Red rose	70	70
2956	50c. Christmas star decorations	70	70
2950/6 Set of 7		3·75	3·75

Nos. 2950/6 were printed together, se-tenant, in sheetlets of seven stamps alternated with eight stamp-size labels inscribed 'Personalised Stamps'.

670 Southern Cross and 0.5m Zeiss Telescope at Stardome Observatory, Auckland

671 "good as gold"

(Des Capiche Design. Litho SEP Sprint)

2007 (6 June). Southern Skies. T **670** and similar horiz designs. Multicoloured. Phosphorised paper. P 13×13½.

2957	50c. Type **670**	1·50	45
2958	$1 Pleiades and 1m McLellan telescope, Mt. John Observatory, Tekapo	2·00	1·00
2959	$1.50 Trifid Nebula and 24cm telescope, Ward Observatory, Wanganui	2·75	2·25
2960	$2 Southern Pinwheel and 1.8m MOA telescope, Mt. John Observatory	3·25	4·00
2961	$2.50 Large Magellanic Cloud and 11m Southern African large telescope	4·00	4·50
2957/61 Set of 5		12·00	11·00

The stamps also exist in six miniature sheets, each 150×110 mm with a line of roulettes at left. Five of the miniature sheets contain Nos. 2957/61 as single stamps and the sixth sheet contains all five designs. These miniature sheets are only available from a booklet, No. SP8, containing stamps with a face value of $15, but sold for $19.90.

(Des Stamps Business. Litho Southern Colour Print)

2007 (4 July). 'Classic Kiwi' (Kiwi slang). T **671** and similar horiz designs. Multicoloured. Phosphorised paper. P 14.

2962	50c. Type **671**	70	70
	a. Sheetlet. Nos. 2962/81	12·00	12·00
2963	50c. "sweet as"	70	70
2964	50c. "she'll be right"	70	70
2965	50c. "hissy fit"	70	70
2966	50c. "sparrow fart"	70	70
2967	50c. Kiwi and "cuz"	70	70
2968	50c. "away laughing"	70	70
2969	50c. "tiki tour"	70	70
2970	50c. "away with the fairies"	70	70
2971	50c. "wop-wops"	70	70
2972	50c. "hard yakka"	70	70
2973	50c. "cods wallop"	70	70
2974	50c. "boots and all"	70	70
2975	50c. "shark and taties"	70	70
2976	50c. "knackered"	70	70
2977	50c. "laughing gear"	70	70
2978	50c. "everyman and his dog"	70	70
2979	50c. "bit of a dag"	70	70
2980	50c. "dreaded lurgy"	70	70
2981	50c. "rark up"	70	70
2962/812 Set of 20		12·00	12·00

The shiny black portions at the right of Nos. 2962/81 are printed in thermochromic ink which fades temporarily when exposed to heat, revealing translations of the Kiwi slang on the stamps.

Nos. 2962/81 were printed together, se-tenant, in sheetlets of 20 stamps.

672 Electric Fence (Bill Gallagher), 1969

673 Girl releasing Peace Dove

(Des Tim Garman. Litho Southern Colour Print)

2007 (1 Aug). "Clever Kiwis". New Zealand Inventions. T **672** and similar horiz designs. Multicoloured. Phosphorised paper. P 14.

2982	50c. Type **672**	60	30
2983	$1 Spreadable butter (Norris and Illingworth)	1·25	1·10

2984	$1.50 Mountain buggy, 1992	2·00	2·00
2985	$2 Jet boat (Bill Hamilton)	3·25	3·75
2986	$2.50 Tranquilliser gun (Colin Murdoch), 1950s	3·75	4·00
2982/6 Set of 5		9·75	10·00

(Des Stamps Business. Litho Southern Colour Print)

2007 (3 Aug). Bangkok 2007 20th Asian International Stamp Exhibition. Sheet 80×70 mm. Phosphorised paper. P 14×14½.
MS2987 Nos. 2735/6 .... 4·00 4·00

(Des Stamps Business. Litho Southern Colour Print, Dunedin)

2007 (31 Aug). Huttpex 2007 Stampshow (National Exhibition), Lower Hutt. Sheet 120×90 mm. Phosphorised paper. P 14.
MS2988 Nos. 2960/1 .... 5·50 5·50

(Des Donna McKenna. Litho Southern Colour Print, Dunedin)

2007 (5 Sept). Children's Health. Peaceful World. T **673** and similar vert designs. Multicoloured.

(a) Size 30×40 mm. Ordinary gum. Phosphorised paper. P 14

2989	50c. +10c. Type **673**	1·00	1·00
2990	$1 +10c. Boy holding Japanese crane	1·75	1·75
MS2991 100×90 mm. 50c.+10c. Girls with peace lily (24×29 mm) (P 14½×14) and Nos. 2989/90		3·00	3·00
	a. Perf 14½×14×13½ (Girls with peace lily design), Perf 13½ (others)	3·00	3·00

(b) Size 24×29 mm. Self-adhesive. Irregular phosphor frame. P 10

2992	50c. +10c. Girls with peace lily	1·50	1·50

674 Queen Elizabeth II and Prince Philip, c. 2007

675 Christmas Symbols (Sione Vao)

(Des Communication Arts. Litho Southern Colour Print, Dunedin)

2007 (5 Sept). Diamond Wedding of Queen Elizabeth II and Prince Philip. T **674** and similar vert design. Multicoloured. Phosphorised paper. P 14.

2993	50c. Type **674**	50	50
2994	$2 On their wedding day, 1947	2·75	2·75
MS2995 110×90 mm. Nos. 2993/4		3·25	3·25

(Adapted by Communication Arts) Litho Pemara, Australia (Nos. 3000/1) or Southern Colour Print (others))

2007 (3 Oct). Christmas. T **675** and similar multicoloured designs showing winning entries in children's stamp design competition 'Christmas Symbols'.

(a) Ordinary gum. Litho Southern Colour Print, Dunedin. Designs 34×34 mm. Phosphorised paper. P 14½

2996	50c. Type **675**	60	10
2997	$1 Robin wearing Santa hat (Reece Cateley)	1·10	40
2998	$1.50 Baby Jesus (Emily Wang)	2·25	2·00
2999	$2 Beach cricket (Alexandra Eathorne)	3·00	3·50
3000	$2.50 Fantail (Jake Hooper)	3·75	4·50
2996/3000 Set of 5		9·50	9·50

(b) Self-adhesive. Litho SEP Sprint, Australia. Size 24×29 mm. Partial phosphor frame (at left and foot). Die-cut perf 11½ (Nos. 3001/2) or 13 (Nos. 3001b/2b)

3001	50c. As Type **675**	60	50
	a. Booklet pane. No. 3001×10	6·00	
	b. Perf 13	60	50
	ba. Horiz pair. Nos. 3001b/2b	2·25	2·75
3002	$1.50 As No. 2998	1·75	1·75
	a. Booklet pane. No. 3002×10	17·00	
	b. Perf 13	1·75	2·25

No. 3001 was issued in $4.50 stamp booklets, No. SB138.
No. 3002 was issued in stamp booklets (No. SB139) sold at $13.50, providing a discount of $1.50 off the face value of the stamps.
No. 3001b was issued in rolls of 100.
Nos. 3001b/2b could be purchased as *se-tenant* pairs from the Philatelic Bureau.

676 "GO YOU GOOD THING"

(Des Saatchi & Saatchi. Litho Southern Colour Print, Dunedin)

2007 (7 Nov). Personalised Stamps. T **676** and similar horiz designs. Multicoloured. Phosphorised paper. P 14.

3003	50c. Type **676**	75	75
	a. Sheetlet. Nos. 3003/12	11·00	11·00
3004	50c. "Look Who it is!"	75	75
3005	50c. "Love Always"	75	75
3006	50c. "THANKS A MILLION"	75	75
3007	50c. "WE'VE GOT NEWS"	75	75
3008	50c. "Wish you were here"	75	75
3009	$1 "Time to Celebrate"	1·40	1·40
3010	$1 "Kia Ora"	1·40	1·40
3011	$1.50 "You gotta love Christmas"	2·25	2·25
3012	$2 Chinese inscription	3·00	3·00
3003/12 Set of 10		11·00	11·00

Nos. 3003/12 were printed together, *se-tenant*, in sheetlets of ten stamps and five stamp-size labels.

"BEST OF 2007". A further set of miniature sheets as described below No. 2042 were distributed by the Philatelic Bureau to customers purchasing a certain amount of material during 2007. The sheets comprised: 1. Nos. 2934, 2929 and 2960; 2. Nos. 2948/9 and 2985; 3. Nos. 2998, 2994 and 3012.

Imperforate sheets of Nos. 2957/61 and a perforated *se-tenant* strip comprising the same five stamps were also distributed.

677 Dusky Sound, Fiordland **678** Rabbits

(Des Tim Garman)

2008 (9 Jan). Underwater Reefs. T **677** and similar horiz designs. Multicoloured.

(a) Ordinary gum. Litho Cartor. Designs 39×29 mm. Phosphorised paper. P 13×13½

3013	50c. Type **677**	75	30
3014	$1 *Callanthias australis* (splendid perch) and *Ecklonia radiata* (common kelp), Mayor Island, Bay of Plenty	1·50	1·25
3015	$1.50 Hydrocoral *Errina novaezelandiae* (red coral), Fiordland	2·25	2·50
3016	$2 *Diadema palmeri* (diadema urchin), Volkner Rocks, White Island, Bay of Plenty	3·00	3·50
3013/16 Set of 4		6·75	6·75
MS3017 120×80 mm. Nos. 3013/16		11·00	11·00

(b) Self-adhesive. Litho SEP Sprint, Australia. Size 29×24 mm. Phosphor frame. Die-cut perf 11½

3018	50c. Type **677**	75	75
	a. Booklet pane. No. 3018×10	7·50	
	b. Horiz pair. Nos. 3018/19	2·10	2·50
3019	$1 As No. 3014	1·40	1·75
	a. Booklet pane. No. 3019×10	14·00	

No. 3018 was issued in rolls of 100 and $5 stamp booklets, No. SB140.
No. 3019 was issued in $10 stamp booklets, No. SB141.
Nos. 3018/19 could be purchased as *se-tenant* pairs (No. 3018b) from the Philatelic Bureau.

(Des Lindy Fisher. Litho Southern Colour Print, Dunedin)

2008 (7 Feb). Chinese New Year (Year of the Rat). Pocket Pets. T **678** and similar horiz designs. Multicoloured. Phosphorised paper. P 14.

3020	50c. Type **678**	1·00	30
3021	$1 Guinea Pigs	1·75	1·25
3022	$1.50 Rats	2·50	3·00
3023	$2 Mice	3·25	3·50
3020/3 Set of 4		7·75	7·25
MS3024 125×90 mm. Nos. 3022/3		6·50	7·50

679 Drought, 1997–98

(Des Vertigo Design. Litho Southern Colour Print)

2008 (5 Mar). Weather Extremes. T **679** and similar horiz designs. Multicoloured. Phosphorised paper. P 14.

3025	50c. Type **679**	1·00	75
3026	50c. Pedestrians in gale, Auckland, March 2007	1·00	75
	a. Magenta, yellow and orange-brown omitted	£1200	

3027	$1 Storm waves, Evans Bay, Wellington, January 2001	1·60	1·40
3028	$1.50 Flooded farmland, Hikurangi, 2007	2·50	2·25
3029	$2 Snow storm, Ohai, Southland, May 2001	3·00	3·50
3030	$2.50 Heat, Matarangi beach, Coromandel, 2005	4·00	3·75
3025/30	Set of 6	12·00	11·00

2008 (7 Mar). Taipei 2008 21st Asian International Stamp Exhibition. Sheet 120×90 mm. Phosphorised paper.

MS3031	No. 3012 (P 14) and as No. 3023 (P 13½)	5·75	5·75

680 Sapper John Luamanu and Baby Daughter, ANZAC Day Parade, 2007

(Des Cue Design. Litho Southern Colour Print, Dunedin)

2008 (2 Apr). ANZAC (1st series). T **680** and similar horiz designs. Multicoloured. Phosphorised paper. P 14.

3032	50c. Type **680**	1·00	75
3033	50c. Auckland Infantry Battalion landing at Gallipoli, 25 April 1915	1·00	75
3034	$1 New Zealand soldiers on Western Front, April 1918	1·75	1·40
3035	$1.50 Sling Camp and chalk kiwi on Salisbury Plain, England, 1919	2·75	2·50
3036	$2 Maori Battalion performing haka, Helwan, Egypt, June 1941	3·50	3·25
3037	$2.50 161 Battery, Nui Dat, Vietnam, 1965–71	4·25	4·25
3032/7	Set of 6	13·00	11·50

The stamps also exist in seven miniature sheets, each 148×110 mm with a line of roulettes at left. Six of the miniature sheets contain Nos. 3032/7 as single stamps and the seventh sheet contains all six designs. These miniature sheets are only obtainable from a booklet, No. SP9, containing stamps with a face value of $16 but sold for $19.90.

See also No. 3131/6, 3199/3204, 3441/**MS**3447 and 3541/**MS**3553.

681 Miro Whero, Miro Ma, Miro Pango

682 The Pevensie Children playing in the Surf

(Des Len Hetet. Litho Southern Colour Print, Dunedin)

2008 (2 May). 150 Years of Kingitanga (Maori King) Movement. T **681** and similar multicoloured designs showing art by Fred Graham. Phosphorised paper. P 14.

3038	50c. Type **681**	75	40
3039	$1.50 He Piko He Taniwha	2·00	2·25
3040	$2.50 Kia Mau (horiz)	3·75	4·00
3038/40	Set of 3	6·00	6·00

(Des CommArts, Wellington. Litho Sprintpak, Australia)

2008 (7 May). Making of The Chronicles of Narnia: Prince Caspian (film). T **682** and similar horiz designs. Multicoloured. Phosphorised paper. P 14½×14.

3041	50c. Type **682**	1·25	45
3042	$1 Queen Susan	2·00	1·50
3043	$1.50 High King Peter	3·25	4·00
3044	$2 Prince Caspian	4·00	4·50
3041/4	Set of 4	9·50	9·50

Nos. 3041/4 also exist as a set of four miniature sheets, each containing a single stamp, which were sold at $7, a premium of $2 over the face value.

683 "Ranginui" (sky)

(Des Len Hetet. Litho Southern Colour Print)

2008 (5 June). Matariki (Maori New Year). T **683** and similar horiz designs. Multicoloured. P 14.

3045	50c. Type **683**	75	60
3046	50c. "Te Moana Nui A Kiwa" (prow of war canoe and Pacific Ocean)	75	60
3047	$1 "Papatuanuku" (land) (silver fern fronds)	1·50	1·10
3048	$1.50 "Whakapapa" (genealogy) (sunset)	2·50	2·25
3049	$2 "Takoha" (passing of tiki neck pendant to next generation)	3·00	3·50
3050	$2.50 "Te Tau Hou" (woodcarving and moon rising over sea)	4·00	4·50
3045/50	Set of 6	11·00	11·00
MS3051	150×90 mm. Nos. 3045/50	11·00	11·00

684 Girl riding Bicycle ("INSPIRE")

(Des Martin Bailey. Litho Southern Colour Print)

2008 (2 July). Children's Health. T **684** and similar diamond-shaped designs. Multicoloured.

(a) Ordinary gum. Phosphorised paper. P 14½

3052	50c. +10c. Type **684**	1·25	1·25
3053	$1 +10c. Boy kayaking ("PASSION")	1·60	1·75
MS3054	140×90 mm. 50c. +10c. Boy with arms outstretched in triumph (34×32 mm) (P 14×14½) and Nos. 3052/3	3·00	3·00

(b) Self-adhesive. P 10

3055	50c. +10c. Boy with arms outstretched in triumph ("EXCEL") (34×32 mm)	1·00	1·00

685 Rower ("CELEBRATE")

(Des Martin Bailey. Litho Southern Colour Print)

2008 (2 July). Olympic Games, Beijing. T **685** and similar diamond-shaped designs. Multicoloured. Phosphorised paper. P 14½.

3056	50c. Type **685**	1·25	1·00
3057	50c. Cyclist ("PASSION")	2·00	1·00
3058	$1 Kayaker ("SUCCEED")	2·00	1·50
3059	$2 Athlete ("MOTIVATE")	3·25	4·00
3056/9	Set of 4	7·75	7·00

686 "a" is for Aotearoa

687 Last Spike Ceremony, Manganui-o-te-Ao, 1908

(Des Clemenger BBDO. Litho Southern Colour Print)

2008 (6 Aug). The A to Z of New Zealand. T **686** and similar horiz designs. Multicoloured. Phosphorised paper. P 14½.

3060	50c. Type **686**	80	80
	a. Sheetlet. Nos. 3060/85	18·00	18·00

3061	50c. B is for Beehive (Parliament House, Wellington)	80	80
3062	50c. C is for Cook (Captain Cook)	80	80
3063	50c. D is for Dog (from Footrot Flats cartoon strip)	80	80
3064	50c. E is for Edmonds (Thomas Edmonds)	80	80
3065	50c. F is for Fantail (bird)	80	80
3066	50c. G is for *Goodnight Kiwi* (TV cartoon)	80	80
3067	50c. H is for Haka	80	80
3068	50c. I is for *Interislander* (ferry)	80	80
3069	50c. J is for Jelly Tip (ice cream)	80	80
3070	50c. K is for Kia Ora	80	80
3071	50c. L is for log o'wood (Ranfurly Shield rugby trophy)	80	80
3072	50c. M is for Mudpools	80	80
3073	50c. N is for Nuclear Free	80	80
3074	50c. O is for O.E. (overseas experience)	80	80
3075	50c. P is for Pinetree (All Black player Colin Meads)	80	80
3076	50c. Q is for Quake (earthquakes)	80	80
3077	50c. R is for Rutherford (nuclear physicist Sir Ernest Rutherford)	80	80
3078	50c. S is for Southern Cross	80	80
3079	50c. T is for Tiki (carved by Lewis Gardiner)	80	80
3080	50c. U is for Upham (Captain Charles Upham's Victoria Cross)	80	80
3081	50c. V is for Vote (suffragette Kate Sheppard)	80	80
3082	50c. W is for Weta (model of insect)	80	80
3083	50c. X is for x-treme sports	80	80
3084	50c. Y is for Yarn	80	80
3085	50c. Z is for Zeeland (explorer Abel Tasman)	80	80
3060/85 *Set of 26*		18·00	18·00

Nos. 3060/85 were printed together, *se-tenant*, in sheetlets of 26 stamps.

(Des Communication Arts. Litho Southern Colour Print)

2008 (3 Sept). Centenary of the North Island Main Trunk Railway Line. T **687** and similar horiz designs. Multicoloured. Phosphorised paper. P 14.

3086	50c. Type **687**	1·00	40
3087	$1 KA 947 class steam locomotive on display at Taumarunui, 1958	1·75	1·10
3088	$1.50 Steam hauled goods train on Makatote Viaduct, 1963	2·25	2·00
3089	$2 Steam hauled goods train climbing the Raurimu Spiral, 1964	3·00	3·75
3090	$2.50 EF powered "Overlander" crossing Hapuawhenua Viaduct, 2003	4·00	4·50
3086/90 *Set of 5*		11·00	10·50

2008 (18 Sept). WIPA08 International Stamp Exhibition, Vienna. Sheet 121×85 mm. Phosphorised paper. P 14.

MS3091 Nos. 3046 and 3048/9		4·50	4·75

688 Nativity

689 Sheep wearing Santa Hat and Jandals (Kirsten Fisher-Marsters)

(Des Martin Bailey. Litho Southern Colour Print (Nos. 3092/4) or Sprintpak, Australia (3095/6))

2008 (1 Oct). Christmas (1st issue). T **688** and similar square designs. Multicoloured.

(a) Ordinary gum. Phosphorised paper. P 14½

3092	50c. Type **688**	60	10
3093	$1 Holy Family	1·10	40
3094	$1.50 Mary and baby Jesus	1·75	2·25
3092/4 *Set of 3*		3·00	2·50

(b) Self-adhesive. Size 24×29 mm. Phosphor frame. Die-cut perf 11½ (Nos. 3095/6) or 13 (3095b/6b)

3095	50c. As Type **688**	60	50
	a. Booklet pane. No. 3095×10	6·00	
	b. Perf 13	65	50
	ba. Horiz pair. Nos. 3095b/6b	2·25	2·50
3096	$1.50 As No. 3094	1·60	1·75
	a. Booklet pane. No. 3096×10	16·00	
	b. Perf 13	1·60	2·00

No. 3095 was issued in $5 booklets, No. SB142, and No. 3096 in $15 booklets, No. SB143.

No. 3095b was issued in rolls of 100.

Nos. 3095b/6b could be purchased in *se-tenant* pairs from the Philatelic Bureau.

(Adapted Communication Arts. Litho Southern Colour Print)

2008 (1 Oct). Christmas (2nd issue). T **689** and similar square designs showing winning entries in children's stamp design competition 'Kiwi Christmas'. Multicoloured. Phosphorised paper. P 14½.

3097	50c. Type **689**	60	10
3098	$2 Pohutukawa flowers and koru (Tamara Jenkin)	2·25	2·75
3099	$2.50 Kiwi wearing Santa hat (Molly Bruhns)	2·50	3·25
3097/9 *Set of 3*		4·75	5·50

(Litho Southern Colour Print)

2008 (20 Oct). 90th Anniv of the End of World War I. Sheet 150×90 mm. Multicoloured. P 14.

MS3100 Nos. 3033/5		6·50	6·50

690 Sir Edmund Hillary

691 Pencarrow Lighthouse

(Des Vertigo Design. Litho Southern Colour Print)

2008 (5 Nov). Sir Edmund Hillary Commemoration. T **690** and similar vert designs. Multicoloured. Phosphorised paper. P 15.

3101	50c. Type **690**	1·00	40
3102	$1 Edmund Hillary and Tenzing Norgay during first ascent of Mt. Everest, 1953	1·75	1·10
3103	$1.50 On tracked vehicle, Trans-Antarctic Expedition, 1957–8	2·50	2·25
3104	$2 Sir Edmund Hillary (founder of Himalayan Trust, 1960) with Nepalese children	3·00	3·50
3105	$2.50 Appointed to the Order of the Garter, 1995	3·00	3·50
3101/5 *Set of 5*		10·00	9·75

(Litho Southern Colour Print)

2008 (7 Nov). Tarapex 2008 National Stamp Exhibition, New Plymouth. Sheet 138×86 mm. Multicoloured. P 13½.

MS3106 $4.50 As Nos. 2609 and 2869 but without imprint dates		5·00	5·00

"**BEST OF 2008**." A further set of miniature sheets as described below No. 2042 were distributed by the Philatelic Bureau to customers purchasing a certain amount of material durring 2008. The sheets comprised: 1. Nos. 3016, 3023 and 3030; 2. Nos. 3037, 3040 and 3050; 3. Nos. 3090, 3094 and 3105.

Imperforate sheets of Nos. 3025/30 and a perforated *se-tenant* block comprising the same six stamps were also distributed.

(Des Vertigo Design. Litho Sprintpak)

2009 (7 Jan). Lighthouses of New Zealand. T **691** and similar horiz designs. Multicoloured. Phosphorised paper. P 13.

3107	50c. Type **691**	1·00	45
3108	$1 Dog Island Lighthouse	1·75	1·00
3109	$1.50 Cape Brett Lighthouse	2·50	2·50
3110	$2 Cape Egmont Lighthouse	3·50	4·00
3111	$2.50 Cape Reinga Lighthouse	3·75	1·25
3107/11 *Set of 5*		11·00	11·00

Nos. 3107/11 commemorate the 150th anniversary of New Zealand's first lighthouse (Pencarrow Head).

The beams of light shining from the lighthouses on Nos. 3107/11 are printed in luminous ink.

692 Lunar Ox Symbol

693 Scott Dixon in Honda Indycar

(Des Bananaworks. Litho Cartor)

2009 (7 Jan). Chinese New Year (Year of the Ox). T **692** and similar vert designs. Multicoloured. Phosphorised paper. P 13.

3112	50c. Type **692**..	80	65
3113	$1 Ox..	1·40	1·40
3114	$2 Chinese lanterns and Auckland Harbour Bridge	2·75	3·50
3112/14 Set of 3		4·50	5·00
MS3115 Nos. 3112/14		4·50	5·00

(Des Communication Arts. Litho Southern Colour Print)

2009 (4 Feb). New Zealand Champions of Motorsport. T **693** and similar horiz designs. Multicoloured.

(a) Ordinary gum. Phosphorised paper. P 14

3116	50c. Type **693**..	1·25	45
3117	$1 Bruce McLaren in Formula One car....	2·00	1·25
3118	$1.50 Ivan Mauger on speedway motorcycle ..	2·75	2·50
3119	$2 Denny Hulme in Formula One car............	3·50	3·50
3120	$2.50 Hugh Anderson on Grand Prix motorcycle	4·00	4·25
3116/20 Set of 5		12·00	11·00
MS3121 150×90 mm. Nos. 3116/20.........................		12·00	11·00

(b) Self-adhesive. Size 30×25 mm. Phosphor frame. Die-cut perf 10×9½

3122	50c. As Type **693**..	1·00	1·00
	a. Booklet pane. No. 3122×10....................	9·00	
3123	$1 As No. 3117.......................................	1·50	1·50
	a. Booklet pane. No. 3123×10....................	13·50	

No. 3122 was issued in $5 booklets, No. SB142, and also in rolls of 100. No. 3123 was issued in $10 booklets, No. SB143.
Nos. 3122/3 could be purchased in *se-tenant* pairs from the Philatelic Bureau.

694 Giant Moa

(Des Dave Gunson. Litho Southern Colour Print)

2009 (4 Mar). Giants of New Zealand. T **694** and similar horiz designs. Multicoloured. Phosphorised paper. P 14½.

3124	50c. Type **694**..	1·50	65
3125	$1 Colossal Squid.....................................	2·25	1·25
3126	$1.50 Southern Right Whale	3·50	2·75
3127	$2 Giant Eagle..	4·25	4·50
3128	$2.50 Giant Weta	4·50	4·75
3124/8 Set of 5		14·50	12·50
MS3129 179×90 mm. Nos. 3124/8.........................		14·50	13·50

2009 (4 Mar). International Polar Year 2007–2009. Sheet 120×80 mm. Multicoloured. P 13×13½.

MS3130 As No. 2871×2 but without imprint dates.........	7·50	7·50

695 Funeral Procession of the Unknown Warrior, Wellington, 2004

(Des Communication Arts. Litho Southern Colour Print)

2009 (1 Apr). ANZAC (2nd series). "Comrades in Arms". T **695** and similar horiz designs. Multicoloured. P 13½×13.

3131	50c. Type **695**..	1·40	1·00
3132	50c. N.Z. (Maori) Pioneer Battalion on break from trench improvement, World War I..	1·40	1·00
3133	$1 No. 75 (N.Z.) Squadron R.A.F. and Wellington bomber, World War II.............	2·75	1·75
3134	$1.50 H.M.S. *Achilles* (Leander class cruiser), World War II	3·00	2·50
3135	$2 Kayforce gun crew in action, Korea, 1 April 1952..................................	3·75	4·00
3136	$2.50 Soldiers of ANZAC Battalion boarding R.A.A.F. Iroquois helicopter, Vietnam, 23 March 1968................................	4·00	4·25
3131/6 Set of 6		14·50	13·00

The stamps also exist in seven miniature sheets, each 151×110 mm with a line of roulettes at left. Six of the miniature sheets contain Nos. 3131/6 as single stamps and the seventh sheet contains all six designs. Stamps from these miniature sheets are all perforated 14. The miniature sheets are only obtainable from a booklet, No. SP10, containing stamps with a face value of $16 but sold for $19.90.

2009 (1 Apr). China 2009 World Stamp Exhibition, Luoyang, China. Sheet 95×90 mm. Multicoloured. P 13×13½.

MS3137 Nos. 3010, 3012 and 3113...........................	5·25	5·50

No. **MS**3137 is cut in a semicircle at left and foot.

696 Pedestrians crossing Bridge before its opening to Traffic, 1959

(Des Mata Limited. Litho Southern Colour Print)

2009 (1 May). 50th Anniv of Auckland Harbour Bridge. T **696** and similar horiz designs. Multicoloured. Phosphorised paper. P 13½×13.

3138	50c. Type **696**..	1·00	40
3139	$1 Auckland Harbour Bridge (with two extra lanes) in 2009.........................	1·50	1·10
3140	$1.50 Auckland Harbour Bridge in 1961	2·50	3·00
3141	$2 Auckland Harbour Bridge at night, 2009..................................	3·00	3·25
3138/41 Set of 4		7·25	7·00

A 50c. self-adhesive stamp as Type **696** was only available from the Philatelic Bureau as a single stamp or from PostShops as part of the set.

697 Heitiki from "Te Maori" Exhibition, 1984

(Des Len Hetet. Litho Southern Colour Print)

2009 (24 June). Matariki (Maori New Year). T **697** and similar vert designs. Multicoloured.

(a) Self-adhesive. Die-cut perf 10×9½

3143	50c. Type **697**..	75	45
	a. Pane. No. 3143/8................................	12·00	12·00
3144	$1 Heitiki by Raponi..............................	1·40	1·10
3145	$1.50 Heitiki made from corian by Rangi Kipa	2·25	2·25
3146	$1.80 Female heitiki made from greenstone....	2·50	2·50
3147	$2 Female heitiki, c. 1849, from the Museum of New Zealand..........................	3·00	3·25
3148	$2.30 Heitiki made from paraoa by Rangi Hetet, 1991..................................	3·50	3·75
3143/8 Set of 6		12·00	12·00

(b) Ordinary gum. Phosphorised paper. P 13×13½

MS3149 150×90 mm. As Nos. 3143/8....................	12·00	12·00

Nos. 3143/8 were issued in separate sheets of 25. The *se-tenant* pane, No. 3143a, was only available from the Philatelic Bureau.
A *se-tenant* strip of six stamps containing Nos. 3143/8 was only available from presentation packs and the limited edition pack.

(Des Stamps Business, New Zealand Post. Litho Southern Colour Print)

2009 (1 July). New Zealand Landscapes (2nd series). Horiz designs as T **622**. Multicoloured.

(a) Ordinary gum. P 13×13½

3150	30c. Tolaga Bay...	75	45
3151	$1.80 Russell...	3·00	3·00
3152	$2.30 Lake Wanaka......................................	3·50	3·50
3153	$2.80 Auckland..	3·75	3·75
3154	$3.30 Rakaia River......................................	4·25	4·25
3155	$4 Wellington.......................................	5·50	6·00
3150/5 Set of 6		19·00	19·00

(b) Self-adhesive. Phosphor frame. P 10×9½

3156	$1.80 As No. 3151.....................................	2·75	3·00
	a. Booklet pane. No. 3156×5 and 2 International Air labels.....................	12·00	

No. 3156 was issued in $9 booklets, No. SB146.

698 Lighthouse (Cape Reinga) and Angler

699 1996 Child Safety 40c.+5c. Stamp

(Des Assignment Group. Litho Southern Colour Print)

2009 (5 Aug). A Tiki Tour of New Zealand (1st issue). Sheet 190×280 mm containing T **698** and similar square designs. Multicoloured. Phosphorised paper. P 14.

MS3157	50c.×24 Type **698**; Hole in the Rock Tour (Cape Brett); Maui snaring the sun (Maori legend); Yachting; Sky Tower (Auckland) and surf boat; Marlin fishing; Waikato rugby (Mooloos); Rower, statue of shearer and Maori carving; Pohutukawa tree, east coast style whare (meeting house), surfing and horse-riding; Mt. Taranaki; Gumboot and wind turbines; Gannet (Cape Kidnappers); Tribute state (Greymouth) and Municipal Building (Westport); Grapes, fly-fishing and glass blowing; Richard Seddon statue (Parliament) and windsurfer; Mount Cook lily and statue of Mackenzie's dog (Lake Tekapo); Roadside crayfish caravan (Kaikoura) and Neil Dawson's Chalice sculpture (Christchurch); Whale watching; Crayfish, black robin and fishing boat (Chatham Islands); Milford Sound and jetboat (Shotover river); 'Wings over Wanaka' (biplane); Kakapo; Curling; Stewart Island Shag and chain sculpture (Rakiura track, Oban)	20·00	24·00	

No. **MS**3157 contains 24 stamps and one stamp-size label, the backgrounds forming a composite design of a map of New Zealand.
See also No. **MS**3379.

(Des Hamish Thompson. Litho Southern Colour Print, New Zealand)

2009 (7 Sept). 80th Anniv of Children's Health Stamps. T **699** and similar vert designs. Multicoloured. Phosphorised paper.

(a) Ordinary gum. P 13×13½

3158	50c. +10c. Type **699**		1·75	1·75
3159	$1 +10c. 1932 Hygeia 1d.+1d. Health stamp		2·25	2·25
MS3160	100×90 mm. 50c.+10c. 1943 Princess Elizabeth 2d.+1d. Health stamp (25×30 mm) (P 14×14½) and as Nos. 3158/9 (P 14)		3·25	3·25

(b) Self-adhesive. Die-cut perf 9½×10

3161	50c. +10c. 1943 Princess Elizabeth 2d.+1d. Health stamp (25×30 mm)		1·75	1·75

700 Beach Cricket

701 Three Shepherds

(Des Robertson Communications. Litho Australia Post Sprintpak (Nos. 3162C/71C) or Southern Colour Print (others))

2009 (7 Sept). KiwiStamps (1st issue). T **700** and similar vert designs. Multicoloured. Self-adhesive. Die-cut.

(a) Folded sheets of 50. Design size 21½×26½ mm. P 10×9½

3162A	(50c.) Type **700**		1·00	1·00
3163A	(50c.) Kiwi fruit		1·00	1·00
3164A	(50c.) State Highway 1 road sign		1·00	1·00
3165A	(50c.) Windfarm and umbrella blown inside out		1·00	1·00
3166A	(50c.) Lawnmower		1·00	1·00
3167A	(50c.) Caravan		1·00	1·00
3168A	(50c.) Flying duck wall ornaments		1·00	1·00
3169A	(50c.) Fish and chips at the beach		1·00	1·00
3170A	(50c.) Swanndri jacket on barbed wire		1·00	1·00
3171A	(50c.) Sausage on fork and barbecue		1·00	1·00
3162A/71A	*Set of 10*		9·00	9·00

(b) Coil stamps. Design size 21x26 mm. P 9½×10

3162B	(50c.) Type **700**		1·00	1·00
	a. Pane of 10. Nos. 3162B/71B		9·00	9·00
	b. Vert strip of 10. Nos. 3162B/71B		9·00	9·00
3163B	(50c.) As No. 3163A		1·00	1·00

3164B	(50c.) As No. 3164A		1·00	1·00
3165B	(50c.) As No. 3165A		1·00	1·00
3166B	(50c.) As No. 3166A		1·00	1·00
3167B	(50c.) As No. 3167A		1·00	1·00
3168B	(50c.) As No. 3168A		1·00	1·00
3169B	(50c.) As No. 3169A		1·00	1·00
3170B	(50c.) As No. 3170A		1·00	1·00
3171B	(50c.) As No. 3171A		1·00	1·00
3162B/71B	*Set of 10*		9·00	9·00

(c) Booklet stamps. Design size 21x26 mm. P 11

3162C	(50c.) Type **700**		1·00	1·00
	a. Booklet pane of 10. Nos. 3162C/71C		9·00	
3163C	(50c.) As No. 3163A		1·00	1·00
3164C	(50c.) As No. 3164A		1·00	1·00
3165C	(50c.) As No. 3165A		1·00	1·00
3166C	(50c.) As No. 3166A		1·00	1·00
3167C	(50c.) As No. 3167A		1·00	1·00
3168C	(50c.) As No. 3168A		1·00	1·00
3169C	(50c.) As No. 3169A		1·00	1·00
3170C	(50c.) As No. 3170A		1·00	1·00
3171C	(50c.) As No. 3171A		1·00	1·00
3162C/71C	*Set of 10*		9·00	9·00

Nos. 3162A/71C were all inscribed "Kiwistamp" and were valid for standard post letters within New Zealand.

Nos. 3162A/71A were issued in sheets of 50, containing five stamps of each design in different combinations *se-tenant* throughout the sheet.

Nos. 3162B/71B were issued in rolls of 100, containing all ten designs in sequence, with a "join" every 20 stamps. They were also available in "Jumbo" panes of ten (5x2), originally produced for first day covers (No. 3162Ba), these were only available from the philatelic bureau.

Nos. 3162C/71C were issued in booklets of ten, No SB147, originally sold for $5.

There are design differences between the sheet, coil and booklet stamps due to varied scaling and cropping of the original artwork.

As well as the size and perforation differences, stamps from the different sources may be identified by the fact that the sheet stamps have "interlocking" perforations with no matrix between the stamps; booklet stamps and stamps from the "Jumbo" coil pane (3162Ba) are separated by a matrix which is intact; stamps from the coils of 100 have the matrix removed.

Stamps in these designs but with silver foil "Kiwistamp" and silver fern emblems were issued in numbered sheets of 50 and numbered booklets of ten in limited quantities (11,000 booklets and 3000 sheets).
See also Nos. 3269/73.

(Des Stephen Fuller. Litho Southern Colour Print)

2009 (7 Oct). Christmas (1st issue). T **701** and similar square designs. Multicoloured.

(a) Ordinary gum. Phosphorised paper. P 14

3172	50c. Type **701**		75	10
3173	$1 Mary, Joseph and Infant Jesus		1·50	80
3174	$1.80 Three magi with gifts		2·50	3·50
3172/4	*Set of 3*		4·25	4·00

(b) Self-adhesive. Size 30×25 mm. Die-cut perf 10×9½

3175	50c. As Type **701**		75	75
	a. Booklet pane. No. 3175×10		6·50	
	b. Horiz pair. Nos. 3175/6		3·00	3·00
3176	$1.80 As No. 3174		2·25	2·25
	a. Booklet pane. No. 3176×10		22·00	

No. 3175 was issued in $5 booklets, No. SB148, and in rolls of 100.

No. 3176 was issued in booklets (No. SB149) sold at $15, providing a $3 discount off the face value of the stamps.

The *se-tenant* pair, No. 3175b, could be purchased from the Philatelic Bureau.

702 Seaside Chair and Pohutukawa Tree
(Felix Wang)

703 Sir Peter Blake ("Inspirational Leader")

(Des Communication Arts. Litho Southern Colour Print)

2009 (7 Oct). Christmas (2nd issue). T **702** and similar square designs showing winning entries in children's stamp design competition "What do you love about Christmas?". Multicoloured. Phosphorised paper. P 14.

3177	50c. Type **702**		75	10
3178	$2.30 New Zealand pigeon wearing Christmas hat (Dannielle Aldworth)		3·00	3·75
3179	$2.80 Christmas presents (Apun Bakshi)		4·25	4·50
3177/9	*Set of 3*		7·25	7·50

2009 (16 Oct). Timpex 2009 National Stamp Exhibition, Timaru. Sheet 170×90 mm. Multicoloured.
MS3180 As Nos. 3101/2 and 3105 (all P 14) and specimen
stamp as Type **501** (P 14½×15)............ 7·00 7·00

No. **MS**3180 was sold for $6.50, with a $2.50 surcharge to fund the Philatelic Trust.

The $20 specimen stamp as Type **501** differs from No. 1784 by being printed in lithography and having no watermark. It was not valid for postage.

(Des Cue Design. Litho Southern Colour Print)

2009 (25 Nov). Sir Peter Blake (yachtsman) Commemoration. T **703** and similar vert designs. Multicoloured. Phosphorised paper. P 13½.
3181   50c. Type **703**............................ 1·00 45
3182 $1 Sir Peter Blake at wheel and yacht
             ("Whitbread Round the World
             Yachtsman")................................ 1·75 1·25
3183 $1.80 Sir Peter Blake using winch and catamaran
             ("Jules Verne Trophy Record Breaker")....... 3·00 2·75
3184 $2.30 Sir Peter Blake, Americas Cup trophy and
             yacht New Zealand ("Passionate Kiwi") ... 4·00 4·50
3185 $2.80 Sir Peter Blake and yacht Seamaster
             on expedition in Antarctica
             ("Environmentalist")..................... 4·50 4·75
3181/5 Set of 5.................................... 13·00 12·50
MS3186 160×58 mm. Nos. 3181/5................. 13·00 13·00

"BEST OF 2009". a further set of miniature sheets as described below No. 2042 were distributed by the Philatelic Bureau to customers purchasing a certain amount of philatelic material during 2009. The sheets comprised: 1. Nos. 3111, 3114 and 3120. 2. Nos. 3128, 3136 and 3141. 3. Nos. 3148, 3174 and 3185.

Imperforate sheets of Nos. 3150/5 and a perforated se-tenant block comprising the same six stamps were also distributed.

704 Lunar Tiger
Symbol

705 Heitiki

(Des Bananaworks. Litho Southern Colour Print)

2010 (6 Jan). Chinese New Year. (Year of the Tiger). T **704** and similar vert designs. Multicoloured. P 14 (3187/90) or 13½ (**MS**3191).
3187   50c. Type **704**............................ 1·00 75
3188 $1 Tiger.................................... 1·90 1·90
3189 $1.80 Head of tiger........................ 2·75 2·75
3190 $2.30 Beehive (Parliament House, Wellington) 3·75 4·00
3187/90 Set of 4.................................. 8·50 8·50
MS3191 150×90 mm. Nos. 3187/90................ 8·50 8·50

(Des YouXD. Litho Southern Colour Print)

2010 (10 Feb). Personalised Stamps. Sheet 94×82 mm containing T **705** and designs as Nos. 2876, 2879 and 2881 but 35×20 mm and with new values. Multicoloured. Phosphorised paper. P 15×14.
MS3192 $1.80 Type **705**; $2.30 As Type **660**; $2.30
Engagement and wedding rings; $2.30 Pohutukawa
flower... 13·00 14·00

No. **MS**3192 contains four stamps in two horizontal pairs separated by two stamp-size labels inscribed 'Personalised Stamps 2010'.

706 Allosaurus

(Des Eklektus Inc. Litho Southern Colour Print)

2010 (3 Mar). Dinosaurs of New Zealand. T **706** and similar horiz designs. Multicoloured.

(a) Ordinary gum. Phosphorised paper. P 14½
3193   50c. Type **706**............................ 95 85

3194 $1 Anhanguera.............................. 2·25 2·25
3195 $1.80 Titanosaurus......................... 3·00 3·00
3196 $2.30 Moanasaurus.......................... 3·75 3·75
3197 $2.80 Mauisaurus........................... 4·50 4·50
3193/7 Set of 5................................... 13·00 13·00

(b) Self-adhesive. Sheet 230×200 mm. Partial phosphor frames.
Die-cut perf 10×9½
MS3198 As Nos. 3193/7......................... 13·00 13·00

Stamps from **MS**3198 have a phosphor frame at left, right and foot of the stamps.

A gummed miniature sheet containing Nos. 3193/7 was only sold in a limited edition pack.

707 ANZAC Soldier

708 Peony and Pohutukawa Flowers

(Des Cue Design. Litho Southern Colour Print, New Zealand)

2010 (7 Apr). ANZAC (3rd series). Remembrance. T **707** and similar horiz designs. Multicoloured. Phosphorised paper. P 13½.
3199   50c. Type **707**............................ 1·50 1·25
3200   50c. Gallipoli veterans marching, ANZAC Day,
             1958..................................... 1·50 1·25
3201 $1 Posthumous VC Award Ceremony for
             Second Lieutenant Te Moana-Nui-a-Kiwa
             Ngarimu, Ruatoria, 1943.................. 2·50 1·75
3202 $1.80 Nurses laying wreath, Cairo Cemetery,
             ANZAC Day, 1940........................... 3·50 3·00
3203 $2.30 ANZAC War Memorial, Port Said, Egypt,
             1932..................................... 4·50 5·00
3204 $2.80 Veteran at Sangro War Cemetery, Italy,
             2004..................................... 4·50 5·00
3199/204 Set of 6................................. 16·00 15·00

The stamps also exist in seven miniature sheets, each 151×110 mm, with a line of roulettes at left. Six of the miniature sheets contain Nos. 3199/3204 as single stamps and the seventh sheet contains all six designs. Stamps from these miniature sheets are all perforated 14. The miniature sheets are only obtainable from a booklet, No. SP11, containing stamps with a face value of $17.80 but sold for $19.90.

(Des Assignment Group. Litho Southern Colour Print)

2010 (30 Apr). Expo 2010, Shanghai, China. T **708** and similar vert designs, with the two images on each stamp laid tete-beche. Multicoloured. Phosphorised paper. P 14.
3205   50c. Type **708**............................ 95 95
3206 $1 Maori Kaitiaki (carved by Lyonel Grant
             for New Zealand pavilion) and Chinese
             Fu Dog................................... 1·75 1·75
3207 $1.80 Pan Gu (Chinese creation story) and Tane
             creating world of light (Maori legend).... 2·25 2·25
3208 $2.30 Shanghai and Auckland skylines ...... 2·50 2·75
3209 $2.80 Jade cong (Chinese good luck symbol)
             and jade heitiki......................... 2·75 3·00
3205/9 Set of 5................................... 9·00 9·50
MS3210 180×140 mm. As Nos. 3205/9 .... 9·00 9·50

Nos. 3205/9 have text in English and Chinese printed on the back of the stamps.

Stamps from **MS**3210 do not have text printed on the reverse.

(Litho Southern Colour Print)

2010 (30 Apr). London 2010 Festival of Stamps. Sheet 130×90 mm. Multicoloured. P 14.
MS3211 Nos. 3199 and 3203/4.................. 9·00 9·00

709 Manu Aute   **710** Centenary Series
Jersey

(Des Len Hetet. Litho Southern Colour Print)

2010 (9 June). Matariki. Manu Tukutuku (traditional Maori
kites). T **709** and similar multicoloured designs. Phosphorised
paper. P 14.

3212	50c. Type **709**	1·00	80
3213	$1 Manu patiki (*vert*)	1·75	1·75
3214	$1.80 Manu taratahi (*vert*)	3·00	3·00
3215	$2.30 Upoko tangata	3·75	4·50
3212/15 *Set of 4*		8·50	9·00
MS3216 150×90 mm. Nos. 3212/15		8·75	9·00

(Des Len Hetet. Litho Southern Colour Print)

2010 (9 June). Centenary of Maori Rugby. T **710** and similar vert
design. Multicoloured. Phosphorised paper. P 14.

3217	50c. Type **710**	1·25	80
3218	$1.80 Centenary logo	3·00	3·00
MS3219 160×90 mm. Nos. 3217/18		3·50	3·50

711 Monarch Butterfly

(Des YouXD. Litho Southern Colour Print)

2010 (7 July). Children's Health. Butterflies. T **711** and similar
multicoloured designs.

(a) Ordinary gum. Phosphorised paper. P 14

3220	50c. +10c. Type **711**	1·50	1·50
3221	$1 +10c. Tussock Butterfly	2·00	2·00
MS3222 166×95 mm. 50c.+10c. Boulder Copper			
Butterfly (26×30 *mm*) and Nos. 3220/1		3·25	3·25

(b) Self-adhesive. Size 25×30 mm. Die-cut perf 9½×10

3223	50c. +10c. Boulder Copper Butterfly	1·50	1·50

No. **MS**3222 is cut around in the shape of a butterfly.

712 Silver Fern (All Blacks
emblem)

2010 (4 Aug). All Blacks (national rugby team). Phosphorised paper.
P 13½.

3224	**712** 60c. black	1·00	80
3225	$1.90 black	5·00	7·00
MS3226 90×78 mm. As Nos. 3224/5 but 35×20 mm			
(P 15×14½) and Nos. 3224/5		4·00	4·00

(Litho Southern Colour Print)

2010 (4 Aug)–**12**. New Zealand Landscapes (3rd series). Horiz designs
as T **622**. Multicoloured.

(a) Ordinary gum. Phosphorised paper. P 13½

3227	$1.20 Mitre Peak, Milford Sound	1·60	1·60
3228	$1.90 Queenstown	2·75	2·75
3229	$2.40 Lake Rotorua	3·75	3·75
3230	$2.90 Kaikoura	4·50	4·50
3231	$3.40 River Avon at Christchurch	5·50	5·50
3227/31 *Set of 5*		16·00	16·00

(b) Self-adhesive. Phosphor frame. Die-cut perf 10×9½

3232	$1.20 As No. 3227	1·75	1·75
	a. Booklet pane. No. 3232×10	16·00	

3233	$1.90 As No. 3228	3·00	3·00
	a. Booklet pane. No. 3233×5 and 2		
	International Air labels	13·00	
3233b	$2.40 As No. 3229 (1.2.12)	3·75	3·75
	ba. Booklet pane. No. 3233b×5 and 2		
	International Air labels	17·00	
3232/3b *Set of 3*		7·75	7·75

Nos. 3232/3 were normally only available from separate $9.50 or $12
booklets, Nos. SB150/1, but the set of single stamps with plain
backing paper could be purchased from the Philatelic Bureau. No. 3233b
was available in $12 booklets, No. SB159, and also as a single stamp with
plain backing paper from the Philatelic Bureau. Nos. 3232/3b all have the
surplus self-adhesive paper around each stamp retained.

713 Emblem   **714** Tane Mahuta (oldest
tree), Kerikeri Stone Store
and Treaty House at Waitangi

(Litho Southern Colour Print)

2010 (9 Sept). Rugby World Cup, New Zealand (2011). Phosphorised
paper. P 13½.

3234	**713** 60c. multicoloured	1·00	1·00
3235	**713** $1.90 multicoloured	3·00	3·00
MS3236 91×79 mm. As Nos. 3234/5 but 35×20 mm			
(P 15×14½) and Nos. 3234/5		7·75	7·75

Stamps as Nos. 3234/5 but 35×20 mm as in **MS**3236 were sold in sheets
of 20 as personalised stamps.

(Des YouXD. Litho Southern Colour Print)

2010 (9 Sept). Personalised Stamps. As Nos. 2950/5 with new
values and new design and as No. **MS**3192 with new values.
Multicoloured. Phosphorised paper. P 15×14½.

MS3237 165×82 mm. 60c.×8 As Type **660**; Buzzy Bee			
(toy); Silver fern; Pohutukawa flower; Engagement			
and wedding rings; Red rose; As Type **705**; Teddy			
bear		7·50	7·50
MS3238 94×82 mm. $1.90 As Type **705**; $2.40 As			
Type **660**; $2.40 Engagement and wedding rings;			
$2.40 Pohutukawa flower		18·00	19·00

(Des Assignment Group. Litho Southern Colour Print)

2010 (6 Oct). 'New Zealand A Slice of Heaven'. Sheet
185×254 mm containing T **714** and similar vert designs.
Multicoloured. Phosphorised paper. P 14.

MS3239 60c.×25 Type **714**; Fountain and waterfront,			
Oriental Bay, Wellington; Octagon Plaza with Dunedin			
Cathedral and St. Paul's Church, Dunedin; Auckland			
Ferry Terminal; The Beehive, Wellington; Sky Tower,			
Auckland; One Tree Hill, Auckland; Mt. Ruapehu and			
Waikato River; Hot air balloons shaped as sheep,			
cow's head and kiwi; Christchurch Cathedral and			
River Avon; Horse race; Rural garage, coffee shop			
and church; Mt. Cook, helicopter and plane; War			
memorial, ploughed field and lake shore; Lake Taupo,			
Huka Falls and bridge; Champagne Pool, geysers, mud			
pools and marae; Rugby match; Queenstown, Lake			
Wakatipu and the Remarkables Range; Skiers, biplane,			
glider and golf course; Shotover River and Skippers			
Suspension Bridge; Seaside caravan park; Titahi Bay			
boatsheds; Hawke's Bay vineyard; Farm with sheep in			
pens; Nugget Point		27·00	28·00

The stamps and margins of No. **MS**3239 form a composite design.

An imperforate version of No. **MS**3239 was included in "The New
Zealand Collection 2010" Yearbook.

715 1960 2d. *The Adoration
of the Shepherds*
(Rembrandt) Stamp

(Des Hamish Thompson. Litho Southern Colour Print)

2010 (20 Oct). Christmas. 50th Anniv of New Zealand Christmas Stamps. T **715** and similar vert designs showing stamps. Multicoloured.

(a) Phosphorised paper. P 13½

3240	60c. Type **715**	1·00	30
3241	$1.20 1970 3c. stamp showing "The Holy Family" stained glass window from Invercargill Presbyterian Church	2·75	1·50
3242	$1.90 1979 35c. Pohutukawa tree stamp	3·00	3·00
3243	$2.40 1983 45c. "The Glory of Christmas" stamp showing star and flowers	4·00	4·75
3244	$2.90 2000 40c. Virgin Mary and Baby Jesus stamp	4·75	5·00
3240/4	Set of 5	14·00	13·00

(b) Self-adhesive. Size 25×30 mm. Phosphor frame. Die-cut perf 11

3245	60c. As Type **715**	1·00	1·00
	a. Booklet pane. No. 3245×10	9·00	
	b. Perf 12½	1·00	1·00
	ba. Horiz pair. Nos. 3245b/6b	2·00	2·00
3246	$1.90 As No. 3242	2·75	3·00
	a. Booklet pane. No. 3246×10	25·00	
	b. Perf 12½	2·75	3·00

No. 3245 was issued in booklets, No. SB152, sold at $5.40, a 60c. discount off the face value of the stamps.

No. 3245b was issued in rolls of 100.

The *se-tenant* pair, No. 3245ba, could be purchased from the Philatelic Bureau.

No. 3246 was issued in booklets, No. SB153, sold at $16, a $3 discount off the face value of the stamps.

716 Surf Lifeguard with Rescue Tube

717 Rabbit Symbol

(Des Creature. Litho Cartor)

2010 (3 Nov). Centenary of Surf Life Saving. T **716** and similar horiz designs. Multicoloured. Phosphorised paper. P 13×13½.

3247	60c. Type **716**	1·10	60
3248	$1.20 Lifeguards in inflatable rescue boat (IRB)	2·25	1·40
3249	$1.90 Ski paddlers in Surf Life Saving Championships	2·75	2·75
3250	$2.40 Surf boat	3·75	4·25
3251	$2.90 March past of lifeguards in 1930s surf carnival	5·00	5·00
3247/51	Set of 5	13·50	12·50

(Litho Southern Colour Print)

2010 (12 Nov). Palmpex 2010 National Stamp Exhibition, Palmerston North. Sheet 150×90 mm. Phosphorised paper. P 14.

MS3252	No. 2090*b*×3	7·50	7·50

"BEST OF 2010". A further set of miniature sheets as described below No. 2042 were distributed by the Philatelic Bureau to customers purchasing a certain amount of philatelic material during 2010. The sheets comprised: 1. Nos. 3190, 3197 and 3204. 2. Nos. 3209, 3215 and 3221. 3. Nos. 3230, 3244 and 3251.

Imperforate sheets of Nos. 3212/15 and a perforated *se-tenant* block of the same four stamps were also distributed.

(Des AsiaWorks. Litho Cartor)

2011 (12 Jan). Chinese New Year. Year of the Rabbit. T **717** and similar vert designs. Multicoloured. Phosphorised paper. P 13½×13.

3253	60c. Type **717**	1·10	60
3254	$1.20 Chinese style rabbit	1·90	1·50
3255	$1.90 Leaping rabbit	3·25	3·50
3256	$2.40 Christchurch Cathedral and Chinese kite	3·75	4·25
3253/6	Set of 4	9·00	9·00
MS3257	150×90 mm. Nos. 3253/6	10·00	10·00

(Litho Southern Colour Print)

2011 (12 Feb). INDIPEX 2011 World Philatelic Exhibition, New Delhi. Sheet 120×90 mm. Multicoloured. P 13½.

MS3258	Nos. 3227/9	9·00	9·00

718 Whakaeke (choreographed entrance)

719 Prince William and Miss Catherine Middleton

(Des Tai Kerekere, KE Design. Litho Southern Colour Print)

2011 (17 Feb). Kapa Haka (Maori performing arts). T **718** and similar vert designs. Multicoloured.

(a) Self-adhesive. Die-cut perf 10×9½

3259	60c. Type **718**	1·10	1·10
	a. Block of 6. Nos. 3259/64	13·50	13·50
3260	60c. Poi (dancer swinging taupo ball on flax cord)	1·10	1·10
3261	$1.20 Waiata-a-ringa (action songs)	2·25	2·25
3262	$1.90 Haka	3·25	3·25
3263	$2.40 Whakawatea (choreographed exit)	3·75	3·75
3264	$2.90 Moteatea (traditional chant)	4·50	4·50
3259/64	Set of 6	13·50	13·50

(b) Ordinary gum. Phosphorised paper. P 13½

MS3265	150×90 mm. As Nos. 3259/64	13·50	16·00

Nos. 3259/64 were each issued in separate sheets of 25. The *se-tenant* block, No. 3259a, is probably from the jumbo roll printing.

(Des Datam. Litho Southern Colour Print)

2011 (23 Mar). Royal Wedding. T **719** and similar vert design. Multicoloured. Phosphorised paper. P 14½.

3266	$2.40 Type **719**	4·00	4·00
	a. Horiz pair. Nos. 3266/7	8·00	8·00
3267	$2.40 Prince William and Miss Catherine Middleton embracing	4·00	4·00
MS3268	135×91 mm. Nos. 3266/7	8·00	8·00

Nos. 3266/7 were printed together, *se-tenant*, as horizontal pairs in sheets of 20.

720 Hokey Pokey (vanilla and crunchy toffee ice cream)

721 Charles Heaphy, 11 February 1864, Waikato, New Zealand

(Des Datam. Litho Southern Colour Print or Australia Post Sprintpak (Nos. 3269b/73b, first three printings))

2011 (23 Mar). KiwiStamps (2nd issue). T **720** and similar horiz designs. Multicoloured. Self-adhesive. Phosphor frame. Die-cut perf 10.

3269	(60c.) Type **720**	95	95
	a. Horiz strip of 5. Nos. 3269/73	4·25	4·25
	b. Perf 11	95	95
	ba. Booklet pane. Nos. 3269b/73b, each×2	8·50	
3270	(60c.) Kiwi road sign	95	95
	b. Perf 11	95	95
3271	(60c.) Beach	95	95
	b. Perf 11	95	95
3272	(60c.) Trout fishing	95	95
	b. Perf 11	95	95
3273	(60c.) Mountain biking	95	95
	b. Perf 11	95	95
3269/73	Set of 5	4·25	4·25

Nos. 3269/73b were all inscr 'KiwiStamp' and were valid for Standard Post medium letters in New Zealand (originally 60c. each).

Nos. 3269/73 were issued in sheets and in rolls of 100 containing all five designs in sequence.

Nos. 3269b/73b were issued in booklets of ten, No. SB154, originally sold for $6. Prior to May 2014 printing was by Australia Post Sprintpak but after that date Southern Colour Print took over the booklet printing contract.

(Des Cue Design. Litho Southern Colour Print)

2011 (14 Apr). Victoria Cross. The New Zealand Story. T **721** and similar vert designs showing New Zealand recipients of Victoria Cross. Multicoloured. Phosphorised paper. P 13½.

3274	60c. Type **721**	1·25	1·25
	a. Sheetlet. Nos. 3274/95	25·00	25·00
3275	60c. William James Hardham, 28 January 1901, South Africa	1·25	1·25
3276	60c. Cyril Royston Guyton Bassett, 7 August 1915, Gallipoli	1·25	1·25
3277	60c. Donald Forrester Brown,15 September 1916, High Wood, France	1·25	1·25
3278	60c. Samuel Frickleton, 7 June 1917, Messines, Belgium	1·25	1·25
3279	60c. Leslie Wilton Andrew, 31 July 1917, La Basse Ville, France	1·25	1·25
3280	60c. Henry James Nicholas, 3 December 1917, Polderboek, Belgium	1·25	1·25
3281	60c. Richard Charles Travis, 24 July 1918, Hébuterne, France	1·25	1·25
3282	60c. Samuel Forsyth, 24 August 1918, Grévillers, France	1·25	1·25
3283	60c. Reginald Stanley Judson, 26 August 1918, Bapaume, France	1·25	1·25
3284	60c. Harry John Laurent, 12 September 1918, Gouzeaucourt Wood, France	1·25	1·25
3285	60c. James Crichton, 30 September 1918, Crevecoeur, France	1·25	1·25
3286	60c. John Gildroy Grant, 1 September 1918, Bancourt, France	1·25	1·25
3287	60c. James Edward Allen Ward, 7 July 1941, on operations over Holland	1·25	1·25
3288	60c. Charles Hazlitt Upham, 22–30 May 1941, Crete and 14–15 July 1942, Western Desert	1·25	1·25
3289	60c. Alfred Clive Hulme, 20–28 May 1941, Crete	1·25	1·25
3290	60c. John Daniel Hinton, 28–29 April 1941, Greece	1·25	1·25
3291	60c. Keith Elliott, 15 July 1942, Western Desert	1·25	1·25
3292	60c. Moana-Nui-a-Kiwa Ngarimu, 26–27 March 1943, Tunisia	1·25	1·25
3293	60c. Lloyd Allen Trigg, 11 August 1943, sea patrol, Atlantic Ocean	1·25	1·25
3294	60c. Leonard Henry Trent, 3 May 1943, on operation over Holland	1·25	1·25
3295	60c. Victoria Cross of New Zealand (awarded to Bill Henry Apiata, 2004, Afghanistan)	1·25	1·25
3274/95	Set of 22	25·00	25·00

Nos. 3274/95 were printed together, *se-tenant*, in sheetlets of 22 stamps. An imperforate version of the sheetlet, No. 3274a, was included in "The New Zealand Collection 2011" Yearbook.

722 Humpback Whale

723 Modern Greenstone Hei Matau by Lewis Gardiner

(Des Dave Gunson. Litho Southern Colour Print)

2011 (4 May). "Beyond the Coast". Sheet 180×250 mm containing T **722** and similar multicoloured designs. Self-adhesive. Phosphorised paper. Die-cut perf 10×9½ (vert) or 9½×10 (horiz).

MS3296	60c.×10 Type **722**; White-faced Storm Petrel (*horiz*); John Dory (*horiz*); Yellowfin Tuna (*horiz*); Hammerhead Shark (*horiz*); Kingfish (*horiz*); Lord Howe Coralfish; Snapper (*horiz*); Arrow Squid (*horiz*); Orange Roughy (*horiz*) $1.90 Yellow Moray Eel (*horiz*); $1.90 King Crab	17·00	18·00

The stamps and margins of **MS**3296 form a composite design showing marine life from the surface to the sea bed.

(Des Len Hetet. Litho Southern Colour Print)

2011 (1 June). Matariki. Hei Matau. T **723** and similar vert designs. Multicoloured. Phosphorised paper.

(a) Self-adhesive. Die-cut perf 10×9½

3297	60c. Type **723**	1·00	1·00
	a. Block of 6. Nos. 3297/3302	14·50	14·50
3298	60c. Functional whalebone fish hook, 1500–1800	1·00	1·00
3299	$1.20 Inanga greenstone hei matau, *c.* 1800	2·25	2·25
3300	$1.90 Modern hei matau in multiple materials by Lewis Gardiner	3·25	3·25
3301	$2.40 Wooden hei matau with bone barb, *c.* 1800	3·75	3·75

3302	$2.90 Symbolic Maui's hook made from whalebone, 1750–1850	5·00	5·00
3297/302	Set of 6	14·50	14·50

(b) Ordinary gum. P 13½

MS3303	150×90 mm. As Nos. 3297/3302	14·50	16·00

Nos. 3297/3302 were each issued in separate sheets of 25, and also in a *se-tenant* block, No. 3297a.

724 Kiwi

725 1 State Highway

(Litho Southern Colour Print)

2011 (6 July). Children's Health. Flightless Birds. T **724** and similar multicoloured designs.

(a) Ordinary gum. Phosphorised paper. P 14

3304	60c. +10c. Type **724**	1·75	1·75
3305	$1.20 +10c. Kakapo	2·75	3·00
MS3306	130×90 mm. 60c.+10c. Takahe (26×30 *mm*) and Nos. 3304/5	4·75	4·75

(b) Self-adhesive. Size 26×30 mm. Die-cut perf 9½×10

3307	60c. +10c. Takahe	1·75	1·75

The upper and left portions of No. **MS**3306 are cut around in the shape of a takahe.

(Litho Southern Colour Print)

2011 (6 July). Round Kiwi Stamps. Phosphorised paper. P 14½.

3308	**445**	$1.20 black	3·25	3·50
		a. Horiz strip of 3. Nos. 3308/10	10·00	11·50
3309	**445**	$1.90 silver	3·75	4·50
3310	**445**	$2.40 blue	4·00	5·00
3308/10	Set of 3		10·00	11·50

Nos. 3308/10 were each perforated in a circle contained within an outer perforated square which had a silver fern leaf in the four corners. The design of the stamp was also altered, to include the NZ Post Silver Fern logo above the Kiwi's neck.

Nos. 3308/10 were each printed in sheets of ten.

Nos. 3308/10 were also available in a horizontal strip of three, No. 3308a.

(Litho Southern Colour Print)

2011 (28 July). Philanippon 2011 World Stamp Exhibition, Yokohama, Japan. Sheet 130×90 mm. Phosphorised paper. P 14½ (circular Kiwi stamp as No. 3309) or 13½ (others).

MS3311	No. 3225×2 and No. 3309	10·50	10·50

(Des Assignment Group. Litho Southern Colour Print)

2011 (10 Aug). Counting in Kiwi. Sheet 190×226 mm containing T **725** and similar vert designs. Multicoloured. Phosphorised paper. P 14.

MS3312	60c.×21 Type **725**; 2 jandals; 3 hour ferry ride across Cook Strait (seagull and ferry); 4 stars of Southern Cross; 5 year old starting school; 6 runs in cricket - out of the park; 7 players in netball team (ball landing in net); Number 8 wire; 9 dressed to the nines; 10 guitar; First 11; 12 Bluff Oysters; 13 lamingtons (cakes); 14 national parks (fish and lake); 15 players in rugby team; 16 driving age (car mirror and dice); 17 Captain Cook's landing, 1769; 18 voting age; 19 protected surf breaks (surfboard and wave); 20 bucks (parrot wearing crown); 21 key to the door	23·00	23·00

726 Webb Ellis Cup
(Motionstamp HDR 3D Technology
Outer Aspect, Auckland)

2011 (7 Sept). Webb Ellis Cup (World Cup Rugby, New Zealand). Die-cut perf 10.

3313	**726**	$15 gold, black and grey	27·00	35·00

No. 3313 was produced using Motionstamp technology, giving a three dimensional effect to the trophy. It is laser perforated.

No. 3313 was only available mounted in a display card or as a first day cover.

727 Hiker   **728** Baby Jesus in Manger

(Des Cue Design. Litho Southern Colour Print, New Zealand)

2011 (5 Oct). "The New Zealand Experience". T **727** and similar vert designs. Multicoloured. Phosphorised paper. P 14.

3314	60c. Type **727**	1·40	1·25
3315	60c. Sailing dinghy, motor boat and windsurfer	1·40	1·25
3316	$1.20 Fishing	2·25	2·00
3317	$1.90 Maori man performing kapa haka and marae	3·50	3·75
3318	$2.40 Skier and helicopter	4·00	4·75
3319	$2.90 Bungy jumping	5·00	5·50
3314/19	*Set of 6*	16·00	17·00
MS3320	160×90 mm. Nos. 3314/19	16·00	17·00

(Des Karen Mounsey-Smith. Litho Australia Post Sprintpak (Nos. 3326b/ba) or Southern Colour Print (others))

2011 (2 Nov). Christmas. T **728** and similar multicoloured designs.

(a) Ordinary paper. Phosphorised paper. P 14

3321	60c. Type **728**	1·90	60
3322	$1.20 Angel appearing to shepherds	2·75	1·75
3323	$1.90 Mary, Joseph and baby Jesus	3·25	3·25
3324	$2.40 Shepherds with baby Jesus	3·75	4·25
3325	$2.90 Wise men with baby Jesus	5·00	7·00
3321/5	*Set of 5*	15·00	15·00

(b) Self-adhesive. Size 25×30 mm. Die-cut perf 9½×10

3326	60c. As Type **728**	1·60	1·00
	a. Horiz strip of 3. Nos. 3326/8	8·50	9·50
	b. With phosphor frame. Perf 11	1·40	1·00
	ba. Booklet pane. No. 3326b×10	12·00	
3327	$1.90 As No. 3323	3·25	3·50
	a. Booklet pane. No. 3327×10	30·00	
3328	$2.40 As No. 3324	4·25	4·50
	a. Booklet pane. No. 3328×10	35·00	
3326/8	*Set of 3*	8·50	8·50

No. 3326 was issued in rolls of 100.

The *se-tenant* strip, No. 3326a, could be purchased from the Philatelic Bureau.

No. 3326b was issued in $6 booklets, No. SB155.

No. 3327 was issued in booklets, No. SB156, sold at $17.10, a $1.90 discount off the face value of the stamps.

No. 3328 was issued in booklets, No. SB157, sold at $21.60, a $2.40 discount off the face value of the stamps.

(Litho Southern Colour Print)

2011 (11 Nov). China 2011 27th Asian International Stamp Exhibition, Wuxi, China. Sheet 130×90 mm. Multicoloured. Phosphorised paper. P 14½.

MS3329	Nos. 3308/10	9·25	9·25

"BEST OF 2011". A further set of miniature sheets as described below No. 2042 were distributed by the Philatelic Bureau to customers purchasing a certain amount of philatelic material during 2011. The sheets comprised: 1. Nos. 3256, 3267 and 3264. 2. Nos. 3295, 3305 and 3302. 3. Nos. 3319, 3310 and 3325.

Imperforate sheets of Nos. 3321/5 and a perforated *se-tenant* strip comprising the same five stamps were also distributed.

729 Chinese Character for Dragon

(Des Bananaworks. Litho Cartor)

2012 (5 Jan). Chinese New Year. (Year of the Dragon). T **729** and similar vert designs. Multicoloured. Phosphorised paper. P 13.

3330	60c. Type **729**	1·25	60

3331	$1.20 Paper-cut dragon	2·00	1·50
3332	$1.90 Dragon lantern	2·50	2·50
3333	$2.40 Dunedin Railway Station and pair of swallows	6·00	7·00
3330/3	*Set of 4*	10·50	10·50
MS3334	150×90 mm. Nos. 3330/3	10·75	10·75

See also No. **MS**3423.

730 Pohutukawa   **731** Tiger Moth ("The Beginning")
(*Metrosideros exselsa*)

(Des 2Di4 Design. Litho Southern Colour Print)

2012 (1 Feb). Native Trees. T **730** and similar vert designs. Multicoloured. Phosphorised paper. P 13×13½.

3335	60c. Type **730**	1·50	60
3336	$1.20 Cabbage tree (*Cordyline australis*)	2·50	2·00
3337	$1.90 Kowhai (*Sophora microphylla*)	3·25	2·75
3338	$2.40 Nikau (*Rhopalostylis sapida*)	4·75	5·00
3339	$2.90 Manuka (*Leptospermum scoparium*)	5·50	6·00
3335/9	*Set of 5*	16·00	14·50
MS3340	160×90 mm. Nos. 3335/9	16·00	16·00

(Des Strategy Design and Advertising. Litho Southern Colour Print)

2012 (15 Mar). 75th Anniv of the RNZAF (Royal New Zealand Air Force). T **731** and similar horiz designs. Multicoloured. Phosphorised paper. P 14½.

3341	60c. Type **731**	1·75	1·75
	a. Sheetlet. Nos. 3341/55	24·00	24·00
3342	60c. Air Training Corps cadets	1·75	1·75
3343	60c. Pilot and navigator in cockpit of Wellington bomber ("WWII Europe")	1·75	1·75
3344	60c. Women's Auxiliary Air Force members in front of de Havilland Express aircraft	1·75	1·75
3345	60c. Servicing Unit aircraft maintenance area, Ondonga, New Georgia, 1943 ("WWII Pacific")	1·75	1·75
3346	60c. Loading hopper into modified bomb bay of Avenger NZ2504 for aerial topdressing trials, Masterton Aerodrome, 1949	1·75	1·75
3347	60c. Territorial Air Force No. 3 (Canterbury) Squadron	1·75	1·75
3348	60c. de Havilland Venom WK428 of 14 Squadron over RAF Station, Changi, Singapore ("South East Asia")	1·75	1·75
3349	60c. RNZAF A-4 Skyhawk and HMAS *Adelaide* off Perth, 1996 ('ANZAC")	1·75	1·75
3350	60c. Super Sea Sprite helicopter SH-2G taking off from flight deck of Anzac-class ship HMNZS *Te-Mana* ("Naval Support")	1·75	1·75
3351	60c. RNZAF Hercules at McMurdo Base, Antarctica ("Transport")	1·75	1·75
3352	60c. Three 'Huey' Iroquois helicopters, Timor, 2001 ("Peacekeeping")	1·75	1·75
3353	60c. Search and rescue training and RNZAF Iroquois helicopter	1·75	1·75
3354	60c. Aircraft flying in 'missing man' formation ("Remembrance")	1·75	1·75
3355	60c. NH90 advance medium utility helicopter ("The Future")	1·75	1·75
3341/55	*Set of 15*	24·00	24·00

Nos. 3341/55 were printed together, *se-tenant*, in sheetlets of 14 stamps. The stamps also exist in eight miniature sheets, each 135×150 mm, with a line of roulettes at left. The miniature sheets contain: Nos. 3341/2, each×2; Nos. 3343/4, each×2; Nos. 3345/6, each×2; Nos. 3347/8, each×2; Nos. 3349/50, each×2; Nos. 3351/2, each×2; Nos. 3353 and 3355, each×2; No. 3354×2. These miniature sheets were only available from a booklet, No. SP12, containing stamps with a face value of $18 but sold for $19.90.

732 Official New Zealand Portrait of Queen Elizabeth II

(Des Capiche Design. Litho Southern Colour Print)

2012 (9 May). Diamond Jubilee. T **732** and similar vert designs. Multicoloured. Phosphorised paper. P 13×13½.

3356	70c. Type **732**	1·75	1·75
3357	70c. Official New Zealand portrait of Queen Elizabeth II and Duke of Edinburgh	1·75	1·75
3358	$1.40 Queen Elizabeth II and Duke of Edinburgh wearing ceremonial cloaks for Maori reception, Hastings, New Zealand, 1986	3·25	3·25
3359	$1.90 Queen Elizabeth II and Duke of Edinburgh waving from car, Wellington, 1981	4·50	4·50
3360	$2.40 Queen Elizabeth II and Duke of Edinburgh on Silver Jubilee tour, Wellington, 1981	5·00	5·50
3361	$2.90 Queen Elizabeth II giving Christmas broadcast from Government House, Auckland, 1953	6·00	6·50
3356/61	Set of 6	20·00	21·00
MS3362	101×97 mm. Nos. 3356/61	22·00	23·00

(Litho Southern Colour Print)

2012 (23 May). New Zealand Landscapes (4th series). Horiz designs as T **622**. Multicoloured.

(a) Ordinary gum. Phosphorised paper. P 13×13½

3363	$1.40 Cape Reinga	2·50	2·50
3364	$2.10 Stewart Island	3·75	4·00
3365	$3.50 Lake Matheson	6·25	7·00
3363/5	Set of 3	11·00	12·00

(b) Self-adhesive. Phosphor frame. Die-cut perf 10×9½

3366	$1.40 As No. 3363	2·50	2·75
	a. Booklet pane. No. 3366×10	22·00	
	b. Horiz pair. Nos. 3366/7	6·25	7·00
3367	$2.10 As No. 3364	3·75	4·25
	a. Booklet pane. No. 3367×5	16·00	

Nos. 3366/7 were issued in separate booklets, Nos. SB159/60. The *se-tenant* pair, No. 3266b, could be purchased from the Philatelic Bureau.

(Litho Southern Colour Print)

2012 (23 May). All Blacks (national rugby team). As Nos. 3224 and **MS**3226 with new face value. P 13½.

3368	**712**	70c. black	1·75	1·75
MS3369	90×61 mm. As No. 3368 but 35×20 mm (P 15×14½) and No. 3368			2·50	2·50

733 Pouakai (birdman), Pareora

(Des Dave Burke. Litho Southern Colour Print)

2012 (6 June). Matariki. Maori Rock Art. T **733** and similar horiz designs. Multicoloured. Phosphorised paper.

(a) Self-adhesive. Die-cut perf 9½×10

3370	70c. Type **733**	1·25	1·25
	a. Pane. Nos. 3370/5	16·00	16·00
3371	70c. Seated tiki figure on ceiling of shelter, Maerewhenua	1·25	1·25
3372	$1.40 Two people on mokihi (bulrush water craft), Opihi	2·50	2·50
3373	$1.90 Te Puawaitanga, Waitaki	3·50	3·50
3374	$2.40 Tiki figure, Te Ana a Wai	4·25	4·25
3375	$2.90 Taniwha on ceiling of shelter, Opihi	5·25	5·25
3370/5	Set of 6	16·00	16·00

(b) Ordinary gum. P 13½

MS3376	150×91 mm. As Nos. 3370/5	16·00	16·00

(Litho)

2012 (6 June). Personalised Stamps. As No. **MS**3237 with new face values. Multicoloured. P 15×14½.

MS3377 70c.×8 As Type **660**; Buzzy Bee (toy); Silver Fern; Pohutukawa flower; Engagement and wedding rings; Red rose; As Type **705**; Teddy bear .... 9·00 9·00

No. **MS**3377 contains two horizontal strips of four stamps separated by a gutter containing labels inscribed 'Personalised Stamps 2012'.

(Litho Southern Colour Print)

2012 (18 June). Indonesia 2012 World Stamp Championship and Exhibition, Jakarta. Sheet 120×90 mm containing Nos. 3335 and 3337/8. Phosphorised paper. P 13×13½.

MS3378 Nos. 3335 and 3337/8 .... 8·00 8·00

734 Cape Reinga and Kaitaia

735 Selu Tuiga depicting Samoan Parliament and Beehive, Wellington

(Des Evan Purdie and Geoff Francis, Assignment Group. Litho Southern Colour Print)

2012 (4 July). Tiki Tour of New Zealand (2nd issue). Sheet 185×254 mm containing T **734** and similar vert designs. Multicoloured. Phosphorised paper. P 14.

MS3379 70c.×20 Type **734**; Whangarei and Bay of Islands; Cape Brett; Lion Rock; Auckland, Hamilton and Tauranga; White Island and East Cape; Mt. Taranaki, New Plymouth and Hawera; Rotorua, Taupo and Palmerston North; Napier and Gisborne; Fish and boat; Westport and Greymouth; Nelson and Kaikoura; Wellington; Chatham Islands; Milford Sound and Mitre Peak; Mt. Cook, Queenstown and Timaru; Christchurch; Invercargill, Gore and Stewart Island; Dunedin; Taiaroa Head........ 29·00 30·00

The stamps and background of No. **MS**3379 form a composite design showing a map of New Zealand.

An imperforate version of No. **MS**3379 was included in "The New Zealand Collection 2012" yearbook.

(Des Michael Tuffery. Litho Southern Colour Print)

2012 (1 Aug). 50th Anniv of Treaty of Friendship between New Zealand and Samoa. Selu Tuiga (Samoan head comb in shape of traditional tuiga headdress). T **735** and similar vert designs. Multicoloured. Phosphorised paper. P 14.

3380	70c. Type **735**	1·25	1·25
3381	$1.40 Tuiga with niu (coconut tree) design	2·50	2·50
3382	$1.90 Selu Tuiga depicting Maota Fa'amasino (Courthouse, Apia)	3·50	3·50
3383	$2.40 Selu Tuiga with tatau (tattoo) motifs and patterns	4·25	4·25
3384	$2.90 Selu Tuiga depicting Immaculate Conception of Mary Cathedral, Mulivai....	5·25	5·25
3380/4	Set of 5	15·00	15·00
MS3385	150×90 mm. Nos. 3380/4	15·00	15·00

736 Sea Lion Pup

737 Aramoana (Picton to Wellington ferry, 1962–84)

(Litho Southern Colour Print)

2012 (1 Aug). Children's Health. New Zealand Sea Lion (*Phocarctos hookeri*). T **736** and similar multicoloured designs.

(a) Ordinary gum. Phosphorised paper. P 14

3386	70c. +10c. Type **736**	1·75	1·75
3387	$1.40 +10c. Sub-adult male	3·00	3·25
MS3388	147×91 mm. 70c.+10c. Sea lion pup (head) (26×30 mm) and Nos. 3386/7	7·00	7·50

(b) Self-adhesive. Size 26×30 mm. Phosphor frame. Die-cut perf 9½×10

3389	70c. +10c. Sea lion pup (head)	1·75	1·75

No. **MS**3388 is cut in the shape of a female sea lion and pup.

(Des Creature, Wellington. Litho Southern Colour Print)

2012 (5 Sept). Great Voyages of New Zealand. T **737** and similar horiz designs. Multicoloured. Phosphorised paper (3390/4) or ordinary paper (**MS**3395). P 14.

3390	70c. Type **737**	2·00	1·25
3391	$1.40 Waka (Maori canoe) crossing Cook Strait..	2·75	2·50
3392	$1.90 *Earnslaw* (Kingston - Queenstown - Glenorchy steamer), Lake Wakatipu..........	4·25	3·50
3393	$2.40 *Dunedin* (Port Chalmers to London, 1874–90)	5·00	5·50
3394	$2.90 *Rotomahana* (Wellington to Lyttelton, Australia), 1870s-1925	6·50	6·50
3390/4	Set of 5	18·00	17·00
MS3395	136 mm × 75 mm. Nos. 3390/4	16·00	16·00

738 Mary, Joseph and Baby Jesus   **739** Bilbo Baggins

(Des Donna MacKenna. Litho Southern Colour Print (3396/3400, 3401b) or Australia Post Sprintpak (3401/3))

2012 (3 Oct). Christmas. T **738** and similar vert designs. Multicoloured.

(a) Ordinary gum. Phosphorised paper. P 14

3396	70c. Type **738**	1·25	60
3397	$1.40 Shepherds	2·50	1·25
3398	$1.90 Angel	3·50	3·25
3399	$2.40 Three Wise Men offering gifts	4·25	4·75
3400	$2.90 Journey of the Three Wise Men	5·25	5·75
3396/400	*Set of 5*	15·00	14·00

(b) Self-adhesive. Size 25×30 mm. Die-cut perf 9½×10 (3401b) or 11 (others)

3401	70c. As Type **738**	1·25	1·25
	a. Booklet pane. No. 3401×10	11·00	
	b. Partial phosphor frame only. Die-cut perf 9½×10	1·25	1·25
	c. Phosphor as No. 3401 but baby has phosphor halo only. Perf 11	1·25	1·25
	ca. Horiz strip of 3. Nos. 3401c/3	8·00	8·00
3402	$1.90 As No. 3398	3·50	3·50
	a. Booklet pane. No. 3402×10	30·00	
3403	$2.40 As No. 3399	4·25	4·25
	a. Booklet pane. No. 3403×10	35·00	

No. 3401b, issued in rolls of 100, has a partial phosphor frame at the foot and part way up the sides of the stamp.

No. 3401c has a phosphor band at the foot of the stamp, phosphor haloes for the Holy Family and phosphor around the sides of the filigree frame of the stamp design. It was only issued in horizontal strips of three with Nos. 3402/3 and could be purchased from the Philatelic Bureau.

No. 3401, issued in $7 booklets, No. SB161, has phosphor as No. 3401c but with the addition of phosphor over the baby's clothes.

Nos. 3402/3 were issued in $17.10 or $21.60 booklets, Nos. SB162/3.

(Litho Southern Colour Print)

2012 (12 Oct). Blenpex 2012 National Stamp Exhibition, Marlborough. Sheet 131×91 mm. Phosphorised paper. P 13×13½.

MS3404	Nos. 3356, 3359 and 3361	9·00	9·00

(Litho Southern Colour Print (3405/10) or Australia Post Sprintpak (3417/22))

2012 (1 Nov). *The Hobbit* (film trilogy): *An Unexpected Journey* (1st issue). T **739** and similar multicoloured designs.

(a) Ordinary gum. Phosphorised paper. P 14½×14 (vert) or 14×14½ (horiz)

3405	70c. Type **739**	1·50	70
3406	$1.40 Gollum (Andy Serkis)	2·75	1·50
3407	$1.90 Gandalf (Ian McKellen) (*horiz*)	3·75	4·00
3408	$2.10 Thorin Oakenshield (Richard Armitage) (*horiz*)	4·00	4·50
3409	$2.40 Radagast (Sylvester McCoy)	4·50	4·75
3410	$2.90 Elrond (Hugo Weaving)	5·50	6·50
3405/10	*Set of 6*	20·00	20·00

(b) Self-adhesive. Size 26×37 mm (vert) or 37×26 mm (horiz). Die-cut perf 11½

3417	70c. As Type **739**	1·25	1·25
	a. Booklet pane. Nos. 3417×4, 3418×2 and 3419/22	25·00	
	b. Pane. Nos. 3417/22	18·00	18·00
3418	$1.40 As No. 3406	2·50	2·50
3419	$1.90 As No. 3407	3·50	3·50
3420	$2.10 As No. 3408	3·75	3·75
3421	$2.40 As No. 3409	4·25	4·25
3422	$2.90 As No. 3410	5·25	5·25
3417/22	*Set of 6*	18·00	18·00

A set of six miniature sheets containing Nos. 3405/10 as single stamps were sold at $14.40 per set, a $3 premium over face value.

Nos. 3417/22 were issued in $14.90 stamp booklets, No. SB164.

No. 3417b could be purchased from the Philatelic Bureau.

See also Nos. 3312/23 and 3623/35.

Nos. 3411/16 are vacant.

(Litho Southern Colour Print)

2012 (2 Nov). Beijing 2012 International Stamp and Coin Expo. Sheet 121×90 mm. Phosphorised paper. P 13×13½.

MS3423	As Nos. 3330 and 3332/3	7·00	7·00

"BEST OF 2012". A further set of miniature sheets as described below No. 2042 were distributed by the Philatelic Bureau to customers purchasing a certain amount of philatelic material during 2012. The sheets comprised: 1. Nos. 3333, 3339 and 3355. 2. Nos. 3361, 3375 and 3384. 3. The Taiaroa Head stamp from **MS**3379 and Nos. 3387 and 3394.

Imperforate sheets of Nos. 3390/4 and a perforated *se-tenant* strip comprising the same four stamps were also distributed.

740 Calligraphic Snake by Zhao Meng-fu (1254–1322)   **741** Hen and Chickens Fern (*Asplenium bulbiferum*)

(Des Bananaworks, Auckland. Litho Cartor)

2013 (9 Jan). Chinese New Year. (Year of the Snake). T **740** and similar vert designs. Multicoloured. Phosphorised paper. P 13½×13.

3424	70c. Type **740**	1·25	60
3425	$1.40 Paper-cut greeting snake patterned with silver ferns and pomegranates	2·50	1·50
3426	$1.90 Lantern with koru-shaped snake design	3·50	4·00
3427	$2.40 Koru-snake lanterns on Skyline Gondola, Queenstown	4·25	4·75
3424/7	*Set of 4*	10·50	9·75
MS3428	150×90 mm. Nos. 3424/7	10·50	10·50

(Des 2Di4 Design, Wellington. Litho Cartor)

2013 (7 Feb). Native Ferns. T **741** and similar horiz designs. Multicoloured. Phosphorised paper. P 13×13½.

3429	70c. Type **741**	1·25	60
3430	$1.40 Kidney Fern (*Cardiomanes reniforme*)	2·50	1·50
3431	$1.90 Colenso's Hard Fern (*Blechnum colensoi*)	3·50	3·50
3432	$2.40 Umbrella Fern (*Sticherus cunninghamii*)	4·25	4·75
3433	$2.90 Silver Fern (*Cyathea dealbata*)	5·25	5·75
3429/33	*Set of 5*	15·00	14·50
MS3434	160×90 mm. Nos. 3429/33	15·00	15·00

742 A Lion in the Meadow

(Des Tim Garman, Silver-i-Design Associates. Litho Southern Colour Print)

2013 (13 Mar). Margaret Mahy (children's writer) Commemoration. T **742** and similar horiz designs. Multicoloured. Phosphorised paper. P 14.

3435	70c. Type **742**	1·25	60
3436	$1.40 *A Summery Saturday Morning*	2·50	1·50
3437	$1.90 *The Word Witch*	3·50	3·50
3438	$2.40 *The Great White Man-eating Shark*	4·25	4·75
3439	$2.90 *The Changeover*	5·25	5·75
3435/9	*Set of 5*	15·00	14·50
MS3440	140×85 mm. Nos. 3435/9	15·00	15·00

743 Kiwi Team One on Patrol, North-east Bamyan, Afghanistan, 2011

(Des Strategy Design and Advertising, Wellington. Litho Southern Colour Print)

2013 (10 Apr). ANZAC (4th series). New Zealanders serving Abroad. T **743** and similar horiz designs. Multicoloured. Phosphorised paper. P 14.

3441	70c. Type **743**	1·25	1·25
3442	70c. RNZAF Iroquois helicopter carrying Australian troops, Dili, Timor-Leste, 2008	1·25	1·25

3443	$1.40 Territorial Army members performing haka, Honiara, Solomon Islands, 2009	2·50	2·50
3444	$1.90 M113A1 tank of Queen Alexandra's Mounted Rifles on checkpoint duty, Bosnia-Herzegovina, 2007	3·50	3·50
3445	$2.40 ANZAC class frigate *Te Kaha* on patrol off Antarctica, 1999	4·25	4·25
3446	$2.90 Kiwi symbol on hillside at post Armistice Korean headquarters of 16th Field Regiment, Royal New Zealand Artillery, 1953	5·25	5·25
3441/6 *Set of 6*		16·00	16·00

MS3447 Seven sheets, each 155×110 mm. (a) No. 3441. (b) No. 3442. (c) No. 3443. (d) No. 3444. (e) No. 3445. (f) No. 3446. (g) Nos. 3441/6 .... 32·00 32·00

Nos. **MS**3447 were only available from $19.90 stamp booklets, No. SB165, with each miniature sheet having a line of roulettes at left.

744 Portrait by Mary Gillick, 1953

745 Piko (Silver Fern) and Tane Mahuta (God of the Forest)

(Recess and litho Southern Colour Print)

2013 (8 May). 60th Anniv of the Coronation. Portraits of Queen Elizabeth II from New Zealand Coins. T **744** and similar vert designs. Multicoloured. Phosphorised paper. P 14.

3448	70c. Type **744**	1·75	1·50
3449	70c. Re-engraved portrait by Mary Gillick, 1956	1·75	1·50
3450	$1.40 Portrait by Arnold Machin, 1967	3·00	2·50
3451	$1.90 Portrait by James Berry, 1979	4·00	3·75
3452	$2.40 Portrait by Raphael Maklouf, 1986	4·75	5·50
3453	$2.90 Portrait by Ian Rank-Broadley, 1999	5·50	6·00
3448/53 *Set of 6*		19·00	19·00
MS3454 150×90 mm. Nos. 3448/53		22·00	22·00

2013 (10 May). Australia 2013 World Stamp Exhibition, Melbourne. Sheet 150×91 mm. Phosphorised paper. P 14.

MS3455 Nos. 3448, 3450 and 3453 .... 9·00 9·00

(Des Dave Burke Design. Litho Southern Colour Print)

2013 (5 June). Matariki. Koru (pattern derived from Silver Fern frond, symbolising renewal). T **745** and similar horiz designs. Multicoloured. Phosphorised paper.

(a) Self-adhesive. Die-cut perf 9½×10

3456	70c. Type **745**	1·25	1·25
	a. Pane. Nos. 3456/61	16·00	16·00
3457	70c. Manu Tukutuku (kite) and koru pattern symbolising wind	1·25	1·25
3458	$1.40 Nguru (flute) and Hine Raukatauri (Goddess of Flute Music)	2·50	2·50
3459	$1.90 Pataka (storehouse) covered in Koru	3·50	3·50
3460	$2.40 Kotiate (club) and Mangopare design representing Hammerhead Shark	4·25	4·25
3461	$2.90 Patiki (flounder) design symbolising hospitality	5·25	5·25
3456/61 *Set of 6*		16·00	16·00

(b) Ordinary gum. P 13½

MS3462 151×91 mm. Nos. 3456/61		16·00	16·00

746 Bee gathering Nectar

(Des Strategy Design and Advertising, Wellington. Litho Southern Colour Print)

2013 (3 July). Honey Bees. T **746** and similar horiz designs. Multicoloured. Phosphorised paper. P 14.

3463	70c. Type **746**	1·00	1·50
3464	$1.40 Bees returning to hive	1·75	1·50
3465	$1.90 Worker bees transferring nectar to honey storage area of hive	2·50	2·50
3466	$2.40 Beekeeper removing honeycomb	3·75	4·25
3467	$2.90 Honey	4·50	4·75

3463/7 *Set of 5*		12·00	12·00
MS3468 137×81 mm. Nos. 3463/7		12·00	12·00

747 Napier, 1933

(Des Hamish Thompson. Litho Southern Colour Print)

2013 (7 Aug). Classic Travel Posters. T **747** and similar vert designs. Multicoloured. Phosphorised paper. P 14×14½.

3469	70c. Type **747**	1·25	1·25
	a. Sheetlet. Nos. 3469/88	22·00	22·00
3470	70c. New Zealand The Sportsman's Paradise (game fishing - hooked marlin)	1·25	1·25
3471	70c. Tree Fern	1·25	1·25
3472	70c. Rata Blossom Franz Josef Glacier	1·25	1·25
3473	70c. For the Worlds Best Sport (angler)	1·25	1·25
3474	70c. Cities of New Zealand Wellington	1·25	1·25
3475	70c. Your New Zealand Holiday Fly Teal (carved Maori figure, Arthur Thompson), 1950s	1·25	1·25
3476	70c. Get in the Queue for Queenstown	1·25	1·25
3477	70c. Timaru by the Sea	1·25	1·25
3478	70c. New Zealand (lake and mountains)	1·25	1·25
3479	70c. Tauranga for Winter Sunshine	1·25	1·25
3480	70c. Kea (Alpine Parrot)	1·25	1·25
3481	70c. Southern Alps Travel the Mount Cook way!	1·25	1·25
3482	70c. Marlborough Sounds	1·25	1·25
3483	70c. Sheep Droving in New Zealand	1·25	1·25
3484	70c. New Zealand for your next holiday (Maori woman)	1·25	1·25
3485	70c. For Winter Thrills Mt. Cook Train to Timaru (skiier)	1·25	1·25
3486	70c. Mt. Egmont 8,260 ft	1·25	1·25
3487	70c. Fly Teal to nearby New Zealand (Maori figures, geyser and Mt. Cook)	1·25	1·25
3488	70c. Blue Baths, Rotorua	1·25	1·25
3469/88 *Set of 20*		22·00	22·00

Nos. 3469/88 were printed together, *se-tenant*, in sheetlets of 20.

An imperforate version of the sheetlet, No. 3469a, was included in "The New Zealand Collection 2013" yearbook.

748 Castlepoint (centenary of lighthouse), Wairarapa Coast

(Des Creature, Wellington. Litho Southern Colour Print)

2013 (4 Sept). Coastlines. T **748** and similar horiz designs. Multicoloured. Phosphorised paper. P 13×13½.

3489	70c. Type **748**	1·00	60
3490	$1.40 Nugget Point	1·75	1·50
3491	$1.90 East Cape	2·50	3·00
3492	$2.40 Pencarrow Head, near Wellington	3·75	4·50
3493	$2.90 Cape Campbell	4·50	5·50
3489/93 *Set of 5*		12·00	13·50
MS3494 160×91 mm. Nos. 3489/93		12·00	13·50

749 Boy with Pet Lamb

(Des Stephen Fuller. Litho Southern Colour Print)

2013 (4 Sept). Children's Health. Country Pets. T **749** and similar vert designs. Multicoloured.

(a) Ordinary gum. Phosphorised paper. P 13½ (MS3497) or 14 (others)

3495	70c. +10c. Type **749**	1·50	1·50
3496	$1.40 +10c. Girl with piglet	2·00	2·25
MS3497	140×90 mm. Nos. 3495/6 and 70c.+10c. Boy with goat on school Pet Day (25×30 mm)	4·25	5·00

(b) Self-adhesive. Size 25×30 mm. Phosphor frame. Die-cut perf 9½×10

3498	70c. +10c. Boy with goat on school Pet Day .	1·50	1·75

750 Duke and Duchess of Cambridge with Prince George outside St. Mary's Hospital, 22 July 2013

751 Giving Christmas Present

(Litho Southern Colour Print)

2013 (11 Sept). Birth of Prince George of Cambridge. T **750** and similar vert designs. Multicoloured. P 14½.

3499	70c. Type **750**	2·00	2·25
	a. Horiz strip of 4. Nos. 3499/3502	13·00	14·00
3500	$1.90 Prince William holding Prince George	3·25	3·75
3501	$2.40 Duke and Duchess of Cambridge, Duchess holding Prince George	4·25	4·75
3502	$2.90 Catherine, Duchess of Cambridge holding Prince George	4·75	5·00
3499/502	*Set of 4*	13·00	14·00

No. 3499a could be purchased from the Philatelic Bureau at $7.90 per strip. It was not available in sheets.

(Litho Southern Colour Print)

2013 (13 Sept). Upper Hutt 2013 National Stamp Show. Sheet 141×80 mm. Phosphorised paper. P 13½.

MS3503	As Nos. 3432/3	9·50	10·50

(Des Martin Bailey. Litho Southern Colour Print)

2013 (2 Oct). Christmas. T **751** and similar square designs. Multicoloured. Phosphorised paper.

(a) Ordinary gum. P 14

3504	70c. Type **751**	1·00	50
3505	$1.40 Christmas lunch	1·75	1·10
3506	$1.90 Decorating the tree	2·50	2·75
3507	$2.40 Cricket on the beach	3·75	4·50
3508	$2.90 Carol singing	4·50	5·50
3504/8	*Set of 5*	12·00	13·00

(b) Self-adhesive. Size 25×30 mm. Die-cut perf 9½×10

(i) Domestic mail

3509	70c. As Type **751**	1·00	70
	a. Booklet pane. No. 3509×10	9·00	
	b. With phosphor bar at foot	1·00	70
	ba. Horiz strip of 3. Nos. 3509b/11	6·50	7·50

(ii) International Post

3510	$1.90 As No. 3506	2·50	3·00
	a. Booklet pane. No. 3510×10	22·00	
3511	$2.40 As No. 3507	3·75	4·50
	a. Booklet pane. No. 3511×10	30·00	
3509/11	*Set of 3*	6·50	7·50

No. 3509 was issued in $7 booklets, No. SB166. No. 3509b was issued in rolls of 100 and in No. 3509ba. No. 3510 was issued in booklets (SB167) sold at $17.10, providing a $1.90 discount off the face value of the stamps. No. 3511 was issued in booklets (SB168) sold at $21.60, providing a $2.40 discount off the face value of the stamps.
The se-tenant strip of three, No. 3509ba, could be purchased from the Philatelic Bureau.

(Litho Southern Colour Print)

2013 (1 Nov). The Hobbit (film trilogy): The Desolation of Smaug (2nd issue). Multicoloured designs as T **739**.

(a) Ordinary gum. Phosphorised paper. P 14½×14 (vert) or 14×14½ (horiz)

3512	70c. Thorin Oakenshield (Richard Armitage).	1·50	70
3513	$1.40 Gandalf (Ian McKellen)	2·25	1·50
3514	$1.90 Tauriel (Evangeline Lilly) (horiz)	3·00	2·50
3515	$2.10 Bilbo Baggins (Martin Freeman) (horiz)..	3·00	3·00

3516	$2.40 Legolas Greenleaf (Orlando Bloom)	4·00	4·25
3517	$2.90 Bard the Bowman (Luke Evans)	4·50	4·75
3512/17	*Set of 6*	16·00	15·00

(b) Self-adhesive. Size 26×37 mm (vert) or 37×26 mm (horiz). Phosphor frame. Die-cut perf 10×9½ (vert) or 9½×10 (horiz)

3518	70c. As No. 3512	1·00	1·00
	a. Booklet pane. Nos. 3518×4, 3519×2 and 3520/3	20·00	
	b. Pane. Nos. 3518/23	16·00	18·00
3519	$1.40 As No. 3513	1·75	1·75
3520	$1.90 As No. 3514	3·00	3·50
3521	$2.10 As No. 3515	3·25	3·75
3522	$2.40 As No. 3516	4·50	5·00
3523	$2.90 As No. 3517	4·75	5·50
3518/23	*Set of 6*	16·00	18·00

A set of six miniature sheets containing Nos. 3512/17 as single stamps were sold at $14.40 per set, a $3 premium over face value.
Nos. 3518/23 were issued in $14.90 stamp booklets, No. SB169.
No. 3518b could be purchased from the Philatelic Bureau.

"BEST OF 2013". A further set of miniature sheets as described below No. 2042 were distributed by the Philatelic Bureau to customers purchasing a certain amount of philatelic material during 2013. The sheets comprised: 1. Nos. 3433, 3427 and 3439. 2. Nos. 3446, 3461 and 3467. 3. Nos. 3470, 3493 and 3508.

Imperforate sheets of Nos. 3463/7 and a perforated se-tenant strip of the same five values were also distributed.

752 Horse Pictogram

753 *Hormosira banksii* (Neptune's Necklace)

(Des Asiaworks, Auckland. Litho Cartor)

2014 (8 Jan). Chinese New Year. (Year of the Horse). T **752** and similar vert designs. Multicoloured. P 13½×13.

3524	70c. Type **752**	1·00	60
3525	$1.40 Paper-cut horse	1·75	1·25
3526	$1.90 Show-jumping	2·50	2·50
3527	$2.40 Rotorua Museum of Art and History	3·75	4·50
3524/7	*Set of 4*	8·00	8·00
MS3528	150×90 mm. Nos. 3524/7	8·00	8·00

(Des 2Di4 Design. Litho Southern Colour Print)

2014 (5 Feb). Native Seaweeds. T **753** and similar vert designs. Multicoloured. Phosphorised paper. P 13½ (MS3534) or 14 (others).

3529	70c. Type **753**	1·00	60
3530	$1.40 *Landsburgia quercifolia*	1·75	1·25
3531	$1.90 *Caulerpa brownii* (sea rimu)	2·50	2·25
3532	$2.40 *Marginariella boryana*	3·75	4·50
3533	$2.90 *Pterocladia lucida* (agar weed)	4·50	5·00
3529/33	*Set of 5*	12·00	12·00
MS3534	160×90 mm. Nos. 3529/33	12·00	12·00

754 Colonial Cottage

(Litho Southern Colour Print)

2014 (5 Mar). Construction of a Nation. T **754** and similar horiz designs. Multicoloured. Phosphorised paper. P 14.

3535	70c. Type **754**	1·00	60
3536	$1.40 Villa	1·75	1·25
3537	$1.90 Californian bungalow	2·50	2·25
3538	$2.40 Art Deco house	3·75	4·50
3539	$2.90 State House	4·50	5·00
3535/9	*Set of 5*	12·00	12·00
MS3540	130×89 mm. Nos. 3535/9	12·00	12·00

The top margin of No. **MS**3540 is cut around in the shape of a house roof.

755 Recruitment Poster for Air Training Corps, 1942

756 Duke and Duchess of Cambridge with Prince George, August 2013

(Litho Southern Colour Print, New Zealand)

2014 (2 Apr). ANZAC (5th series). World War II Poster Art. T **755** and similar vert designs. Multicoloured. Phosphorised paper. P 14½.

3541	70c. Type **755**	1·25	1·25
3542	70c. Woman driving tractor ('HELP FARM FOR VICTORY', Women's Land Service), October 1943	1·25	1·25
3543	$1.40 Pilot ('THE AIR FORCE NEEDS MEN!', Royal New Zealand Air Force), February 1941	2·50	2·50
3544	$1.90 Warship ('NAVY WEEK') on fund raising poster for 3rd Liberty Loan, June 1943	3·50	3·50
3545	$2.40 Soldier throwing grenade ('ARMY WEEK') on fund raising poster for 3rd Liberty Loan, June 1943	4·25	4·25
3546	$2.90 Maori soldier and fund raising poster in Maori language ('TARINGA WHAKARONGO!'), 1941	5·25	5·25
3541/6	Set of 6	16·00	16·00
MS3547	165×110 mm. No. 3541	1·25	1·25
MS3548	165×110 mm. No. 3542	1·25	1·25
MS3549	165×110 mm. No. 3543	2·50	2·50
MS3550	165×110 mm. No. 3544	3·50	3·50
MS3551	165×110 mm. No. 3545	4·25	4·25
MS3552	165×110 mm. No. 3546	5·25	5·25
MS3553	165×110 mm. No. 3541/6	16·00	16·00

Nos. MS3547/53 were only available from $19.90 stamp booklets, No. SB170, containing stamps with a face value of $20.

(Litho Southern Colour Print)

2014 (7 Apr). Visit of Duke and Duchess of Cambridge to New Zealand, April 2014. T **756** and similar vert design. Multicoloured. Phosphorised paper. P 14½.

3554	70c. Type **756**	1·25	1·25
3555	$2.40 Official Christening photograph, Clarence House, London	4·25	4·25

757 Franz Josef Glacier

(Litho Southern Colour Print)

2014 (7 May). New Zealand Landscapes (5th series). T **757** and similar horiz designs. Multicoloured.

(a) Ordinary gum. Phosphorised paper. P 13×13½.

3556	60c. Type **757**	1·10	1·10
3557	$1.60 Moeraki Boulders	3·00	3·00
3558	$2.50 Pancake Rocks	4·50	4·50
3559	$3.60 Waikato River	6·50	6·50
3556/9	Set of 4	13·50	13·50

(b) Self-adhesive. Phosphor frame. Die-cut perf 10×9½.

3560	$2 Mount Taranaki	3·50	3·50
	a. Booklet pane. No. 3560×5	16·00	
	b. Horiz pair. Nos. 3560/1	8·00	8·00
3561	$2.50 As No. 3558	4·50	4·50
	a. Booklet pane. No. 3561×5	20·00	

Nos. 3560/1 were issued in $10 or $12.50 booklets, Nos. SB171/2.

(Litho Southern Colour Print)

2014 (7 May). All Blacks (national rugby team). As Nos. 3224/MS3226 with new face values. P 13½.

3562	**712**	80c. black	1·40	1·40
3563		$2.50 black	4·50	4·50
MS3564	90×80 mm. As Nos. 3562/3 but 35×19 mm (P 15×14½) and Nos. 3562/3		11·00	11·00

758 Wedding Rings

(Litho Southern Colour Print)

2014 (7 May). Personalised Stamps. T **758** and similar horiz designs. Multicoloured. P 15×14½.

MS3565	164×82 mm. 80c.×8 Type **758**; Silver Fern; 'love'; Two glasses of champagne; Teddy bear; Pohutukawa flowers; Cupcake with birthday candles; Balloons	8·75	7·50
MS3566	94×82 mm. $2 As Type **758**; $2 Silver Fern; $2.50 Two glasses of champagne; $2.50 Pohutukawa flowers	12·50	13·50

No. MS3565 contains two horizontal strips of four stamps separated by a gutter containing labels inscribed '2014 Personalised Stamps'.

759 Te wehenga o Rangi raua ko Papa (Cliff Whiting)

760 Giant Peaches, Cromwell

(Des Rangi Kipa, Te Atiawa, Taranaki Tuturu. Litho Southern Colour Print)

2014 (4 June). Matariki. Papatuanuku and Ranginui. T **759** and similar multicoloured designs.

(a) Self-adhesive. Die-cut perf 10×9½ (vert) or 9½×10 (horiz).

3567	80c. Type **759**	1·10	95
	a. Pane. Nos. 3567/72	13·00	13·50
3568	80c. Rangi and Papa (Phil Mokaraka Berry)	1·10	95
3569	$1.40 Te whakamamae o te wehenga (Kura Te Waru Rewiri)	2·00	1·60
3570	$2 The Separation of Rangi and Papa (Fred Graham) (horiz)	2·75	2·75
3571	$2.50 The Children of Rangi and Papa (Pauline Kahurangi Yearbury) (horiz)	3·50	4·00
3572	$3 The Ranginui Doorway (Robert Jahnke) (horiz)	4·25	4·75
3567/72	Set of 6	13·00	13·50

(b) Ordinary gum. P 13½.

MS3573	150×90 mm. As Nos. 3567/72	14·50	15·00

(Des Graeme Mowday and Tim Christie. Litho Southern Colour Print)

2014 (2 July). Legendary Landmarks (town icons). T **760** and similar square designs. Multicoloured. Phosphorised paper. P 14½.

3574	80c. Type **760**	1·10	95
	a. Sheetlet. Nos. 3574/91	19·00	17·00
3575	80c. New Zealand flag on giant kiwi ('Otorohanga Kiwiana Town')	1·10	95
3576	80c. Kiwi fruit ('TEPUKE HEART OF KIWI FRUIT COUNTRY')	1·10	95
3577	80c. Lemon and Paeroa bottle ('PAEROA HOME OF A KIWI FAVOURITE')	1·10	95
3578	80c. Deer statue ('MOSSBURN Deer capital of NZ')	1·10	95
3579	80c. Surfer on wave ('Surf's Up at Colac Bay')	1·10	95
3580	80c. Giant carrot ('OHAKUNE CARROT CAPITAL OF NZ')	1·10	95
3581	80c. Giant fish ('Rakaia means great fishing')	1·10	95
3582	80c. Giant sheep's head ('Tirau's Big Sheep')	1·10	95
3583	80c. Multicoloured giant gumboot ('TAIHAPE WHERE GUMBOOTS RULE')	1·10	95
3584	80c. Chain-link sculpture ('Rakiura the chain holding us together')	1·10	95
3585	80c. Bronze statue of child with Opo the dolphin ('Opononi HOME OF THE FRIENDLY DOLPHIN')	1·10	95
3586	80c. Dog statue ('HUNTERVILLE THE HUNTAWAY'S HOME')	1·10	95
3587	80c. Bicycle with cyclist in front wheel ('TAUPO THE CYCLIST'S DELIGHT')	1·10	95
3588	80c. Giant Sandfly ('PUKEKURA'S GIANT SANDFLY')	1·10	95
3589	80c. Sculpture of shepherd and dog ('Feilding celebrating the land')	1·10	95

3590	80c. Cart horses ('Clinton celebrates our rural heritage')	1·10	95
3591	80c. Loaf of bread ('Farewell from MANAIA BREAD CAPITAL')	1·10	95
3574/91	*Set of 18*	19·00	17·00

Nos. 3574/91 were printed together, *se-tenant*, in sheetlets of 18 stamps, each sheetlet forming a composite background design depicting postcards stuck on a fridge.

761 Lord Kitchener (1850–1916)

(Des Strategy Design and Advertising, Wellington. Litho Southern Colour Print)

2014 (29 July). Centenary of the First World War (1st issue). 1914 For King and Empire. T **761** and similar square designs. Multicoloured. Phosphorised paper. P 14½.

3592	80c. Type **761**	1·10	95
	a. Block of 6. Nos. 3592/7	6·50	5·75
3593	80c. Military training poster ('New Zealand called to prepare')	1·10	95
3594	80c. Governor of New Zealand (Earl of Liverpool) with New Zealand Parliament reading message from King George V ('War announced')	1·10	95
3595	80c. Melville Mirfin ('Serving his country')	1·10	95
3596	80c. Mirfin family ('Family portrait')	1·10	95
3597	80c. New Zealand Expeditionary Force aboard the troopship *Limerick*, 1914 ('Troopships depart')	1·10	95
3598	$2 Training camp, Canterbury	2·75	2·75
	a. Horiz pair. Nos. 3598/9	5·50	5·50
3599	$2 Karaka Bay, Wellington, 1914 ('The home front')	2·75	2·75
3600	$2.50 Letter from Melville Mirfin to his father ('Letters and stories from Samoa')	3·50	4·00
	a. Horiz pair. Nos. 3600/1	7·00	8·00
3601	$2.50 New Zealand Expeditionary Force by the Pyramids, Egypt, 1914 ('Serving abroad')	3·50	4·00
3592/601	*Set of 10*	17·00	17·00
MS3602	175×90 mm. Nos. 3592/7	6·50	5·75
MS3603	141×90 mm. Nos. 3598/3601	12·50	13·50

Nos. 3592/7 were printed together, *se-tenant*, as blocks of six stamps in sheets of 24 (6×4). Nos. 3598/9 and 3600/1 were each printed together, *se-tenant*, as horizontal pairs in sheets of 24 (6×4).

Nos. 3592/3601 were also issued in premium booklets, No. SP13, containing stamps with a face value of $27.60 but sold for $39.90.

See also Nos. 3663/**MS**3674 and 3760/**MS**3771.

762 Antipodean Albatross   **763** Girl holding Carrots

(Litho Southern Colour Print)

2014 (3 Sept). Endangered Seabirds. T **762** and similar horiz designs. Multicoloured. P 14 (3604/8) or 13½ (**MS**3609).

3604	80c. Type **762**	1·10	95
3605	$1.40 New Zealand Fairy Tern	2·00	1·60
3606	$2 Chatham Island Shag	2·75	2·75
3607	$2.50 Black-billed Gull	3·50	4·00
3608	$3 Chatham Island Taiko	4·25	4·75
3605/8	*Set of 5*	12·00	12·50
MS3609	160×74 mm. Nos. 3604/8	13·50	14·00

(Des Insight, Wellington. Litho Southern Colour Print)

2014 (3 Sept). Children's Health. Growing a Healthy Future. T **763** and similar vert designs.

*(a) Ordinary gum. Phosphorised paper. P 13½ (**MS**3612) or 14 (others).*

3610	80c. Type **763**	1·10	95
3611	$1.40 Boy holding apples on shoulders	2·00	1·60
MS3612	140×90 mm. As Nos. 3610/11 and boy holding pumpkin (25×30 *mm*)	3·00	2·50

(b) Self-adhesive. Size 25×30 mm. Phosphor frame. Die-cut perf 9½×10.

3613	80c. Boy holding pumpkin	1·25	1·00

764 Mary and Jesus

(Des Lindy Fisher. Litho Southern Colour Print)

2014 (1 Oct). Christmas. Children in Nativity Play. T **764** and similar horiz designs. Multicoloured.

(a) Ordinary gum. P 14.

3614	80c. Type **764**	1·10	95
3615	$1.40 Joseph	2·00	1·60
3616	$2 Wise man	2·75	2·75
3617	$2.50 Angel	3·50	4·00
3618	$3 Shepherd	4·25	4·75
3614/18	*Set of 5*	12·00	12·50

(b) Self-adhesive. Size 30×25 mm.

(i) Domestic mail. Die-cut perf 10×9½.

3619	80c. As Type **764**	1·10	95
	a. Booklet pane. No. 3619×10	10·00	
	b. With irregular phosphor bar at left	1·10	95
	ba. Horiz strip of 3. Nos. 3619b/21b	7·25	7·50

(ii) International Post. Die-cut perf 10×9½.

3620	$2 As No. 3616	2·75	2·75
	a. Booklet pane. No. 3620×10	25·00	
	b. With irregular phosphor bar at left	2·75	2·75
3621	$2.50 As No. 3617	3·50	4·00
	a. Booklet pane. No. 3621×10	32·00	
	b. With irregular phosphor bar at left	3·50	4·00
3619/21	*Set of 3*	6·50	7·00

No. 3619 was issued in $8 booklets, No. SB173.

Nos. 3619/21b were issued in No. 3619ba.

No. 3620 was issued in booklets (SB174) sold at $18, providing a $2 discount off the face value of the stamps.

No. 3621 was issued in booklets (SB175) sold at $22.50, providing a $2.50 discount off the face value of the stamps. The *se-tenant* strip of three, No. 3619ba, could be purchased from the Philatelic Bureau.

765 Gandalf and the Companions

(Litho Southern Colour Print)

2014 (15 Oct). Personalised Stamps. The Hobbit. Multicoloured. Phosphorised paper. P 15×14½.

MS3622 110×66 mm. 80c. Type **765**; $2.50 As Type **765**   4·50   5·00

(Litho Southern Colour Print)

2014 (12 Nov). The Hobbit (film trilogy): The Battle of the Five Armies (3rd issue). Multicoloured designs as T **739**.

(a) Ordinary gum. Phosphorised paper. P 14½×14 (vert) or 14×14½ (horiz).

3623	80c. Smaug the Dragon	1·10	95
3624	$1.40 Bilbo Baggins	2·00	1·60
3625	$2 Gandalf (*horiz*)	2·75	2·75
3626	$2.10 Thranduil (*horiz*)	3·00	3·50
3627	$2.50 Bard the Bowman	3·50	4·00
3628	$2.50 Door to Bag End	3·50	4·00
3629	$3 Tauriel	4·25	4·75
3623/9	*Set of 7*	18·00	19·00

(b) Self-adhesive. Size 26×37 mm or 37×26 mm. Die-cut perf 10×9½ (vert) or 9½×10 (horiz).

3630	80c. As No. 3623	1·10	95
	a. Booklet pane. Nos. 3630×4, 3631×2 and 3632/5	20·00	
	b. Pane. Nos. 3630/5	15·00	16·00
3631	$1.40 As No. 3624	2·00	1·60
3632	$2 As No. 3625	2·75	2·75
3633	$2.10 As No. 3626	3·00	3·50
3634	$2.50 As No. 3627	3·50	4·00
3635	$3 As No. 3629	4·25	4·75
3630/5	*Set of 6*	15·00	16·00

No. 3628 has ground wood from the Hobbiton film set affixed to the Bag End door.

A set of seven miniature sheets containing Nos. 3623/9 as single stamps were sold at $17.80 per set, a $3.50 premium over face value.

Nos. 3630/5 were issued in $15.60 stamp booklet, No. SB176.

No. 3630b could be purchased from the Philatelic Bureau.

(Litho Southern Colour Print)

2014 (14 Nov). BAYPEX 2014 National Stamp Exhibition, Hawke's Bay. Sheet 140×90 mm. Phosphorised paper. P 14½.
MS3636 Nos. 3597/8 and 3601............................. 10·50   11·50
No. **MS**3636 was sold at $7.50, a $2.50 premium over face value. The surcharge was for the Philatelic Trust.

766 Chinese Character for Sheep

(Des Asiaworks. Litho Southern Colour Print)

2015 (14 Jan). Chinese New Year. Year of the Sheep. T **766** and similar vert designs. Multicoloured. Phosphorised paper. P 14 (3637/40) or 13½ (**MS**3641).
3637	80c. Type **766**....................................	1·10	95
3638	$1.40 Paper-cut of sheep decorated with traditional Chinese patterns...............	2·00	1·50
3639	$2 Sheep pasture in New Zealand.................	2·75	2·75
3640	$2.50 Church of the Good Shepherd, Lake Tekapo.......................................	3·50	4·00
3637/40 Set of 4..		8·50	8·25
MS3641 150×90 mm. Nos. 3637/40...............		9·00	9·00

767 ZK-AMA *Aotearoa* Short S.30 Empire Class Flying Boat on First TEAL Flight Auckland to Sydney, 30 April 1940

(Des Insight Creative. Litho Southern Colour Print)

2015 (14 Jan). 75th Anniv of New Zealand National Airlines 'Connecting New Zealand and the World'. T **767** and similar horiz designs. Multicoloured. Phosphorised paper. P 14½.
3642	80c. Type **767**....................................	1·10	95
3643	$1.40 Mrs. Margaret Gould, NAC's first ground stewardess with child and Kawatere NZNAC Lockheed Lodestar on ground, 1948 ('Travelling the Country with NAC')...	2·00	1·50
3644	$2 TEAL (Tasman Empire Airways Ltd) coral route luggage label, 1951 to 1960 ('Exploring the Pacific with TEAL')...........	2·75	2·75
3645	$2.50 Two children on board Douglas DC-10 Series 30, 1977 ('Sharing the Flying Experience') (NAC merged with Air New Zealand, 1978).............................	3·50	4·00
3646	$3 Air New Zealand Boeing 787-9 taking off, 2014...	4·25	4·75
3642/6 Set of 5..		12·00	12·50
MS3647 119×91 mm. Nos. 3642/6.................		13·00	13·00

768 India

(Litho Southern Colour Print)

2015 (4 Feb). ICC Cricket World Cup, New Zealand and Australia. T **768** and similar round designs showing emblem and national flags of participating countries on cricket balls. Multicoloured. Phosphorised paper. Self-adhesive. Die-cut.
3648	80c. Type **768**....................................	1·10	95
	a. Sheetlet. Nos. 3648/61	15·00	13·00

3649	80c. England (white ball)....................	1·10	95
3650	80c. South Africa (bright blue-green ball)......	1·10	95
3651	80c. Pakistan (bright yellow-green ball).........	1·10	95
3652	80c. Unted Arab Emirates (grey ball)	1·10	95
3653	80c. Sri Lanka (Royal blue ball)..........................	1·10	95
3654	80c. West Indies (lake ball)...............................	1·10	95
3655	80c. Afghanistan (bright blue ball)..................	1·10	95
3656	80c. Ireland (emerald ball)................................	1·10	95
3657	80c. Bangladesh (bright scarlet ball, green dotted lines).............................	1·10	95
3658	80c. Australia (greenish yellow ball).................	1·10	95
3659	80c. New Zealand (grey ball)	1·10	95
3660	80c. Zimbabwe (bright scarlet ball, white dotted lines).............................	1·10	95
3661	80c. Scotland (deep dull blue)............................	1·10	95
3648/61 Set of 14..		15·00	13·00

Nos. 3648/61 were printed together in sheetlets of 14 stamps.

769 Ngapuhi Chief Tamati Waka Nene shaking hands with William Hobson (first Governor of New Zealand)

770 Catafalque Sentry, Bugler, Australian Golden Wattle and Anzac Cove

(Des Rangi Kipa, Te Atiawa, Taranaki Tuturu and Roy McDougall. Litho Southern Colour Print)

2015 (4 Feb). 175th Anniv of the Treaty of Waitangi. Sheet 149×90 mm. W **502**. P 14×14½.
MS3662 **769** $2.50 multicoloured .... 3·50   4·00

(Des Strategy Design and Advertising, Wellington. Litho Southern Colour Print)

2015 (23 Mar). Centenary of the First World War (2nd issue). 1915 The Spirit of ANZAC. Square designs as T **261**. Multicoloured. Phosphorised paper. P 14½.
3663	80c. Evelyn Brooke (matron in New Zealand Army Nursing Service)...................	1·10	95
	a. Block of 6. Nos. 3663/8.................	6·50	5·75
3664	80c. Postcard from Egypt, 1915	1·10	95
3665	80c. Landing at Anzac Cove, 1915.......	1·10	95
3666	80c. The Battle of Chunuk Bair, 8 August 1915 (Ion Brown).............................	1·10	95
3667	80c. '"HELP OUR WOUNDED" in lights, Queen Carnival, Auckland, 1915...........	1·10	95
3668	80c. Stained glass window depicting First and Second World War nurses, Marquette Memorial Chapel, Christchurch	1·10	95
3669	$2 Watercolour *The Sapper and his Donkey* (Horace Moore-Jones).....................	2·75	2·75
	a. Horiz pair. Nos. 3669/70.............	5·50	5·50
3670	$2 War Census, 1915............................	2·75	2·75
3671	$2.50 Hospital ship NZHS *Maheno* ...	3·50	4·00
	a. Horiz pair. Nos. 3671/2...............	7·00	8·00
3672	$2.50 Poster of Australian and New Zealand soldiers bearing Union Jack flags (Otho Hewett)..	3·50	4·00
3663/72 Set of 10..		17·00	17·00
MS3673 175×90 mm. Nos. 3663/8.................		6·00	6·00
MS3674 140×90 mm. Nos. 3669/72...............		12·00	13·00

Nos. 3663/72 were printed together, *se-tenant*, as blocks of six stamps in sheets of 24 (6×4).

Nos. 3669/70 and 3671/2 were each printed together, *se-tenant*, as horizontal pairs in sheets of 24 (6×4).

Nos. 3663/72 were also issued in premium booklets, No. SP14, containing stamps with a face value of $27.60 but sold for $39.90.

(Des Australia Post Design Studio. Litho McKellar Renown)

2015 (7 Apr). ANZAC Centenary. T **770** and similar vert design. Multicoloured. Phosphorised paper. P 14½×14.
3675	80c. Type **770**....................................	1·10	95
3676	$2 Bugler, catafalque sentry, New Zealand silver Fern and ANZAC Cove...............	2·75	2·75
MS3677 105×70 mm. Nos. 3675/6.................		3·75	3·75

Similar designs were issued on the same date by Austalia.

771 Silver Paua
(*Haliotis australis*)

772 *Digiwhaiwhai*
(Johnson Witehira)

(Litho Southern Colour Print)

2015 (6 May). Native Seashells. T **771** and similar vert designs. Multicoloured. Phosphorised paper. P 14 (3678/82) or 13½ (**MS**3683).

3678	80c. Type **771**	1·10	95
3679	$1.40 Scott's Murex (*Rolandiella scotti*)	2·00	1·50
3680	$2 Golden Volute (*Provocator mirabilis*)	2·75	2·75
3681	$2.50 Fan Shell (*Talochlamys gemmulata*)	3·50	4·00
3682	$3 Opal Top Shell (*Cantharidus opalus*)	4·25	4·75
3679/82	Set of 5	12·00	12·50
MS3683	140×90 mm. Nos. 3678/82	13·00	13·00

(Des Rangi Kipa and Roy McDougall. Litho Southern Colour Print)

2015 (3 June). Matariki. Kowhaiwhai. T **772** and similar multicoloured designs.

(a) Self-adhesive. Die-cut perf 10×9½ (vert) or 9½×10 (horiz).

3684	80c. Type **772**	1·10	95
	a. Pane. Nos. 3684/9	13·00	13·50
3685	80c. *Tenai au tenai au* (This is me, this is me) (Kura Te Waru Rewiri)	1·10	95
3686	$1.40 *Haki* from the series *Whakahokia mai te mauri* (Kylie Tiuka)	2·00	1·50
3687	$2 *Banner Moon* from the series *Land Protest 1975–1976*, reworked 1982 (Buck Nin) (*horiz*)	2·75	2·75
3688	$2.50 Part of the *Te Hatete o te Reo* series (Ngatai Taepa) (*horiz*)	3·50	4·00
3689	$3 *Taona Marama* (Night Lights of the City) (Sandy Adsett)	4·25	4·75
3684/9	Set of 6	13·00	13·50

(b) Ordinary gum. P 14.

MS3690	150×90 mm. As Nos. 3684/9	14·00	14·00

773 Asparagus Rolls

774 Emerald Lakes, Tongariro National Park

(Des Jason Kelly. Litho Southern Colour Print)

2015 (1 July). Kiwi Kitchen. T **773** and similar square designs. Multicoloured. Phosphorised paper. P 14½.

3691	80c. Type **773**	1·10	95
	a. Sheetlet. Nos. 3691/3708	19·00	17·00
3692	80c. Kiwi Onion Dip	1·10	95
3693	80c. Puha Pork	1·10	95
3694	80c. Bluff Oysters	1·10	95
3695	80c. Meat Loaf	1·10	95
3696	80c. Hokey Pokey ice cream	1·10	95
3697	80c. Shrimp Cocktail	1·10	95
3698	80c. Cheese Rolls	1·10	95
3699	80c. Pikelets	1·10	95
3700	80c. Lambington	1·10	95
3701	80c. Mince on Toast	1·10	95
3702	80c. Whitebait Fritters	1·10	95
3703	80c. Curried Egg	1·10	95
3704	70c. Saveloy and Tomato Sauce	1·10	95
3705	80c. Bacon and Egg	1·10	95
3706	80c. Pavlova	1·10	95
3707	80c. Fairy Bread	1·10	95
3708	80c. Mousetrap	1·10	95
3691/708	Set of 18	19·00	17·00

Nos. 3691/3708 were printed together, *se-tenant*, in sheetlets of 18 stamps.

(Litho Southern Colour Print)

2015 (5 Aug). UNESCO World Heritage Sites. Multicoloured. Phosphorised paper. P 14.

3709	80c. Type **774**	1·10	95
3710	$1.40 Franz Josef Glacier, Te Wahipounamu (south-west New Zealand)	2·00	1·60
3711	$2 Enderby Island, New Zealand sub Antarctic islands	2·75	2·75
3712	$2.20 Mt Ngauruhoe, Tongariro National Park	3·00	3·50
3713	$2.50 Lake MacKenzie, Te Wahipounamu (south-west New Zealand)	3·50	4·00
3714	$3 Campbell Island, New Zealand sub Antarctic islands	4·25	4·75
3710/14	Set of 6	15·00	16·00
MS3715	160×90 mm. Nos. 3709/14	16·00	16·00

775 Parliament House, Wellington, New Zealand

776 Girl under Sun Umbrella

(Litho Southern Colour Print)

2015 (14 Aug). World Stamp Exhibition, Singapore. T **775** and similar horiz designs. Multicoloured. Phosphorised paper. P 14.

3716	$2.50 Type **775**	3·50	4·00
MS3717	120×80 mm. 70c. Parliament House, Canberra, Australia; $1.30 Parliament House, Singapore; No. 3716	2·75	2·75

Similar designs were issued by Australia and Singapore.

(Des Donna McKenna. Litho Southern Colour Print)

2015 (2 Sept). Children's Health. Being Sunsmart. 'Slip, Slop, Slap & Wrap'. T **776** and similar vert designs. Multicoloured.

*(a) Ordinary gum. Phosphorised paper. P 14 (3718/20) or 13½ (**MS**3721).*

3718	80c. Type **776**	1·25	1·00
3719	$1.40 Boy wearing cap with flaps and applying sunscreen	2·00	1·50
3720	$2 Girl with huge wide-brimmed hat	3·00	3·50
3718/20	Set of 3	5·75	5·50
MS3721	149×90 mm. As Nos. 3718/20 and 80c.+10c. Boy with huge sunglasses (25×30 mm)	7·00	7·00

(b) Self-adhesive. Size 25×30 mm. Die-cut perf 9½×10.

3722	80c. +10c. Boy with huge sunglasses (25×30 mm)	1·25	1·00

The top of **MS**3721 is cut around in the shape of a sun umbrella. This miniature sheet contains photochromic ink and the sun umbrella on the upper sheet margin turns from yellow and white to purple and green when exposed to sunlight.

777 All Blacks Jersey

(Des Dave Burke. Litho Southern Colour Print)

2015 (2 Sept). All Blacks (national rugby team) Jersey. Phosphorised paper. P 13½.

3723	**777** $15 multicoloured	20·00	25·00

No. 3723 was issued in a folder sold for $15. The "shirt" was of screen-printed fabric affixed to the background frame.

A sheet containing six $2.50 All Blacks stamps as No. 3563 was issued on 1 November 2015 to mark New Zealand's victory in the Rugby World Cup and sold by New Zealand Post for $19.90 per sheet.

778 Queen Elizabeth II, 1950s

779 Angel (from St. Mark's Church, Carterton)

(Litho Southern Colour Print)

2015 (7 Oct). Queen Elizabeth II - New Zealand's Longest Reigning Monarch. T **778** and similar vert designs. Multicoloured. Phosphorised paper. P 14½.

3724	80c. Type **778**	1·10	95
3725	80c. Queen Elizabeth II, 1960s	1·10	95
3726	$1.40 Queen Elizabeth II, 1970s	2·00	1·50
3727	$2 Queen Elizabeth II, 1980s	2·75	2·75
3728	$2.20 Queen Elizabeth II, 1990s	3·00	3·50
3729	$2.50 Queen Elizabeth II, 2000s	3·50	4·00
3730	$3 Queen Elizabeth II, 2010s	4·25	4·75
3725/30 *Set of 7*		16·00	16·50
MS3731 158×85 mm. Nos. 3724/30		17·00	17·00

(Litho Southern Colour Print)

2015 (23 Oct). The Capital Stamp Show, Wellington. Sheet 130×90 mm containing Nos. 3665, 3669 and 3671. Phosphorised paper. P 14½.

MS3732 Nos. 3665, 3669 and 3671		7·00	7·00

(Des Hannah Stancliffe-White. Litho Southern Colour Print)

2015 (4 Nov). Christmas. Stained Glass Windows. T **779** and similar vert designs. Multicoloured. Phosphorised paper (ex **MS**3738).

(a) Ordinary gum. P 14.

3733	80c. Type **779**	1·10	95
3734	$1.40 Dove (from St. Aidan's Anglican Church, Remuera, Auckland)	2·00	1·50
3735	$2 Mary and Jesus (from St. Mary's-in-Holy Trinity Cathedral, Parnell, Auckland)	2·75	2·75
3736	$2.50 Pohutukawa (from Christchurch Hospital Nurses Memorial Chapel)	3·50	4·00
3737	$3 Three Wise Men (from St. Benedict's Church, Auckland)	4·25	4·75
3733/7 *Set of 5*		12·00	12·50
MS3738 177×79 mm. As Nos. 3733/7			

(b) Self-adhesive. Size 25×30 mm.

(i) Domestic mail. Die-cut perf 9½×10.

3739	80c. As Type **779**	1·10	95
	a. Booklet pane. No. 3739×10	10·00	
	b. Horiz strip of 3. Nos. 3739/41	7·25	7·50

(ii) International Post. Die-cut perf 9½×10.

3740	$2 As No. 3735	2·75	2·75
	a. Booklet pane. No. 3740×10	25·00	
3741	$2.50 As No. 3736	3·50	4·00
	a. Booklet pane. No. 3741×10	32·00	
3739/41 *Set of 3*		6·50	7·00

No. 3739 was issued in $8 booklets, No. SB177.

No. 3740 was issued in booklets (SB179) sold at $18, providing a $2 discount off the face value of the stamps.

No. 3741 was issued in booklets (SB179) sold at $22.50, providing a $2.50 discount off the face value of the stamps.

The *se-tenant* strip of three, No. 3739b, could be purchased from the Philatelic Bureau.

"Best of 2015" A further set of miniature sheets as described below No. 2041 were distributed by the Philatelic Bureau to customers purchasing a certain amount of philatelic material during 2015. The sheets comprised: 1. Nos. 3640, the $2·50 stamp from **MS**3662 and 3689. 2. Nos. 3682, 3646 and 3670. 3. Nos. 3714, 3730 and 3737.

Imperforate sheets of No. 3676/82 and a *se-tenant* strip of the same five values was also distributed.

780 Pictogram

(Des Asiaworks, Auckland. Litho Southern Colour Print, New Zealand)

2016 (13 Jan). Chinese New Year. Year of the Monkey. T **780** and similar vert designs. Multicoloured. Phosphorised paper. P 14 (3742/5) or 13½ (**MS**3746).

3742	80c. Type **780**	1·10	95
3743	$1.40 Paper-cut monkey holding peach	2·00	1·50
3744	$2 Monkey	2·75	2·75
3745	$2.50 Monkey Island	3·50	4·00
3742/5 *Set of 4*		8·50	8·25
MS3746 150×90 mm. As Nos. 3742/5		9·00	9·00

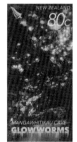

781 National Meeting of Returned Soldiers, Wellington, 28 April 1916 ('THE RETURNED')

782 Glowworms, Mangawhitikau Cave

(Des Richard Payne. Litho Southern Colour Print)

2016 (3 Feb). Centenary of RSA (Royal New Zealand Returned and Services' Association). T **781** and similar square designs. Multicoloured. Phosphorised paper. P 14½.

3747	80c. Type **781**	1·10	95
3748	$1.40 'THE POPPY'	2·00	1·50
3749	$2 'SUPPORTING THOSE WHO SERVED'	2·75	2·75
3750	$2.20 Inside RSA clubroom ('AT THE RSA')	3·00	3·50
3751	$2.50 RSA badge ('THE BADGE')	3·50	4·00
3752	$3 'WE WILL REMEMBER THEM'	4·25	4·75
3748/52 *Set of 6*		15·00	15·50
MS3753 165×90 mm. Nos. 3747/52		16·00	16·00

(Des Hannah Stancliffe-White. Litho Southern Colour Print)

2016 (2 Mar). New Zealand Native Glowworms (*Arachnocampa luminosa*). T **782** and similar vert designs. Multicoloured.

(a) Ordinary gum. Phosphorised paper. P 14½×14.

3754	80c. Type **782**	1·10	95
3755	$1.40 Nicau Cave	2·00	1·50
3756	$2 Ruakuri Cave	2·75	2·75
3757	$2.50 Waipu Cave	3·50	4·00
3754/7 *Set of 4*		8·50	8·25
MS3758 149×70 mm. Nos. 3754/7		9·00	9·00

(b) Self-adhesive. Size 25×36 mm. Die-cut perf 9½×10.

3759	$2 As No. 3756	2·75	2·75
	a. Booklet pane. No. 3759×10	25·00	

Nos. 3754/9 were printed using glow-in-the-dark ink, and will light up if exposed to sunlight and then taken into a dark place.

No. 3759 was issued in $20 stamp booklets, No. SB180. It was also available as a self-adhesive stamp on plain white backing paper.

(Des Strategy Design and Advertising. Litho Southern Colour Print)

2016 (6 Apr). Centenary of the First World War (3rd issue). 1916 Courage and Commitment. Square designs as T **761**. Multicoloured. Phosphorised paper. P 14½.

3760	80c. Solomon Isaacs in uniform, February 1916	1·10	95
	a. Block of 6. Nos. 3760/5	6·50	5·75
3761	80c. Pioneer Battalion	1·10	95
3762	80c. Graffiti 'KIAORA NZ' by the New Zealand Tunnelling Company (NZTC) in the Arras tunnels	1·10	95
3763	80c. Newspaper headline of 26 August 1916 'CONSCRIPTION COMES!'	1·10	95
3764	80c. New Zealand Mounted Rifles in the Middle East	1·10	95
3765	80c. The Somme	1·10	95
3766	$2 Service on church steps, Nelson, 25 April 1916 ('The first Anzac Day')	2·75	2·75
	a. Horiz pair. Nos. 3766/7	5·50	5·50
3767	$2 NZEF Headquarters, Bloomsbury Square, London ('Away from the front')	2·75	2·75
3768	$2.50 Indefatigable-class battlecruiser HMS *New Zealand*, 31 May 1916 ('Battle of Jutland')	3·50	4·00
	a. Horiz pair. Nos. 3768/9	7·00	8·00
3769	$2.50 Kaikoura Post & Telegraph office ('The home front')	3·50	4·00
3760/9 *Set of 10*		17·00	17·00

MS3770 174×89 mm. Nos. 3760/5		6·50	5·75
MS3771 137×89 mm. Nos. 3766/9		12·50	13·00

Nos. 3760/5 were printed together, *se-tenant*, as blocks of six stamps in sheets of 24 (6×4).

Nos. 3766/7 and 3768/9 were each printed together, *se-tenant*, as horizontal pairs in sheets of 24 (6×4).

Nos. 3760/9 were also issued in premium booklets, No. SP15, containing stamps with a face value of $27.60 but sold for $39.90.

783 Duke and Duchess of York with Baby Elizabeth, 1926

(Des Jonathan Gray. UV offset printing Enschedé)

2016 (4 May). 90th Birthday of Queen Elizabeth II. Sheet 179×92 mm containing T **783** and similar horiz designs. Multicoloured. Self-adhesive. Die-cut.

MS3772 Type **783**, Princess Elizabeth and Duke of Edinburgh with Prince Charles, 1949, Queen Elizabeth II in New Zealand, 2016; $5 Young Princesses Elizabeth and Margaret, 1936, Queen Elizabeth II and Duke of Edinburgh opening New Zealand's Parliament, 1963, Queen Elizabeth II, New Zealand, 2002; $5 Wedding of Princess Elizabeth, 1947, Queen Elizabeth II, New Zealand, 1977, Queen Elizabeth II, New Zealand, 2016		20·00	25·00

No. **MS**3772 contains three lenticular stamps, each stamp containing three images which change as the miniature sheet is tilted.

(Des Richard Payne. Litho Southern Colour Print)

2016 (18 May). New Zealand Landscapes (6th series). Horiz designs as T **757**. Multicoloured.

(a) Ordinary gum. Phosphorised paper. P 13×13½.

3773	40c. Church of the Good Shepherd, Lake Tekapo		55	45
3774	80c. Chatham Islands		1·10	95
3775	$2.20 Awaroa Bay, Abel Tasman Scenic Reserve		3·00	3·50
3776	$2.70 Vineyards, Marlborough		3·75	4·25
3777	$3.30 Dunedin Railway Station		4·50	5·00
3778	$3.80 Te Mata Peak, Hawke's Bay		5·25	5·75
3773/8 *Set of 6*			16·00	18·00

(b) Self-adhesive. Phosphor frame. Die-cut perf 10×9½.

3779	$2.20 As No. 3775		3·00	3·50
	a. Booklet pane. No. 3779×5		13·50	
	b. Horiz pair. Nos. 3779/80		6·75	7·75
3780	$2.70 As No. 3776		3·75	4·25
	a. Booklet pane. No. 3780×5		17·00	

No. 3779 was issued in $11 booklets, No. SB181.
No. 3780 was issued in $13.50 booklets, No. SB182.

784 Kete Taniko with Serpent's Teeth and Duck's Feet Pattern (Cori Marsters)

(Des Rangi Kipa and Roy McDougall. Litho Southern Colour Print)

2016 (1 June). Matariki. Kete. T **784** and similar multicoloured designs. Phosphorised paper.

(a) Self-adhesive. Die-cut perf 10×9½ (vert) or 9½×10 (horiz).

3781	$1 Type **784**		1·40	1·10
	a. Pane. Nos. 3781/6		15·00	15·00
3782	$1 Basket with plaited bottom (Pip Devonshire)		1·40	1·10
3783	$1.80 Poutama (male lineage) design (Te Atiwei Ririnui)		2·50	2·00
3784	$2.20 Mount Taranaki and Royal Albatross feather design (Audra Potaka) (*horiz*)		3·00	3·50

3785	$2.70 Aramoana (navigate the ocean) design (Matthew McIntyre Wilson) (*horiz*)		3·75	4·25
3786	$3.30 Tatai whetu ki te rangi (clusters of stars in the heavens) (Sonia Snowden)		4·50	5·00
3781/6 *Set of 6*			15·00	15·00

(b) Ordinary gum. P 13½.

MS3787 150×90 mm. As Nos. 3781/6		15·00	15·00

(Litho Southern Colour Print)

2016 (22 June). Personalised Stamps. Horiz designs as T **758**. Multicoloured. Phosphorised paper. P 14½.

3788	$1 As Type **758**		1·40	1·40
	a. Sheetlet. Nos. 3788/97		18·00	18·00
3789	$1 Silver Fern		1·40	1·40
3790	$1 'love'		1·40	1·40
3791	$1 Two glasses of champagne		1·40	1·40
3792	$1 Teddy bear		1·40	1·40
3793	$1 Pohutukawa flowers		1·40	1·40
3794	$1 Balloons		1·40	1·40
3795	$2.20 As No. 3789		3·00	3·00
3796	$2.20 As Type **758**		3·00	3·00
3797	$2.70 As No. 3793		3·75	3·75
3788/97 *Set of 10*			18·00	18·00

Nos. 3788/97 were printed together, *se-tenant*, in sheetlets of ten stamps containing two horizontal strips of five stamps separated by a gutter containing stamp-size labels inscribed '2016 Personalised Stamps'.

785 Athlete and New Zealand Landscape

(Des Jonathan Gray. Litho Southern Colour Print)

2016 (6 July). Olympic Games, Rio de Janeiro, Brazil. Road to Rio. T **785** and similar parallelogram designs showing silhouettes of athletes in New Zealand landscapes. Multicoloured. Phosphorised paper. P 14.

3798	$1 Type **785**		1·40	1·40
	a. Block of 10. Nos. 3798/3807		12·50	12·50
3799	$1 Boxer		1·40	1·40
3800	$1 Canoeist (on mountain river with gravel banks)		1·40	1·40
3801	$1 Swimmer		1·40	1·40
3802	$1 Equestrian		1·40	1·40
3803	$1 Hockey player		1·40	1·40
3804	$1 Triathlete		1·40	1·40
3805	$1 Cyclist		1·40	1·40
3806	$1 Rower (on river with forested banks)		1·40	1·40
3807	$1 Sailor		1·40	1·40
3798/807 *Set of 10*			12·50	12·50

Nos. 3798/3807 were printed together, *se-tenant*, as blocks of ten stamps in sheetlets of 20 (5×4).

786 Natalie Rooney (silver, shooting: trap – women)

(Des Jonathan Gray. Litho. New Zealand Post)

2016 (8 Aug). New Zealand Olympic Medal Winners, Rio de Janeiro, Brazil. T **786** and similar parallelogram designs. Multicoloured. Phosphorised paper. P 14.

3808	$1 Type **786**		1·40	1·40
	a. Sheetlet. Nos. 3808×6		8·00	
	b. Sheetlet. Nos. 3808/25		24·00	
3809	$1 New Zealand team (silver, rugby sevens: women)		1·40	1·40
	a. Sheetlet. No. 3809×6		8·00	
3810	$1 Eric Murray and Hamish Bond (gold, rowing: pair – men)		1·40	1·40
	a. Sheetlet. No. 3810×6		8·00	
3811	$1 Luuka Jones (silver, slalom: K-1 – women)		1·40	1·40
	a. Sheetlet. No. 3811×6		8·00	

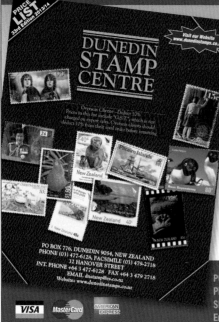

3812	$1	Ethan Mitchell, Sam Webster and Eddie Dawkins (silver, cycling – track: team sprint – men)	1·40	1·40
	a.	Sheetlet. No. 3812×6	8·00	
3813	$1	Genevieve Behrent and Rebecca Scown (silver, rowing: pair – women)	1·40	1·40
	a.	Sheetlet. No. 3813×6	8·00	
3814	$1	Valerie Adams (silver, athletics: shot put – women)	1·40	1·40
	a.	Sheetlet. No. 3814×6	8·00	
3815	$1	Mahe Drysdale (gold, rowing: single scull – men)	1·40	1·40
	a.	Sheetlet. No. 3815×6	8·00	
3816	$1	Lisa Carrington (gold, sprint: K-1 – 200m – women)	1·40	1·40
	a.	Sheetlet. No. 3816×6	8·00	
3817	$1	Sam Meech (bronze, sailing: laser – men)	1·40	1·40
	a.	Sheetlet. No. 3817×6	8·00	
3818	$1	Lisa Carrington (bronze, sprint: K-1 – 500m – women)	1·40	1·40
	a.	Sheetlet. No. 3818×6	8·00	
3819	$1	Jo Aleh and Polly Powrie (silver, sailing: 470 – women)	1·40	1·40
	a.	Sheetlet. No. 3819×6	8·00	
3820	$1	Peter Burling and Blair Tuke (gold, sailing: 49er – men)	1·40	1·40
	a.	Sheetlet. No. 3820×6	8·00	
3821	$1	Molly Meech and Alex Maloney (silver, sailing: 49er – women)	1·40	1·40
	a.	Sheetlet. No. 3821×6	8·00	
3822	$1	Tomas Walsh (athletics: shot put – men)	1·40	1·40
	a.	Sheetlet. No. 3822×6	8·00	
3823	$1	Eliza McCartney (bronze, athletics: pole vault – women)	1·40	1·40
	a.	Sheetlet. No. 3823×6	8·00	
3824	$1	Lydia Ko (silver, golf: individual – women)	1·40	1·40
	a.	Sheetlet. No. 3824×6	8·00	
3825	$1	Nick Willis (bronze, athletics: 1500m – men)	1·40	1·40
	a.	Sheetlet. No. 3825×6	8·00	
3808/25	Set of 18		24·00	24·00

Nos. 3808/25 were issued in a *se-tenant* sheetlet containing the 18 designs and two labels.

Nos. 3808/25 were also each issued in sheetlets of six stamps of the same design.

787 'At that moment Trev had a bit of an idea'

(Des Chris Davidson (illustration), Graeme Mowday and Jack Faulkner. Litho Southern Colour Print)

2016 (7 Sept). It's a Kiwi Thing. T **787** and similar square designs. Multicoloured. Phosphorised paper. P 14½.

3826	$1	Type **787**	1·40	1·40
	a.	Sheetlet. Nos. 3826/39	18·00	18·00
3827	$1	'I'll have a trim, decaf latte with a twist and a...'	1·40	1·40
3828	$1	'Breaking the tackle in the big game' (streaker on rugby pitch)	1·40	1·40
3829	$1	'The traditional Kiwi sand-wich'	1·40	1·40
3830	$1	'GONE BUT NOT FORGOTTEN 2011–2016 (jandals)	1·40	1·40
3831	$1	'A kea ate my car'	1·40	1·40
3832	$1	'Catching a glimpse of our national bird'	1·40	1·40
3833	$1	'A cool splash followed by a hot dash' (hot beach sand)	1·40	1·40
3834	$1	'Water skiing on Lake Taupo' (angler towed by trout)	1·40	1·40
3835	$1	'Another smooth landing in the capital'.	1·40	1·40
3836	$1	'At this time of year we'd be lucky to see a whale'	1·40	1·40
3837	$1	'Another successful day's whitebaiting'.	1·40	1·40
3838	$1	'Just a friendly game of beach cricket'....	1·40	1·40
3839	$1	'Always blow on the pie'	1·40	1·40
3826/39	Set of 14		18·00	18·00

Nos. 3826/39 were printed together, *se-tenant*, in sheetlets of 14 stamps.

788 Children playing Touch Rugby (Aerobic)

(Des Stephen and Di Fuller. Litho Southern Colour Print)

2016 (7 Sept). Children's Health. Being Active. T **788** and similar horiz designs. Multicoloured. Phosphorised paper. P 14.

3840	$1 +10c.Type **788**		1·50	1·25
	a.	Horiz strip of 3. Nos. 3840/2	7·00	6·75
3841	$1.80 +10c Children playing tug of war (Strength)		2·75	2·40
3842	$2.20 +10c. Stretching exercises (Flexibility)....		3·25	3·75
3840/2	Set of 3		7·00	6·75
MS3843	150×90 mm. Nos. 3840/2		7·00	6·75

No. 3840a could be purchased from the Philatelic Bureau.

789 Bruce and William Anderson (Loss of HMS *Neptune*)

(Des Helcia Knap. Litho Southern Colour Print)

2016 (5 Oct). 75th Anniv of the Royal New Zealand Navy (RNZN). T **789** and similar horiz designs. Multicoloured. Phosphorised paper. P 14½×14.

3844	$1	Type **789**	1·40	1·10
3845	$1	Frigate RNZN *Pukaki* (Conflict in Korea) .	1·40	1·10
3846	$1.80	Women at sea	2·50	2·00
3847	$2.20	Frigate HMNZS Te *Mana*, 2004 (Supporting the United Nations)	3·00	3·50
3848	$2.70	Disaster relief in Christchurch, 2011	3·75	4·25
3849	$3.30	The Navy family	4·50	5·00
3844/9	Set of 6		15·00	15·00
MS3850	160×110 mm. Nos. 3844/9		15·00	15·00

Nos. 3844/9 and the stamps within **MS**3850 each show an image, coated with spot UV to give the effect of looking through glass, within a brass scuttle recovered from the wreck of the *Moa* In 1943.

A $10 miniature sheet containing a circular stamp with the 'One Ring' embossed in 22 carat gold foil was issued on 19 October 2016. It was sold for $10.50, a 50c. premium over face value.

MACHINE LABELS

An automatic machine dispensing labels, ranging in value from 1c. to $99.99, was installed at the Queen Street Post Office, Auckland, on 3 September 1984 for a trial period. The oblong designs, framed by simulated perforations at top and bottom and vertical rules at the sides, showed the "Southern Cross", face value and vertical column of six horizontal lines between the "NEW ZEALAND" and "POSTAGE" inscriptions. The trial period ended abruptly on 16 October 1984.

Similar labels, with the face value and inscriptions within a plain oblong, were introduced on 12 February 1986 and from 22 August 1988 they were printed on paper showing New Zealand flags. On 12 September 1990 the design printed on the paper was changed to show seaplanes and on 12 August 1992 to a Maori pattern. A further Maori pattern, taken from rafters, in green and grey appeared on 21 February 1996.

A commemorative label was available at "NEW ZEALAND '90" held at Auckland between 24 August and 2 September 1990.

CUSTOMISED ADVERTISING LABELS (CALs)

These labels, formerly known as Personalised Advertising Labels, are produced for customers by NZ Post and feature the NZ Post 'envelope' logo. Although valid for postage, they are not generally available through NZ Post outlets and are, thus, outside the scope of this catalogue.

The first such label was issued at the Wellington Arts Festival in February 2004, a 40c. value depicting a bright red Kiwi. Subsequent issues have usually been at the standard inland postage rate, although higher values have been produced. The majority are self-adhesive but several designs have ordinary gum and, although the design size has been consistent at 29x21mm, the format may be vertical or horizontal.

Early labels were printed by Kinetic Vision or Southern Colour Print, but since 2006 printing has been by NZ Post in Wanganui.

In 2009 the first booklets were released (for Maui Gas), containing ten different 50c. values, and in 2010 the first 'regional' booklets, known as 'i-site' booklets, were issued, initially containing 70c. and $1.90 labels and later 80c. and $2 values. Since early 2007 NZ Post has produced an annual pack containing all the labels released during the previous calendar year.

STAMP BOOKLETS

Nos. SB1 to SB24 are stapled.
Nos. SB1/5 were sold at ½d. above the face value of the stamps to cover the cost of manufacture.

1901 (1 Apr). White card covers with postage rates.
SB1   1s.½d. booklet containing twelve 1d. (No. 278) in
         blocks of 6.. £2250
SB2   2s. 6½d. booklet containing thirty 1d. (No. 278) in
         blocks of 6.. £3000
         Original printings of Nos. SB1/2 showed the face value on the cover in small figures. Subsequent printings show large figures of value on the covers and the prices quoted are for this type.

1902 (21 Aug)–**05**. White card covers with postage rates.
SB3   1s.½d. booklet containing twelve 1d. in panes of 6
         (Nos. 303b or 303cb)................................... £1800
SB4   2s.½d. booklet containing twenty-four 1d. in panes of
         6 (Nos. 303b or 303cb) (21.3.05)............. £2250
SB5   2s. 6½d. booklet containing thirty 1d. in panes of 6
         (Nos. 303b or 303cb)................................... £2750

1910 (Apr). White card cover with postage rates.
SB6   2s. booklet containing eleven ½d. in pane of 5 with
         one label (Nos. 387b or 387c) and pane of 6
         (No. 387d), and eighteen 1d. in three panes of 6
         (No. 405b)... £5000

1912 (May). White card cover.
SB7   2s. booklet containing twelve ½d. and eighteen
         1d. in panes of 6 with bars on the selvedge
         (Nos. 387e, 405c).. £3000

1915 (Feb). Red card cover.
SB8   2s. booklet containing twelve ½d. and eighteen 1d.
         in panes of 6 with bars on the selvedge (Nos. 435a
         or 435ba, 405c).. £1800
         a. Grey cover ....
         b. Blue cover ....
         c. Yellow-buff cover ....
         d. Purple-buff cover ....

1924 (1 Dec)–**25**. Cover inscription within frame.
SB9   2s. booklet containing twelve ½d. and eighteen
         1d. in panes of 6 with bars on the selvedge
         (Nos. 441a, 406b) (lilac cover).................. £2000
         a. Grey cover ....
         b. Pale blue cover.. £2250
SB10   2s. booklet containing twelve ½d. and eighteen 1d.
         in panes of 6 with bars and advertisements on
         the selvedge (Nos. 446a, 410b) (yellow-buff cover)
         (1925)... £2500
         a. Grey-green cover....................................... £2500
         b. Grey-buff cover... £2500
         c. Grey-pink cover... £2500

1928–34.
SB11   2s. booklet containing twelve ½d. (P 14×15) and
         eighteen 1d. in panes of 6 with bars on the
         selvedge (Nos. 446ab, 468b)...................... £3000
         a. As No. SB11, but ½d. (P 14) (Nos. 446ca, 468b).... £1800
         b. As No. SB11 but panes with bars and
         advertisements on the selvedge (Nos. 446cb,
         468c).. £2000
SB12   2s. booklet containing twenty-four 1d. (P 14) in
         panes of 6 with bars and advertisements on the
         selvedge (No. 468c) (1930)........................ £1800
         a. As No. SB12, but 1d. (P 14×15) (No. 468ea) (1934) £1700

1935 (18 Nov).
SB15   2s. booklet containing twenty-four 1d., in panes of 6
         with advertisements on the selvedge (No. 557ca) £375

1936 (Nov).
SB16   2s. booklet containing twenty-four 1d. (No. 578) in
         blocks of 6... £250

B **1**

1938 (1 July). Cream cover as Type B **1**.
SB17   2s. booklet containing twenty-four 1d. (No. 605) in
         blocks of 6... £375

1938 (Nov). Cream (No. SB18) or blue (No. SB19) covers as Type B **1**.
SB18   2s. booklet containing twelve ½d. and eighteen 1d.
         (Nos. 603, 605) in blocks of 6.................... £475
SB19   2s.3d. booklet containing eighteen 1½d. (No. 607) in
         blocks of 6... £400

B **2**

1954 (1 Apr)–**55**. Black and green on cream cover as Type B **2**.
SB20   4s. booklet containing twelve 1d. and 3d. (Nos. 724,
         727), each in blocks of 6............................. 4·00
         a. Contents as SB20 but with one pane of air mail
         labels (9.55)... 21·00

1956 (1 May). Black and green on cream cover as Type B **2**.
SB21   4s. booklet containing twelve 1d. and 3d. (Nos. 724,
         748), each in blocks of 6, and one pane of air mail
         labels.. 10·00

1957 (5 Sept). Black and green on cream cover as Type B **2**.
SB22   4s. booklet containing twelve 1d. and 3d. (Nos. 745,
         748), each in blocks of 6, and one pane of air mail
         labels.. 9·00

B **3**

1960 (1 Sept). Black and red on cream cover as Type B **3**.
SB23   4s. booklet containing twelve 1d. and 3d. (Nos. 782,
         785), each in blocks of 6, and one pane of air mail
         labels.. 14·00

1962 (21 May). Black and red on cream cover as Type B **3**.
SB24   4s.6d. booklet containing twelve ½d., 1d. and 3d.
         (Nos. 781, 782, 785), each in blocks of 6, and one
         pane of air mail labels................................ 50·00

1964. Black and carmine on cream cover as Type B **3**. Stitched.
SB25   4s.3d. booklet containing six ½d. and twelve 1d. and
         3d. (Nos. 781/2, 785), each in blocks of 6, and one
         pane of air mail labels................................ 16·00

B **4** Maori Art

1967 (10 July). Black and carmine on pale lemon cover as Type B **4**. Stitched.
SB26   50c. booklet containing ½c. (No. 845) in block of 6,
         eleven 1c. in block of 6 (No. 846) and pane of 5
         stamps and one label (No. 846a), and twelve 3c.
         (No. 849) in blocks of 6.............................. 6·50

B **5** Native Trees

1971 (6 July). Multicoloured cover 70×49 mm, as Type B **5**. Stitched.
SB27   75c. booklet containing nine 1c. (No. 915b) in block of 6 and in pane of 3 stamps and three labels (No. 915ba), six 3c. (No. 918b) and twelve 4c. (No. 919b), each in blocks of 6 with sideways inverted or sideways watermarks .... 5·50

1974 (Aug). Multicoloured cover 70×49 mm, as Type B **5**. Stitched.
SB28   75c. booklet. As No. SB27 but containing stamps without watermark (Nos. 1008/a, 1010/11) .... 5·50
        a. Revised cover design ....

The front cover of No. SB28a was printed in four colours instead of three, with the foliage to the left of the design being in grey-green instead of myrtle-green. The stamps were printed on paper with bluish gum and there were changes to the advertisements.

All booklets from No. SB29 onwards have their panes attached by the selvedge, *unless otherwise stated*.

B **6** Garden Rose "Josephine Bruce"

1977 (May). Multicoloured cover 80×58 mm, as Type B **6**.
SB29   80c. booklet containing 8c. (No. 1093a) in block of 10 .... 3·00

B **7**

1977 (May). Blue and black printed cover 89×49 mm, as Type B **7**.
SB30 $1 booklet containing 10c. (No. 1017) in block of 10 .... 8·00

B **8**

Two settings of Booklet Cover for No. SB31:
Setting I. Inscription at foot. "c" aligned at top of "10" (similar to Type B **8**).
Setting II. Inscription at top. "c" aligned at bottom of "10".

1978 (Aug)–**79**. Black and ultramarine printed cover 80×58 mm, as Type B **8**.
SB31 $1 booklet containing 10c. (No. 1094a) in block of 10 (Cover Setting I) .... 9·00
        a. Cover Setting II .... 27·00
        b. Containing 10c. (No. 1094ab) (Cover Setting I) (1979) .... 21·00

1978 (Aug). Black and orange cover 80×58 mm, as Type B **8**.
SB32 $1.20 booklet containing 12c. (No. 1096) in block of 10 .... 2·75

1980 (1 Mar). Black and red cover 80×58 mm, as Type B **8**.
SB33 $1.40 booklet containing 14c. (No. 1098) in block of 10 .... 2·75

B **9**

1980 (12 May). Black and green cover 80×59 mm, as Type B **9**.
SB34 $1.40 booklet containing 14c. (No. 1098) in block of 10 .... 2·50
        The cover of No. SB34 is inscribed "$1.54" which included a premium payable when purchased from commercial outlets authorized to sell booklets. It was available at $1.40 (value of contents) from the Post Office Philatelic Bureau.

B **10**

1981. Black and blue cover 95×50 mm, as Type B **10**.
SB35 $2 booklet containing 20c. (No. 1099) in block of 10 .... 2·25

B **11**

1981. Black and green cover 95×50 mm, as Type B **11**.
SB36 $2 booklet containing 20c. (No. 1099) in block of 10 .... 2·25
        The cover of No. SB36 is inscribed "$2.20". See note below No. SB34.

1982 (1 Apr)–**83**. Black and green cover 83×60 mm, as Type B **8**.
SB37 $2.40 booklet containing 24c. (P 12½) (No. 1261) in block of 10 .... 4·75
        a. Containing 24c. (P 14½×14) (No. 1261a) (3.83) .... 14·00

1982 (1 Apr)–**85**. Black and blue cover 83×60 mm, as Type B **9**.
SB38 $2.40 booklet containing 24c. (P 12½) (No. 1261) in block of 10 .... 3·50
        a. Containing 24c. (P 14½×14) (No. 1261a) (3.85) ... 20·00
        The covers of Nos. SB38/a are inscribed "$2.64". See note below No. SB34.

B **12** Lake Tekapo, South Island

1985 (1 July). Multicoloured cover as Type B **12** with design continuing on back cover.
SB39 $2.50 booklet (Type B **12**) containing 25c. (No. 1370) in block of 10 .... 5·00
SB40 $2.50 booklet (Tongariro Park, North Island) containing 25c. (No. 1370) in block of 10 .... 6·00
        The cover of No. SB40 is inscribed "$2.75". See note below No. SB34.

1986 (1 May). Multicoloured covers as Type B **12**, but 115×60 mm, with the design continuing on back cover.

SB41	$3 booklet (Matukituki Valley, Otago) containing 30c. (No. 1288) in block of 10	4·00
SB42	$3 booklet (Stream and native bush, Canterbury) containing 30c. (No. 1288) in block of 10	4·00

The cover of No. SB42 is inscribed "$3.30". See note below No. SB34.

Nos. SB41/2 exist overprinted on the front cover with the "Stockholmia" logo for sale at the International Philatelic Exhibition in Sweden.

1987 (2 Feb–June). Multicoloured covers as Type B **12**, but 115×60 mm with the design continuing on back cover.

SB43	$4 booklet (Ahuriri Valley, Otago) containing 40c. (No. 1289) in block of 10	18·00
	a. Revised "NZ POST" logo without crown (6.87)	18·00
SB44	$4 booklet (Totaranui Beach, Abel Tasman National Park, Nelson) containing 40c. (No. 1289) in block of 10	18·00
	a. Revised "NZ POST" logo without crown (6.87)	30·00

The covers of booklets Nos. SB44/a are inscribed "$4.40". See note below No. SB34.

Nos. SB43a and SB44a exist overprinted on the front cover with the "CAPEX" logo for sale at the International Philatelic Exhibition in Toronto.

1987 (Nov). Multicoloured covers as Type B **12**, but 115×60 mm, with the design continuing on back cover. New "NZ POST" logo as shown on Type B **14**.

SB45	$4 booklet (Wellington by night) containing 40c. (No. 1289) in block of 10	6·00
SB46	$4 booklet (Katiki Point) containing 40c. (No. 1289) in block of 10	29·00

The cover of No. SB46 is inscribed "$4.40". See note below No. SB34.

B **13**

1988 (18 May). "Personal Message Stamps". Multicoloured cover, 101×60 mm, as Type B **13**.

SB47	$2 booklet containing pane of 5 different 40c. (No. 1455a)	3·25

No. SB47 exists overprinted on the front cover with the "WORLD STAMP EXPO '89" logo for sale at the International Stamp Exhibition in Washington, U.S.A.

B **14**

1988 (7 June). "Fast Post" Service. Black, bright scarlet and new blue cover, 88×60 mm, as Type B **14**.

SB48	$7 booklet containing 70c. (No. 1466) in block of 10	6·50

B **15**

1988 (14 Sept). Christmas. Multicoloured cover, 116×59 mm, as Type B **15**.

SB49	$3.50 booklet containing 35c. (No. 1480) in block of 10	3·50

B **16**

1988 (19 Oct). Multicoloured cover, 86×55 mm, as Type B **16**.

SB50	$6 booklet containing pane of 6 $1 (No. 1490a)	11·00

B **17** Mt Cook from the Hooker Valley, South Canterbury

1988 (2 Nov). Multicoloured cover, 88×60 mm, as Type B **17** with design continuing on back cover.

SB51	$4 booklet containing 40c. (No. 1463) in block of 10	5·50

No. SB51 exist overprinted on the front cover with the "Stamp World London '90" logo for sale at the International Stamp Exhibition in Great Britain.

1989 (13 Sept). Christmas. Multicoloured cover, 16×59 mm, as Type B **15**.

SB52	$3.50 booklet containing 35c. (No. 1520) in block of 10	3·25

B **18**

1990 (Aug). Black and white cover, 61×96 mm, as Type B **18** showing multicoloured stamp No. 1463.

SB53	$4 booklet containing 40c. (No. 1463) in block of 10 with three fastPOST labels	10·00

No. SB53 has a slot in the cover for hanging display. Booklets in this format were produced for self-service sales.

B **19**

1991 (15 May). "Happy Birthday". Multicoloured cover, 101×60 mm, as
Type B **19**.
SB54 $2 booklet containing pane of 5 different 40c.
(No. 1594a)...   3·25

B **20**

1991 (15 May). "Thinking of You". Multicoloured cover, 101×60 mm, as
Type B **20**.
SB55 $2 booklet containing pane of 5 different 40c.
(No. 1604a)...   3·25

B **20a**   B **20b**

1991 (1 July). Blue and white cover, 61×96 mm, as
Type B **18** showing multicoloured stamp No. 1463b. B **20a** in
hanging display format with slotted tab as Type B **18**.
SB56 $4.50 booklet containing 45c. (No. 1463b) in
block of 10...   4·00

1991 (1 July). "Happy Birthday". Multicoloured vert cover, 61×100 mm,
as Type B **20b**.
SB57 $2.25 booklet containing pane of 5 different 45c.
(No. 1599a)...   3·25

B **20c**

1991 (1 July). "Thinking of You". Multicoloured cover, 60×100 mm,
as Type B **20c** with slotted tab in hanging display format as
Type B **20b**.
SB58 $2.25 booklet containing pane of 5 different 45c.
(No. 1609a)...   3·25

BARCODES. All booklets from No. SB59 show a barcode on the reverse,
unless indicated otherwise.

B **21**

1991 (1 Oct)–**92**. Bright red and black cover, 86×50 mm, as Type B **21**
showing multicoloured stamp No. 1463b. Roman "I" on back.
SB59 $4.50 booklet containing 45c. (No. 1463b) in
block of 10...   4·00
a. Roman "II" on back (5.92) ....   9·50
b. With additional slotted tab at right. Containing
45c. in pane of 10 (No. 1463ba) ("I" on back) ....   5·50
ba. Containing 45c. (No. 1463b) in block of 10 ("II" on
back)..   11·00

B **21a**

1992 (Mar–27 May). Bright blue and black cover, 86×50 mm, as
Type B **21a**. No barcode on reverse.
SB60 $4 booklet containing 80c. (No. 1467) in strip of 5
and pane of six fastPOST labels.................................   4·00
SB61 $8 booklet containing 80c. (No. 1467) in block of 10
and pane of ten fastPOST labels ....   30·00
a. Barcode on back (27.5) ....   8·00

B **21b**

1992 (1 Sept)–**93**. Landscapes. Bright red and black cover 86×51 mm, as Type B **21b** showing multicoloured stamp No. 1693. Roman "I" on back.

SB62	$4.50 booklet containing pane of 10 different 45c. (No. 1690a)...	5·50
	a. Roman "II" on back (1993)............................	13·00
	b. Roman "III" on back (1993)..........................	35·00
	c. With additional slotted tab at right ("I" on back).	5·50
	ca. Roman "II" on back (1993).........................	16·00
	cb. Roman "III" on back (1993)........................	35·00

1993 (31 Mar)–**95**. Bright blue and black cover, 86×50 mm, as Type B **21a**.

SB63	$8 booklet containing 80c. (No. 1467a) in block of 10 and block of 10 fastPOST labels.........................	8·00
	a. Containing pane No. 1467ab (P 12) (7.94).............	16·00
	ab. With additional slotted tab at right (7.95)..............	

B **21c**

1993 (9 June). Endangered Species Conservation. Bright red and black cover, 85×50 mm, as Type B **21c** showing multicoloured illustration of Tusked Weta.

SB64	$4.50 booklet containing 45c. (No. 1740) in block of 10..	6·50
	a. With additional slotted tab at right....................	9·00

B **21d**

1993 (1 Sept). Marine Life. Bright red and black cover, 86×50 mm, as Type B **21d** showing multicoloured illustration of Grouper (fish).

SB65	$4.50 booklet containing pane of 10 different 45c. (No. 1752a)..	11·00
	a. With additional slotted tab at right....................	13·00

B **21e**

1993 (1 Oct). Prehistoric Animals. Bright red and black cover, 86×51 mm, as Type B **21e** showing multicoloured illustration of Carnosaur.

SB66	$4.50 booklet containing pane of ten 45c. plus two labels (No. 1767a)..	6·50
	a. With additional slotted tab at right....................	8·00

B **21f**

1993 (3 Nov). Christmas. Bright red and black cover 86×50 mm as Type B **21f** showing multicoloured illustration of Christmas Pudding.

SB67	$4.50 booklet containing pane of ten 45c. (No. 1746ba)..	12·00
	a. With additional slotted tab at right....................	12·00

B **21g**

1994 (19 Jan–Aug). Tourism. Bright red and black cover, 86×50 mm, as Type B **21g** showing multicoloured illustration of White Water Rafting.

SB68	$4.50 booklet containing pane of ten 45c. and four half stamp-size labels (No. 1782a) (horiz format).........	4·00
	a. Roman "II" on back (8.94)............................	10·00
	b. Vert format with additional slotted tab at top.....	8·00
	ba. Roman "II" on back (8.94)...........................	12·00

1994 (27 Apr). New Zealand Life. Bright red and black cover as Type B **21** showing multicoloured illustration of Buzzy Bee.

SB69	$4.50 booklet containing pane of ten different 45c. (No. 1797a) (horiz format)..............................	2·75
	a. Vert format with additional slotted tab at right ..	3·50

1994 (21 Sept). Christmas. Multicoloured covers as Type B **21** showing illustration of Father Christmas and children.

SB70	$4.50 booklet containing 45c. (No. 1832) in block of 10 (horiz format)..	3·50
	a. Vert format with additional slotted tab at top.....	4·25

1994 (2 Nov). Centenary of New Zealand Cricket Council. Multicoloured covers as Type B **21** showing illustration of father and son playing cricket.

SB71	$4.50 booklet containing pane of ten 45c. (No. 1840a) (horiz format)..	6·50
	a. Vert format with additional slotted tab at top.....	9·00

B **22**   B **22a**

1995 (22 Mar). Environment. Bright red and black cover, 51×101 mm, as Type B **22** showing multicoloured illustration of backpackers.

SB72	$4.50 booklet containing pane of ten 45c. (No. 1865a) inserted sideways in the vertical cover..................	6·00

1995 (26 July). Centenary of Rugby League. Multicoloured cover, 51×99 mm, as Type B **22a** showing New Zealand and Australian Players.

SB73	$4.50 booklet containing pane of ten 45c. (No. 1892a)	4·50

B **23**   B **23a**

1995 (1 Sept). Black and bright royal blue cover, 50×99 mm, as
  Type B **23** inscribed "airPOST INTERNATIONAL".
SB74 $5 booklet containing pane of five $1 and five labels
        (No. 1645a) inserted sideways in the cover .... 21·00

1995 (1 Sept–2 Oct). Farmyard Animals. Multicoloured covers,
  51×99 mm, as Typr B **23a** showing illustration of sow and piglets.
SB75 $4 booklet containing pane of ten 40c. (No. 1894a)
        inserted sideways in the cover (2.10) .... 7·00
SB76 $4.50 booklet containing pane of ten 45c. (No. 1904a)
        inserted sideways in the cover .... 7·00

B **23b**

1995 (9 Nov). Christmas. Multicoloured cover, 51×100 mm, as
  Type B **23b** showing illustration of Angel holding trumpet.
SB77 $4 booklet containing pane of ten 40c.
        (No. 1923a).. 5·00

B **24** (*Illustration reduced. Actual size 166×110 mm*)

1996 (24 Jan). Famous Racehorses. Multicoloured cover as Type B **24**
  showing illustrations of harness and horse races.
SB78 $13.40 booklet containing seven miniature sheets (Nos.
        MS1951a/g) .... 16·00

B **24a**   B **25**

1996 (21 Feb). Seaside Environment. Multicoloured cover, 50×100 mm,
  as Type B **24a** but vert, showing illustration of sea shore.
SB79 $4 booklet containing pane of ten 40c. (No. 1958a)... 6·25

1996 (7 Aug). Seaside Environment. Multicoloured cover as No. SB79,
  but 58×78 mm. Self-adhesive.
SB80 $4 booklet containing pane of ten 40c.
        (No. 1968a).. 5·00

1996 (7 Aug)–**99**. Multicoloured cover, 60×99 mm, as Type B **25**
  showing illustration of Pohutukawa tree. "New Zealand Post" and
  logo in white on ultramarine background. Self-adhesive.
SB81 $5 booklet containing pane of five $1 (No. 1991a)... 5·00
        a. "New Zealand Post" and logo redrawn larger in
           black and red on white panel (2.99) .... 4·50

B **26**   B **26a**

1996 (4 Sept). Christmas. Multicoloured cover, 58×78 mm as
  Type B **26** showing illustration of King. Self-adhesive.
SB82 $4 booklet containing pane of ten 40c. (No. 2027a)... 4·25

1996 (2 Oct). Extinct Birds. Multicoloured cover, 58×79 mm, as
  Type B **26a** showing illustration of Stout-legged Wren. Self-
  adhesive.
SB83 $4 booklet containing pane of ten 40c. (No. 2035a)... 4·75

B **26b**

1996 (13 Nov)–**2000**. Multicoloured cover, 59×78 mm, as Type B **26b**
  inscr "fastPOST" with illustration of Doubtful Sound. Self-adhesive.
SB84 $8 booklet containing pane of ten 80c. (No. 1990a)
        incorporating ten half-width "fastPOST" labels on
        the inner cover... 8·00

a. Incorporating ten full width "fastPOST" labels with
barcode on inner cover (1.99)... 8·50
ab. No stamps on first panel, two stamps on last
panel. Correction to extra large envelope size on
first panel (12.99)... 10·00
ac. Layout as above, extra large envelope size
information shown correctly (8.2000)............................ 10·00
No. SB84a also shows "New Zealand Post" and logo redrawn larger.
On Nos. SB84/a there are two stamps on the first panel and none
on the last.
No. SB84ab (1 kiwi ptg) shows the incorrect extra large envelope size
obliterated by a black bar with a correction beneath.
No. SB84ac (2 or 3 kiwi ptgs) shows the extra large envelope size
printed correctly. The 3 kiwi printing includes increases for some rates
in the first panel.

B **27** (*Illustration reduced. Actual size 166×110 mm*)

1997 (19 Mar). New Zealand Vineyards. Multicoloured cover as
Type B **27**.
SB85 $13.40 booklet containing seven miniature sheets (Nos.
MS2063a/g).. 11·00

B **27a**   B **27b**

1997 (19 Mar). Curious Letterboxes. Multicoloured cover, 58×79 mm,
as Type B **27a**, showing letterbox. Self-adhesive.
SB86 $4 booklet containing pane of ten 40c.
(No. 2064a)... 4·50

1997 (3 Sept). Christmas. Multicoloured cover, 59×78 mm, as
Type B **27b**, showing illustration of Memorial Cross, Pohutukawa,
and Bay of Islands. Self-adhesive.
SB87 $4 booklet containing pane of ten 40c. (No. 2103a).... 4·00

B **27c**   B **27d**

1997 (1 Oct). Insects. Multicoloured cover, 59×79 mm, as Type B **27c**
showing illustration of Grasshopper's head. Self-adhesive.
SB88 $4 booklet containing pane of ten 40c. (No. 2104a)... 4·50

1998 (14 Jan)–**2001**. Multicoloured (background vermilion) cover,
58×79 mm, as Type B **27d** showing New Zealand scenery. Self-
adhesive.
SB89 $4 booklet containing pane of ten 40c. (No. 1984ba)
(*Motoring Guide* advertisement on inner cover) .... 3·25
a. Background of cover deep rose-red (Scenic Skies
presentation pack advertisement on inner cover)
(8.98) .... 3·25
ab. Town Icons presentation pack advertisement on
inner cover (5.99) .... 3·25
ac. U-BIX Rugby Super 12 Championship stamp packs
advertisement on inner cover (10.6.99) .... 3·25
aca. Stamps printed on backing paper............................. 60·00
ad. "Stamp Focus" advertisement on inner cover
(5.2000) .... 3·75
ae. "Stamp Hunters" advertisement on inner cover
(6.2000) .... 3·75
af. "New Zealand Stamp Collection 2000"
advertisement on inner cover (20.2.01) .... 4·25
ag. Threatened Birds presentation pack advertisement
on inner cover (20.2.01).. 4·25
Nos. SB89a/ac also show "New Zealand" and logo redrawn larger.
Nos. SB89ad/ae, but not Nos. SB89af/ag, omit the black border to the
central star-shaped cutout on the front cover.
For explanation of No. SB89aca see after Nos. 1984/91.

B **28** (*Illustration reduced. Actual size 164×110 mm*)

1998 (14 Jan). Performing Arts. Multicoloured cover as Type B **28**
showing illustration of performers.
SB90 $13.40 booklet containing seven miniature sheets (Nos.
MS2130a/g).. 10·00

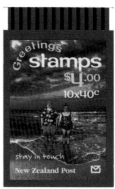   

B **28a**   B **28b**

1998 (15 Apr). "Stay in Touch" Greetings Stamps. Multicoloured cover,
60×96 mm, as Type B **28a** showing couple on beach. Self-
adhesive.
SB91 $4 booklet containing pane of ten 40c. (No. 2148a)... 3·25

1998 (2 Sept). Christmas. Multicoloured cover, 58×79 mm, as
Type B **28b** showing illustration of Virgin Mary and Christ Child.
Self-adhesive.
SB92 $4 booklet containing pane of ten 40c. (No. 2195a)... 3·50

B **28c**   B **29**

1998 (7 Oct). Town Icons. Multicoloured cover, 60×100 mm, as Type B **28c**, showing illustration of town symbols. Self-adhesive.
SB93 $4 booklet containing *se-tenant* pane of ten 40c.
(No. 2196a).. 3·75

1999 (7 Apr). New Zealand U-Bix Rugby Super 12 Championship. Multicoloured covers, 60×96 mm, as Type B **29** showing team logos. Self-adhesive.
SB94 $4 booklet containing pane of ten 40c. (No. 2258a)
(Type B **29**)... 2·75
SB95 $4 booklet containing pane of ten 40c. (No. 2260a)
(Chiefs)... 2·75
SB96 $4 booklet containing pane of ten 40c. (No. 2262a)
(Wellington Hurricanes)................................. 2·75
SB97 $4 booklet containing pane of ten 40c. (No. 2264a)
(Canterbury Crusaders)................................. 2·75
SB98 $4 booklet containing pane of ten 40c. (No. 2266a)
(Otago Highlanders)...................................... 2·75

B **30** (*Illustration reduced. Actual size 168×110 mm*)

1999 (28 July). Scenic Walks. Multicoloured cover as Type B **30** showing illustration of man reading map.
SB99 $13.40 booklet containing seven miniature sheets (Nos.
MS2285a/g)... 11·00

B **31** "Optimist" Sailing Dinghy   B **32** Baby Jesus with Animals

1999 (20 Oct). Yachting. Multicoloured cover, 58×78 mm, as Type B **31**. Self-adhesive.
SB100 $4 booklet containing pane of ten 40c.
(No. 2303a).. 3·00

1999 (1 Nov). Christmas. Multicoloured cover, 59×79 mm, as Type B **32**. Self-adhesive.
SB101 $4 booklet containing pane of ten 40c. (No. 2294a).... 3·00

B **32a**   B **32b**

2000 (3 Apr). Multicoloured (background ultramarine) cover, 59×88 mm, as Type B **32a** showing Kaikoura Coast. Self-adhesive.
SB102 $5.50 booklet containing pane of five $1.10
(No. 1991ba).. 4·50

2000 (3 Apr). New Zealand Life (2nd series). Bright red and black cover, 59×79 mm, as Type B **32b**, showing Kiwi with envelope. Self-adhesive.
SB103 $4 booklet containing *se-tenant* pane of ten 40c.
(No. 2318a).. 3·25

B **32c**   B **34** Bungy Jumping

2000 (1 Nov). Christmas. Multicoloured cover, 58×78 mm, as Type B **32c** showing Madonna and Child. Self-adhesive.
SB105 $4 booklet containing pane of ten 40c.
(No. 2359a).. 3·25

2001 (4 July). Tourism Centenary. Multicoloured covers as Type B **34**. Self-adhesive.
SB106 $4 booklet containing pane of ten 40c. stamps (5×2)
(No. 2431b) (cover Type B **34**, 58×79 mm)............ 4·00
SB107 $7.50 booklet containing pane of five $1.50 stamps
and five "air post international" labels (No. 2433a)
(cover 58×88 mm showing Sea-kayaking in Abel
Tasman National Park)...................................... 6·50
SB108 $9 booklet containing pane of ten 90c. stamps (5×2)
(No. 2432a) (cover 58×79 mm showing sightseeing
from Mount Alfred)... 7·50
No. SB106 and SB108 each include ten "fastpost" self-adhesive labels on the inner cover.

B **34a**   B **35** Gandalf (Sir Ian McKellen)

2001 (7 Nov). Christmas. Multicoloured cover, 58×78 mm, as Type B **34a** showing Madonna, Child and angels. Self-adhesive.

SB109 $4 booklet containing pane of ten 40c.
(No. 2445b) .... 4·00

2001 (4 Dec). Making of *The Lord of the Rings* Film Trilogy (1st issue): *The Fellowship of the Ring*. Multicoloured cover, 61×96 mm, as Type B **35**. Self-adhesive.

SB110 $9 booklet containing *se-tenant* pane of ten
(No. 2464b) .... 7·00

B **36** Tongaporutu Cliffs, Taranaki

B **37** Altar, St. Werenfrieds Church, Tokaanu

2002 (3 July)–**3**. Coastlines. Multicoloured covers as Type B **36**, each repeating the design of the contents. Self-adhesive.

SB111 $4 booklet containing pane of ten 40c. (No. 2516b)
(cover 58×78 mm) .... 3·25
a. Containing pane No. 2516ca (P 11) (27.5.03) .... 3·25
SB112 $9 booklet containing pane of ten 90c. (No. 2517b)
(cover 58×88 mm) .... 7·00
SB113 $7.50 booklet containing pane of five $1.50, (No. 2518b)
(cover 58×78 mm) .... 6·50

2002 (4 Sept). Christmas. Church Interiors. Multicoloured cover, 58×78 mm, as Type B **37**. Self-adhesive.

SB114 $4 booklet containing pane of ten 40c.
(No. 2530ab) .... 3·50

B **37a**

B **38** Arrowtown

2002 (4 Dec). Making of *The Lord of the Rings* Film Trilogy (2nd issue): *The Two Towers*. Multicoloured cover, 60×96 mm, as Type B **37a** showing the Ring. Self-adhesive.

SB115 $9 booklet containing pane of ten (No. 2556b) .... 6·50

2003 (7 May). New Zealand Landscapes. Multicoloured cover, 59×90 mm, as Type B **38**. Self-adhesive.

SB116 $7.50 booklet containing pane of five $1.50, (No. 2614a) .. 7·50

B **39** Christ Child in Crib

2003 (1 Oct). Christmas. Decorations. Multicoloured covers, 59×78 mm, as Type B **39**, each repeating the design of the contents. Self-adhesive.

SB117 $4 booklet containing pane of ten 40c.
(No. 2649b) .... 4·50
SB118 $8 booklet containing pane of eight $1 (No. 2650a)
and pane of eight International Economy labels ... 8·00

B **39a**

B **40** Hamadryas Baboon

2003 (5 Nov). Making of *The Lord of the Rings* Film Trilogy (3rd issue): *The Return of the King*. Multicoloured cover as 61×95 mm, as Type B **39a** showing Gandalf and other horsemen on journey. Self-adhesive.

SB119 $9 booklet containing pane of ten (No. 2658b) .... 9·50

2004 (28 Jan). Zoo Animals. Multicoloured cover, 59×79 mm, as Type B **40**. Self-adhesive.

SB120 $4 booklet containing pane of ten 40c. (No. 2671ab) ... 5·00

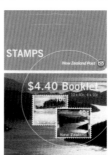
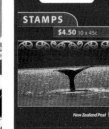

B **41** Stamps and Tory Channel, Marlborough Sounds

B **41a** Kaikoura

2004 (28 Jan). Multicoloured cover, 58×83 mm, as Type B **41**. Self-adhesive.

SB121 $4.40 booklet containing pane of four 10c. and ten 40c.
(No. 1983ab) .... 6·00

2004 (22 Mar). New Zealand Landscapes. Multicoloured cover, 58×79 mm, as Type B **41a**. Self-adhesive.

SB122 $4.50 booklet containing pane of ten 45c. (No. 2611a).... 5·50
No. SB122 was re-issued as a one kiwi reprint on 3rd September 2004, two kiwi reprint in March 2005, three and four kiwi reprints both on 20 October 2005, five kiwi reprint in April 2006, six kiwi reprint on 26 September 2006 and seven kiwi reprint on 11 January 2007.
The six and seven kiwi reprints show minor variations in the text on the back covers.

B **41b** Rangitoto Island

B **42** Aragorn, Legolas, Gimli and Gandalf the White

2004 (5 Apr). New Zealand Scenery. Multicoloured cover, 58×79 mm, as Type B **41b**. Self-adhesive.
SB123 $9 booklet containing pane of ten 90c. (1990ba) .....   8·00
No. SB123 was re-issued as a one kiwi reprint on 3rd May 2005 and as a two kiwi reprint on 19 May 2006. The two kiwi reprint shows minor variations in the text on the back cover.

2004 (7 July). Making of *The Lord of the Rings* Film Trilogy (4th issue): *Home of Middle Earth*. Multicoloured cover, 58×79 mm, as Type B **42**. Self-adhesive.
SB124 $6.30 booklet containing pane of ten stamps
(No. 2723ba)..   5·50

B **43** Christmas Dinner   B **43a**

2004 (4 Oct). Christmas. Multicoloured covers, 59×78 mm, as Type B **43**. Self-adhesive.
SB125 $4.50 booklet containing pane of ten 45c. (No. 2747a)
(cover Type B **43**)................................   4·00
SB126 $8 booklet containing pane of eight $1 (No. 2749a)
and pane of eight International Economy labels
(cover showing Christmas cake and cards) ....   7·00

2005 (12 Jan). Farmyard Animals and Chinese New Year ("Year of the Rooster"). Multicoloured cover, 59×79 mm, as Type B **43a**. Self-adhesive.
SB127 $4.50 booklet containing pane of ten 45c. (No. 2763a).....   4·00

B **44**   B **45** Baby Jesus

2005 (6 Apr). 150th Anniv of New Zealand Stamps (2nd issue). Stamps of 1905–1955. Multicoloured covers, 58×78 mm, as Type B**44**. Self-adhesive.
SB128 $4.50 booklet   containing   pane   of   ten   45c.
(No. 2783ba)..   4·50
SB129 $9 booklet   containing   pane   of   ten   90c.
(No. 2784ba)..   7·00

2005 (5 Oct–2 Nov). Christmas. Multicoloured covers, 58×78 mm, as Type B **45**. Self-adhesive.
SB130 $4.50 booklet containing pane of ten 45c. (No. 2825a)
(2.11) (cover Type B **45**) ....   4·00
SB131 $10 booklet containing pane of ten 45c. (No. 2826a) and
pane of ten International Economy labels (cover
showing gifts on straw) ....   7·50

B **46** Labrador Retriever Guide   B **47** Decorated Silver Fern
Dog   (Hanna McLachlan)

2006 (4 Jan). Chinese New Year ("Year of the Dog"). Multicoloured covers, 57×78 mm, as Type B **46**. Self-adhesive.
SB132 $4.50 booklet containing pane of ten 45c. (No. 2847a)....   5·00

2006 (4 Oct). Christmas. Multicoloured covers, as Type B **47**. Self-adhesive.
SB133 $4.50 booklet containing pane of ten 45c. (No. 2915a)
(cover Type B **47**, 58×79 mm)..........................   5·00
SB134 $13.50 booklet containing pane of ten $1.50, ten
International Air and ten International Economy
labels (No. 2916a) (cover 58×83 *mm* showing
stamp No. 2916)..   14·00
No. SB134 was sold at $13.50, providing a discount of $1.50 off the face value of the stamps.

B **48**   B **49**

2007 (27 Mar)–**09**. New Zealand Landscapes. Multicoloured cover, 59×78 mm, as Type B **48** showing stamp No. 2614. Self-adhesive.
SB135 $7.50 booklet containing pane of five $1.50, five
International Economy and five International Air
labels (No. 2614b) ....   10·00
a. Containing pane No. 2614ca (ordinary paper)
(2.3.09)..   10·00
b. Containing pane No. 2614d (18.5.09).....................   10·00
c. Containing pane No. 2614a (30.10.09)..................   7·50
No. SB135 was issued as a one kiwi reprint of No. SB116, but the cover and contents are different.
No. SB135 was re-issued as a two kiwi reprint on 19 November 2007, a three kiwi reprint on 8 July 2008 and a four kiwi reprint on 19 November. The three and four kiwi printings have "RRP" and "(Recommended Retail Price)" added to the inscriptions on the front cover. The two and three kiwi printings have minor variations to the text on the back cover.
Nos. SB135a/c all have "RRP" and "(Recommended Retail Price)" added to the inscriptions on the front cover.
No. SB135c was issued as one and two kiwi reprints, both on 30 October 2009, a three kiwi reprint in March 2010 and four kiwi reprint on 2 July 2010.

2007 (9 May). New Zealand Landscapes. Multicoloured covers, 59×78 mm, as Type B **49** each showing the stamp contained in the booklet. Self-adhesive.
SB136 $5 booklet containing pane of ten 50c. (No. 2612a).....   6·25
SB137 $10 booklet containing pane of ten $1 (No. 2613a) ...   12·50
No. SB136 was re-issued as a one kiwi reprint on 3 March 2008, a two kiwi reprint on 19 June 2008 and a three kiwi reprint on 25 November 2008. The two and three kiwi printings have "RRP" and "(Recommended Retail Price)" added to the inscriptions on the front cover. Both the one and two kiwi reprints show variations to the table inside the front cover and the text on the back cover.
No. SB137 was issued as a one kiwi reprint on 12 December 2007, a two kiwi reprint on 3 March 2008, a three kiwi reprint on 2 July 2008, a four kiwi reprint on 19 November 2008 and a five kiwi reprint on 2 July 2010. The three, four and five kiwi printings have "RRP" and "(Recommended Retail Price)" added to the inscriptions on the front cover. The one, two, three and five kiwi printings show variations to the text on the back cover, and the two, three and five kiwi printings also to the table inside the front cover.

2007 (3 Oct). Christmas. Multicoloured covers as Type B **47**. Self-adhesive.

SB138 $5 booklet containing pane of ten 50c. (No. 3001a) (cover 58×79 mm, showing stamp Type **675**) ......   6·00

SB139 $13.50 booklet containing pane of ten $1.50, ten International Air and ten International Economy labels (No. 3002a) (cover, 58×83 mm, showing stamp No. 3002) ....   17·00

No. SB139 was sold at $13.50, providing a discount of $1.50 off the face value of the stamps.

B **51**   B **52**

2008 (9 Jan). Underwater Reefs. Multicoloured covers, 59×78 mm, as Type B **51**, each showing the stamp contained in the booklet. Self-adhesive.

SB140 $5 booklet containing pane of ten 50c. (No. 3018a) .....   7·50

SB141 $10 booklet containing pane of ten $1 (No. 3019a) ....   14·00

2008 (1 Oct). Christmas. Multicoloured covers as Type B **52**. Self-adhesive.

SB142 $5 booklet containing pane of ten 50c. (No. 3095a) (cover 58×78 mm, Type B **52**).................................   6·00

SB143 $15 booklet containing pane of ten $1.50, ten International Air and ten International Economy labels (No. 3096a) (cover 58×83 mm, showing stamp No. 3096)...   16·00

B **53**   B **54** Russell

2009 (4 Feb). New Zealand Champions of World Motorsport. Multicoloured covers, 58×78 mm, as Type B **53**, each showing the stamp contained in the booklet. Self-adhesive.

SB144 $5 booklet containing pane of ten 50c. (No. 3122a) ...   9·00

SB145 $10 booklet containing pane of ten $1 (No. 3123a) ...   13·50

2009 (1 July). New Zealand Landscapes. Multicoloured cover, 59×79 mm, as Type B **54**. Self-adhesive.

SB146 $9 booklet containing pane of five $1.80 (No. 3156a) ...   12·00

No. SB146 was re-issued as a one kiwi reprint in February 2010 and as a two kiwi reprint in January 2011.

B **55** State Highway 1 Road Sign   B **56** Three Shepherds

2009 (7 Sept). KiwiStamps. Multicoloured cover, 61×79 mm, as Type B **55**. Self-adhesive.

SB147   ($5) booklet containing pane of ten KiwiStamps (No. 3162Ca)...   9·00

2009 (7 Oct). Christmas. Multicoloured covers, 58×78 mm, as Type B **56**. Self-adhesive.

SB148 $5 booklet containing pane of ten 50c. (No. 3175a) (cover Type B **56**).................................   6·50

SB149 $15 booklet containing pane of ten $1.80 (No. 3176a) (green cover showing stamp No. 3174) ....   22·00

No. SB149 was sold at $15, providing a discount of $3 off the face value of the stamps. The cover was inscr "International Buy 10 pay $15 save $3".

B **57** Queenstown   B **58** New Zealand 1960 2d. Christmas Stamps

2010 (4 Aug). New Zealand Landscapes. Multicoloured covers, 59×79 mm, as Type B **57**. Self-adhesive.

SB150 $9.50 booklet containing pane of five $1.90 (No. 3233a)...   13·00

SB151 $12 booklet containing pane of ten $1.20 (No. 3232a)...   16·00

No. SB150 was reissued as one, two, three and four kiwi reprints. The two, three, four and five kiwi reprints differ in the wording on the booklet pane about air service indicator stickers. The one and two kiwi reprints were issued in 2011, the three kiwi in 2012 and the four and five kiwi reprints in 2013.

2010 (20 Oct). Christmas. Multicoloured covers, 58×79 mm, as Type B **58**. Self-adhesive.

SB152 $5.40 booklet containing pane of ten 60c. (No. 3245a) (cover Type B **58**) ....   9·00

SB153 $16 booklet containing pane of ten (No. 3246a) (green cover showing stamp No. 3242)................   25·00

B **59** Kiwi Road Sign   B **60** Baby Jesus in Manger

2011 (23 Mar). KiwiStamps. Multicoloured cover, 60×79 mm, as Type B **59**. Self-adhesive.

SB154   ($6) booklet containing pane of ten KiwiStamps (No. 3269ba)...   8·50

No. SB154 was reissued as one kiwi and two kiwi reprints. The table of required postage is upside down on the original and one kiwi printings only. A new printing by Southern Colour Print, issued in May 2014, had no kiwis. Subsequent Southern Colour Print booklets have one, two, three, four or five kiwis.

2011 (2 Nov). Christmas. Multicoloured covers, 58×79 mm, as Type B **60**. Self-adhesive.

SB155 $6 booklet containing pane of ten 60c. (No. 3326ba) (cover Type B **60**).................................   12·00

SB156 $17.10 Booklet containing pane of ten $1.90 (No. 3327a) (blue cover showing stamp No. 3327) ....   30·00

SB157 $21.60 booklet containing pane of ten $2.40 (No. 3328a) (blue cover showing stamp No. 3328) ....   35·00

B **61** Lake Rotorua   B **62** Stewart Island

2012 (1 Feb). New Zealand Landscapes. Multicoloured cover, 58×78 mm, as Type B **61**. Self-adhesive.
SB158 $12 booklet containing pane of five $2.40 (No. 3233ba)...   17·00
    No. SB158 was reissued as a one kiwi reprint on 29 November 2012, a two kiwi reprint on 1 November 2013 and three and four kiwi reprints in 2015.

2012 (23 May). New Zealand Landscapes. Multicoloured covers, 59×79 mm, as Type B **62**. Self-adhesive.
SB159 $10.50 booklet containing pane of five $2.10 (No. 3367a)
              (Type B **62**)..   16·00
SB160 $14 booklet containing pane of ten $1.40 (No. 3366a)
              (cover showing stamp No. 3366) ....   22·00
    SB159 was reissued as a one kiwi reprint on 10 May 2013 and a two kiwi reprint on 1 November 2013.
    SB160 was reissued as a one kiwi reprint on 10 April 2013 and a two kiwi reprint in 2015.

B **63** Mary, Joseph and Baby Jesus   B **64** Bilbo Baggins

2012 (3 Oct). Christmas. Multicoloured covers as Type B **63**. Self-adhesive.
SB161 $7 booklet containing pane of ten 70c. (No. 3401a)
              (cover Type B **63**, 58×78 mm).................................   11·00
SB162 $17.10 booklet containing pane of ten $1.90 and ten International Air labels (No. 3402a) (blue cover showing stamp No. 3402, 58×82 mm).....................   30·00
SB163 $21.60 booklet containing pane of ten $2.40 and ten International Air labels (No. 3403a) (blue cover showing stamp No. 3403, 58×82 mm).....................   35·00
    No. SB162 was sold at $17.10, providing a discount of $1.90 off the face value of the stamps. The cover was inscr 'International $1.90 Buy 10 pay for 9'.
    No. SB163 was sold at $21.60, providing a discount of $2.40 off the face value of the stamps. The cover was inscr 'International $2.40 Buy 10 pay for 9'.

2012 (1 Nov). The Hobbit: (film trilogy): An Unexpected Journey (1st issue). Multicoloured cover, 60×95 mm, as Type B **64**. Self-adhesive.
SB164 $14.90 booklet containing pane of ten stamps
              (No. 3417a)..   25·00

B **65** Poppy and Bugle

2013 (10 Apr). ANZAC (4th series). New Zealanders serving Abroad. Multicoloured cover, 165×110 mm, as Type B **65**.
SB165 $19.90 booklet containing seven miniature sheets (Nos.
              MS3447a/g)..   32·00

B **66** Giving Christmas Present

2013 (2 Oct). Christmas. Multicoloured covers as Type B **66**. Self-adhesive.
SB166 $7 booklet containing pane of ten 70c. (No. 3509a)
              (cover 59×79 mm)..   9·00
SB167 $17.10 booklet containing pane of ten $1.90 and ten International Air labels (No. 3510a) (cover 59×82 mm, showing stamp No. 3510)....................   22·00
SB168 $21.60 booklet containing pane of ten $2.40 and ten International Air labels (No. 3511a) (cover 59×82 mm, showing stamp No. 3511)....................   30·00
    No. SB167 was sold at $17.10, providing a discount of $1.90 off the face value of the stamps. The cover was inscr 'International $1.90 Buy 10 pay for 9 For International sending (Australia and South Pacific only)'.
    No. SB168 was sold at $21.60, providing a discount of $2.40 off the face value of the stamps. The cover was inscr 'International $2.40 Buy 10 pay for 9 For International sending'.

2013 (1 Nov). The Hobbit (film trilogy): The Desolation of Smaug (2nd issue). Multicoloured cover, 60×95 mm, as Type B **64**. Self-adhesive.
SB169 $14.90 booklet containing pane of ten stamps
              (No. 3518a)..   20·00

B **67** Air Training Corps Recruit playing Bugle

2014 (2 Apr). ANZAC (5th series). World War II Poster Art. Multicoloured cover, 165×110 mm, as Type B **67**.
SB170 $19.90 booklet containing seven miniature sheets (Nos.
              MS3547/53)..   30·00

B **68** Mount Taranaki   B **69** Mary and Jesus

2014 (7 May). New Zealand Landscapes. Multicoloured covers, 59×78 mm, as Type B **68**. Self-adhesive.
SB171 $10 booklet containing pane of five $2 and two International Air labels (No. 3560a) (Type B **68**) ..   16·00

SB172 $12.50 booklet containing pane of five $2.50 and two International Air labels (No. 3561a) (cover showing stamp No. 3561)........................ 20·00

No. SB172 was reissued as one and two kiwi reprints in 2015.

No. SB173 was reissued as one, two and three kiwi reprints in 2015, four kiwi reprint on 11 December 2015 and five kiwi reprint on 12 February 2016.

2014 (1 Oct). Christmas. Children in Nativity Play. Multicoloured covers as Type B **69**. Self-adhesive.
SB173 $8 booklet containing pane of ten 80c. (No. 3619a) (cover 58×79 mm)..................................
SB174 $18 booklet containing pane of ten $2 and ten International Air labels (No. 3620a) (cover 58×82 mm, showing stamp No. 3620)..................... 25·00
SB175 $22.50 booklet containing pane of ten $2.50 and ten International Air labels (No. 3621a) (cover 58×82 mm, showing stamp No. 3621)..................... 32·00

No. SB174 was sold at $18, providing a discount of $2 off the face value of the stamps. The cover was inscr 'International $2.00 Buy 10 pay for 9 For International sending (Australia & South Pacific only)'.

No. SB175 was sold at $22.50, providing a discount of $2.50 off the face value of the stamps. The cover was inscr 'International $2.50 Buy 10 pay for 9 For International sending'.

2014 (12 Nov). *The Hobbit* (film trilogy): *The Battle of the Five Armies* (3rd issue). Multicoloured cover, 60×95 mm, as Type B **64**. Self-adhesive.
SB176 $15.60 booklet containing pane of ten stamps (No. 3630a)... 20·00

B **70** Angel   B **71** Glowworms, Ruakuri Cave

2015 (4 Nov). Christmas. Multicoloured covers as Type B **70**. Self-adhesive.
SB177 $8 booklet containing pane of ten 80c. (No. 3739a) (cover Type B **70**, 58×78 mm)....................
SB178 $18 booklet containing pane of ten $2 and ten International Air labels (No. 3740a) (cover 58×82 mm, showing stamp No. 3740)..................... 25·00
SB179 $22.50 booklet containing pane of ten $2.50 and ten International Air labels (No. 3741a) (cover 58×82 mm, showing stamp No. 3741)..................... 32·00

No. SB174 was sold at $18, providing a discount of $2 off the face value of the stamps. The cover was inscr 'International $2.00 Buy 10 pay for 9 For International sending (Australia & South Pacific only)'.

No. SB175 was sold at $22.50, providing a discount of $2.50 off the face value of the stamps. The cover was inscr 'International $2.50 Buy 10 pay for 9 For International sending'.

2016 (2 Mar). New Zealand Native Glowworms (*Arachnocampa luminosa*). Multicoloured cover, 60×95 mm, as Type B **71**. Self-adhesive.
SB180 $20 booklet containing pane of ten $2 stamps (No. 3759a)... 25·00

B **72** Awaroa Bay, Abel Tasman Scenic Reserve

2016 (18 May). New Zealand Landscapes. Multicoloured covers, 58×78 mm, as Type B **72**. Self-adhesive.
SB181 $11 booklet containing pane of five $2.20 (No. 3779a) (Type B **72**)............................... 13·50
SB182 $13.50 booklet containing pane of five $2.70 (No. 3780a) (Vineyards, Marlborough).............................. 17·00

PREMIUM BOOKLETS

The following booklets were sold at a premium over the face value of the stamps. All are stitched and have text and illustrations on panes and interleaving pages. All (except SP12) measure 165×110 mm and are illustrated at one-third actual size.

P **1** Ford Zephyr

2000 (1 June). "On The Road". Motor Cars. Multicoloured cover as Type P **1**. Stitched.
SP1 $14.95 booklet containing seven miniature sheet panes, six containing Nos. 2329/34 as single stamps and the seventh containing all six designs.................... 11·00
Face value: $13.60.

P **2** de Havilland Tiger Moth

2001 (2 May). Aircraft. Multicoloured cover as Type P **2**. Stitched.
SP2 $19.95 booklet containing seven miniature sheet panes, six containing Nos. 2408/13 as single stamps and the seventh containing all six designs.................... 15·00
Face value: $13.80.

P **3**

2002 (3 Apr). Architectural Heritage. Multicoloured cover as Type P **3**. Stitched.
SP3 $16.95 booklet containing seven miniature sheet panes, six containing Nos. 2484/9 as single stamps and the seventh containing all six designs.................... 12·00
Face value: $13.80.

P **4**

2003 (2 Apr). New Zealand Military Uniforms. Multicoloured cover as Type P **4**. Stitched.
SP4 $19.95 booklet containing five miniature sheet panes containing two examples each of Nos. 2577/80, 2581/4, 2585/8, 2589/92 and 2593/6 .... 21·00
    Face value: $16.

P **5** Heavy Horses Pulling Farm Equipment

2004 (5 Apr). Historic Farm Equipment. Multicoloured cover as Type P **5**. Stitched.
SP5 $19.95 booklet containing six miniature sheet panes, five containing Nos. 2695/9 as single stamps and the sixth containing all five designs .... 18·00
    Face value: $12.40.

P **6** Whitewater Rafting

2004 (1 Dec). Extreme Sports. Multicoloured cover as Type P **6**. Stitched.
SP6 $14.95 booklet containing six miniature sheet panes, five containing Nos. 2751/5 as single stamps and the sixth containing all five designs .... 14·00
    Face value: $12.40.

P **7** Street with Wrecked Car and Fallen Masonry

2006 (3 Feb). 75th Anniv of the Hawke's Bay Earthquake. Grey, brownish grey and red cover as Type P **7**. Stitched.
SP7 $19.95 booklet containing seven miniature sheet panes containing two examples each of Nos. 2848/50, 2865/7, 2851/3, 2854/5 (with two half stamp-size central labels), 2856, 2858 and 2863, 2857 and 2859/60 and 2861/2 and 2864.................................. 23·00
    Face value: $18.80.

P **8** Trifid Nebula

2007 (6 June). Southern Skies. Multicoloured cover as Type P **8**. Stitched.
SP8 $19.90 booklet containing six miniature sheet panes, five containing Nos. 2957/61 as single stamps and the sixth containing all five designs .... 19·00
    Face value: $15.

P **9** Sapper John Luamanu and Baby Daughter, ANZAC Day Parade, 2007

2008 (2 Apr). ANZAC (1st series). Multicoloured cover as Type P **9**. Stitched.
SP9 $19.90 booklet containing seven miniature sheet panes, six containing Nos. 3032/7 as single stamps and the seventh containing all six designs..................... 25·00
    Face value: $16.

P **10** Guns and Transport under Simulated Attack by RNZAF Mosquito Aircraft, Final Manoeuvres, Waiouru, 1950

2009 (1 Apr). ANZAC (2nd series). "Comrades in Arms". Multicoloured cover as Type P **10**. Booklet contains text and illustrations on interleaving pages. Stitched.
SP10 $19.90 booklet containing seven miniature sheet panes, six containing Nos. 3131/6 as single stamps and the seventh containing all six designs..................... 26·00
    Face value: $16
    Stamps from booklet SP10 are all perforated 14.

P **11** Carillon Dedication, 25 April 1932

2010 (7 Apr). ANZAC (3rd series). Remembrance. Black, grey and red cover as Type P **11**. Booklet contains text and illustrations on interleaving pages. Stitched.
SP11 $19.90 booklet containing seven miniature sheet panes, six containing Nos. 3199/3204 as single stamps and the seventh containing all six designs............ 30·00
    Face value: $17.80
    Stamps from booklet SP11 are all perforated 14.

P **12**

2012 (15 Mar). 75th Anniv of the RNZAF (Royal New Zealand Air Force). Deep blue cover with silver inscription, 150×150 mm, as Type P **12**. Booklet contains text and illustrations on interleaving pages.
SP12 $19.90 booklet containing eight miniature sheet panes as follows: Nos. 3341/2, each×2; Nos. 3343/4, each×2; Nos. 3345/6, each×2; Nos. 3347/8, each×2; Nos. 3349/50, each×2; Nos. 3351/2, each×2; Nos. 3353 and 3355, each×2; No. 3354×2 .... 32·00
Face value: $18.

P **13** Melville Mirfin

2014 (29 July). Centenary of the First World War (1st issue). Grey-black and gold cover, 105×180 mm, as Type P **13**. Booklet contains text and illustrations on interleaving pages.
SP13 $39.90 booklet containing Nos. 3592/3601 in panes of single stamps and Nos. 3592/7 and 3600/1 in *se-tenant* panes.. 55·00
Face value: $27.60

2015 (23 Mar). Centenary of the First World War (2nd issue). 1915 The Spirit of ANZAC. Grey-black and gold cover, 105×180 mm, as Type P **13**. but inscr '1915 THE SPIRIT OF ANZAC NEW ZEALAND'S STORY'. Booklet contains text and illustrations on panes and interleaving pages.
SP14 $39.90 booklet containing Nos. 3663/72 in panes of single stamps and in *se-tenant* panes.................... 55·00
Face value: $27.60

2016 (6 Apr). Centenary of the First World War (3rd issue). 1916 Courage and Commitment. Grey-black, grey and gold cover, 104×179 mm, as Type P **13**. but inscr '1916 COURAGE & COMMITMENT NEW ZEALAND'S STORY'. Booklet contains text and illustrations on panes and interleaving pages.
SP15 $39.90 booklet containing Nos. 3760/9 in panes of single stamps and in *se-tenant* panes................. 55·00
Face value: $27.60

EXPRESS DELIVERY STAMPS

E **1**

(Typo Govt Printing Office, Wellington)
1903 (9 Feb). Value in first colour. W **43** (sideways). P 11.
E1   E **1**   6d. red and violet .... 38·00   23·00

1926–36. Thick, white, opaque chalk-surfaced "Cowan" paper. W **43**.

(a) P 14×14½
E2   E **1**   6d. vermilion and bright violet .... 50·00   26·00
    w. Wmk inverted £300

(b) P 14×15 (1936)
E3   E **1**   6d. carmine and bright violet .... 70·00   60·00

1937–39. Thin, hard, chalk-surfaced "Wiggins Teape" paper.

(a) P 14×14½
E4   E **1**   6d. carmine and bright violet .... £110   50·00

(b) P 14×15 (4.39)
E5   E **1**   6d. vermilion and bright violet £180   £350

E **2** Express Mail Delivery Van

(Des J. Berry. Eng Stamp Ptg Office, Melbourne. Recess Govt Ptg Office, Wellington)
1939 (16 Aug). W **43**. P 14.
E6   E **2**   6d. violet .... 1·50   1·75
    w. Wmk inverted .... 90·00
No. E6 was withdrawn on 30 June 1948, when the Express Delivery Service ceased.

POSTAGE DUE STAMPS

D **1**

(I)

(II)

3D.   **5D.**
(a) Large "D"   *(b)* Small "D"

(Typo Govt Printing Office, Wellington)
1899 (1 Dec). Coarse paper. W **12b**. P 11.

I. Type I. Circle of 14 ornaments 17 dots over "N.Z.", "N.Z." large

(a) Large "D"
D1   D **1**   ½d. carmine and green .... 35·00   45·00
    a. No stop after "D" (Right pane
      R. 2/3)... £200   £250
D2   8d. carmine and green .... 60·00   85·00
    a. Carmine "8D." printed double ....
D3   1s. carmine and green .... 70·00   95·00
D4   2s. carmine and green £120   £150
D1/4 *Set of 4* £250   £325
To avoid further subdivision the 1s. and 2s. are placed with the *pence* values, although the two types of "D" do not apply to the higher values.

(b) Small "D"
D6   D **1**   5d. carmine and green .... 35·00   50·00
D7   6d. carmine and green .... 48·00   50·00
D8   10d. carmine and green .... 75·00   £100
D6/8 *Set of 3* £130   £180

II. Type II. Circle of 13 ornaments, 15 dots over "N.Z.", "N.Z." small

(a) Large "D"
D9   D **1**   ½d. vermilion and green........................ 4·25   16·00
    a. No stop after "D" (Right pane
      R. 2/3)... 65·00   £120
D10   1d. vermilion and green........................... 22·00   3·75
D11   2d. vermilion and green........................... 55·00   9·00
D12   3d. vermilion and green........................... 17·00   7·00
D9/12 *Set of 4* .... 85·00   32·00

(b) Small "D"
D14   D **1**   1d. vermilion and green........................ 21·00   3·75
D15   2d. vermilion and green........................... 55·00   9·50
D16   4d. vermilion and green........................... 40·00   21·00
D14/16 *Set of 3* .... £100   30·00
Nos. D9/16 were printed from a common frame plate of 240 (4 panes of 60) used in conjunction with centre plates of 120 (2 panes of 60) for the ½d. and 4d. or 240 for the other values. Sheets of the 1d. and 2d. each contained two panes with large "D" and two panes with small "D".

D **2**    D **3**

(Des W. R. Bock. Typo Govt Printing Office)

1902 (28 Feb). No wmk. P 11.
D17   D **2**   ½d. red and deep green .... 3·00   9·00

1904–08. "Cowan" unsurfaced paper. W **43** (sideways).

(a) P 11
D18   D **2**   ½d. red and green (4.04)........................ 3·00   3·00
          a. Imperf between (horiz pair)............... £1400
D19   1d. red and green (5.12.05)................. 22·00   3·50
D20   2d. red and green (5.4.06) £110   £110
D18/20 *Set of 3* £120   £110

(b) P 14
D21   D **2**   1d. carmine and green (12.06) .... 26·00   1·50
          a. Rose-pink and green (9.07) .... 15·00   1·50
D22   2d. carmine and green (10.06)................ 15·00   11·00
          a. Rose-pink and green (6.08) .... 8·50   3·00
The note regarding sideways watermark varieties below No. 299 applies here also.

1919 (Jan)–**20.** "De La Rue" chalky paper. Toned gum. W **43.** P 14×15.
D23   D **2**   ½d. carmine and green (6.19)................. 3·75   5·50
D24   1d. carmine and green .... 9·00   50
          w. Wmk inverted .... †   —
D25   2d. carmine and green (8.20)................. 26·00   4·50
D23/5 *Set of 3* .... 35·00   9·50

1925 (May). "Jones" chalky paper. White gum. W **43.** P 14×15.
D26   D **2**   ½d. carmine and green .... 45·00   55·00

1925 (July). No wmk, but bluish "N Z" and Star lithographed on back. P 14×15.
D27   D **2**   ½d. carmine and green .... 2·00   25·00
D28   2d. carmine and green .... 3·50   35·00

1925 (Nov)–**35.** "Cowan" thick, opaque chalky paper. W **43.**

(a) P 14×15
D29   D **2**   ½d. carmine and green (12.26) .... 1·75   14·00
D30   1d. carmine and green .... 3·75   80
D31   2d. carmine and green (6.26)................ 28·00   4·25
          x. Wmk reversed .... 55·00   28·00
D32   3d. carmine and green (6.35)................ 50·00   55·00
D29/32 *Set of 4* .... 75·00   65·00

(b) P 14
D33   D **2**   ½d. carmine and green (10.28)............. 50·00   32·00
D34   1d. rose and pale yellow-green (6.28) .. 4·00   1·25
D35   2d. carmine and green (10.29)............. 7·00   3·00
D36   3d. carmine and green (5.28)................ 15·00   50·00
D33/6 *Set of 4* .... 70·00   75·00

1937–38. "Wiggins Teape" thin, hard chalky paper. W **43.** P 14×15.
D37   D **2**   ½d. carmine and yellow-green (2.38) .... 45·00   45·00
D38   1d. carmine and yellow-green (1.37)....... 17·00   4·25
D39   2d. carmine and yellow-green (6.37)....... 55·00   21·00
D40   3d. carmine and yellow-green (11.37)...... £100   75·00
D37/40 *Set of 4* £190   £130

(Des J. Berry. Typo Govt Printing Office, Wellington)

1939–49. P 15×14.

*(a) W **43** (sideways inverted) (16.8.39)*
D41   D **3**   ½d. turquoise-green............................ 5·00   5·00
D42   1d. carmine.. 4·00   4·00
          w. Wmk sideways.............................. £200   9·50
D43   2d. bright blue.................................... 6·00   2·75
          w. Wmk sideways.............................. £250
D44   3d. orange-brown.............................. 35·00   25·00
          w. Wmk sideways.............................. £190
D41/4 *Set of 4* .... 45·00   32·00

*(b) W **98** (sideways (1d.), sideways inverted (2d.) or upright (3d.)*
D45   D **3**   1d. carmine (4.49)................................ 20·00   7·50
D46   2d. bright blue (12.46)........................ 11·00   4·75
          w. Wmk sideways (4.49)..................... 2·75   12·00
D47   3d. orange-brown (1943)...................... 60·00   50·00
          a. Wmk sideways inverted (6.45) .... 30·00   17·00
          aw. Wmk sideways (28.11.49)............... 9·00   22·00
D45/7aw *Set of 3* .... 29·00   26·00*
*The use of Postage Due stamps ceased on 30 September 1951, our used price for No. D45 being for stamps postmarked after this date (*price for examples clearly cancelled 1949–51, £30*).

OFFICIAL STAMPS

1891 (Dec)–**1906.** Contemporary issues handstamped "O.P.S.O." in 3½mm capital letters.

(a) Stamps of 1873 type optd in violet. P 12½
O1   **3**   ½d. pale dull rose (W **4**) (No. 149)........... —   £1400
O2   ½d. bright rose (W **12b**) (No. 151) .... —   £900

*(b) Stamps of 1882–97 optd in rose/magenta. W **12b***
O3   **13**   ½d. black (P 10) (No. 217)...................... —   £800
          a. Violet opt .... —   £950
O4   ½d. black (P 10×11) (No. 227).................. —   £800
O5   1d. rose (P 12×11½) (No. 195b).............. —   £800
          a. Violet opt .... —
O6   1d. rose (P 10) (violet opt) (No. 218)...... —
O7   1d. rose (P 11) (No. 237)........................ —   £800
          a. Violet opt .... —
O8   2d. purple (P 11) (No. 238)..................... —   £850
          a. Violet opt .... —
O9   2d. mauve-lilac (P 10) (No. 219).............. —   £850
          a. Advert on back (3rd setting)............ —
          b. Violet opt .... —   £1200
          ba. Advert on back............................. —
O10   2½d. blue (P 12×11½) (violet opt) (No. 197) —
O11   2½d. blue (P 11) (violet opt) (No. 239)...... —   £850
O12   2½d. ultramarine (P 10) (No. 220)............ —   £850
          a. Advert on back................................ —
          b. Violet opt .... —
          ba. Green advert (2nd setting) .... —
          bb. Mauve advert (3rd setting) .... —
O13   2½d. ultramarine (P 10×11) (No. 230)....... —   £850
          a. Violet opt .... —
O14   5d. olive-black (P 12×11½) (No. 200)....... —   £1100
          a. violet opt .... —
O15   6d. brown (P 12½×11½) (No. 201)............ —   £1300

(c) Stamps of 1898–1903 optd in violet. P 11

(i) No wmk
O16   ½d. green (P 14) (No. 294)...................... —   £800
          a. Rose or magenta opt .... —
O17   2½d. blue (P 12-16) (No. 249).................. —   £1200
O18   2½d. blue (No. 260).............................. —   £950
          a. Rose/magenta opt .... —
O19   4d. indigo and brown (No. 262)............. —   £1100
O20   5d. purple-brown (No. 263)................... —   £1100
          a. Rose/magenta opt .... —
          b. Greenish blue opt .... —
O21   8d. Indigo (No. 266)............................ —   £1300
O22   1s. red (No. 268)................................. —   £2500

*(ii) W **38***
O23   ½d. green (No. 273b)............................ —
O24   1d. carmine (No. 278).......................... —   £850
          a. Blue opt.. —

*(iii) W **43** (sideways on 3d. 5d., 1s.)*
O25   ½d. green (P 14) (No. 302)..................... —
          a. Rose or magenta opt .... —
O26   1d. carmine (P 14) (No. 303).................. —   £850
          a. Green opt .... —   £850
O27   1d. carmine (P 14) (No. 349).................. —
O28   1d. carmine (P 14) (No. 356).................. —   £850
O29   1d. carmine (No. 357) (black opt).......... —
O30   2½d. blue (No. 308)............................ —   £900
O31   3d. yellow-brown (No. 309)................... —   £1100
O32   5d. red-brown (No. 311)....................... —
O33   1s. orange-red (No. 315b)..................... —   £2500
O34   2s. green (No. 316).............................. —   £3750
The letters signify "On Public Service Only" and stamps so overprinted were used exclusively at the General Post Office, Wellington, on official correspondence to foreign countries between December 1891 and 31 December 1906.
Four different handstamps were used, differing slightly in the length of the overprint. The handstamp was normally applied diagonally reading upwards but other positions are known.
The stamps were not available unused and such examples with the "O.P.S.O." handstamp are generally considered to be reprints.

OFFICIAL.

(O **3**)

1907–11. Stamps of 1902–6 optd with Type O **3** (vertically, upwards). W **43** (sideways on 3d, 6d., 1s. and 5s.). P 14.
O59   **23**   ½d. yellow-green .... 18·00   75
          a. Perf 11×14.................................... £300
          b. Mixed perfs................................. £300   £300
O60   **42**   1d. carmine (No. 303) (1.7.07*).............. 14·00   22·00
          a. Booklet pane of 6......................... 55·00
          ab. Imperf horiz (booklet pane of 6).... £2750
O60b   1d. rose-carmine (Waterlow) (No. 352)... 28·00   70
          ba. Perf 11×14................................. —   £500
          bb. Mixed perfs............................... —   £475

		bc. Perf 14×11	—	£1000
O60*c*		1d. carmine (Royle)	60·00	70
		ca. Perf 11×14	£375	£600
		cb. Mixed perfs	£375	£475
O61	**41**	2d. purple	17·00	1·75
		a. *Bright reddish purple*	8·50	1·60
		ab. Mixed perfs	£550	£425
O63	**28**	3d. bistre-brown	50·00	1·75
		a. Mixed perfs	—	£1600
O64	**31**	6d. bright carmine-pink	£250	25·00
		a. Imperf vert (horiz pair)	£1500	
		b. Mixed perfs	£1000	£750
		c. Opt inverted (reading downwards)	†	£4250
O65	**34**	1s. orange-red	£110	22·00
O66	**35**	2s. blue-green	85·00	£140
		a. Imperf between (pair)	£4000	
		b. Imperf vert (horiz pair)	£2750	
		w. Wmk inverted	£750	£550
O67	**36**	5s. deep red	£170	£190
		a. Wmk upright (1911)	£1200	£1200

*Though issued in 1907 a large quantity of booklets was mislaid and not utilized until they were found in 1930.

1908–09. Optd as Type O **3**. W **43**.

O69	**23**	½d. green (P 14×15)	18·00	6·00
O70	**50**	1d. carmine (P 14×15)	70·00	5·50
O71	**48**	6d. pink (P 14×13, 13½)	£200	48·00
O72		6d. pink (P 14×15) (1909)	£225	35·00
O72*a*	F **4**	£1 rose-pink (P 14) (No. F89)	£650	£450

1910. No. 387 optd with Type O **3**.

O73	**51**	½d. yellow-green	17·00	40
		a. Opt inverted (reading downwards)	†	£3000

1910–16. Nos. 389 and 392/4 optd with Type O **3**. P 14×14½.

O74	**52**	3d. chestnut	14·00	80
		a. Perf 14×13½ (1915)	65·00	£130
		ab. Vert pair. Nos. O74/a	£350	£750
O75	–	6d. carmine	19·00	5·50
		a. Perf 14 (line) (No. 398)	†	£3750
		b. *Deep carmine*	25·00	6·00
		w. Wmk inverted		
O76	–	8d. indigo-blue (R.) (5.16)	12·00	29·00
		aw. Wmk inverted	75·00	85·00
		b. Perf 14×13½	12·00	29·00
		bw. Wmk inverted	75·00	85·00
		c. Vert pair, Nos. O76 and O76b	70·00	£140
		cw. Wmk inverted	£275	£325
O77		1s. vermilion	55·00	20·00
O74/7 *Set of 4*			90·00	50·00

1910–26. Optd with Type O **3**.

*(a) W **43**. De La Rue chalk-surfaced paper with toned gum*

O78	**53**	1d. carmine (No. 405)	5·50	10
		a. "Feather" flaw	70·00	12·00
		b. "Globe" flaw	70·00	12·00
		c. "Q" flaw	75·00	45·00
		y. Wmk inverted and reversed		

*(b) W **43**. Jones chalk-surfaced paper with white gum*

O79	**53**	1d. deep carmine (No. 406) (1925)	15·00	11·00
		a. "Feather" flaw	£150	75·00
		b. "Globe" flaw	£150	75·00

(c) No wmk, but bluish "NZ" and Star lithographed on back. Art paper

O80	**53**	1d. rose-carmine (No. 409) (1925)	7·00	22·00
		a. "Feather" flaw	75·00	
		b. "Globe" flaw	75·00	

*(d) W **43**. Cowan thick, opaque, chalk-surfaced paper with white gum*

O81	**53**	1d. deep carmine (No. 410) (1925)	8·00	1·25
		a. "Feather" flaw	75·00	32·00
		b. "Globe" flaw	75·00	32·00
		c. "N" flaw	£180	£100
		x. Wmk reversed (1926)	50·00	38·00
		xa. "Feather" flaw	£325	£225
		xb. "Globe" flaw	£325	£225
		xc. "N" flaw	£325	£225

1913–25. Postal Fiscal stamps optd with Type O **3**.

(i) Chalk-surfaced De La Rue paper

(a) P 14 (1913–14)

O82	F **4**	2s. blue (30.9.14)	65·00	60·00
O83		5s. yellow-green (13.6.13)	90·00	£130
O84		£1 rose-carmine (1913)	£650	£550
O82/4 *Set of 3*			£750	£650

(b) P 14½×14, comb (1915)

O85	F **4**	2s. deep blue (8.15)	65·00	60·00
		a. No stop after "OFFICIAL" (R. 2/5)	£180	£160
O86		5s. yellow-green (1.15)	90·00	£130
		a. No stop after "OFFICIAL" (R. 2/5)	£275	£350

(ii) Thick, white, opaque chalk-surfaced Cowan paper. P 14½×14 (1925)

O87	F **4**	2s. blue	85·00	£100
		a. No stop after "OFFICIAL"(R. 2/5)	£250	£300

The overprint on these last, and on Nos. O69 and O72*a* is from a new set of type, giving a rather sharper impression than Type O **3**, but otherwise resembling it closely.

1915 (12 Oct)–**34**. Optd with Type O **3**. P 14×15.

(a) On Nos. 435/40 (De La Rue chalk-surfaced paper with toned gum)

O88	**61**	½d. green	1·25	20
O89	**62**	1½d. grey-black (6.16)	8·50	2·75
O90	**61**	1½d. slate (12.16)	5·50	1·00
O91		1½d. orange-brown (4.19)	5·00	30
O92		2d. yellow (4.17)	13·00	20
O93		3d. chocolate (11.19)	12·00	1·00
O88/93 *Set of 6*			40·00	5·00

(b) On Nos. 441 and 443 (Jones chalk-surfaced paper with white gum)

O94	**61**	½d. green (1924)	4·50	3·50
O95		3d. deep chocolate (1924)	50·00	9·50

(c) On Nos. 446/7 and 448a/9 (Cowan thick, opaque, chalk surfaced paper with white gum)

O96	**61**	½d. green (1925)	5·50	10
		ax. Wmk reversed (1927)	80·00	27·00
		ay. Wmk inverted and reversed (1927)	£300	65·00
		b. Perf 14 (1929)	3·75	70
		ba. No stop after "OFFICIAL"	32·00	40·00
O97		1½d. orange-brown (P 14) (1929)	14·00	17·00
		a. No stop after "OFFICIAL"	£100	£100
		b. Perf 14×15 (1934)	50·00	42·00
O98		2d. yellow (P 14) (1931)	2·50	50
		a. No stop after "OFFICIAL"	75·00	80·00
O99		3d. chocolate (1925)	7·00	70
		a. No stop after "OFFICIAL"	75·00	55·00
		b. Perf 14 (1930)	70·00	14·00
		ba. No stop after "OFFICIAL"	£250	£190
O96/9 *Set of 4*			25·00	17·00

1915 (Dec)–**27**. Optd with Type O **3**. P 14×13½.

(a) Nos. 420, 422, 425, 428 and 429/30 (Cowan unsurfaced paper)

O100	**60**	3d. chocolate	4·50	1·50
		aw. Wmk inverted	32·00	7·00
		b. Perf 14×14½	4·50	1·75
		bw. Wmk inverted	50·00	12·00
		c. Vert pair, Nos. O100 and O100b	40·00	£120
		cw. Wmk inverted	£140	£225
		d. Opt double	†	£1400
O101		4d. bright violet (4.25)	14·00	7·50
		a. Re-entry (Pl 20 R. 1/6)	85·00	60·00
		b. Re-entry (Pl 20 R. 4/10)	90·00	70·00
		c. Perf 14×14½ (*Deep purple*) (4.27)	40·00	1·25
O102		6d. carmine (6.16)	5·00	75
		aw. Wmk inverted	£140	
		b. Perf 14×14½	5·00	2·00
		c. Vert pair, Nos. O102 and O102b	55·00	£140
O103		8d. red-brown (8.22)	65·00	£190
O104		9d. sage-green (4.25)	42·00	38·00
O105		1s. vermilion (9.16)	24·00	14·00
		aw. Wmk inverted	£275	£170
		b. Perf 14×14½	7·00	2·00
		ba. Pale orange-red	15·00	20·00
		bw. Wmk inverted	£250	£275
		c. Vert pair. Nos. O105 and O105b	65·00	£190
		cw. Wmk inverted	£650	
O100/5 *Set of 6*			£120	£200

(b) No. 433 (Thin paper with widely spaced sideways wmk)

O106	**60**	3d. chocolate (P 14) (7.16)	3·00	15·00
		a. No wmk	50·00	80·00

1927–33. Optd with Type O **3**. W **43**. P 14.

O111	**71**	1d. rose-carmine (No. 468)	2·00	20
		a. No stop after "OFFICIAL" (R. 1/2, 5/24)	42·00	£110
		bw. Wmk inverted	†	50·00
		c. Perf 14×15	8·00	20
O112	**72**	2s. light blue (No. 469) (2.28)	85·00	£130
O113	F **6**	5s. green (1933)	£325	£375
O111/13 *Set of 3*			£375	£475

Unused examples of No. O111 are known printed on Cowan unsurfaced paper.

Official (O **4**)   *Official* (O **5**)

1936–61. Pictorial issue optd horiz or vert (2s.) with Type O **4**.

*(a) W **43** (Single "N Z" and Star)*

O115	**82**	1d. scarlet (Die I) (P 14×13½) (21.3.36).	10·00	1·25
		a. Perf 13½×14	£140	85·00
O116	**83**	1½d. red-brown (P 13½×14) (3.36)	45·00	35·00
		a. Perf 14×13½	£20000	
O118	**92**	1s. deep green (P 14×13½) (3.36)	50·00	65·00
		w. Wmk inverted	†	£650
O119	F **6**	5s. green (P 14) (12.38)	£160	65·00
O115/19 *Set of 4*			£225	£160

The watermark of No. O119 is almost invisible.

Only four examples of No. O116a exist. The error occurred when a sheet of No. 558a was found to have a block of four missing. This was replaced by a block of No. 558 and the sheet was then sent for overprinting.

(b) W **98** *(Mult "N Z" and Star)*

O120	81	½d. bright green, P 14×13½ (7.37)	7·50	4·50
O121	82	1d. scarlet (Die II), P 14×13½ (11.36)	12·00	50
		w. Wmk inverted (2.37)	48·00	55·00
O122	83	1½d. red-brown, P 14×13½ (7.36)	35·00	4·75
O123	84	2d. orange, P 14×13½ (1.38)	13·00	10
		aw. Wmk inverted	—	£400
		b. Perf 12½ (1941)	£200	60·00
		c. Perf 14 (1941)	65·00	16·00
O124	85	2½d. chocolate and slate, P 13-14×13½		
		(26.7.38)	70·00	£110
		a. Perf 14 (1938)	14·00	21·00
O125	86	3d. brown, P 14×13½ (1.3.38)	48·00	3·50
		w. Wmk inverted	—	£400
O126	87	4d. black and sepia, P 14×13½ (8.36) ...	22·00	1·10
		a. Perf 14 (8.41)	24·00	4·50
		b. Perf 12½ (12.41)	24·00	10·00
		c. Perf 14×13½ (10.42)	10·00	1·00
		cw. Wmk inverted	—	£800
O127	89	6d. scarlet, P 13½×14 (12.37)	40·00	80
		aw. Wmk inverted	†	£750
		b. Perf 12½ (1941)	15·00	10·00
		c. Perf 14½×14 (7.42)	17·00	40
O128	90	8d. chocolate, P 12½ (wmk sideways)		
		(8.42)	23·00	17·00
		a. Perf 14×14½ (wmk sideways)		
		(8.45)	8·50	16·00
		b. Perf 14×13½ (1942)	†	£3250
O129	91	9d. red and grey-black (G.) (No. 587b),		
		P 13½×14 (1.3.38)	90·00	40·00
O130		9d. scarlet and black (chalk-surfaced		
		paper) (Blk.) (No. 631), P 14×15		
		(10.43)	20·00	22·00
O131	92	1s. deep green, P 14×13½ (2.37)	50·00	1·50
		aw. Wmk inverted	—	£750
		b. Perf 12½ (4.42)	40·00	3·00
O132	93	2s. olive-green, P 13–14×13½ (5.37)	80·00	42·00
		a. "CAPTAIN COQK"	£225	£120
		b. Perf 13½×14 (5.39)	£250	11·00
		ba. "CAPTAIN COQK"	£350	85·00
		c. Perf 12½ (3.42)	80·00	22·00
		ca. "CAPTAIN COQK"	£225	85·00
		d. Perf 14×13½ (1944)	50·00	11·00
		da. "CAPTAIN COQK"	£500	£225
O133	F 6	5s. green (chalk-surfaced paper), P 14		
		(3.43)	50·00	6·00
		aw. Wmk inverted	40·00	6·00
		b. Perf 14×13½. Yellow-green		
		(ordinary paper) (10.61)	14·00	30·00
O120/33 Set of 14			£350	£120

The opt on No. O127b was sometimes applied at the top of the stamp, instead of always at the bottom as on No. O127.

All examples of No. O128b were used by a government office in Whangarei.

The 5s. value on ordinary paper perforated 14×13½ does not exist without the "Official" overprint.

See notes on perforations after No. 590c.

1938–51. Nos. 603 etc., optd with Type O **4**.

O134	108	½d. green (1.3.38)	28·00	2·25
O135		½d. brown-orange (1946)	2·75	4·25
O136		1d. scarlet (1.7.38)	38·00	15
O137		1d. green (10.7.41)	7·00	10
O138	108a	1½d. purple-brown (26.7.38)	75·00	24·00
O139		1½d. scarlet (2.4.51)	17·00	12·00
O140		3d. blue (16.10.41)	7·50	10
O134/40 Set of 7			£160	38·00

1940 (2 Jan–8 Mar). Centennial. Nos. 613, etc., optd with Type O **5**.

O141		½d. blue-green (R.)	3·00	35
		a. "ff" joined, as Type O **4**	55·00	65·00
O142		1d. chocolate and scarlet	7·50	10
		a. "ff" joined, as Type O **4**	50·00	60·00
O143		1½d. light blue and mauve	6·50	2·00
O144		2d. blue-green and chocolate	9·00	10
		a. "ff" joined, as Type O **4**	65·00	65·00
O145		2½d. blue-green and ultramarine	5·00	2·75
		a. "ff" joined, as Type O **4**	50·00	75·00
O146		3d. purple and carmine (R.)	8·00	1·00
		a. "ff" joined, as Type O **4**	45·00	55·00
O147		4d. chocolate and lake	42·00	1·50
		a. "ff" joined, as Type O **4**	£120	£100
O148		6d. emerald-green and violet	35·00	1·50
		a. "ff" joined, as Type O **4**	80·00	75·00
O149		8d. black and red (8.3)	35·00	17·00
		a. "ff" joined, as Type O **4**	80·00	£120
O150		9d. olive-green and vermilion	14·00	4·00
O151		1s. sage-green and deep green	50·00	3·00
O141/51 Set of 11			£190	30·00

For this issue the Type O **4** overprint occurs on R. 4/3 of the 2½d. and on R. 1/10 of the other values.

1947 (1 May)**–51.** Nos. 680, etc., optd with Type O **4**.

O152	108a	2d. orange	7·00	10
O153		4d. bright purple	4·75	4·25
O154		6d. carmine	21·00	50
O155		8d. violet	8·00	7·50

O156		9d. purple-brown	9·00	6·50
O157	144	1s. red-brown and carmine (wmk		
		upright) (Plate 1)	17·00	1·00
		a. Wmk sideways (Plate 1) (6.49)	8·50	12·00
		aw. Wmk sideways inverted	45·00	25·00
		b. Wmk upright (Plate 2) (4.51)	24·00	7·50
		bw. Wmk inverted	£150	50·00
O158		2s. brown-orange and green (wmk		
		sideways) (Plate 1)	42·00	16·00
		a. Wmk upright (Plate 1)	35·00	48·00
O152/8 Set of 7			80·00	32·00

O **6** Queen   (O **7**)
Elizabeth II

(Des J. Berry. Recess B.W.)

1954 (1 Mar)**–63.** W. **98.** P 14×13½.

O159	**06**	1d. orange	75	1·00
		a. White opaque paper (8.7.59)	50	1·00
O160		1½d. brown-lake	3·75	5·50
O161		2d. bluish green	50	50
		a. White opaque paper (11.12.58)	40	60
O162		2½d. olive (white opaque paper) (1.3.63).	3·00	1·50
O163		3d. vermilion	70	10
		a. White opaque paper (1960)	40	10
		aw. Wmk inverted	38·00	24·00
O164		4d. blue	1·50	75
		a. Printed on the gummed side	£200	
		b. White opaque paper (1.9.61)	1·00	50
O165		9d. carmine	9·50	3·25
O166		1s. purple	1·25	30
		a. White opaque paper (2.10.61)	2·50	1·00
O167		3s. slate (white opaque paper) (1.3.63).	22·00	40·00
O159/67 Set of 9			38·00	48·00

See note *re* white opaque paper after No. 736.
No. O164a shows the watermark inverted and reversed.

1959 (1 Oct). No. O160 surch with Type O **7**.

O168	O **6**	6d. on 1½d. brown-lake	50	1·10

1961 (1 Sept). No. O161 surch as Type O **7**.

O169	O **6**	2½d. on 2d. bluish green	1·25	2·50

Owing to the greater use of franking machines by Government Departments, the use of official stamps was discontinued on 31 March 1965, but they remained on sale at the G.P.O. until 31 December 1965.

STAMP BOOKLET

1907 (1 July). White card cover.

OB1		10s. booklet containing one hundred and twenty	
		1d. in panes of 6 (No. O60a)...............	£1200

**PROVISIONALS ISSUED AT REEFTON AND USED BY
THE POLICE DEPARTMENT**

1907 (Jan). Current stamps of 1906, optd "Official", in red manuscript and handstamped with a circular "Greymouth—PAID—3". P 14.

P1	**23**	½d. green	£1300	£1600
P2	**40**	1d. carmine	£1300	£1500
P3	**38**	2d. purple	£1500	£2000
P4	**28**	3d. bistre		£2250
P5	**31**	6d. pink		£2250
P6	**34**	1s. orange-red		£3000
P7	**35**	2s. green		£8500

Only the ½d., 1d. and 2d. are known postally used, cancelled with the Reefton squared circle postmark. The 3d. and 6d. were later cancelled by favour at Wanganui.

LIFE INSURANCE DEPARTMENT

L **1**   L **2**   **2d.** "Z" flaw. (R. 1/6,
Lighthouse   Lighthouse   upper right pane)

(Des W. B. Hudson and J. F. Rogers; Eng. A. E. Cousins. Typo Govt Printing Office, Wellington)

1891 (2 Jan)**–98.**

A. W **12c.** P 12×11½

L1	L **1**	½d. bright purple	£110	6·00
		a. Mixed perf 12×11 and 12½..............	†	—

	x. Wmk reversed	†	£190
L2	1d. blue	90·00	4·00
	ax. Wmk reversed	†	£190
	ay. Wmk inverted and reversed	†	£110
	b. Wmk **12b**	£170	27·00
	bx. Wmk reversed	†	£500
L3	2d. brown-red	£170	15·00
	ax. Wmk reversed	†	£160
	b. Wmk **12b**	£180	21·00
L4	3d. deep brown	£325	38·00
L5	6d. green	£400	80·00
L6	1s. rose	£600	£150
L1/6 *Set of 6*		£1500	£250

B. W 12b (1893–98)

(a) P 10 (1893)

L7	L **1**	½d. bright purple	£110	21·00
L8		1d. blue	90·00	1·75
L9		2d. brown-red	£150	3·75
		a. "Z" flaw	—	£110
L7/9 *Set of 3*			£300	24·00

(b) P 11×10

L10	L **1**	½d. bright purple (1896)	£120	28·00
		a. Perf 10×11	£300	£110
L11		1d. blue (1897)	†	90·00
		a. Perf 10×11	£110	14·00

(c) Mixed perfs 10 and 11 (1897)

L12	L **1**	2d. brown-red	£1400	£1000

(d) P 11 (1897–98)

L13	L **1**	½d. bright purple	95·00	4·00
		a. Thin coarse toned paper (1898)	£180	14·00
L14		1d. blue	90·00	75
		a. Thin coarse toned paper (1898)	£190	6·00
		x. Wmk reversed	£275	55·00
		y. Wmk inverted and reversed	£275	60·00
L15		2d. brown-red	£170	3·50
		a. Chocolate	£190	25·00
		b. Thin coarse toned paper (1898)	£300	6·00
		c. "Z" flaw	—	£110
L13/15 *Set of 3*			£300	7·50

1902–04. W **43** (sideways).

(a) P 11

L16	L **1**	½d. bright purple (1903)	£110	14·00
L17		1d. blue (1902)	90·00	3·25
L18		2d. brown-red (1904)	£225	22·00
L16/18 *Set of 3*			£375	35·00

(b) P 14×11

L19	L **1**	½d. bright purple (1903)	£2500	£1500
L20		1d. blue (1904)	£160	12·00

Nos. L16/17 and L20 are known without watermark from the margins of the sheet. Note that the Type W **43** watermark may be found both sideways and sideways inverted.

1905–06. Redrawn, with "V.R." omitted. W **43** (sideways).

(a) P 11

L21	L **2**	2d. brown-red (12.05)	£1500	£130

(b) P 14

L22	L **2**	1d. blue (7.06)	£275	30·00

(c) P 14×11

L23	L **2**	1d. blue (7.06)	£850	£225
		a. Mixed perfs	†	£750

Between January 1907 and the end of 1912 the Life Insurance Department used ordinary Official stamps.

1913 (2 Jan)**–37.** New values and colours. W **43**.

(a) "De La Rue" paper. P 14×15

L24	L **2**	½d. green	22·00	2·50
		a. Yellow-green	22·00	2·50
L25		1d. carmine	20·00	1·25
		a. Carmine-pink	23·00	1·75
L26		1½d. black (1917)	50·00	8·50
L27		1½d. chestnut-brown (1919)	1·50	3·00
L28		2d. bright purple	60·00	35·00
		w. Wmk inverted	†	£350
L29		2d. yellow (1920)	12·00	4·00
L30		3d. yellow-brown	55·00	38·00
L31		6d. carmine-pink	48·00	35·00
L24/31 *Set of 8*			£225	£110

(b) "Cowan" paper

(i) P 14×15

L31a	L **2**	½d. yellow-green (1925)	45·00	4·50
L31b		1d. carmine-pink (1925)	42·00	3·50
		bw. Wmk inverted	£200	75·00

(ii) P 14

L32	L **2**	½d. yellow-green (1926)	24·00	4·00
		w. Wmk inverted	†	90·00
L33		1d. scarlet (1931)	8·50	2·00
		w. Wmk inverted	£100	50·00
L34		2d. yellow (1937)	7·00	13·00
		w. Wmk inverted	£100	£130
L35		3d. brown-lake (1931)	14·00	24·00
		a. "HREE" for "THREE" (R. 7/11)	£375	

L36		6d. pink (1925)	55·00	60·00
L32/6 *Set of 5*			95·00	90·00

(c) "Wiggins Teape" paper. P 14×15

L36a	L **2**	½d. yellow-green (3.37)	8·00	12·00
L36b		1d. scarlet (3.37)	22·00	3·25
L36c		6d. pink (7.37)	35·00	40·00
L36a/c *Set of 3*			60·00	50·00

For descriptions of the various types of paper, see after No. 385. In the 1½d. the word "POSTAGE" is in both the side-labels instead of at left only.

1944–47. W **98**. P 14×15.

L37	L **2**	½d. yellow-green (7.47)	8·50	9·00
L38		1d. scarlet (6.44)	3·25	2·00
L39		2d. yellow (1946)	17·00	35·00
L40		3d. brown-lake (10.46)	32·00	38·00
		a. "HREE" for "THREE" (R. 7/11)	£400	
L41		6d. pink (7.47)	20·00	45·00
L37/41 *Set of 5*			70·00	£110

L **3** Castlepoint lighthouse    L **4** Taiaroa lighthouse

L **5** Cape Palliser lighthouse    L **6** Cape Campbell lighthouse    L **7** Eddystone lighthouse

L **8** Stephens Island lighthouse    L **9** The Brothers lighthouse    L **10** Cape Brett lighthouse

(Des J. Berry. Recess B.W.)

1947 (1 Aug)**–65.** Type L **3/10**. W **98** (sideways inverted on 1d., 2d., sideways on 2½d.). P 13½.

L42	L **3**	½d. grey-green and orange-red	2·25	70
L43	L **4**	1d. olive-green and pale blue	1·75	1·25
L44	L **5**	2d. deep blue and grey-black	3·75	1·00
L45	L **6**	2½d. black and bright blue (*white opaque paper*) (4.11.63)	9·50	13·00
L46	L **7**	3d. mauve and pale blue	4·50	1·25
L47	L **8**	4d. brown and yellow-orange	4·25	1·75
		a. Wmk sideways (*white opaque paper*) (13.10.65)	3·50	14·00
L48	L **9**	6d. chocolate and blue	4·50	2·75
L49	L **10**	1s. red-brown and blue	4·75	4·00
L42/49 *Set of 8*			30·00	23·00

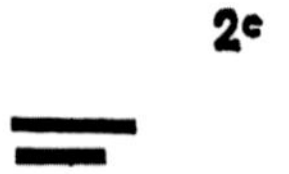

(L **11**)    (L **12**)

1967 (10 July)**–68.** Decimal currency. Stamps of 1947–65, surch as Type L **12** or L **11** (2c.).

L50		1c. on 1d. (No. L43)	2·25	4·25
		a. Wmk upright (*white opaque paper*) (10.5.68)	1·00	7·00
L51		2c. on 2½d. (No. L45)	8·00	14·00
L52		2½c. on 3d. (No. L46)	1·25	4·00
		a. Horiz pair, one without surcharge	£4250	
		b. Wmk sideways (*white opaque paper*) (4.68?)	1·90	4·75
L53		3c. on 4d. (No. L47a)	2·75	5·00
		w. Wmk sideways inverted	£1600	£750
L54		5c. on 6d. (No. L48)	75	6·50
		a. White opaque paper	1·50	6·50

L55	10c. on 1s. (No. L49)........................			1·50	10·00
	a. Wmk sideways (*white opaque paper*)........			75	4·00
	aw. Wmk sideways inverted...........................			†	£475
L50/5a *Set of 6*				13·00	32·00

See note *re* white paper below No. 736.

L **13** Moeraki Point lighthouse   L **14** Puysegur Point lighthouse

L **14a** Baring Head lighthouse   L **14b** Cape Egmont lighthouse

L **14c** East Cape   L **14d** Farewell Spit   L **15** Dog Island lighthouse

(Des J. Berry. Litho B.W.)

1969 (27 Mar)–**76**. Types L **13/15**. No wmk. Chalk-surfaced paper (8, 10c.), ordinary paper (others). P 14 (8, 10c.) or 13½ (others).

L56	L **13**	½c. greenish yellow, red and deep blue	65	1·50
L57	L **14**	2½c. ultramarine, green and pale buff.	50	1·00
L58	L **14a**	3c. reddish brown and yellow...............	50	60
		a. Chalk-surfaced paper (1974)..........	50	2·75
L59	L **14b**	4c. light new blue, yellowish green and apple-green	50	75
		a. Chalk-surfaced paper (1975)..........	50	2·25
L60	L **14c**	8c. multicoloured (17.11.76)...............	40	2·00
L61	L **14d**	10c. multicoloured (17.11.76).................	40	2·00
L62	L **15**	15c. black, light yellow and ultramarine..	40	1·25
		a. Chalk-surfaced paper (3.75)............	20·00	22·00
		ab. Perf 14 (24.12.76)....................	90	3·50
L56/62 *Set of 7*			3·00	8·00

The ordinary paper stamps have shiny gum and fluoresce brightly under UV light. The chalk-surfaced paper stamps have matt, PVA gum and the front of the stamps give a dull reaction under UV light.

L **16**

1978 (8 Mar). As No. L 57 but with the addition of new value as Type L **16**. Chalky paper.

L63	L **14**	25c. on 2½c. ultramarine, green and buff...	75	1·75

L **17**

(Des A. G. Mitchell. Litho Harrison)

1981 (3 June). P 14½.

L64	L **17**	5c. multicoloured	10	10
L65		10c. multicoloured	10	10
L66		20c. multicoloured	15	15
L67		30c. multicoloured	25	25
L68		40c. multicoloured	30	30
L69		50c. multicoloured	30	45
L64/9 *Set of 6*			1·00	1·25

Issues for the Government Life Insurance Department were withdrawn on 1 December 1989 when it became the privatised Tower Corporation.

POSTAL FISCAL STAMPS

As from 1 April 1882 fiscal stamps were authorised for postal use and conversely postage stamps became valid for fiscal use. Stamps in the designs of 1867 with "STAMP DUTY" above the Queen's head were withdrawn and although some passed through the mail quite legitimately they were mainly "philatelic" and we no longer list them. The issue which was specifically authorised in 1882 was the one which had originally been put on sale for fiscal use in 1880.

There is strong evidence that the authorities used up existing low value revenue stamps for postage, delaying the general release of the new "Postage and Revenue" low values (T **14**, **15** and **18-22**) to achieve this. Used prices for such stamps are for examples with 1882–3 postal cancellations.

Although all fiscal stamps were legally valid for postage, only values between 2s. and £1 were stocked at ordinary post offices. Other values could only be obtained by request from the G.P.O., Wellington or from offices of the Stamp Duties Department. Later the Arms types above £1 could also be obtained from the head post offices in Auckland, Christchurch, Dunedin and also a branch post office at Christchurch North where there was a local demand for them.

It seems sensible to list under Postal Fiscals the Queen Victoria stamps up to the £1 value and the Arms types up to the £5 because by 1931 the higher values were genuinely needed for postal purposes. The £10 was occasionally used on insured airmail parcels and is therefore also listed.

Although 2s. and 5s. values were included in the 1898 pictorial issue, it was the general practice for the Postal Department to limit the postage issues to 1s. until 1926 when the 2s. and 3s. appeared. These were then dropped from the fiscal issues and when in turn the 5s. and 10s. were introduced in 1953 and the £1 in 1960 no further printings of these values occurred in the fiscal series.

FORGED POSTMARKS. Our prices are for stamps with genuine postal cancellations. Beware of forged postmarks on stamps from which fiscal cancellations have been cleaned off.

Many small post offices acted as agents for government departments and it was the practice to use ordinary postal date-stamps on stamps used fiscally, so that when they are removed from documents they are indistinguishable from postally used specimens unless impressed with the embossed seal of the Stamp Duties Department.

Date-stamps very similar to postal date-stamps were sometimes supplied to offices of the Stamp Duties Department and it is not clear when this practice ceased. Prior to the Arms types the only sure proof of the postal use of off-cover fiscal stamps is when they bear a distinctive duplex, registered or parcel post cancellation, but beware of forgeries of the first two.

F **1**   F **2**   F **3**

(Die eng W. R. Bock. Typo Govt Ptg Office)

1882 (Feb). W **12a**. P 12×11½.

F1	F **1**	1d. lilac.........................	£1100	£600
F2		1d. blue...........................	£275	45·00
		w. Wmk inverted	—	£250

The 1d. fiscal was specifically authorised for postal use in February 1882 owing to a shortage of the 1d. Type **5** and pending the introduction of the 1d. Type **14** on 1 April.

The 1d. lilac fiscal had been replaced by the 1d. blue in 1878 but postally used copies with 1882 duplex postmarks are known although most postally used examples are dated from 1890 and these must have been philatelic.

1882 (early). W **12a**. P 12×11½.

F3	F **2**	1s. grey-green	
F4	F **3**	1s. grey-green and red.........................	
F4*a*		2s. rose and blue.........................	

Examples of these are known postally used in 1882 and although not specifically authorised for postal use it is believed that their use was permitted where there was a shortage of the appropriate postage value.

WMK TYPE F **5**. The balance of the paper employed for the 1867 issue was used for early printings of Type F **4** introduced in 1880 before changing over to the "N Z" and Star watermark. The values we list with this watermark are known with 1882–83 postal date stamps. Others have later dates and are considered to be philatelic but should they be found with 1882–83 postal dates we would be prepared to add them to the list.

F 4   F 5

The 12s.6d. value has the head in an oval (as Type **10**), and the 15s. and £1 values have it in a broken circle (as Type **7**).

(Dies eng W.R. Bock. Typo Govt Ptg Office)

1882 (1 Apr)–**1930**. Type F **4** and similar types. "De La Rue" paper.

A. W **12a** *(6 mm)*

(a) P 12 (1882)

F5	4d. orange-red (Wmk F **5**)	—	£425
F6	6d. lake-brown	—	£325
	a. Wmk F **5**		£850
F7	8d. green (Wmk F **5**)	—	£850
F8	1s. pink	—	£400
	a. Wmk F **5**		£400
F9	2s. blue	£140	9.50
F10	2s.6d. grey-brown	£190	9.50
	a. Wmk F **5**		
F11	3s. mauve	£250	13.00
F12	4s. brown-rose	£300	20.00
	a. Wmk F **5**		
F13	5s. green	£350	19.00
	a. Yellow-green	£350	19.00
F14	6s. rose	£375	50.00
	a. Wmk F **5**		
F15	7s. ultramarine	£400	90.00
	a. Wmk F **5**		
F16	7s.6d. bronze-grey	£1500	£250
F17	8s. deep blue	£475	£110
	a. Wmk F **5**		
F18	9s. orange	£550	£120
F19	10s. brown-red	£350	30.00
	a. Wmk F **5**		
F20	15s. green	£1100	£200
F21	£1 rose-pink	£550	90.00

(b) P 12½ (1886)

F22	2s. blue	£140	9.50
F23	2s.6d. grey-brown	£190	9.50
F24	3s. mauve	£275	13.00
F25	4s. purple-claret	£300	20.00
	a. Brown-rose	£300	20.00
F26	5s. green	£350	19.00
	a. Yellow-green	£350	19.00
F27	6s. rose	£425	50.00
F28	7s. ultramarine	£425	90.00
F29	8s. deep blue	£475	£110
F30	9s. orange	£550	£120
F31	10s. brown-red	£350	30.00
F32	15s. green	£1100	£200
F33	£1 rose-pink	£550	90.00

B. W **12b** *(7 mm). P 12½ (1888)*

F34	2s. blue	£140	9.50
F35	2s.6d. grey-brown	£190	9.50
F36	3s. mauve	£250	13.00
F37	4s. brown-rose	£275	20.00
	a. Brown-red	£275	20.00
F38	5s. green	£325	19.00
	a. Yellow-green	£325	19.00
F39	6s. rose	£425	50.00
F40	7s. ultramarine	£450	90.00
F41	7s.6d. bronze-grey	£1500	£250
F42	8s. deep blue	£475	£110
F43	9s. orange	£550	£120
F44	10s. brown-red	£350	29.00
	a. Maroon	£350	29.00
F45	£1 pink	£550	90.00

C. W **12c** *(4 mm). P 12½ (1890)*

F46	2s. blue	£200	22.00
F46a	2s.6d. grey-brown	£300	24.00
F47	3s. mauve	£400	55.00
F48	4s. brown-red	£350	35.00
F49	5s. green	£375	24.00
F50	6s. rose	£475	60.00
F51	7s. ultramarine	£550	£110
F52	8s. deep blue	£550	£130
F53	9s. orange	£600	£150
F54	10s. brown-red	£450	40.00
F55	15s. green	£1400	£250

D. Continuation of W **12b**. *P 11 (1895–1901)*

F56	2s. blue	90.00	9.50
F57	2s.6d. grey-brown	£180	9.00
	a. Inscr "COUNTERPART" (1901)*	£200	£300

F58	3s. mauve	£225	12.00
F59	4s. brown-red	£275	18.00
F60	5s. yellow-green	£325	19.00
F61	6s. rose	£375	50.00
F62	7s. pale blue	£425	90.00
F63	7s.6d. bronze-grey	£1500	£250
F64	8s. deep blue	£475	£100
F65	9s. orange	£550	£140
	a. Imperf between (horiz pair)	£3500	
F66	10s. brown-red	£350	28.00
	a. Maroon	£350	28.00
F67	15s. green	£1100	£200
F68	£1 rose-pink	£550	90.00

*The plate normally printed in yellow and inscribed "COUNTERPART" just above the bottom value panel, was for use on the counterparts of documents but was issued in error in the colour of the normal fiscal stamp and accepted for use.

E. W **43** *(sideways)*

(i) Unsurfaced "Cowan" paper

(a) P 11 (1903)

F69	2s.6d. grey-brown	£225	9.00
F70	3s. mauve	£275	13.00
F71	4s. orange-red	£275	18.00
F72	6s. rose	£350	50.00
F73	7s. pale blue	£450	95.00
F74	8s. deep blue	£475	£100
F75	10s. brown-red	£350	30.00
	a. Maroon	£350	30.00
F76	15s. green	£1200	£200
F77	£1 rose-pink	£500	90.00

(b) P 14 (1906)

F78	2s.6d. grey-brown	£150	9.00
F79	3s. mauve	£200	12.00
F80	4s. orange-red	£200	16.00
F81	5s. yellow-green	£225	16.00
F82	6s. rose	£325	50.00
F83	7s. pale blue	£375	90.00
F84	7s.6d. bronze-grey	£1400	£225
F85	8s. deep blue	£450	£100
F86	9s. orange	£475	£110
F87	10s. maroon	£325	29.00
F88	15s. green	£1200	£200
F89	£1 rose-pink	£475	90.00

(c) P 14½×14, comb (clean-cut) (1907)

F90	2s. blue	90.00	8.50
F91	2s.6d. grey-brown	£180	9.00
F92	3s. mauve	£225	13.00
F93	4s. orange-red	£225	17.00
F94	6s. rose	£350	50.00
F95	10s. maroon	£325	28.00
F96	15s. green	£1200	£200
F97	£1 rose-pink	£475	90.00

(ii) Chalk-surfaced "De la Rue" paper

(a) P 14 (1913)

F98	2s. blue	70.00	8.00
	a. Imperf horiz (vert pair)	£2000	
F99	2s.6d. grey-brown	85.00	9.00
F100	3s. purple	£170	12.00
F101	4s. orange-red	£170	14.00
F102	5s. yellow-green	£180	15.00
F103	6s. rose	£300	32.00
F104	7s. pale blue	£325	55.00
F105	7s.6d. bronze-grey	£1500	£250
F106	8s. deep blue	£425	65.00
F107	9s. orange	£500	£110
F108	10s. maroon	£325	27.00
F109	15s. green	£1200	£200
F110	£1 rose-carmine	£450	90.00

(b) P 14½×14, comb (1913–21)

F111	2s. deep blue	70.00	8.00
F112	2s.6d. grey-brown	85.00	9.00
F113	3s. purple	£170	11.00
F114	4s. orange-red	£170	14.00
F115	5s. yellow-green	£180	15.00
F116	6s. rose	£300	32.00
F117	7s. pale blue	£325	55.00
F118	8s. deep blue	£425	65.00
F119	9s. orange	£475	£110
F120	10s. maroon	£325	27.00
F121	12s.6d. deep plum (1921)	£13000	£5000
F122	15s. green	£1200	£200
F123	£1 rose-carmine	£425	90.00

The "De La Rue" paper has a smooth finish and has toned gum which is strongly resistant to soaking.

(iii) Chalk-surfaced "Jones" paper. P 14½×14, comb (1924)

F124	2s. blue	£100	11.00
F125	2s.6d. deep grey-brown	£110	12.00
F126	3s. purple	£225	15.00
F127	5s. yellow-green	£225	19.00
F128	10s. brown-red	£375	30.00
F129	12s.6d. deep purple	£13000	£5000
F130	15s. green	£1000	£225

The "Jones" paper has a coarser texture, is poorly surfaced and the ink tends to peel. The outline of the watermark commonly shows on the surface of the stamp. The gum is colourless or only slightly toned and washes off readily.

(iv) Thick, opaque, chalk-surfaced "Cowan" paper. P 14½×14, comb (1925–30)

F131	2s. blue	75·00	9·50
F132	2s.6d. deep grey-brown	90·00	10·00
F133	3s. mauve	£225	19·00
F134	4s. orange-red	£170	19·00
F135	5s. yellow-green	£180	21·00
	x. Wmk reversed (1927)	£275	42·00
F136	6s. rose	£300	38·00
F137	7s. pale blue	£325	60·00
F138	8s. deep blue	£500	70·00
	a. *Blue* (1930)	£550	
F139	10s. brown-red	£325	32·00
	x. Wmk reversed (1927)	£400	£275
F140	12s.6d. blackish purple	£13000	£5000
F141	15s. green	£1100	£225
F142	£1 rose-pink	£425	95·00

The "Cowan" paper is white and opaque and the watermark, which is usually smaller than in the "Jones" paper, is often barely visible.

(v) Thin, hard, chalk-surfaced "Wiggins Teape" paper. P 14½×14, comb (1926)

F143	4s. orange-red	£190	26·00
F144	£1 rose-pink	£475	£170

The "Wiggins Teape" paper has a horizontal mesh, in relation to the design, with narrow watermark, whereas other chalk-surfaced papers with this perforation have a vertical mesh and wider watermark.

F 6   **35/-**   **(F 7)**

PRICES. Collectors should note that in the F **6** "Arms" design, prices quoted for unused examples refer to hinged mint for Nos. F145/68*a*. Unused prices for Nos. F169/85 and all subsequent issues are for unmounted examples.

(Des H. L. Richardson. Typo Govt Ptg Office)
1931–40. As Type F **6** (various frames). W **43**. P 14.

(i) Thick, opaque, chalk-surfaced "Cowan" paper, with horizontal mesh (1931–35)

F145	1s.3d. lemon (4.31)	6·50	48·00
F146	1s.3d. orange-yellow	17·00	20·00
F147	2s.6d. deep brown	16·00	4·50
F148	4s. red	15·00	11·00
F149	5s. green	40·00	16·00
F150	6s. carmine-rose	32·00	16·00
F151	7s. blue	28·00	27·00
F152	7s.6d. olive-grey	85·00	£110
F153	8s. slate-violet	32·00	35·00
F154	9s. brown-orange	32·00	29·00
F155	10s. carmine-lake	24·00	10·00
F156	12s.6d. deep plum (9.35)	£170	£170
F157	15s. sage-green	95·00	42·00
F158	£1 pink	85·00	19·00
F159	25s. greenish blue	£700	£950
F160	30s. brown (1935)	£425	£250
F161	35s. orange-yellow	£5500	£6500
F162	£2 bright purple	£425	85·00
F163	£2.10s. red	£500	£650
F164	£3 green	£700	£350
F165	£3 10s. rose (1935)	£2250	£2750
F166	£4 light blue (1935)	£600	£250
F167	£4.10s. deep olive-grey (1935)	£2000	£2250
F168	£5 indigo-blue	£475	£150
F168*a*	£10 deep blue	£1600	£500

(ii) Thin, hard 'Wiggins Teape" paper with vertical mesh (1936–40)

(a) Chalk-surfaced (1936–39)

F169	1s.3d. pale orange-yellow	48·00	5·00
F170	2s.6d. dull brown	£130	4·00
F171	4s. pale red-brown	£170	21·00
F172	5s. green	£170	7·00
	w. Wmk inverted	—	£475
F173	6s. carmine-rose	£180	55·00
F174	7s. pale blue	£300	60·00
F175	8s. slate-violet	£325	85·00
F176	9s. brown-orange	£350	£110
F177	10s. pale carmine-lake	£300	7·00
F178	15s. sage-green	£450	85·00
F179	£1 pink	£300	42·00
F180	30s. brown (1.39)	£800	£250
F181	35s. orange-yellow	£8000	£7500
F182	£2 bright purple (1937)	£1200	£160
	w. Wmk inverted	£3500	
F183	£3 green (1937)	£1600	£475
F184	£5 indigo-blue (1937)	£2000	£400

(b) Unsurfaced paper (1940)

F185	7s.6d. olive-grey	£250	90·00

Not all values listed above were stocked at ordinary post offices as some of them were primarily required for fiscal purposes but all were valid for postage.

1939. No. F161 and F168*a* surch as Type F **7**.

F186	35/- on 35s. orange-yellow	£850	£400
F186*a*	£10 on £10 deep blue	£2250	£500
	aw. Wmk inverted		

Because the 35s. orange-yellow could so easily be confused with the 1s.3d. and the £10 with the £5 in similar colours, they were surcharged.

1940 (June). New values surch as Type F **7**. "Wiggins Teape" chalk-surfaced paper. W **43**. P 14.

F187	3/6 on 3s.6d. grey-green	80·00	38·00
F188	5/6 on 5s.6d. lilac	£140	75·00
F189	11/- on 11s. yellow	£275	£225
F190	22/- on 22s. scarlet	£700	£500
F187/90 *Set of 4*		£1100	£750

These values were primarily needed for fiscal use.

1940–58. As Type F **6** (various frames). W **98**. P 14.

(i) "Wiggins Teape" chalk-surfaced paper with vertical mesh (1940–56)

F191	1s.3d. orange-yellow	25·00	4·25
	w. Wmk inverted	—	£325
F192	1s.3d. yellow and black (wmk inverted) (14.6.55)	9·00	4·50
	aw. Wmk upright (9.9.55)	35·00	35·00
	b. Error. Yellow and blue (wmk inverted) (7.56)	4·75	4·50
F193	2s.6d. deep brown	17·00	1·40
	w. Wmk inverted (3.49)	19·00	1·50
F194	4s. red-brown	38·00	2·00
	w. Wmk inverted (3.49)	45·00	2·75
F195	5s. green	24·00	1·25
	w. Wmk inverted (1.5.50)	29·00	1·25
F196	6s. carmine-rose	55·00	3·75
	w. Wmk inverted (1948)	65·00	3·75
F197	7s. pale blue	55·00	6·00
F198	7s.6d. olive-grey (wmk inverted) (21.12.50)	85·00	95·00
F199	8s. slate-violet	95·00	17·00
	w. Wmk inverted (6.12.50)	£110	22·00
F200	9s. brown-orange (1.46)	50·00	60·00
	w. Wmk inverted (9.1.51)	£100	50·00
F201	10s. carmine-lake	60·00	2·50
	w. Wmk inverted (4.50)	70·00	2·50
F202	15s. sage-green	90·00	25·00
	w. Wmk inverted (8.12.50)	£110	26·00
F203	£1 pink	32·00	3·75
	w. Wmk inverted (1.2.50)	65·00	5·50
F204	25s. greenish blue (1946)	£800	£800
	w. Wmk inverted (7.53)	£1000	£1000
F205	30s. brown (1946)	£475	£190
	w. Wmk inverted (9.49)	£400	£170
F206	£2 bright purple (1946)	£225	32·00
	w. Wmk inverted (17.6.52)	£200	22·00
F207	£2.10s. red (wmk inverted) (9.8.51)	£475	£500
F208	£3 green (1946)	£300	60·00
	w. Wmk inverted (17.6.52)	£250	65·00
F209	£3.10s. rose (11.48)	£3500	£2250
	w. Wmk inverted (5.52)	£3500	£2250
F210	£4 light blue (wmk inverted) (12.2.52)	£350	£200
	w. Wmk upright	†	£1700
F211	£5 indigo-blue	£700	£100
	w. Wmk inverted (11.9.50)	£400	70·00
F191/211 *Set of 21*		£6250	£3750

3s.6d.

Type I. Broad serifed capitals

Type II. Taller capitals, without serifs

*Surcharged as Type F **7**.*

F212	3/6 on 3s.6d. grey-green (I) (1942)	21·00	8·50
	w. Wmk inverted (12.10.50)	45·00	22·00
F213	3/6 on 3s.6d. grey-green (II) (6.53)	17·00	50·00
	w. Wmk inverted (6.53)	55·00	55·00
F214	5/6 on 5s.6d. lilac (1944)	70·00	27·00
	w. Wmk inverted (13.9.50)	80·00	18·00
F215	11/- on 11s. yellow (1942)	£100	48·00
F216	22/- on 22s. scarlet (1945)	£450	£200
	aw. Wmk inverted (1.3.50)	£475	£225
F216*b*	£10 on £10 deep blue	£1700	£450
	bw. Wmk inverted		
F212/16 *Set of 5*		£600	£275

(ii) P 14×13½. "Wiggins Teape" unsurfaced paper with horizontal mesh (1956–58)

F217	1s.3d. yellow and black (11.56)	4·75	5·00
	w. Wmk inverted	45·00	45·00
F218	£1 pink (20.10.58)	40·00	12·00

No. F192b had the inscription printed in blue in error but as many as 378,000 were printed.

From 1949–53 inferior paper had to be used and for technical reasons it was necessary to feed the paper into the machine in a certain way which resulted in whole printings with the watermark inverted for most values.

F **8**

1967 (10 July)–**84**. Decimal currency. W **98** (sideways inverted). Unsurfaced paper. P 14 (line).

F219	F **8**	$4 deep reddish violet	8·00	7·00
		a. Perf 14 (comb) (wmk sideways)		
		(17.9.68)	2·50	1·50
		aw. Wmk sideways inverted (6.7.84)	3·75	11·00
F220		$6 emerald	12·00	21·00
		a. Perf 14 (comb) (wmk sideways)		
		(17.9.68)	3·00	3·50
		aw. Wmk sideways inverted (6.7.84)	3·75	13·00
F221		$8 light greenish blue	26·00	35·00
		a. Perf 14 (comb) (wmk sideways)		
		(20.6.68)	3·00	4·50
		aw. Wmk sideways inverted (6.7.84)		
F222		$10 deep ultramarine	28·00	20·00
		a. Perf 14 (comb) (wmk sideways)		
		(20.6.68)	3·00	3·50
		aw. Wmk sideways inverted (6.7.84)	25·00	30·00
F219/22 *Set of 4*			65·00	75·00
F219a/22a *Set of 4*			10·50	11·50

The original printings were line perforated on paper with the watermark sideways inverted (top of star pointing to left, *when viewed from the back*). In 1968 the stamps appeared comb perforated with the watermark sideways (top of star to right). A further comb perforated printing in July 1984 showed the sideways inverted watermark.

1986 (Apr.). As Nos. F220/2 but without wmk. Chalk-surfaced paper. P 14 (comb).

F223	F **8**	$6 bright green	6·50	4·50
F224		$8 light greenish blue	7·00	14·00
F225		$10 deep ultramarine	8·00	7·00
F223/5 *Set of 3*			19·00	23·00

ANTARCTIC EXPEDITIONS

VICTORIA LAND

These issues were made under authority of the New Zealand Postal Department and, while not strictly necessary, they actually franked correspondence to New Zealand. They were sold to the public at a premium.

(A **1**)

1908 (15 Jan). Shackleton Expedition. T **42** of New Zealand (P 14), optd with Type A **1**, by Coulls, Culling and Co., Wellington.

A1		1d. rose-carmine (No. 356 Royle) (G.)	£475	42·00
		a. Opt double	†	£1600
A1b		1d. rose-carmine (No. 352c Waterlow) (G.)	£1600	£850

Nos. A1/1b were used on board the expedition ship, *Nimrod*, and at the Cape Royds base in McMurdo Sound. Due to adverse conditions Shackleton landed in Victoria Land rather than King Edward VII Land, the intended destination.

VICTORIA LAND.   VICTORIA LAND.

(A **2**)   (A **3**)

1911 (9 Feb)–**13**. Scott Expedition. Stamps of New Zealand optd with Types A **2** (½d.) or A **3** (1d.) by Govt Printer, Wellington.

A2	**51**	½d. deep green (No. 387aa) (18.1.13)	£750	£850
A3	**53**	1d. carmine (No. 405)	55·00	£120
		a. No stop after "LAND" (R. 7/5)	£425	£120
		b. "Q" flaw		£650

Nos. A2/3 were used at the Cape Evans base on McMurdo Sound or on the *Terra Nova*.

ROSS DEPENDENCY

This comprises a sector of the Antarctic continent and a number of islands. It was claimed by Great Britain on 30 July 1923 and soon afterward put under the jurisdiction of New Zealand.

1 H.M.S. *Erebus*   **2** Shackleton and Scott

3 Map of Ross   **4** Queen
Dependency and   Elizabeth II
New Zealand

(Des E. M. Taylor (3d.), L. C. Mitchell (4d.), R. Smith (8d.), J. Berry (1s.6d.). Recess D.L.R.)

1957 (11 Jan). W **98** of New Zealand (Mult N Z and Star). P 13 (1s.6d.) or 14 (others).

1	**1**	3d. indigo	1·00	60
2	**2**	4d. carmine-red	1·00	60
3	**3**	8d. bright carmine-red and ultramarine	1·00	60
		a. Bright carmine-red and blue	4·75	4·50
4	**4**	1s.6d. slate-purple	1·00	60
1/4 *Set of 4*			3·50	2·25

(New Currency. 100 cents = 1 New Zealand dollar)

5 H.M.S. *Erebus*

1967 (10 July). Decimal currency. As Nos. 1/4 but with values inscr in decimal currency as T **5**. Chalky paper (except 15c.). W **98** of New Zealand (sideways on 7c.). P 13 (15c.) or 14 (others).

5	**5**	2c. indigo	9·00	8·00
		a. Deep blue	18·00	9·50
6	**2**	3c. carmine-red	2·50	4·25
		w. Wmk inverted	75·00	
7	**3**	7c. bright carmine-red and ultramarine	2·75	5·00
8	**4**	15c. slate-purple	2·00	10·00
		w. Wmk inverted	£100	
5/8 *Set of 4*			14·50	25·00

6 McCormick's Skua   **7** Scott Base

(Des M. Cleverley. Litho B.W.)

1972 (18 Jan)–**79**. Horiz designs as T **6** (3 to 8c.) or **7** (10, 18c.). Ordinary paper. P 14½×14 (10, 18c.) or 13 (others).

9		3c. black, brownish grey and pale blue	1·25	1·40
		a. Chalk-surfaced paper (2.79)	70	1·75
10		4c. black, royal blue and violet	50	1·40
		a. Chalk-surfaced paper (2.79)	15	1·75
11		5c. black, brownish grey and rose-lilac	35	1·40
		a. Chalk-surfaced paper (2.79)	15	1·75
12		8c. black, yellow-brown and brownish grey	35	1·40
		a. Chalk-surfaced paper (2.79)	15	1·75
13		10c. black, turquoise-green and slate-green	35	1·50
		a. Perf 13½×13. Chalk-surfaced paper (2.79)	15	1·75
14		18c. black, violet and bright violet	50	2·50
		a. Perf 13½×13. Chalk-surfaced paper (2.79)	15	1·75
9/14 *Set of 6*			3·00	8·50
9a/14a *Set of 6*			1·25	9·50

Designs:—4c. Lockheed C-130 Hercules aircraft at Williams Field; 5c. Shackleton's Hut; 8c. Supply ship H.M.N.Z.S. *Endeavour*; 18c. Tabular ice floe.

8 Adélie Penguins

9 McCormick's Skua

(Des R. Conly. Litho Asher and Co, Melbourne)

1982 (20 Jan). Horiz designs as T **8**. Multicoloured. P 15½.

15	5c. Type **8**	1·25	1·60
16	10c. Tracked vehicles	20	1·50
17	20c. Scott Base	20	75
18	30c. Field party	20	40
19	40c. Vanda Station	20	40
20	50c. Scott's hut, Cape Evans	20	40
15/20 Set of 6		2·00	4·50

The post office at Scott Base closed on 30 September 1987 and Nos. 15/20 were withdrawn from sale at philatelic counters in New Zealand on 31 December 1987. Local stamps were subsequently issued by the Armed Forces Canteen Council to cover the cost of mail carriage from Scott Base to New Zealand. These are not listed as they had no national or international validity.

Sets of stamps, showing whales, Antarctic birds and seals, inscribed "NEW ZEALAND ROSS DEPENDENCY", were issued in 1988, 1990 and 1992. These were available from post offices throughout New Zealand, but not in the Ross Dependency.

Separate issues for Ross Dependency were resumed in November 1994. Such stamps were only valid on mail from Scott Base, but were not postmarked until arrival at the New Zealand Post Ross Dependency Agency situated at Christchurch.

(Des G. Millen. Litho Southern Colour Print, Dunedin)

1994 (2 Nov)–**95**. Wildlife. T **9** and similar horiz designs. Multicoloured. P 13½.

21	5c. Type **9**	55	75
22	10c. Snow Petrel chick	65	80
23	20c. Black-browed Albatross	1·00	1·00
24	40c. Emperor Penguins (2.10.95)	3·50	2·50
25	45c. As 40c.	1·60	1·00
26	50c. Chinstrap Penguins	1·60	1·25
27	70c. Adélie Penguin	2·00	1·75
28	80c. Elephant Seals	1·75	1·50
29	$1 Leopard Seal	1·75	1·50
30	$2 Weddell Seal	2·25	2·75
31	$3 Crabeater Seal pup	3·00	3·75
21/31 Set of 11		17·00	17·00

10 Capt. James Cook with H.M.S. *Resolution* and H.M.S. *Adventure*

11 Inside Ice Cave

(Des G. Fuller. Litho Questa)

1995 (9 Nov). Antarctic Explorers. T **10** and similar horiz designs. Multicoloured. P 14½.

32	40c. Type **10**	1·50	1·50
33	80c. James Clark Ross with H.M.S. *Erebus* and H.M.S. *Terror*	1·75	1·75
34	$1 Roald Amundsen and *Fram*	2·00	2·00
35	$1.20 Robert Scott with *Terra Nova*	2·50	2·50
36	$1.50 Ernest Shackleton with *Endurance*	2·75	2·75
37	$1.80 Richard Byrd with Ford 4-AT-B Trimotor *Floyd Bennett* (aircraft)	2·75	2·75
32/7 Set of 6		12·00	12·00

(Des Diane Prosser. Litho Enschedé)

1996 (13 Nov). Antarctic Landscapes. T **11** and similar multicoloured designs. P 14½×14 (vert) or 14×14½ (horiz).

38	40c. Type **11**	75	55
39	80c. Base of glacier	1·25	1·00
40	$1 Glacier ice fall	1·50	1·40
41	$1.20 Climbers on crater rim (*horiz*)	1·75	1·75
42	$1.50 Pressure ridges (*horiz*)	2·00	2·50
43	$1.80 Fumarole ice tower (*horiz*)	2·25	2·75
38/43 Set of 6		8·50	9·00

12 Snow Petrel

13 Sculptured Sea Ice

(Des P. Martinson. Litho Southern Colour Print, Dunedin)

1997 (12 Nov). Antarctic Seabirds. T **12** and similar vert designs. Multicoloured. P 14.

(a) With "W.W.F." panda emblem

44	40c. Type **12**	80	60
45	80c. Cape Petrel	1·25	1·00
46	$1.20 Antarctic Fulmar	1·60	1·50
47	$1.50 Antarctic Petrel	1·60	1·50

(b) Without "W.W.F." panda emblem

48	40c. Type **12**	2·75	2·75
	a. Block of 6. Nos. 48/53	17·00	16·00
49	80c. Cape Petrel	3·00	2·75
50	$1 Antarctic Prion	3·00	2·50
51	$1.20 Antarctic Fulmar	3·25	3·25
52	$1.50 Antarctic Petrel	3·25	3·50
53	$1.80 Antarctic Tern	3·25	3·25
44/53 Set of 10		21·00	20·00

Nos. 44/7 were printed in sheets containing stamps of one value.

Nos. 48/53 were printed in sheets containing the six values together, *se-tenant*, with the backgrounds forming a composite design. In addition the $1 and $1.80 were also produced in separate sheets.

(Des S. Fuller. Litho Southern Colour Print, Dunedin)

1998 (11 Nov). Ice Formations. T **13** and similar horiz designs. Multicoloured. P 14.

54	40c. Type **13**	60	40
	a. Block of 6. Nos. 54/9	5·75	5·25
55	80c. Glacial tongue	80	70
56	$1 Stranded tabular iceberg	1·00	90
57	$1.20 Autumn at Cape Evans	1·10	1·00
58	$1.50 Sea ice in summer thaw	1·40	1·25
59	$1.80 Sunset at tabular icebergs	1·50	1·50
54/9 Set of 6		5·75	5·25

Nos. 54/9 were printed in sheets of one value or together *se-tenant*, in blocks of six.

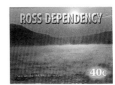

14 Sea Smoke, McMurdo Sound

(Des G. Millen. Litho Southern Colour Print, Dunedin)

1999 (17 Nov). Night Skies. T **14** and similar horiz designs. Multicoloured. P 14.

60	40c. Type **14**	1·00	65
61	80c. Alpenglow, Mount Erebus	1·50	1·00
62	$1.10 Sunset, Black Island	1·60	1·40
63	$1.20 Pressure ridges, Ross Sea	1·90	1·75
64	$1.50 Evening light, Ross Island	2·25	1·90
65	$1.80 Mother of pearl clouds, Ross Island	2·75	2·00
60/5 Set of 6		10·00	8·00

ROSS DEPENDENCY

40c

15 R.N.Z.A.F. C-130 Hercules

(Des Sea Sky Design. Litho Southern Colour Print, Dunedin)

2000 (4 Nov). Antarctic Transport. T **15** and similar horiz designs. Multicoloured. Phosphorised paper. P 14.

66	40c. Type **15**	1·75	75
67	80c. Hagglunds BV206 All Terrain carrier	2·00	1·25
68	$1.10 Tracked 4×4 motorbike	2·25	1·50
69	$1.20 ASV track truck	2·25	1·50
70	$1.50 Squirrel helicopter	2·75	2·75

71	$1.80 Elan skidoo	2·75	2·75
66/71	*Set of 6*	12·50	9·50

(Des Communication Arts Ltd. Litho Southern Colour Print, Dunedin)

2001 (7 Nov). Penguins. Horiz designs as T **604** of New Zealand. Multicoloured. P 14½.

72	40c. Two Emperor Penguins	1·25	75
73	80c. Two Adélie Penguins	1·75	1·25
74	90c. Emperor Penguin leaving water	1·75	1·25
75	$1.30 Adélie Penguin in water	2·00	1·60
76	$1.50 Group of Emperor Penguins	2·25	2·00
77	$2 Group of Adélie Penguins	2·75	2·50
72/77	*Set of 6*	10·50	8·50

16 British Explorers by Sledge

(Des Emdesign. Litho Southern Colour Print, Dunedin)

2002 (6 Nov). Centenary of Discovery Expedition. T **16** and similar horiz designs. Each grey-black, greenish slate and stone. P 14.

78	40c. Type **16**	1·50	75
79	80c. H.M.S. *Discovery* at anchor	2·50	1·25
80	90c. H.M.S. *Discovery* trapped in ice	2·50	1·25
81	$1.30 Sledges and tents on ice	2·75	1·90
82	$1.50 Expedition members	3·25	2·25
83	$2 Scott's hut	3·75	2·75
78/83	*Set of 6*	14·50	9·25

17 *Odontaster validus* (red seastar)

18 Penguin and Chick

(Des Chrometoaster. Litho Cartor)

2003 (1 Oct). Marine Life. T **17** and similar horiz designs. Multicoloured. Phosphorised paper. P 13×13½.

84	40c. Type **17**	1·50	75
85	90c. *Beroe cucumis* (comb jelly)	2·50	1·25
86	$1.30 *Macroptychaster accrescens* (giant seastar)	3·00	1·75
87	$1.50 *Sterechinus neumayeri* (sea urchin)	3·25	2·25
88	$2 *Perkinsiana littoralis* (fan worm)	3·75	2·50
84/8	*Set of 5*	12·50	7·75

(Des Ocean Design. Litho Enschedé)

2004 (3 Nov). Emperor Penguins. T **18** and similar vert designs. Multicoloured. P 13½×14.

89	45c. Type **18**	1·75	85
90	90c. Penguin chick	3·25	1·60
91	$1.35 Penguin feeding chick	3·75	2·00
92	$1.50 Two penguins and chick	3·75	2·50
93	$2 Group of penguins	4·25	3·25
89/93	*Set of 5*	15·00	9·25

19 Dry Valleys (Craig Potton)

(Des CommArts Design. Litho Wyatt & Wilson)

2005 (2 Nov). Photographs of Antarctica. T **19** and similar horiz designs. Multicoloured. Phosphor frame. P 13½.

94	45c. Type **19**	1·50	70
95	90c. Emperor Penguins (Andris Apse)	2·75	1·50
96	$1.35 Antarctic Fur Seal (Mark Mitchell)	3·00	2·25

97	$1.50 Hut of Captain Robert F. Scott (Colin Monteath)	3·50	2·75
98	$2 Antarctic Minke Whale (Kim Westerskov)	4·00	3·00
94/8	*Set of 5*	13·50	9·25

20 Biologist, 1957–8

(Litho Southern Colour Print, Dunedin)

2006 (1 Nov). 50th Anniv of New Zealand Antarctic Programme. T **20** and similar horiz designs. Multicoloured. Phosphorised paper. P 14.

99	45c. Type **20**	1·75	1·00
100	90c. Hydrologists, 1979–80	3·00	2·00
101	$1.35 Geologist, 1984–5	3·50	3·25
102	$1.50 Meteorologists, 1994–5	3·75	4·00
103	$2 Marine biologist, 2004–5	4·25	4·50
99/103	*Set of 5*	14·50	13·50

21 Beaver Aircraft

(Des Cue Design. Litho Southern Colour Print, Dunedin)

2007 (7 Nov). 50th Anniv of Commonwealth Trans-Antarctic Expedition. T **21** and similar horiz designs, each greenish blue and olive-black. Phosphorised paper. P 14.

104	50c. Type **21**	1·75	1·00
105	$1 Harry Ayres and sledge	2·50	1·50
106	$1.50 Sledge dogs	3·50	3·50
107	$2 TE20 Ferguson tractor	3·75	4·00
108	$2.50 H.M.N.Z.S. *Endeavour*	4·75	5·00
104/8	*Set of 5*	14·50	13·50
MS109	120×80 mm. Nos. 107/8	9·00	9·00

22 Departure of *Nimrod* from Lyttelton

(Des Cue Design. Litho Southern Colour Print)

2008 (5 Nov). Centenary of British Antarctic Expedition, 1907–1909. T **22** and similar horiz designs. Multicoloured. Phosphorised paper. P 13½.

110	50c. Type **22**	1·75	1·00
111	$1 Expedition hut, Cape Royds	2·50	1·75
112	$1.50 Arrol-Johnston car (first vehicle on Antarctica)	3·25	3·00
113	$2 Professor Edgeworth David, Douglas Mawson and Alistair Mackay, first to reach South Magnetic Pole, 16 January 1909	3·75	3·75
114	$2.50 Setting out for first ascent of Mount Erebus, 1908	4·25	4·25
110/14	*Set of 5*	14·00	12·50

23 Map of Antarctica

(Des Inhouse Design. Litho Southern Colour Print)

2009 (25 Nov). 50th Anniv of the Antarctic Treaty. T **23** and similar vert designs, each showing silhouettes in Antarctic landscape. Multicoloured. P 13×13½.

115	50c. Type **23**	1·40	1·00
116	$1 Penguins ("Antarctica shall be used for peaceful purposes only")	2·50	2·25
117	$1.80 Scientist ("Freedom of scientific investigation")	3·50	3·50
118	$2.30 Flags ("International co-operation in scientific investigation")	4·25	4·50
119	$2.80 Seal ("Preservation and conservation of living resources")	4·25	4·75
115/19 *Set of 5*		14·00	14·50

24 Sperm Whale

(Des Tim Garman. Litho Southern Colour Print)

2010 (17 Nov). Whales of the Southern Ocean. T **24** and similar horiz designs. Multicoloured. Phosphorised paper. P 14½.

120	60c. Type **24**	1·40	1·10
121	$1.20 Minke Whale	2·50	2·25
122	$1.90 Sei Whale	3·75	3·25
123	$2.40 Killer Whale	4·25	4·50
124	$2.90 Humpback Whale	4·50	4·75
120/24 *Set of 5*		14·50	14·50
MS125 160×85 mm. Nos. 120/4		14·50	14·50

25 Roald Engelbregt Gravning Amundsen and *Fram*

(Des Vertigo. Litho Southern Colour Print)

2011 (2 Nov). "Race to the Pole": Centenary of the Amundsen and Scott Expeditions. T **25** and similar horiz designs. Multicoloured. Phosphorised paper. P 13½.

126	60c. Type **25**	1·40	1·10
127	$1.20 Amundsen triumphs	2·50	2·00
128	$1.90 Robert Falcon Scott and ship *Terra Nova*	3·50	3·50
129	$2.40 Scott's party and memorial cairn at their last camp	4·00	4·25
130	$2.90 Norwegian flag and Union Jack	5·50	6·00
126/30 *Set of 5*		15·00	15·00
MS131 161×91 mm. Nos. 126/30		15·00	15·00

(Litho)

2012 (14 Jan). Christchurch Philatelic Society Centennial Stamp and Postcard Exhibition. Sheet 130×90 mm. Multicoloured. Phosphorised paper. P 13½.

MS132 Nos. 128/9	8·50	8·50

26 Mount Erebus

(Des Gregory Millen. Litho Southern Colour Print, New Zealand)

2012 (21 Nov). Landscapes. T **26** and simiilar horiz designs. Multicoloured. Phosphorised paper. P 13½×13.

133	70c. Type **26**	1·40	1·10
134	$1.40 Beardmore Glacier	2·50	2·25
135	$1.90 Lake Vanda	3·50	3·50
136	$2.40 Cape Adare	4·00	4·25
137	$2.90 Ross Ice Shelf	4·50	4·75
133/7 *Set of 5*		14·50	14·50
MS138 134×88 mm. Nos. 133/7		14·50	14·50

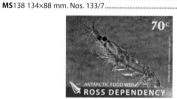

27 Antarctic Krill (*Euphausia superba*)

(Des Gregory Millen. Litho Southern Colour Print, New Zealand)

2013 (20 Nov). Antarctic Food Web. T **27** and similar horiz designs. Multicoloured. P 14.

139	70c. Type **27**	1·40	1·10
140	$1.40 Lesser Snow Petrel (*Pagodroma nivea*)	2·50	2·25
141	$1.90 Adélie Penguin (*Pygoscelis adeliae*)	3·50	3·50
142	$2.40 Crabeater Seal (*Lobodon carcinophaga*)	4·00	4·25
143	$2.90 Blue Whale (*Balaenoptera musculus*)	4·50	4·75
139/43 *Set of 5*		14·50	14·50
MS144 141×90 mm. Nos. 139/43		14·50	14·50

28 Emperor Penguin

(Litho Southern Colour Print)

2014 (19 Nov). Penguins of the Antarctic. T **28** and similar circular designs. Multicoloured. Phosphorised paper. P 14½.

145	80c. Type **28**	1·40	1·10
146	$1.40 Adélie Penguin	2·50	2·25
147	$2 Macaroni Penguin	3·50	3·50
148	$2.50 Gentoo Penguin	4·50	4·75
149	$3 Chinstrap Penguin	5·50	5·75
145/9 *Set of 5*		16·00	16·00
MS150 180×81 mm. Nos. 145/9		17·00	17·00

(Litho)

2014 (19 Nov). From Pole to Pole. Sheet 160×90 mm. Phosphorised paper. P 14½.

MS151 As No. 149	5·50	5·50

No. **MS**151 contains No. 149 and also a circular stamp-size label depicting a Polar Bear. A similar sheet issued by Greenland on the same date contains the Polar Bear design as a Greenland stamp inscr 'KALAALLIT NUNAAT. GRØNLAND 2014 21.50' and a circular stamp-size label in the same design as No. 149 but without inscriptions.

29 Endurance

(Des Jonathan Grey. Litho Southern Colour Print)

2015 (4 Nov). Centenary of the Imperial Trans-Antarctic Expedition, 1914–1917. T **29** and similar horiz designs. Multicoloured. Phosphorised paper. P 14×14½.

152	80c. Type **29**	1·10	95

153		80c. Ocean Camp..............................	1·10	95
154		$1.40 Elephant Island to South Georgia in the		
		lifeboat *James Caird*	2·00	1·50
155		$2 The *Aurora*...............................	2·75	2·75
156		$2.50 Laying the Depots	3·50	4·00
157		$3 Rescue of the Ross Sea Party................	4·25	4·75
152/7 *Set of 6*			13·00	13·00
MS158 162×59 mm. Nos. 152/4.........................			4·00	4·00
MS159 162×59 mm. Nos. 155/7.........................			10·00	10·00

TOKELAU ISLANDS

Formerly known as the Union Islands, and administered as part of the Gilbert & Ellice Islands Colony, Tokelau was transferred to New Zealand on 4 November 1925 and administered with Western Samoa. The Islands were finally incorporated in New Zealand on 1 January 1949 and became a dependency. The name Tokelau was officially adopted on 7 May 1946.

> Stamps of GILBERT AND ELLICE ISLANDS were used in Tokelau from Febuary 1911 until June 1926 when they were replaced by those of SAMOA. These were current until 1948.
> The post office on Atafu opened in 1911, but the cancellations for the other two islands, Fakaofo and Nukunono, did not appear until 1926.

NEW ZEALAND ADMINISTRATION

1 Atafu Village and Map

2 Nukunono hut and map

3 Fakaofo village and map

(Des J. Berry from photographs by T. T. C. Humphrey. Recess B.W.)

1948 (22 June). T **1/3**. Wmk T **98** of New Zealand (Mult N Z and Star). P 13½.

1	**1**	½d. red-brown and purple.........................	15	75
2	**2**	1d. chestnut and green..........................	15	50
		w. Wmk inverted	£275	
3	**3**	2d. green and ultramarine	15	50
1/3 *Set of 3*			40	1·60

Covers are known postmarked 16 June 1948, but this was in error for 16 July.

1953 (16 June*). Coronation. As No. 715 of New Zealand, but inscr "TOKELAU ISLANDS".

4	**164**	3d. brown	1·75	1·75

*This is the date of issue in Tokelau. The stamps were released in New Zealand on 25 May.

ONE SHILLING

(4)

1956 (27 Mar). No. 1 surch with T **4** by Govt Printer, Wellington.

5	**1**	1s. on ½d. red-brown and purple.....................	75	1·25

1966 (8 Nov). Postal fiscal stamps of New Zealand (Type F **6**), but without value, surch as T **5** by Govt Printer, Wellington. W **98** of New Zealand. P 14.

6		6d. light blue	25	80
7		8d. light emerald	25	80
8		2s. light pink	30	80
6/8 *Set of 3*			70	2·25

(New Currency. 100 cents = 1 New Zealand dollar)

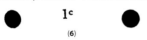

(6)

TOKELAU	
ISLANDS	
(7)	

1967 (4 Sept*)–**68**. Decimal currency.

(a) Nos. 1/3 surch in decimal currency as T **6** by Govt Printer, Wellington

9		1c. on 1d....................................	20	1·00
10		2c. on 2d....................................	30	1·50
11		10c. on ½d....................................	70	2·00

R. 7/1

Normal

On R .7/1 of Nos. 12/15 the words "TOKELAU" and "ISLANDS" are ½ mm apart instead of 1½ mm.

(b) Postal Fiscal stamps of New Zealand (Type F **6**), but without value, surch as T **7** by Govt Printer, Wellington. W **98** of New Zealand (sideways). P 14 (line or comb)

12	F **6**	3c. reddish lilac	30	20
		a. Narrow setting	10·00	10·00
13		5c. light blue	30	20
		a. Narrow setting	10·00	10·00
		b. *Pale blue* (second setting) (18.9.68)...	2·00	2·50
14		7c. light emerald	30	20
		a. Narrow setting	10·00	10·00
15		20c. light pink	30	30
		a. Narrow setting	10·00	10·00
9/15 *Set of 7*			2·25	4·75

*This is the date of issue in Tokelau. The stamps were released in New Zealand on 10 July.

In the second setting of the 5c. the words "TOKELAU" and "ISLANDS" are in thinner letters and almost 2 mm apart.

8 British Protectorate (1877)

(Des New Zealand P.O. artists from suggestions by Tokelau Administration. Litho B.W.)

1969 (8 Aug). History of Tokelau. T **8** and similar horiz designs. W **98** of New Zealand. P 13×12½.

16		5c. ultramarine, yellow and black................	15	10
17		10c. vermilion, yellow and black................	15	10
18		15c. green, yellow and black....................	20	15
19		20c. yellow-brown, yellow and black...............	25	15
16/19 *Set of 4*			65	45

Designs:—10c. Annexed to Gilbert and Ellice Islands, 1916: 15c. New Zealand Administration, 1925; 20c. New Zealand Territory, 1948.

1969 (14 Nov*). Christmas. As T **301** of New Zealand, but inscr "TOKELAU ISLANDS". W **98** of New Zealand. P 13½×14½.

20		2c. multicoloured...............................	10	15

*This is the date of issue in Tokelau. The stamps were released in New Zealand on 1 October.

1970 (15 Nov*). Christmas. As T **314** of New Zealand, but inscr "TOKELAU ISLANDS". P 12½.

21		2c. multicoloured...............................	10	20

*This is the date of issue in Tokelau. The stamps were released in New Zealand on 1 October.

12 H.M.S. *Dolphin*, 1765

(Des D. B. Stevenson. Litho B.W.)

1971 (9 Feb*). Discovery of Tokelau. T **12** and similar multicoloured designs. P 13½.

22	5c. Type **12**	50	35
23	10c. H.M.S. *Pandora*, 1791	50	35
24	25c. *General Jackson* (American whaling ship), 1835 (*horiz*)	70	70
22/4	*Set of 3*	1·50	1·25

*This is the date of issue in Tokelau. The stamps were released in New Zealand on 9 December 1970.

13 Fan

14 Windmill Pump

(Des Enid Hunter. Litho Harrison)

1971 (20 Oct). Various horiz designs as T **13** showing handicrafts. Multicoloured. P 14.

25	1c. Type **13**	15	20
26	2c. Hand-bag	15	30
27	3c. Basket	15	40
28	5c. Hand-bag	15	40
29	10c. Shopping-bag	15	45
30	15c. Fishing box	20	1·00
31	20c. Canoe	20	1·10
32	25c. Fishing hooks	20	1·10
25/32	*Set of 8*	1·25	4·50

(Des A. G. Mitchell. Litho Questa)

1972 (6 Sept). 25th Anniversary of South Pacific Commission. T **14** and similar vert designs. Multicoloured. P 14×13½.

33	5c. Type **14**	20	50
34	10c. Community well	30	60
35	15c. Pest eradication	45	75
36	20c. Flags of member nations	55	80
33/6	*Set of 4*	1·40	2·40

On No. 35 "PACIFIC" is spelt "PACFIC".

15 Horny Coral

16 Hump-back Cowrie

(Des Eileen Mayo. Litho B.W.)

1973 (12 Sept). Coral. T **15** and similar vert designs. Multicoloured. P 13.

37	3c. Type **15**	40	60
38	5c. Soft Coral	40	65
39	15c. Mushroom Coral	60	80
40	25c. Staghorn Coral	60	1·00
37/40	*Set of 4*	1·75	2·75

(Des G. F. Fuller. Litho Questa)

1974 (13 Nov). "Shells of the Coral Reef". T **16** and similar horiz designs. Multicoloured. P 14.

41	3c. Type **16**	40	1·00
42	5c. Tiger Cowrie	40	1·00

43	15c. Mole Cowrie	60	1·25
44	25c. Eyed Cowrie	60	1·50
41/4	*Set of 4*	1·75	4·25

17 Moorish Idol

18 Canoe Building

(Des Eileen Mayo. Litho Questa)

1975 (19 Nov). Fish. T **17** and similar vert designs. Multicoloured. P 14.

45	5c. Type **17**	20	40
46	10c. Long-nosed Butterflyfish	20	45
47	15c. Lined Butterflyfish	30	60
48	25c. Lionfish ("Red Fire Fish")	30	70
45/8	*Set of 4*	80	1·90

(Des F. Paulo. Litho Questa)

1976 (27 Oct)–**81**. T **18** and similar multicoloured designs showing local life. P 14×13½ (9c. to $1) or 13½×14 (others).

49	1c. Type **18**	40	1·25
	a. Perf 14½×15 (15.7.81)	10	15
50	2c. Reef fishing	30	2·25
51	3c. Weaving preparation	25	75
	a. Perf 14½×15 (15.7.81)	10	15
52	5c. Umu (kitchen)	30	75
	a. Perf 14½×15 (15.7.81)	10	15
53	9c. Carving (*vert*)	10	1·00
	a. Perf 15×14½ (15.7.81)	15	15
54	20c. Husking coconuts (*vert*)	15	80
	a. Perf 15×14½ (15.7.81)	15	20
55	50c. Wash day (*vert*)	20	90
	a. Perf 15×14½ (15.7.81)	20	20
56	$1 Meal time (*vert*)	35	2·00
	a. Perf 15×14½ (15.7.81)	30	30
49/56	*Set of 8*	1·60	8·75
49a/56a	*Set of 7*	1·00	1·10

19 White Tern

20 Westminster Abbey

(Des F. Paulo. Litho Questa)

1977 (16 Nov). Birds of Tokelau. T **19** and similar horiz designs. Multicoloured. P 14½.

57	8c. Type **19**	25	30
58	10c. Ruddy Turnstone	30	35
59	15c. White-capped Noddy	35	50
60	30c. Common Noddy	40	70
57/60	*Set of 4*	1·10	1·60

(Des Eileen Mayo. Litho Questa)

1978 (28 June). 25th Anniv of Coronation. T **20** and similar vert designs. Multicoloured. P 14.

61	8c. Type **20**	20	25
62	10c. King Edward's Chair	20	25
63	15c. Coronation regalia	30	40
64	30c. Queen Elizabeth II	50	65
61/4	*Set of 4*	1·10	1·40

21 Canoe Race

22 Rugby

(Des F. Paulo. Photo Heraclio Fournier)

1978 (8 Nov). Canoe Racing. T **21** and similar horiz designs showing races. P 13½×14.

65	8c. multicoloured	20	30
66	12c. multicoloured	20	35
67	15c. multicoloured	20	40
68	30c. multicoloured	30	70
65/8	*Set of 4*	80	1·60

(Des F. Paulo. Photo Heraclio Fournier)

1979 (7 Nov). Sports. T **22** and similar horiz designs. Multicoloured. P 13½.

69	10c. Type **22**	20	30
70	15c. Cricket	75	60
71	20c. Rugby (*different*)	30	45
72	30c. Cricket (*different*)	75	80
69/72	*Set of 4*	1·75	1·90

23 Surfing

24 Pole Vaulting

(Des F. Paulo. Litho J.W.)

1980 (5 Nov). Water Sports. T **23** and similar horiz designs. Multicoloured. P 13.

73	10c. Type **23**	10	15
74	20c. Surfing (*different*)	15	20
75	30c. Swimming	20	25
76	50c. Swimming (*different*)	25	35
73/6	*Set of 4*	60	85

(Des F. Paulo. Photo Heraclio Fournier)

1981 (4 Nov). Sports. T **24** and similar vert designs. Multicoloured. P 14×13½.

77	10c. Type **24**	10	10
78	20c. Volleyball	20	20
79	30c. Running	25	30
80	50c. Volleyball (*different*)	30	35
77/80	*Set of 4*	75	85

25 Wood Carving

26 Octopus Lure

(Des R. Conly. Litho Enschedé)

1982 (5 May). Handicrafts. T **25** and similar vert designs. Multicoloured. P 14×13½.

81	10s. Type **25**	10	20
82	22s. Bow-drilling sea shell	10	35
83	34s. Bowl finishing	15	45
84	60s. Basket weaving	25	80
81/4	*Set of 4*	55	1·60

(Des R. Conly. Litho Questa)

1982 (3 Nov). Fishing Methods. T **26** and similar vert designs. Multicoloured. P 14.

85	5s. Type **26**	10	10
86	18s. Multiple-hook fishing	20	20
87	23s. Ruvettus fishing	25	25
88	34s. Netting flyingfish	25	30
89	63s. Noose fishing	30	40
90	75s. Bonito fishing	40	45
85/90	*Set of 6*	1·25	1·50

27 Outrigger Canoe

28 Javelin Throwing

(Des R. Conly. Litho Cambec Press, Melbourne)

1983 (4 May). Transport. T **27** and similar horiz designs. Multicoloured. P 13×13½.

91	5s. Type **27**	10	10
92	18s. Wooden whaleboat	10	15
93	23s. Aluminium whaleboat	10	20
94	34s. *Alia* (fishing catamaran)	15	25
95	63s. *Frysna* (freighter)	25	40
96	75s. Grumman MacKinnon G-21C Goose flying boat	30	50
91/6	*Set of 6*	85	1·40

(Des R. Conly. Litho Questa)

1983 (2 Nov). Traditional Pastimes. T **28** and similar horiz designs. Multicoloured. P 14.

97	5s. Type **28**	10	10
98	18s. String game	10	15
99	23s. Fire making	10	20
100	34s. Shell throwing	15	25
101	63s. Hand-ball game	20	40
102	75s. Mass wrestling	25	50
97/102	*Set of 6*	70	1·40

29 Planting and Harvesting

30 Convict Tang ("Manini")

(Des R. Conly. Litho J.W.)

1984 (2 May). Copra Industry. T **29** and similar vert designs. Multicoloured. P 13½×13.

103	48s. Type **29**	30	40
	a. Horiz strip of 5. Nos. 103/7	1·40	1·75
104	48s. Husking and splitting	30	40
105	48s. Drying	30	40
106	48s. Bagging	30	40
107	48s. Shipping	30	40
103/7	*Set of 5*	1·40	1·75

Nos. 103/7 were printed together, *se-tenant*, in horizontal strips of five throughout the sheet.

(Des R. Conly. Litho B.D.T.)

1984 (5 Dec). Fish. T **30** and similar horiz designs. Multicoloured. P 15×14.

108	1s. Type **30**	10	10
109	2s. Flyingfish ("Hahave")	10	10
110	5s. Surge Wrasse ("Uloulo")	15	10
111	9s. Unicornfish ("Ume ihu")	15	10
112	23s. Wrasse ("Lafilafi")	20	20
113	34s. Red Snapper ("Fagamea")	25	25
114	50s. Yellow-finned Tuna ("Kakahi")	35	40
115	75s. Oilfish ("Palu po")	45	50
116	$1 Grey Shark ("Mokoha")	45	55
117	$2 Black Marlin ("Hakula")	70	80
108/17	*Set of 10*	2·50	2·75

Examples of Nos. 108/17 are known postmarked at Nukunonu on 23 November 1984.

The 50s., No. 114, was sold at the "STAMPEX 86" Stamp Exhibition, Adelaide, overprinted "STAMPEX 86 4–10 AUGUST 1986" in three lines. These overprinted stamps were not available from post offices in Tokelau. Used examples come from dealers' stocks subsequently sent to the islands for cancellation.

31 *Ficus tinctoria* ("Mati")

32 Administration Centre, Atafu

(Des R. Conly. Litho Wyatt and Wilson Ltd, Christchurch, N.Z.)

1985 (26 June). Native Trees. T **31** and similar vert designs. Multicoloured. P 13.

118	5c. Type **31**	10	10
119	18c. *Morinda citrifolia* ("Nonu")	10	15
120	32c. Breadfruit Tree ("Ulu")	15	25
121	48c. *Pandanus tectorius* ("Fala")	25	40
122	60c. *Cordia subcordata* ("Kanava")	30	45
123	75c. Coconut Palm ("Niu")	35	55
118/23 *Set of 6*		1·10	1·60

Nos. 118/23 were issued with matt, almost invisible, PVA gum.

(Des R. Conly. Litho Questa)

1985 (4 Dec). Tokelau Architecture (1st series). Public Buildings. T **32** and similar horiz designs. Multicoloured. P 14.

124	5c. Type **32**	10	10
125	18c. Administration Centre, Nukunonu	15	15
126	32c. Administration Centre, Fakaofo	15	25
127	48c. Congregational Church, Atafu	20	40
128	60c. Catholic Church, Nukunonu	25	45
129	75c. Congregational Church, Fakaofo	25	55
124/9 *Set of 6*		1·00	1·60

33 Atafu Hospital

(Des R. Conly. Litho Cambec Press, Melbourne)

1986 (7 May). Tokelau Architecture (2nd series). Hospitals and Schools. T **33** and similar horiz designs. Multicoloured. P 13½.

130	5c. Type **33**	10	15
131	18c. St. Joseph's Church, Nukunonu	15	15
132	32c. Fenuafala Hospital, Fakaofo	15	30
133	48c. Matauala School, Atafu	20	45
134	60c. Matiti School, Nukunonu	25	60
135	75c. Fenuafala School, Fakaofo	25	90
130/5 *Set of 6*		1·00	2·25

34 Coconut Crab

(Des R. Conly. Litho Questa)

1986 (3 Dec). Agricultural Livestock. T **34** and similar horiz designs. Multicoloured. P 14.

136	5c. Type **34**	10	15
137	18c. Pigs	10	15
138	32c. Chickens	20	30
139	48c. Reef Hawksbill Turtle	25	45
140	60c. Goats	30	55
141	75c. Ducks	35	70
136/41 *Set of 6*		1·00	2·10

35 *Scaevola taccada* ("Gahu")

(Des R. Conly. Litho Questa)

1987 (6 May). Tokelau Flora. T **35** and similar horiz designs. Multicoloured. P 14.

142	5c. Type **35**	35	50
143	18c. *Hernandia nymphaeifolia* ("Puka")	50	80
144	32c. *Pandanus tectorius* ("Higano")	65	1·10
145	48c. *Gardenia taitensis* ("Tialetiale")	70	1·40
146	60c. *Pemphis acidula* ("Gagie")	80	1·75
147	75c. *Guettarda speciosa* ("Puapua")	90	1·90
142/7 *Set of 6*		3·50	6·75

36 Javelin-throwing

(Des F. Paulo. Litho Leigh-Mardon Ltd, Melbourne)

1987 (2 Dec). Tokelau Olympic Sports. T **36** and similar horiz designs. Multicoloured. P 14×14½.

148	5c. Type **36**	20	30
149	18c. Shot-putting	30	50
150	32c. Long jumping	40	70
151	48c. Hurdling	50	80
152	60c. Sprinting	55	1·40
153	75c. Wrestling	70	1·60
148/53 *Set of 6*		2·40	4·75

37 Small Boat Flotilla in Sydney Harbour

38 Island Maps and Ministerial Representatives

(Des and litho CPE Australia Ltd, Melbourne)

1988 (30 July). Bicentenary of Australian Settlement and "Sydpex '88" National Stamp Exhibition, Sydney. T **37** and similar square designs. Multicoloured. P 13.

154	50c. Type **37**	2·00	2·25
	a. Horiz strip of 5. Nos. 154/8	9·00	10·00
155	50c. Sailing ships and liners	2·00	2·25
156	50c. Sydney skyline and Opera House	2·00	2·25
157	50c. Sydney Harbour Bridge	2·00	2·25
158	50c. Sydney waterfront	2·00	2·25
154/8 *Set of 5*		9·00	10·00

Nos. 154/8 were printed together, *se-tenant*, in horizontal strips of five throughout the sheet, forming a composite aerial view of the re-enactment of First Fleet's arrival.

(Des F. Paulo. Litho Leigh-Mardon Ltd, Melbourne)

1988 (10 Aug). Political Development. T **38** and similar horiz designs. Multicoloured. P 14½.

159	5c. Type **38** (administration transferred to N.Z. Foreign Affairs Ministry, 1975)	40	60
160	18c. General Fono (island assembly) meeting, 1977	45	55
161	32c. Arms of New Zealand (first visit by New Zealand Prime Minister, 1985)	70	80
162	48c. U.N. logo (first visit by U.N. representative, 1976)	80	1·00
163	60c. Canoe and U.N. logo (first Tokelau delegation to U.N., 1987)	1·00	1·40
164	75c. Secretary and N.Z. flag (first islander appointed as Official Secretary, 1987)	2·25	2·00
159/64 *Set of 6*		5·00	5·75

39 Three Wise Men in Canoe and Star

(Des F. Paulo. Litho Govt Ptg Office, Wellington)

1988 (7 Dec). Christmas. T **39** and similar horiz designs showing Christmas in Tokelau. Multicoloured. P 13½.

165	5c. Type **39**	20	35

166	20c. Tokelau Nativity		25	40
167	40c. Flight to Egypt by canoe		45	70
168	60c. Children's presents		50	80
169	70c. Christ child in Tokelauan basket		60	90
170	$1 Christmas parade		75	1·10
165/70 Set of 6			2·50	3·75

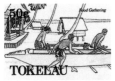

40 Launching Outrigger Canoe   **41** Basketwork

(Des F. Paulo. Litho Leigh-Mardon Ltd, Melbourne)

1989 (28 June). Food Gathering. T **40** and similar horiz designs. Multicoloured. P 14×14½.

171	50c. Type **40**		1·75	2·00
	a. Horiz strip of 3. Nos. 171/3		4·75	5·50
172	50c. Paddling canoe away from shore		1·75	2·00
173	50c. Fishing punt and sailing canoe		1·75	2·00
174	50c. Canoe on beach		1·75	2·00
	a. Horiz strip of 3. Nos. 174/6		4·75	5·50
175	50c. Loading coconuts into canoe		1·75	2·00
176	50c. Tokelauans with produce		1·75	2·00
171/6 Set of 6			9·50	11·00

Nos. 171/3 and 174/6 were each printed together, *se-tenant*, in horizontal strips of three throughout the sheets, forming composite designs.

A $3 miniature sheet commemorating the 150th anniversary of the Penny Black and "Stamp World London 90" International Stamp Exhibition exists, but was not issued or used by the New Zealand Post offices on the islands. Examples were subsequently offered to collectors in January 1994.

(Des F. Paulo. Litho Leigh-Mardon Ltd, Melbourne)

1990 (2 May). Women's Handicrafts. T **41** and similar horiz designs. Multicoloured. P 14½.

177	5c. Type **41**		75	65
178	20c. Preparing cloth		1·25	1·10
179	40c. Tokelau fabrics		1·75	1·50
180	60c. Mat weaving		2·25	2·25
181	80c. Weaving palm fronds		3·00	3·25
182	$1 Basket making		3·25	3·50
177/82 Set of 6			11·00	11·00

42 Man with Adze and Wood Blocks   **43** Swimming

(Des F. Paulo. Litho Wyatt & Wilson, Christchurch)

1990 (1 Aug). Men's Handicrafts. T **42** and similar horiz designs. Multicoloured. P 13.

183	50c. Type **42**		2·00	2·25
	a. Horiz strip of 3. Nos. 183/5		5·50	5·50
184	50c. Making fishing boxes		2·00	2·25
185	50c. Fixing handles to fishing boxes		2·00	2·25
186	50c. Two men decorating fishing boxes		2·00	2·25
	a. Horiz strip of 3. Nos. 186/8		5·50	5·50
187	50c. Canoe building (two men)		2·00	2·25
188	50c. Canoe building (three men)		2·00	2·25
183/8 Set of 6			11·00	12·00

Nos. 183/5 and 186/8 were each printed together, *se-tenant*, in horizontal strips of three throughout the sheets, and have matt, almost invisible, gum.

Under the terms of the Tokelau Post Office Regulations which came into force on 1 March 1991 the responsibility for providing postage stamps for the islands passed from New Zealand Post to the Administrator of Tokelau, based at the Ministry of External Relations, Wellington.

(Des R. Roberts. Litho Southern Colour Print, Dunedin)

1992 (8 July). Olympic Games, Barcelona. T **43** and similar vert designs. Multicoloured. P 13½.

189	40c. Type **43**		60	60
190	60c. Long jumping		80	90
191	$1 Volleyball		1·60	1·75

192	$1.80 Running		2·25	3·25
189/92 Set of 4			4·75	6·00

44 Santa Maria   **45** Queen Elizabeth II in 1953

(Des R. Roberts. Litho Southern Colour Print, Dunedin)

1992 (18 Dec). 500th Anniv of Discovery of America by Columbus. T **44** and similar horiz designs. Multicoloured. P 13½.

193	40c. Type **44**		1·00	1·00
194	60c. Christopher Columbus		1·25	1·40
195	$1.20 Fleet of Columbus		2·75	3·00
196	$1.80 Columbus landing in the New World		3·75	4·00
193/6 Set of 4			8·00	8·50

(Des M. Conly. Litho Southern Colour Print, Dunedin)

1993 (8 July). 40th Anniv of Coronation. T **45** and similar horiz designs. Multicoloured. P 13½.

197	25c. Type **45**		70	80
198	40c. Prince Philip		80	1·00
199	$1 Queen Elizabeth II in 1993		1·25	1·50
200	$2 Queen Elizabeth II and Prince Philip		2·00	2·75
197/200 Set of 4			4·25	5·50

46 Bristle-thighed Curlew

(Des M. Conly. Litho Southern Colour Print, Dunedin)

1993 (15 Dec). Birds of Tokelau. T **46** and similar horiz designs. Multicoloured. P 13½.

201	25c. Type **46**		75	75
202	40c. Red-tailed Tropic Bird		1·10	1·10
203	$1 Reef Heron		1·75	1·75
204	$2 Pacific Golden Plover		2·50	3·25
201/4 Set of 4			5·50	6·25

(Des M. Conly. Litho Southern Colour Print, Dunedin)

1994 (18 Feb). "Hong Kong '94" International Stamp Exhibition. Multicoloured. P 14×14½.

MS205 125×100 mm. As Nos. 201/4 (*sold at $5*) | 5·00 | 6·00

47 Great Egret ("White Heron")

(Des M. Conly. Litho Southern Colour Print, Dunedin)

1994 (16 Aug). "Philakorea '94" International Stamp Exhibition, Seoul. P 12.

206	**47**	$2 multicoloured	2·50	3·25
MS207 110×76 mm. No. 206			4·50	4·50

48 Model Outrigger Canoe   **49** Fishing Pigs

(Des M. Conly. Litho Southern Colour Print, Dunedin)

1994 (19 Dec). Handicrafts. T **48** and similar horiz designs. Multicoloured. P 13½.

208	5c. Type **48**		10	10
209	25c. Plaited fan		20	25
210	40c. Plaited baskets		30	35

211	50c. Fishing box	35	40
212	80c. Water bottle	50	65
213	$1 Fishing hook	60	80
214	$2 Coconut gourds	1·10	1·60
215	$5 Shell necklace	2·75	4·00
208/15	Set of 8	5·50	7·25

(Des M. Conly. Litho Southern Colour Print, Dunedin)

1995 (3 Feb). Chinese New Year (Year of the Pig). Sheet 110×75 mm. P 14×14½.

MS218 **49**	$5 multicoloured	7·00	7·50

1995 (3 Feb). "PostX '95" National Stamp Exhibition, Auckland. No. **MS**218 optd with "PostX '95" emblem on sheet margin in red.

MS219 **49**	$5 multicoloured	12·00	13·00

50 Pacific Pigeon on Branch

51 Long-nosed Butterflyfish

(Des Patricia Altman. Litho Southern Colour Print, Dunedin)

1995 (27 Apr). Endangered Species. Pacific Pigeon. T **50** and similar horiz designs. Multicoloured. P 13½.

220	25c. Type **50**	60	65
221	40c. On branch (different)	85	90
222	$1 On branch with berries	1·40	1·75
223	$2 Chick in nest	2·40	3·25
220/3	Set of 4	4·75	6·00

(Des R. Youmans. Litho Southern Colour Print, Dunedin)

1995 (1 Sept). Reef Fish. T **51** and similar horiz designs. Multicoloured. P 12.

224	25c. Type **51**	35	55
225	40c. Emperor Angelfish	60	75
226	$1 Moorish Idol	1·10	1·60
227	$2 Lined Butterflyfish	1·90	3·00
224/7	Set of 4	3·50	5·50
MS228	130×90 mm. $3 Lionfish (inscr "Red Fire Fish" (39×34 mm)	2·75	4·00

No. **MS**228 includes the "Singapore '95" International Stamp Exhibition logo on the sheet margin.

1995 (1 Sept). "Singapore '95" International Stamp Exhibition. No. **MS**218 optd with exhibition emblem in red on sheet margin.

MS229 **49**	$5 multicoloured	5·50	7·00

52 Danaus plexippus

53 Hawksbill Turtle

(Des Patricia Altman. Litho Southern Colour Print, Dunedin)

1995 (16 Oct). Butterflies and Moths. T **52** and similar vert designs. Multicoloured. P 12.

230	25c. Type **52**	65	65
231	40c. Precis villida samoensis	90	90
232	$1 Hypolimnas bolina	1·75	2·25
233	$2 Euploea lewenii	2·50	3·50
230/3	Set of 4	5·25	6·50

(Des Patricia Altman. Litho Southern Colour Print, Dunedin)

1995 (27 Nov). Year of the Sea Turtle. T **53** and similar horiz designs. Multicoloured. P 12.

234	25c. Type **53**	65	65
235	40c. Leatherback Turtle	90	90
236	$1 Green Turtle	2·00	2·25
237	$2 Loggerhead Turtle	3·00	3·50
234/7	Set of 4	6·00	6·50
MS238	130×90 mm. $3 As $2 (50×40 mm)	4·00	5·50

54 Pacific Rat

(Des Patricia Altman. Litho Southern Colour Print, Dunedin)

1996 (19 Feb). Chinese New Year (Year of the Rat). Sheet 128×97 mm. P 12.

MS239 **54**	$3 multicoloured	4·50	6·00

55 Queen Elizabeth II and Nukunonu

56 Fraser's Dolphin

(Des D. Miller. Litho Enschedé)

1996 (22 Apr). 70th Birthday of Queen Elizabeth II. T **55** and similar vert designs, each incorporating a different photograph of the Queen. Multicoloured. P 13½.

240	40c. Type **55**	50	50
241	$1 Atafu at night	1·40	1·50
242	$1.25 Atafu	1·60	1·75
243	$2 Atafu village	2·00	2·50
240/3	Set of 4	5·00	5·75
MS244	64×66 mm. $3 Queen Elizabeth II	3·25	4·00

1996 (18 May). "CHINA '96" 9th Asian International Stamp Exhibition, Peking. No. **MS**239 optd with exhibition emblem on sheet margin in red.

MS245	128×97 mm. $3 Type **54**	4·00	5·50

(Des R. Youmans. Litho Southern Colour Print, Dunedin)

1996 (15 July). Dolphins. T **56** and similar horiz designs. Multicoloured. P 14.

246	40c. Type **56**	1·00	1·00
247	$1 Common Dolphin	2·00	2·50
248	$1.25 Striped Dolphin	2·00	2·50
249	$2 Spotted Dolphin	3·25	3·50
246/9	Set of 4	7·50	8·50

57 Mole Cowrie

58 Ox

(Des Patricia Altman. Litho Southern Colour Print, Dunedin)

1996 (16 Oct). Sea Shells. T **57** and similar horiz designs. Multicoloured. P 12.

250	40c. Type **57**	60	60
251	$1 Humpback Cowrie	1·25	1·50
252	$1.25 Eyed Cowrie	1·25	1·75
253	$2 Tiger Cowrie	1·75	2·75
250/3	Set of 4	4·25	6·00
MS254	123×83 mm. $3 Humpback Cowrie (different) (50×40 mm)	3·50	4·50

1996 (16 Oct). "TAIPEI '96" Tenth Asian International Stamp Exhibition, Taiwan. No. **MS**239 optd with exhibition emblem on sheet margin in red.

MS255	128×97 mm. $3 Type **54**	3·25	4·00

(Des Patricia Altman. Litho Southern Colour Print, Dunedin)

1997 (12 Feb). Chinese New Year (Year of the Ox). Sheet 120×78 mm. P 15×14½.

MS256 **58**	$2 multicoloured	2·50	3·25

1997 (12 Feb). "HONG KONG '97" International Stamp Exhibition. No. **MS**256 optd with **"HONG KONG '97 STAMP EXHIBITION"** in gold on sheet margin.
MS257 120×78 mm. **58** $2 multicoloured .... 3·00   3·50

1997 (29 May). "Pacific '97" International Stamp Exhibition, San Francisco. No. **MS**256 optd with exhibition emblem in red on sheet margin.
MS258 120×78 mm. **58** $2 multicoloured .... 2·25   3·25

59 Humpback Whale   **60** Church by Lagoon

(Des Patricia Altman. Litho Southern Colour Print, Dunedin)

1997 (10 June). Humpback Whales. T **59** and similar horiz designs. Multicoloured. P 12.
259	40c. Type **59**	50	55
260	$1 Family of Humpback Whales	75	85
261	$1.25 Humpback Whale feeding	1·00	1·50
262	$2 Humpback whale and calf	1·50	2·50
259/62	Set of 4	3·25	4·75
MS263	135×87 mm. $3 Head of Humpback Whale	2·50	3·25

(Des R. Youmans. Litho Southern Colour Print, Dunedin)

1997 (17 Sept). 50th Anniv of South Pacific Commission. T **60** and similar horiz designs showing views of Tokelau. Multicoloured. P 14.
264	40c. Type **60**	45	45
265	$1 Boy looking across lagoon	90	90
266	$1.25 Bungalow on small island	1·25	1·50
267	$2 Tokelau from the air	1·90	2·50
264/7	Set of 4	4·00	5·00

61 Gorgonian Coral and Emperor Angelfish   **62** Tiger

(Des Patricia Altman. Litho Southern Colour Print, Dunedin)

1997 (20 Oct). Pacific Year of the Coral Reef. T **61** and similar horiz designs. Multicoloured. P 13½.
268	$1 Type **61**	1·00	1·25
	a. Horiz strip of 5. Nos. 268/72	4·50	5·50
269	$1 Soft Coral	1·00	1·25
270	$1 Mushroom Coral	1·00	1·25
271	$1 Staghorn Coral	1·00	1·25
272	$1 Staghorn Coral and Moorish Idols	1·00	1·25
268/72	Set of 5	4·50	5·50

Nos. 268/72 were printed together, *se-tenant*, in horizontal strips of five with the backgrounds forming a composite design.

(Des Patricia Altman. Litho Southern Colour Print, Dunedin)

1997 (13 Nov). "Aupex '97" National Stamp Exhibition, Auckland. No. **MS**263 optd **"AUPEX'97 13–16 NOVEMBER NZ NATIONAL STAMP EXHIBITION"** on sheet margin in black. P 12.
MS273 135×87 mm. $3 Head of Humpback Whale .... 2·75   3·50

(Des S. Chan. Litho Southern Colour Print, Dunedin)

1998 (28 Jan). Chinese New Year (Year of the Tiger). Sheet 130×95 mm. P 14×14½.
MS274 **62** $2 multicoloured .... 1·75   2·50

62a Princess Diana   **63** 1948 ½d. Atafu Village Stamp

(Des D. Miller. Litho Questa)

1998 (31 Mar). Diana, Princess of Wales Commemoration. T **62a** and similar vert designs. Multicoloured. P 14½×14.
275	$1 Type **62a**	1·00	1·25

MS276 145×70 mm. $1 Wearing red polka-dot dress; $1 Wearing matching pink hat and jacket; $1 No. 275; $1 In pink and yellow jacket with flowers (*sold at $4+50c. charity premium*) .... 2·00   3·25

(Des Sea Sky Design Studio. Litho Southern Colour Print, Dunedin)

1998 (22 June). 50th Anniv of Tokelau Postage Stamps. Sheet 105×80 mm, containing T **63** and similar horiz designs. Multicoloured. P 14½.
MS277 $1 Type **63**; $1 1948 1d. Nukunono hut stamp; $1 1948 2d. Fakaofo village stamp .... 3·75   4·50

64 *Oryctes rhinoceros*

(Des Patricia Altman. Litho Southern Colour Print, Dunedin)

1998 (23 Aug). Beetles. T **64** and similar horiz designs. Multicoloured. P 14.
278	40c. Type **64**	85	85
279	$1 *Tribolium castaneum*	1·60	1·60
280	$1.25 *Coccinella repanda*	1·75	1·75
281	$2 *Amarygmus hydrophiloides*	2·75	3·25
278/81	Set of 4	6·25	6·75
MS282	125×86 mm. $3 *Coccinella repanda* (*different*)	2·50	3·25

65 *Ipomoea pes-caprae*

(Des Patricia Altman. Litho Southern Colour Print, Dunedin)

1998 (18 Nov). Tropical Flowers. T **65** and similar horiz designs. Multicoloured. P 14.
283	40c. Type **65**	40	50
284	$1 *Ipomoea littoralis*	85	95
285	$1.25 *Scaevola taccada*	1·00	1·40
286	$2 *Thespesia populnea*	1·60	2·25
283/6	Set of 4	3·50	4·50

66 Rabbit

(Des Stan Chan Graphics. Litho Southern Colour Print, Dunedin)

1999 (16 Feb). Chinese New Year (Year of the Rabbit). Sheet 105×70 mm. P 14.
MS287 **66** $3 multicoloured .... 2·25   3·00

67 H.M.S. *Pandora* (frigate)

1999 (19 Mar). "Australia '99" International Stamp Exhibition, Melbourne. Sheet 119×80 mm. P 14.
MS288 **67** $3 multicoloured... 2·75 3·25

1999 (27 Apr). "iBRA '99" International Stamp Exhibition, Nuremberg. No. MS287 optd with the "iBRA" logo on the sheet margin.
MS289 105×70 mm. **66** $3 multicoloured...................... 3·50 4·25

68 Coconut Crab   **69** Lift-off

(Litho Southern Colour Print, Dunedin)

1999 (10 Aug). Pacific Crabs. T **68** and similar horiz designs. Multicoloured. P 14½.
290   40c. Type **68**... 40 40
291        $1 Ghost Crab................................... 85 95
292        $1.25 Land Hermit Crab.................. 1·00 1·40
293        $2 Purple Hermit Crab...................... 1·60 2·25
290/3 *Set of 4*... 3·50 4·50
MS294 127×89 mm. $3 Ghost Crab (*different*) .... 4·00 4·75

(Des N. Shewring. Litho Southern Colour Print, Dunedin)

1999 (31 Aug). 30th Anniv of First Manned Landing on Moon. T **69** and similar vert designs. Multicoloured. P 13½.
295   25c. Type **69**... 40 40
296   50c. Rocket stage separation.............. 60 60
297   75c. Aldrin deploying experiment....... 70 70
298        $1 Planting the flag........................... 85 85
299        $1.25 Separation of command module............. 1·00 1·25
300        $2 Recovery of astronauts .... 1·50 2·00
295/300 *Set of 6*... 4·50 5·25
MS301 90×65 mm. $3 Lunar module, Earth and Jupiter... 3·00 3·50

70 Black-naped Tern Chick and Egg   **71** Dragon

(Des Pat Altman. Litho Southern Colour Print, Dunedin)

1999 (31 Dec). Black-naped Tern. T **70** and similar horiz designs. Multicoloured. P 13½×14.
302   40c. Type **70**... 45 45
303        $1 Black-naped Tern perched on pebbles... 90 90
304        $1.25 Two Black-naped Terns................ 1·10 1·10
305        $2 Two Black-naped Terns in flight......... 1·75 2·00
302/5 *Set of 4*... 3·75 4·00

(Litho Southern Colour Print, Dunedin)

2000 (5 Feb). Chinese New Year (Year of the Dragon). Sheet 105×70 mm. P 14.
MS306 **71** $3 multicoloured..................................... 2·25 3·00

2000 (25 Mar). "Bangkok 2000" World Youth Stamp Exhibition. No. MS306 optd on the margin with **"WORLD YOUTH STAMP EXHIBITION BANGKOK 2000"** in English and Thai. P 14.
MS307 105×70 mm. $3 Type **71** .... 2·25 3·00

72 Nukunonu   **73** Queen Elizabeth the Queen Mother

(Litho Southern Colour Print, Dunedin)

2000 (22 May). "The Stamp Show 2000" International Stamp Exhibition, London. Sheet 105×80 mm. P 14.
MS308 **72** $6 multicoloured..................................... 3·75 5·00

2000 (7 July). "EXPO 2000" World Stamp Exhibition, Anaheim, U.S.A. No. MS301 optd **"WORLD STAMP EXPO 2000 7–16 JULY ANAHEIM–U.S.A."** on sheet margin in silver.
MS309 90×65 mm. $3 Lunar module, Earth and Jupiter .... 3·00 4·00

(Litho Questa)

2000 (4 Aug). Queen Elizabeth the Queen Mother's 100th Birthday. T **73** and similar vert designs. Multicoloured. W w **14**. P 14½.
310   40c. Type **73**... 55 w 35
311        $1.20 Queen Mother waving................. 80 1·00
312        $1.80 Wearing diamond earrings and pearl necklace........................... 1·25 1·75
313        $3 Wearing blue hat and tartan scarf......... 2·00 2·75
310/13 *Set of 4*... 4·25 5·25

74 *Gehyra oceanica*   **75** Snake

(Des Pat Altman. Litho Southern Colour Print, Dunedin)

2001 (1 Feb). Lizards. T **74** and similar horiz designs. Multicoloured. P 14.
314   40c. Type **74**... 80 60
315        $1 *Lepidodactylus lugubris*................. 1·60 1·40
316        $1.25 *Gehyra mutilate* .... 1·75 1·75
317        $2 *Emoia cyanura*............................. 2·75 2·75
314/17 *Set of 4*... 6·25 5·75

(Litho Southern Colour Print, Dunedin)

2001 (1 Feb). Chinese New Year (Year of the Snake). Sheet 105×73 mm. P 14.
MS318 **75** $3 multicoloured..................................... 3·50 4·00

2001 (1 Feb). "Hong Kong 2001" Stamp Exhibition. No. MS318 optd **"HONG KONG 2001"** in English and Chinese on the sheet margin in gold.
MS319 105×73 mm. $3 Type **75** .... 3·50 4·00

76 Yellow and Orange Seahorses   **77** Atafu Island

(Des Patricia Altman. Litho Southern Colour Print, Dunedin)

2001 (23 Aug). Seahorses. T **76** and similar vert designs. Multicoloured. P 14.

320	40c. Type **76**	40	40
321	$1 Baby Seahorses	70	80
322	$1.25 Pink Seahorse	90	1·10
323	$2 Yellow Seahorse	1·40	2·00
320/3 *Set of 4*		3·00	3·75
MS324 104×73 mm. $3 As No. 320		2·25	3·00

(Des W. Paterson and N. Thomson. Litho Southern Colour Print, Dunedin)

2001 (17 Nov). Island Views. T **77** and similar horiz designs. Multicoloured. P 14.

325	40c. Type **77**	70	60
326	$1 Fakaofo	1·25	1·25
327	$2 Sunrise over Nukunonu village	1·90	2·00
328	$2.50 Nukunonu beach	2·00	2·25
325/8 *Set of 4*		5·25	5·50

78 Princess Elizabeth and Lieutenant Philip Mountbatten, 1947

(Des A. Robinson. Litho Questa)

2002 (6 Feb). Golden Jubilee. T **78** and similar designs. W w **14** (sideways). P 14½.

329	40c. agate, claret and gold	55	50
330	$1 multicoloured	75	80
331	$1.25 grey-black, claret and gold	1·00	1·25
332	$2 multicoloured	1·50	1·75
329/32 *Set of 4*		3·50	4·00
MS333 162×95 mm. Nos. 329/32 and $3 multicoloured. P 13½ ($3) or 14½ (others)		5·50	6·50

Designs: Horiz (as Type **78**)—$1 Queen Elizabeth in mauve hat; $1.25, Princess Elizabeth holding Prince Charles, 1948; $2 Queen Elizabeth in Poland, 1996. Vert (38×51 *mm*)—$3 Queen Elizabeth after Annigoni.

Designs as Nos. 329/32 in No. **MS**333 omit the gold frame around each stamp and the "Golden Jubilee 1952–2002" inscription.

79 Horse

(Litho Southern Colour Print, Dunedin)

2002 (12 Feb). Chinese New Year (Year of the Horse). Sheet 105×70 mm. P 14.

MS334 **79** $4 multicoloured	4·00	5·00

2002 (22 Feb). "Stampex 2002" Stamp Exhibition, Hong Kong. No. **MS**334 optd **"STAMPEX 2002 HONG KONG 22–24 FEBRUARY 2002"** in gold on the sheet margin.

MS335 105×70 mm. $4 Type **79**	4·00	5·00

80 Pelagic Thresher Sharks

2002 (2 July). Endangered Species. Pelagic Thresher Shark. T **80** and similar horiz designs showing sharks. Litho. P 14½.

336	40c. multicoloured	50	40
337	$1 multicoloured	90	90
338	$2 multicoloured	1·75	2·00
339	$2.50 multicoloured	1·90	2·50
336/9 *Set of 4*		4·50	5·25

80a Queen Elizabeth   **81** H.M.N.Z.S. *Kaniere* (frigate), 1958–59

(Des A. Robinson. Litho Questa)

2002 (5 Aug). Queen Elizabeth the Queen Mother Commemoration. T **80a** and similar vert designs. W w **14**. P 14½×14.

340	40c. black, gold and purple	50	40
341	$2 multicoloured	2·00	2·25
MS342 145×70 mm. $2.50 black and gold; $4 multicoloured. Wmk sideways		5·00	7·50

Designs:—$2 Queen Mother wearing mauve hat and coat; $2.50, Wearing feathered hat and pearls; $4 Queen Mother smiling.

Designs in No. **MS**342 omit the "1900–2002" inscription and the coloured frame.

(Litho Southern Colour Print, Dunedin)

2002 (19 Dec). Royal New Zealand Navy Ships which have visited Tokelau. T **81** and similar horiz designs. Multicoloured. P 14.

343	40c. Type **81**	1·00	80
344	$1 H.M.N.Z.S. *Endeavour* (supply ship), 1990	1·75	1·75
345	$2 H.M.N.Z.S. *Wellington* (frigate), 1987, 1988, 1990	3·25	3·50
346	$2.50 H.M.N.Z.S. *Monowai* (survey ship), 1979, 1985, 1994	4·00	4·25
343/6 *Set of 4*		9·00	9·25

82 Ram   **82a** Queen Elizabeth II with her Maids of Honour

(Des S. Chan. Litho Southern Colour Print, Dunedin)

2003 (3 Feb). Chinese New Year (Year of the Sheep). Sheet 105×70 mm. P 14.

MS347		**82**
$4 multicoloured	4·25	4·75

(Des A. Robinson. Litho D.L.R.)

2003 (2 June). 50th Anniv of Coronation. T **82a** and similar horiz designs. Multicoloured. W w **14** (sideways). P 14×14½.

348	$2.50 Type **82a**	2·00	3·00
349	$4 Queen and Duke of Edinburgh	3·00	4·25
MS350 95×115 mm. $2.50, As No. 348; $4 As No. 349		5·50	7·50

Nos. 348/9 have scarlet frame; stamps from **MS**350 have no frame and country name in mauve panel.

83 Prince William at Polo Match and at Sighthill Community Education Centre, 2001

84 Shoreline with Palm Trees

(Des A. Robinson. Litho D.L.R.)

2003 (21 June). 21st Birthday of Prince William of Wales. T **83** and similar square designs. Multicoloured. W w **14** (sideways). P 14½.

351	$1.50 Type **83**	2·00	2·50
	a. Horiz pair. Nos. 351/2	4·25	6·00
352	$3 At Tidworth Polo Club, 2002 and at Highgrove, 2000	2·25	3·50

Nos. 351/2 were printed together, *se-tenant*, as horizontal pairs in sheets of ten (2×5) with enlarged illustrated left-hand margins.

2003 (13 Oct). "Bangkok 2003" World Philatelic Exhibition. **MS**347 optd **"BANGKOK 2003"** in English and Thai in gold on the sheet margin.
MS353 105×70 mm. $4 Type **82** .... 3·25 4·00

(Litho Southern Colour Print, Dunedin)

2003 (7 Nov). "Welpex 2003" National Stamp Exhibition, Wellington, New Zealand. Sheet 119×80 mm. P 14.
MS354 **84** $4 multicoloured .... 3·75 4·50

85 Chinese Character and Monkeys

86 Dawn at Atafu

(Litho Southern Colour Print)

2004 (22 Jan). Chinese New Year (Year of the Monkey). Sheet 105×71 mm. P 14.
MS355 **85** $4 bright red, black and gold .... 3·00 3·50

2004 (28 Jan). Hong Kong Stamp Exhibition. No. **MS**355 optd with **"2004 Hong Kong Stamp Expo"** in gold on the margin.
MS356 **85** $4 bright red, black and gold .... 3·00 3·50

(Des W. Paterton and Tracey Winiata. Litho Southern Colour Print, Dunedin)

2004 (30 June). Scenes. T **86** and similar horiz designs. Multicoloured. P 14.

357	40c. Type **86**	1·00	80
358	$1 Fishermen returning to Nukunonu	1·75	1·75
359	$2 Early evening at Fakaofo	3·00	3·50
360	$2.50 Beach scene, Atafu	3·75	4·00
357/60 *Set of 4*		8·50	9·00

NEW ZEALAND PRIME MINISTER'S VISIT AUGUST 2004

(**87**)

2004 (8 Aug). Commemoration of Visit by Prime Minister of New Zealand. No. **MS**354 optd as T **87** in silver with additional rectangular opt on top right of sheet margin.
MS361 **84** $4 multicoloured .... 4·75 6·00

88 Lesser Frigate Bird

(Des Pat Medearis Altman. Litho Southern Colour Print)

2004 (20 Dec). Lesser Frigate Bird. T **88** and similar horiz designs. Multicoloured. P 14.

362	40c. Type **88**	1·00	80
363	$1 Birds in flight	1·75	1·75
364	$2 Two birds in nest	3·25	3·50
365	$2.50 Juvenile bird	4·00	4·25
362/5 *Set of 4*		9·00	9·25

89 Rooster

89a Pope John Paul II

2005 (9 Feb). Chinese New Year (Year of the Rooster). Sheet 115×75 mm. P 14.
MS366 **89** $4 bright vermilion, black and gold .... 7·00 7·50

2005 (21 Apr). Pacific Explorer World Stamp Exhibition. No. **MS**366 optd with Pacific Explorer logo in gold on the margin.
MS367 **89** $4 bright vermilion, black and gold .... 6·00 7·00

(Des A. Robinson. Litho B.D.T.)

2005 (18 Aug). Pope John Paul II Commemoration. T **89a** P 14.

368	**89a**	$1 multicoloured	2·00	2·00

No. 368 was printed in sheetlets of eight stamps with an enlarged, illustrated right margin.

90 H.M.N.Z.S. *Te Kaha* and Launch

(Litho Southern Colour Print, New Zealand)

2005 (15 Dec). H.M.N.Z.S. *Te Kaha* (frigate). T **90** and similar horiz designs. Multicoloured. P 14.

369	40c. Type **90**	1·25	1·00
370	$1 H.M.N.Z.S. *Te Kaha* offshore	2·00	1·75
371	$2 H.M.N.Z.S. *Te Kaha* at sunset	3·50	3·50
372	$2.50 Close up of H.M.N.Z.S. *Te Kaha*	4·25	4·50
369/72 *Set of 4*		10·00	10·00

91 Leaping Dogs and Chinese Characters

(Des O. Bell. Litho Southern Colour Print, New Zealand)

2006 (29 Jan). Chinese New Year (Year of the Dog). Sheet 115×75 mm. P 14.
MS373 **91** vermilion, black and gold .... 6·00 7·00

92 Queen Elizabeth II

(Litho B.D.T.)

2006 (21 Apr). 80th Birthday of Queen Elizabeth II. T **93** and similar horiz designs. Multicoloured. P 14.

374	40c. Type **93**	1·00	85
375	$1 On wedding day	1·75	1·50
376	$2 Wearing tiara	3·25	3·25
377	$2.50 In close-up, wearing hat	3·50	3·75
374/7 *Set of 4*		8·50	8·50
MS378 144×75 mm. $2 As No. 375; $2.50 As No. 376		7·50	7·50

2006 (27 May). Washington 2006 International Stamp Exhibition. Sheet 144×85 mm containing Nos. 325/8. P 14.

MS379 144×85 mm. 40c. Type **77**; $1 Fakaofo; $2 Sunrise over Nukunonu Village; $2.50 Nukunonu beach		10·00	12·00

2006 (2 Nov). Kiwipex National Stamp Exhibition, Christchurch, New Zealand. No. **MS**378 optd "National Stamp Exhibition, Christchurch, New Zealand" in blue foil on the margin.

MS380 144×75 mm. $2 As No. 375 (optd "KIWIPEX"); $2.50 As No. 376 (optd "2006")		6·00	7·00

93 Fishing Pig

2007 (18 Feb). Chinese New Year (Year of the Pig). Sheet 105×70 mm. Litho. P 14.

MS381 **93** $4 multicoloured		6·00	7·00

94 Pacific Golden Plover   **95** Bicolour Angelfish (*Centropyge bicolor*)

(Des Owen Bell. Litho)

2007 (19 Oct). Endangered Species. Pacific Golden Plover (*Pluvialis fulva*). T **94** and similar horiz designs. Multicoloured. Litho. P 14.

382	40c. Type **94**	1·25	1·25
	a. Strip of 4. Nos. 382/5	11·00	11·00
383	$1 Head of plover in breeding plumage	2·25	2·25
384	$2 On ground with wing outstretched (winter plumage)	4·00	4·00
385	$2.50 Pair in winter plumage	4·50	4·50
382/5 *Set of 4*		11·00	11·00

Nos. 382/5 were printed together, *se-tenant*, as horizontal and vertical strips of four stamps in sheetlets of 16, and also in separate sheets of 25.

(Des Owen Bell. Litho Southern Colour Print, New Zealand)

2007 (19 Dec). Marine Life. T **95** and similar horiz designs. Multicoloured. P 14½×14.

386	10c. Type **95**	55	55
	a. Sheetlet. Nos. 386/95	27·00	27·00
387	20c. Staghorn Coral (*Acropora robusta*)	75	75
388	40c. Black-tipped Reef Shark (*Carcharhinus melanopterus*)	1·10	1·10
389	50c. Seastar (*Linckia multiflora*)	1·25	1·25
390	$1 Porcupine Fish (*Diodon hystrix*)	1·75	1·75
391	$1.50 Thorny Seahorse (*Hippocampus histrix*)	2·25	2·25
392	$2 Spotted Eagle Ray (*Aetobatis narinari*)	2·75	2·75
393	$2.50 Small Giant Clam (*Tridacna maxima*)	3·00	3·00
394	$5 Green Turtle (*Chelonia mydas*)	5·50	5·50
395	$10 Slate Pencil Urchin (*Heterocentrotus mammillatus*)	11·00	11·00
386/95 *Set of 10*		27·00	27·00

Nos. 386/95 were printed in separate sheets. They were also printed together, *se-tenant*, in sheetlets of ten.

96 Rat

(Des Stan Chan. Litho Southern Colour Print, New Zealand)

2008 (7 Feb). Chinese New Year (Year of the Rat). Sheet 105×70 mm. P 14.

MS396 **96** $4 multicoloured		6·00	7·00

97 Sir Edmund Hillary

(Litho Southern Colour Print, New Zealand)

2008 (5 Nov). Sir Edmund Hillary Commemoration. T **97** and similar multicoloured designs. P 14.

397	50c. Type **97**	90	1·00
398	$1 Hillary on Mt. Everest (wearing checked shirt)	1·50	1·50
399	$2 Hillary on Mt. Everest (wearing jacket)	2·50	2·75
400	$2.50 As older man	2·75	3·00
397/400 *Set of 4*		7·00	7·50
MS401 110×68 mm. $5 Hillary and Tenzing Norgay on summit of Mt. Everest (*horiz*)		5·50	6·00

98 Houses on Seashore

(Litho Southern Colour Print, New Zealand)

2008 (7 Nov). Scenes of Tokelau. T **98** and similar horiz designs. Multicoloured. P 14 (Nos. 402/5) or 13½×13 (**MS**406).

402	50c. Type **98**	1·50	1·25
403	$1 Small boats off beach with palm trees	2·25	2·00
404	$2 Causeway lined with palm trees	3·75	4·00
405	$2.50 Houses at seashore	4·00	4·50
402/5 *Set of 4*		10·50	10·50
MS406 130×85 mm. $5 Landscape of tropical forest, beach and rocky islets		5·50	6·00

No. **MS**406 also commemorates Tarapex 2008 National Stamp Exhibition, New Plymouth, New Zealand.

99 Ox

2009 (26 Jan). Chinese New Year (Year of the Ox). Sheet 106×70 mm. Litho. P 13½.

MS407 **99** multicoloured		7·50	7·50

100 Chile 1875 One
Peso Coin

101 Tiger

2009 (22 Dec). Coins of the Pacific. T **100** and similar vert designs.
Multicoloured. Litho. P 14.

408	50c. Type **100**	1·00	1·00
409	$1 Great Britain 1911 one sovereign	1·75	1·75
410	$2 New Zealand 1950 half crown	3·25	3·25
411	$2.50 1997 Tokelau ten dollar	3·75	3·75
408/11 *Set of 4*		9·50	9·50
MS412 140×86 mm. Nos. 408/11		9·50	10·00

2010 (12 Feb). Chinese New Year (Year of the Tiger). Sheet
105×70 mm. Litho. P 13½.

MS413 **101** multicoloured		13·00	13·00

2010 (8 May). London 2010 International Stamp Exhibition. No.
MS412 inscr 'London 2010 Stamp Exhibition' in gold on lower left
sheet margin. P 14.

MS414 140×86 mm. Nos. 408/11		8·75	8·75

102 Tokelauan Bible and Atafu
Church

(Litho)

2010 (21 Sept). Tokelauan Bible Translation. T **102** and similar horiz
designs. Multicoloured. P 13½.

415	50c. Type **102**	1·00	1·00
416	$1 Tokelauan Bible and Fakaofo Church	2·00	2·00
417	$2 Tokelauan Bible and Nukunonu Church	3·00	3·00
418	$2.50 Tokelauan Bibles	3·50	3·50
415/18 *Set of 4*		8·50	8·50

103 Rabbits feeding on
Carrots

(Litho)

2011 (3 Feb). Chinese New Year (Year of the Rabbit). Sheet 105×71 mm.
P 13½.

MS419 **103** $5 multicoloured		12·00	12·00

104 Yellow-bellied Sea Snake

(Litho)

2011 (25 Mar). Endangered Species. Yellow-bellied Sea Snake
(*Pelamis platura*). T **104** and similar horiz designs. Multicoloured.
P 13½×13.

420	50c. Type **104**	1·00	1·00
	a. Strip of 4. Nos. 420/3	9·50	9·50
421	$1 Sea Snake on sandy beach	2·00	2·00
422	$2 Sea Snake in sea	3·00	3·00
423	$2.50 Three Sea Snakes in sea	3·50	3·50
420/3 *Set of 4*		9·50	9·50

Nos. 420/3 were printed in ordinary sheets and also *se-tenant* as
horizontal and vertical strips of four in sheetlets of 16.

105 Prince William and Miss
Catherine Middleton

(Litho B.D.T.)

2011 (29 Apr). Royal Wedding. Sheet 118×90 mm. W w **18** (sideways).
P 14½×14.

MS424 **105** $6 multicoloured		10·00	10·00

106 Christmas Tree

(Litho)

2011 (16 Nov). Christmas. T **106** and similar vert designs.
Multicoloured. Phosphorised paper. P 13½.

425	40c. Type **106**	80	80
426	45c. Tree bauble	90	90
427	$1.40 Stocking	2·40	2·40
428	$2 Angel tree decoration	3·00	3·00
425/8 *Set of 4*		6·50	6·50

107 Gathering Coconuts

(Litho)

2012 (11 Apr). Scenic. T **107** and similar horiz designs. Multicoloured.
P 13½.

429	10c. Type **107**	20	20
430	20c. Atoll with palm trees and sandy beach	40	40
431	25c. Small offshore atoll with palm trees and hut	50	50
432	40c. Divers in lagoon	80	80
433	45c. Sailing canoe off coast	90	90
434	50c. Beached canoes and church	1·00	1·00
435	$1 Sandy beach backed by palm trees	2·00	2·00
436	$1.40 Angler and offshore atoll	2·40	2·40
437	$2 Palm forest and sandy beach	3·00	3·00
429/37 *Set of 9*		10·00	10·00

108 Queen Elizabeth II in
Wellington, New Zealand, 1963

(Litho)

2012 (23 May). Diamond Jubilee. T **108** and similar horiz design.
Multicoloured. P 13½.

438	$2 Type **108**	3·00	3·00
439	$3 Official New Zealand Portrait of Queen Elizabeth II, 2012	4·00	4·00
MS440	110×60 mm. Nos. 438/9	7·00	7·00

109 Yellowfin Tuna

(Litho)

2012 (3 Oct). Fish of Tokelau. T **109** and similar horiz designs.
Multicoloured. P 13½.

441	40c. Type **109**	80	80
442	45c. Ruby Snapper	90	90
443	$1.40 Wahoo	2·40	2·40
444	$2 Common Dolphinfish	3·00	3·00
441/4	Set of 4	6·50	6·50
MS445	110×90 mm. Nos. 441/4	7·00	7·00

110 Santa's Sleigh over
Atafu

(Litho New Zealand Post)

2012 (21 Nov). Christmas. T **110** and similar vert designs.
Multicoloured. P 13×13½.

446	45c. Type **110**	90	90
	a. Horiz strip of 3. Nos. 446/8	7·50	7·50
447	$2 Reindeer flying over Nukunonu	3·00	3·00
448	$3 Reindeer flying over Fakaofo	4·00	4·00
446/8	Set of 3	7·50	7·50
MS449	105×62 mm. Nos. 446/8	7·50	7·50

Nos. 446/8 were printed together, se-tenant, as horizontal strips of three
stamps throughout the sheets.

111 Queen Elizabeth II and Duke
of Edinburgh waving from
Buckingham Palace Balcony
after Coronation, 2 June 1953

(Litho New Zealand Post)

2013 (8 May). 60th Anniv of the Coronation. T **111** and similar horiz
design. Multicoloured. P 13½×13.

450	$2 Type **111**	3·00	3·00
451	$3 Coronation portrait of Royal family in Throne Room of Buckingham Palace, 1953	4·00	4·00
MS452	110×60 mm. Nos. 450/1	7·00	7·00

112 Blue Moon Butterfly
(*Hypolimnas bolina pallescens*)
(female)

(Litho New Zealand Post)

2013 (7 Aug). Tokelau Butterflies. T **112** and similar horiz designs.
Multicoloured. P 13½×13.

453	45c. Type **112**	1·00	1·00
454	$1 Blue Moon Butterfly (*Hypolimnas bolina pallescens*) (male)	2·25	2·25
455	$1.40 Common Crow (*Euploea lewinii bourkei*)	2·75	2·75
456	$3 Meadow Argus (*Junonia villida*)	4·25	4·25
453/6	Set of 4	9·25	9·25
MS457	100×85 mm. Nos. 453/6	9·75	9·75

113 Mary and Joseph
on Road to Bethlehem

(Litho New Zealand Post)

2013 (20 Nov). Christmas. T **113** and similar vert designs.
Multicoloured. P 13×13½.

458	45c. Type **113**	90	90
459	$1.40 Nativity	2·40	2·40
460	$2 Shepherds	3·00	3·00
461	$3 Wise Men	4·00	4·00
458/61	Set of 4	9·25	9·25
MS462	135×63 mm. Nos. 458/61	9·75	9·75

114 Taulima (bracelets - made
from processed pandanus leaf)

(Litho New Zealand Post)

2014 (23 Apr). Tokelau Weaving. T **114** and similar horiz designs.
Multicoloured. P 13½.

463	45c. Type **114**	65	65
464	$1.40 Pupu (water holders - made from a coconut shell with wrapping of plaited coconut husk fibres)	2·00	2·00
465	$2 Tapili (decorated fan - made from young coconut leaf and coconut leaf midrib)	2·75	2·75
466	$3 Ato (basket - made from synthetic materials)	4·25	4·25
463/6	Set of 4	8·75	8·75
MS467	191×60 mm. Nos. 463/6	9·50	9·50

115 Vakas

(Litho New Zealand Post)

2014 (18 June). Tokelau Vaka (five man canoe constructed in segments). T **115** and similar vert designs. Multicoloured. P 13½.

468	45c. Type **115**	65	65
469	$1.40 Two men building vaka	2·00	2·00
470	$2 Paddling vaka towards shore	2·75	2·75
471	$3 Two fishermen coming ashore from vaka with catch	4·25	4·25
468/71 *Set of 4*		8·75	8·75
MS472 151×65 mm. Nos. 468/71		9·50	9·50

116 Mālō nī! (Hello)

(Litho New Zealand Post)

2014 (15 Oct). Tokelau Language Week. T **116** and similar horiz designs. Multicoloured. P 13½.

473	45c. Type **116**	65	65
474	$1.40 E ā mai koe? (How are you?)	2·00	2·00
475	$2 Ko ai tō agoa? (What is your name?)	2·75	2·75
476	$3 Tōfā la nī! (Farewell then)	4·25	4·25
473/6 *Set of 4*		8·75	8·75
MS477 Nos. 473/6		9·50	9·50

117 The Shepherds

(Litho New Zealand Post)

2014 (10 Dec). Christmas. T **117** and similar vert designs. Multicoloured. P 13½.

478	45c. Type **117**	65	65
479	$2 Mary, Joseph and Jesus in manger	2·75	2·75
480	$3 Three Wise Men	4·25	4·25
478/80 *Set of 3*		7·00	7·00
MS481 113×54 mm. Nos. 478/80		7·50	7·50

118 Paddling for Atu (Skipjack)

(Litho New Zealand Post)

2015 (7 Apr). Traditional Tokelau Fishing. T **118** and similar horiz designs. Multicoloured. P 13½.

482	45c. Type **118**	65	65
483	$1.40 Netting Manini (Convict Tang)	2·00	2·00
484	$2 Laulaufau (Moorish Idols) trap	2·75	2·75
485	$3 Noosing Pāla (Wahoo)	4·25	4·25
482/5 *Set of 4*		8·75	8·75
MS486 90×70 mm. Nos. 482/5		9·50	9·50

119 Ugauga (*Birgus latro*)

(Litho New Zealand Post)

2015 (3 June). Tokelau Crabs. T **119** and similar horiz designs. Multicoloured. P 13½.

487	45c. Type **119**	65	65
488	$1.40 Tupa (*Cardisoma* sp.)	2·00	2·00
489	$2 Kaviki (*Ocypode* sp.)	2·75	2·75
490	$3 Kamakama (*Grapsus* sp.)	4·25	4·25
487/90 *Set of 4*		8·75	8·75
MS491 170×45 mm. Nos. 487/90		9·50	9·50

120 TAHI TE FALA (ONE PANDANUS TREE)

(Des Hannah Stancliffe-White. Litho New Zealand Post)

2015 (13 Oct). Tokelau Language Week. T **120** and similar vert designs. Multicoloured. P 13½.

492	45c. Type **120**	65	65
	a. Sheetlet. Nos. 492/501	12·50	12·50
493	45c. LUA IA TOLUMA (TWO TACKLE BOXES)	65	65
494	45c. TOLU IA MOTU (THREE ATOLLS)	65	65
495	45c. FA IA OLO (FOUR WICKETS)	65	65
496	45c. LIMA IA TUPA (FIVE CRABS)	65	65
497	$1.40 ONO IA LELEFUA (SIX BUTTERFLIES)	2·00	2·00
498	$1.40 FITU IA IKA (SEVEN FISH)	2·00	2·00
499	$1.40 VALU IA ILI (EIGHT FANS)	2·00	2·00
500	$1.40 IVA IA VAKA (NINE CANOES)	2·00	2·00
501	$1.40 HEFALU IA MATAU (TEN FISHHOOKS)	2·00	2·00
492/501 *Set of 10*		12·50	12·50
MS502 169×59 mm. Nos. 492/6		3·25	3·25
MS503 169×59 mm.Nos. 497/501		10·00	10·00

121 Snowman made from Sand

(Des Jonathan Gray. Litho New Zealand Post)

2015 (25 Nov). Christmas. Kilihimahi. T **121** and similar vert designs. Multicoloured. P 13½.

504	45c. Type **121**	65	65
505	$1.40 Christmas gifts under decorated pandanus tree on beach	2·00	2·00
506	$2 Reindeer making sand angels	2·75	2·75
507	$3 Santa lying on lounger on beach	4·25	4·25
504/7 *Set of 4*		8·75	8·75
MS508 136×56 mm. Nos. 504/7		9·50	9·50

122 Step One

(Des Hannah Stancliffe-White. Litho Southern Colour Print, New Zealand)

2016 (6 Apr). Tokelau Keyhole Gardens – Growing a Sustainable Future. T **122** and similar vert designs. Multicoloured. P 13½.

MS509 210×100 mm. 45c. Type **122** (Tie 120 cm of string between two sticks. Place one stick in the centre of your space and use the other to mark a circle in the ground. Leave a wedge of 60 cm, so you can access the middle); $1 Step Two Create a basket in the centre of your circle using either sticks or cane (at least 130 cm tall). Place the sticks 5-10 cm apart and tie with string. Half fill the basket with soil and straw; $1.40 Step Three Lay stones, bricks or logs around the perimeter to create a wall high enough to keep the soil in. Put a layer of stones and twigs on the bottom of your garden for drainage; $2 Step Four Start filling the garden with the soil and compost. Make sure that the best soil goes on top! Keep piling up the soil until you have a mound that slopes away from the basket; $3 Step Five Let the garden settle for a week before planting your seeds and seedlings. Add water, food waste and compostable material to the basket and watch your produce grow. .... 11·00 11·00

MS510 180×48 mm. 45c. Type **122**; $1 Step Two; $1.40 Step Three; $2 Step Four; $3 Step Five..................... 11·00 11·00

No. **MS**509 has enlarged bottom margins describing the five steps of how to make a keyhole garden. No. **MS**510 contains the same five designs but has smaller margins without the inscriptions.

123 Young Elizabeth with her Mother the Duchess of York

(Des Hannah Stancliffe-White. Litho New Zealand Post)

2016 (4 May). 90th Birthday of Queen Elizabeth II. T **123** and similar vert designs. Multicoloured. P 13½.

511	45c. Type **123**	65	65
512	$1.40 Princess Elizabeth and Duke of Edinburgh with baby Prince Charles, 1948	2·00	2·00
513	$2 Queen Elizabeth and Duke of Edinburgh, 1972	2·75	2·75
514	$3 Queen Elizabeth II, 2010	4·25	4·25
511/14 Set of 4		8·75	8·75

124 MV *Mataliki*

(Des Hannah Stancliffe-White. Litho New Zealand Post)

2016 (3 Aug). Tokelau's New Ferry MV *Mataliki*. T **124** and similar square designs. Multicoloured. P 14½.

515	45c. Type **124**	65	65
516	$1.40 MV *Mataliki* sailing from Apia, Samoa	2·00	2·00
517	$2 MV *Mataliki* in Apia harbour	2·75	2·75
518	$3 Passengers transferring from MV *Mataliki* to Tokelau atoll by barge	4·25	4·25
515/18 Set of 4		8·75	8·75
MS519 154×57 mm. Nos. 515/18		9·50	9·50

125 Popo (Coconut)

(Des Richard Payne. Litho New Zealand Post)

2016 (5 Oct). Tokelau Language Week. T **125** and similar horiz designs. Multicoloured. P 13½.

520	45c. Type **125**	65	65
521	$1.40 Ugauga (Coconut Crab)	2·00	2·00
522	$2 Ika (fish)	2·75	2·75
523	$3 Fuaulu (Breadfruit)	4·25	4·25
520/3 Set of 4		8·75	8·75
MS524 100×88 mm. Nos. 520/3		9·50	9·50

AITUTAKI

The island of Aitutaki, under British protection from 1888, was annexed by New Zealand on 11 June 1901.

NEW ZEALAND DEPENDENCY

Stamps of COOK ISLANDS were used in Aitutaki from 1892 until 1903.

PRICES FOR STAMPS ON COVER TO 1945	
Nos. 1/7	from × 4
Nos. 9/14	from × 3
Nos. 15/29	from × 4
Nos. 30/2	from × 6

Stamps of New Zealand overprinted or surcharged. For illustrations of watermarks and definitive types see New Zealand.

AITUTAKI. **Ava Pene.**
(1) (2) ½d.

Tai Pene. **Rua Pene Ma Te Ava.**
(3) 1d. (4) 2½d.

Toru Pene. **Ono Pene.** **Tai Tiringi.**
(5) 3d. (6) 6d. (7) 1s.

1903 (29 June)–11. T **23**, **27/8**, **31**, **34** and **42** surch with T **1** at top and T **2** to **7** at foot. Thin, hard "Cowan" paper. W **43**.

(a) P 14

1	½d. green (No. 302) (R.)	4·75	6·50
2	1d. carmine (No. 303) (B.)	5·00	5·50
3	2½d. deep blue (No. 320a) (R.) (9.11)	8·00	18·00
	a. "Ava" without stop	£150	£250
1/3 Set of 3		16·00	27·00

(b) P 11

4	2½d. blue (No. 308) (R.)	19·00	12·00
5	3d. yellow-brown (No. 309) (B.)	18·00	15·00
6	6d. rose-red (No. 312a) (B.)	30·00	25·00
7	1s. bright red (No. 315a) (B.)	55·00	90·00
	a. "Tiringi" without stop (R. 7/12)	£650	£950
	b. *Orange-red*	70·00	£100
	ba. "Tiringi" without stop (R. 7/12)	£850	£1100
4/7 Set of 4		£110	£130

Nos. 1/2 and 4/7 were placed on sale in Auckland on 12 June 1903. There were four states of the overprint used for No. 3. On the first the "no stop" variety (No. 3a) occurs on R. 6/8, on the second it appears on R. 1/4, 2/4 and 6/8, on the third on R. 5/8 and 6/8, and on the fourth all stops are present.

AITUTAKI.

Ono Pene.
(8)

1911–16. T **51** and **53** surch with T **1** at top and T **2** or **3** at foot and T **52** surch as T **8**. P 14×15 (½d., 1d.) or 14×14½ (others).

9	½d. green (No. 387) (R.) (9.11)	1·00	8·50
10	1d. carmine (No. 405) (B.) (2.13)	3·00	13·00
11	6d. carmine (No. 392) (B.) (23.5.16)	50·00	£140
12	1s. vermilion (No. 394) (B.) (9.14)	60·00	£150
9/12 Set of 4		£100	£275

1916–17. T **60** (recess) surch as T **8**. W **43**. P 14×13½.

13	6d. carmine (No. 425) (B.) (6.6.16)	9·00	50·00
	a. Perf 14×14½	7·50	27·00
	b. Vert pair. Nos. 13/13a	50·00	£180
14	1s. vermilion (No. 430) (B.) (3.17)	10·00	90·00
	a. Perf 14×14½	12·00	90·00
	ab. "Tai" without dot (R. 8/9, 9/12, 10/12)	£225	£750
	ac. "Tiringi" without dot on second "i" (R. 8/12, 10/7)	£300	£850
	ad. "Tiringi" without dot on third "i" (R. 8/11)	£425	£1100
	b. Vert pair. Nos. 14/14a	£100	£400

1917–18. T **60** (recess) optd **"AITUTAKI"** only, as in T **8**. W **43**. P 14×13½.

15	2½d. blue (No. 419) (R.) (12.18)		2·00	25·00
	a. Perf 14×14½		1·75	16·00
	b. Vert pair. Nos. 15/15a		30·00	£150
16	3d. chocolate (No. 420) (B.) (1.18)		1·75	40·00
	a. Perf 14×14½		1·50	32·00
	b. Vert pair. Nos. 16/16a		30·00	£170
17	6d. carmine (No. 425) (R.) (11.17)		6·00	22·00
	a. Perf 14×14½		4·75	21·00
	b. Vert pair. Nos. 17/17a		40·00	£150
18	1s. vermilion (No. 430) (B.) (11.17)		14·00	48·00
	a. Perf 14×14½		10·00	32·00
	b. Vert pair. Nos. 18/18a		65·00	£225
15/18 *Set of 4*			21·00	£120
15a/18a *Set of 4*			16·00	90·00

1917–20. T **53** and **61** (typo) optd **"AITUTAKI"** only, as in T **8**. W **43**. P 14×15.

19	½d. green (No. 435) (R.) (2.20)		1·00	6·00
20	1d. carmine (No. 405) (R.) (5.20)		4·75	35·00
21	1½d. slate (No. 437) (R.) (11.17)		4·25	30·00
22	1½d. orange-brown (No. 438) (R.) (2.19)		80	7·00
23	3d. chocolate (No. 440) (B.) (6.19)		3·50	21·00
19/23 *Set of 5*			13·00	90·00

(Des and recess Perkins Bacon & Co)

1920 (23 Aug). T **9/14** of Cook Islands, but inscr "AITUTAKI". No wmk. P 14.

24	½d. black and green		3·50	25·00
25	1d. black and dull carmine		3·50	17·00
	a. Double derrick flaw (R. 2/8, 3/6 or 5/2) ..		11·00	
26	1½d. black and sepia		6·00	12·00
27	3d. black and deep blue		2·50	14·00
28	6d. red-brown and slate		5·50	14·00
29	1s. black and purple		9·50	16·00
24/9 *Set of 6*			27·00	90·00

Examples of the 6d. with centre inverted (*price £900, unused*) and the 1s. with frame printed double (*price £225, unused*) come from printer's waste and were not issued.

(Recess Govt Printing Office, Wellington)

1924–27. T **9/10** and **16** of Cook Islands, but inscr "AITUTAKI". W **43** of New Zealand. P 14.

30	½d. black and green (5.27)		2·00	23·00
31	1d. black and deep carmine (10.24)		6·00	12·00
	a. Double derrick flaw (R. 2/8, 3/6 or 5/2) ..		16·00	27·00
32	2½d. black and dull blue (10.27)		7·50	80·00
30/2 *Set of 3*			14·00	£100

Cook Islands stamps superseded those of Aitutaki on 15 March 1932.

COOK ISLANDS

A British Protectorate was declared over this group of 15 islands by the local Vice-Consul on 20 September 1888.

Before the introduction of the Cook Islands Post Office, mail was forwarded via Auckland, New Zealand.

PRICES FOR STAMPS ON COVER TO 1945	
Nos. 1/4	from × 5
Nos. 5/74	from × 4
Nos. 75/145	from × 3

BRITISH PROTECTORATE

1 　　　　**2** Queen　　**3** White Tern or
　　　　　Makea Takau　　　Torea

(Des F. Moss. Typo Govt Printing Office, Wellington)

1892 (19 Apr). No wmk. Toned or white paper. P 12½.

1	**1**	1d. black	35·00	26·00
		a. Imperf between (vert pair)	£10000	
2		1½d. mauve	48·00	38·00
		a. Imperf (pair)	£17000	
3		2½d. blue	48·00	38·00
4		10d. carmine	£140	£130
1/4 *Set of 4*			£225	£200

Nos. 1/4 were printed in sheets of 60 (6×10) from plates constructed from a matrix of six slightly different types.

(Eng A. E. Cousins. Typo Govt Printing Office, Wellington)

1893 (28 July)–**1900**. W **12b** of New Zealand (N Z and Star wide apart) (sideways on T **3**).

(a) P 12×11½

5	**2**	1d. brown	50·00	55·00
6		1d. blue (3.4.94)	13·00	2·00
		a. Perf 12×11½ and 12½ mixed	†	£2250
7		1½d. mauve	18·00	7·00
8		2½d. rose	55·00	23·00
		a. Rose-carmine	65·00	48·00
		ab. Perf 12×11½ and 12½ mixed	£3000	
9		5d. olive-black	23·00	15·00
10		10d. green	85·00	50·00
5/10 *Set of 6*			£200	£130

(b) P 11 (July 1896–1900)

11	**3**	½d. steel blue (1st setting) (11.99)	35·00	48·00
		a. Upper right "d" omitted	£1500	
		b. Second setting	23·00	23·00
		ba. Deep blue (1900)	5·50	15·00
12	**2**	1d. blue	5·00	5·50
13		1d. deep brown/cream (4.99)	30·00	21·00
		a. Wmk sideways	£1600	
		b. Bistre-brown (1900)	30·00	23·00
14		1½d. deep lilac	18·00	7·00
		a. Deep mauve (1900)	12·00	7·00
15	**3**	2d. brown/thin toned (7.98)	18·00	6·50
		a. Deep brown (1900)	15·00	8·50
16	**2**	2½d. pale rose	55·00	38·00
		a. Deep rose (1900)	25·00	14·00
17		5d. olive-black	29·00	19·00
18	**3**	6d. purple/thin toned (7.98)	42·00	40·00
		a. Bright purple (1900)	23·00	27·00
19	**2**	10d. green	18·00	55·00
20	**3**	1s. red/thin toned (7.98)	65·00	75·00
		a. Deep carmine (1900)	48·00	48·00
11ba/20a *Set of 10*			£190	£200

Examples of the 1d., 1½d., 2½d. and 5d. perforated 11 and on laid paper are perforation trials. On the first setting of the ½d. the face values are misplaced in each corner. As corrected in the second setting the face values are correctly positioned in each corner.

ONE
HALF
PENNY
(4)　　　
　　　　　　(5) 

1899 (24 Apr). No. 12 surch with T **4** by Govt Printer, Rarotonga.

21	**2**	½d. on 1d. blue	32·00	48·00
		a. Surch inverted	£850	£900
		b. Surch double	£1000	£900

NEW ZEALAND TERRITORY

On 8 and 9 October 1900 the chiefs of all the main islands, except Aitutaki, ceded their territory to the British Crown. On 11 June 1901 all the islands, including Aitutaki, were transferred by Great Britain to New Zealand control.

1901 (8 Oct). No. 13 optd with T **5** by Govt Printer, Rarotonga.

22	**2**	1d. brown	£180	£140
		a. Crown inverted	£2250	£1700
		c. Optd with crown twice	£1600	£1600

1902. No wmk. P 11.

(a) Medium white Cowan paper (Feb)

23	**3**	½d. blue-green	9·50	9·50
		a. Imperf horiz (vert pair)	£1300	
24	**2**	1d. dull rose	15·00	21·00

(b) Thick white Pirie paper (May)

25	**3**	½d. yellow-green	10·00	4·25
26	**2**	1d. rose-red	19·00	11·00
		a. Rose-lake	18·00	6·50
27		2½d. dull blue	13·00	21·00

NEW ZEALAND WATERMARKS. In W **43** the wmk units are in vertical columns widely spaced and the sheet margins are unwatermarked or wmkd "NEW ZEALAND POSTAGE" in large letters.

In W **98** the wmk units are arranged alternately in horizontal rows closely spaced and are continued into the sheet margins. Stamps with W **98** sideways show the star to the left of NZ, *as seen from the back*. Sideways inverted varieties have the star to the right, *as seen from the back*.

1902 (Sept). W **43** of New Zealand (single-lined NZ and Star, close together; sideways on T **2**). P 11.

28	**3**	½d. yellow-green	4·50	3·25
		a. Grey-green	30·00	70·00
29	**2**	1d. rose-pink	4·00	3·00
30		1½d. deep mauve	4·50	8·50
31	**3**	2d. deep brown	10·00	10·00
		a. No figures of value	£2250	£3500
		b. Perf 11×14	£2500	
32	**2**	2½d. deep blue	3·75	7·00
33		5d. olive-black	35·00	48·00
34	**3**	6d. purple	35·00	28·00

35	**2**	10d. green	50·00	£110
36	**3**	1s. carmine	50·00	80·00
		a. Perf 11×14	£3000	
28/36 *Set of 9*			£170	£275

Stamps in Type **3** were printed from a master plate with the value added by a series of separate duty plates. One sheet of the 2d. missed this second pass through the press and was issued without value.

For Nos. 28/36 Type **3** exists with the watermark in equal quantities either upright or inverted and for Type **2**, on which the watermark is sideways, in equal quantities with the star to the right or left of NZ.

1909–11. W **43** of New Zealand.

37	**3**	½d. green (P 14½×14) (1911)	12·00	8·00
38	**2**	1d. deep red (P 14)	42·00	32·00
		a. Wmk sideways (24.12.09)	14·00	2·50

For Nos. 37/8 the watermark is either upright or inverted. For No. 38a it is sideways, either with star to right or left of NZ.

1913–19. W **43** of New Zealand (sideways on T **3**). Chalk-surfaced paper.

39	**3**	½d. deep green (P 14) (1915)	11·00	15·00
		a. Wmk upright	14·00	24·00
40	**2**	1d. red (P 14) (7.13)	13·00	4·50
41		1d. red (P 14×14½) (1914)	11·00	6·00
42		1½d. deep mauve (P 14) (1915)	90·00	18·00
43		1½d. deep mauve (P 14×15) (1916)	20·00	4·00
44	**3**	2d. deep brown (P 15×14) (1919)	5·00	48·00
45	**2**	10d. green (P 14×15) (1918)	38·00	£110
46	**3**	1s. carmine (P 15×14) (1919)	27·00	£110
39/46 *Set of 6*			£100	£275

RAROTONGA

APA PENE
(**8**)

1919 (Apr–July). Stamps of New Zealand surch as T **8**.

(a) T **53**. W **43**. De La Rue chalk-surfaced paper. P 14×15

47		1d. carmine (No. 405) (B.) (06.19)	1·25	4·75

(b) T **60** (recess). W **43**. Cowan unsurfaced paper. P 14×13½

48		2½d. blue (No. 419) (R.) (06.19)	2·25	6·50
		a. Perf 14×14½	2·00	2·25
		b. Vert pair. Nos. 48/a	20·00	50·00
49		3d. chocolate (No. 420) (B.)	3·25	8·00
		a. Perf 14×14½	3·25	3·75
		b. Vert pair. Nos. 49/a	22·00	60·00
50		4d. bright violet (No. 422) (B.)	2·00	5·50
		a. Re-entry (Pl 20 R. 1/6)	60·00	
		b. Re-entry (Pl 20 R. 4/10)	60·00	
		c. Perf 14×14½	1·75	4·25
		d. Vert pair (Nos. 50 and 50c)	20·00	65·00
51		4½d. deep green (No. 423) (B.)	2·75	7·00
		a. Perf 14×14½	1·75	8·00
		b. Vert pair. Nos. 51/a	20·00	75·00
52		6d. carmine (No. 425) (B.) (06.19)	4·25	8·50
		a. Perf 14×14½	1·75	5·50
		b. Vert pair. Nos. 52/a	38·00	90·00
53		7½d. red-brown (No. 426a) (B.)	1·50	5·50
54		9d. sage-green (No. 429) (R.)	3·75	15·00
		a. Perf 14×14½	2·75	15·00
		b. Vert pair. Nos. 54/a	40·00	£120
55		1s. vermilion (No. 430) (B.) (06.19)	12·00	30·00
		a. Perf 14×14½	2·75	28·00
		b. Vert pair. Nos. 55/a	48·00	£140

(c) T **61** (typo). W **43**. De La Rue chalk-surfaced paper. P 14×15

56		½d. green (No. 435) (R.) (06.19)	40	1·00
57		1½d. orange-brown (No. 438) (R.) (06.19)	50	75
58		2d. yellow (No. 439) (R.)	1·50	1·75
59		3d. chocolate (No. 440) (B.) (07.19)	2·75	13·00
47/59 *Set of 13*			22·00	80·00

Nos. 60 to 69 are vacant.

9 Capt. Cook landing    **10** Wharf at Avarua

11 "Capt. Cook" (Dance)    **12** Palm Tree

13 Huts at Arorangi    **14** Avarua Harbour

R. 2/8   R. 3/6 Double derrick flaws   R. 5/2

(Des, eng and recess Perkins, Bacon & Co)

1920 (23 Aug). No wmk. P 14.

70	**9**	½d. black and green	4·00	28·00
71	**10**	1d. black and carmine-red	4·75	28·00
		a. Double derrick flaw (R. 2/8, 3/6 or 5/2)	13·00	
72	**11**	1½d. black and dull blue	8·50	8·50
73	**12**	3d. black and chocolate	2·25	5·50
74	**13**	6d. brown and yellow-orange	4·50	8·50
75	**14**	1s. black and violet	8·50	17·00
70/5 *Set of 6*			29·00	85·00

Examples of the 1d. and 1s. with centre inverted were not supplied to the Post Office (*Price £850 each, unused*).

RAROTONGA
(**15**)

RAROTONGA
Trimmed overprint (R. 1/6 and R. 3/7)

1921 (Oct)–**23**. Postal Fiscal stamps as Type F **4** of New Zealand optd with T **15**. W **43** (sideways). Chalk-surfaced "De La Rue" paper. P 14½×14.

76		2s. deep blue (No. F111) (R.)	27·00	55·00
		a. Trimmed opt	£120	
		b. Carmine opt (1923)	£200	£225
		ba. Trimmed opt	£600	£650
		c. Optd on "Jones" chalk-surfaced paper	—	£650
77		2s.6d. grey-brown (No. F112) (B.)	19·00	50·00
		a. Trimmed opt	90·00	
78		5s. yellow-green (No. F115) (R.)	27·00	70·00
		a. Trimmed opt	£120	
79		10s. maroon (No. F120) (B.)	85·00	£140
		a. Trimmed opt	£275	
80		£1 rose-carmine (No. F123) (B.)	£140	£250
		a. Trimmed opt	£375	
76/80 *Set of 5*			£275	£500

For details of the "Jones" paper, see below No. 385 of New Zealand. See also Nos. 85/9.

16 Te Po, Rarotongan Chief    **17** Harbour, Rarotonga and Mt. Ikurangi

(2½d. from a print; 4d. des A. H. Messenger. Plates by P.B. Recess Govt Ptg Office, Wellington)

1924–27. W **43** of New Zealand (sideways on 4d.). P 14.

81	**9**	½d. black and green (13.5.26)..................	4·50	8·50
82	**10**	1d. black and deep carmine (10.11.24)...	6·00	2·25
		a. Double derrick flaw (R. 2/8, 3/6 or 5/2).................................	16·00	
		x. Wmk reversed..................................	£200	
83	**16**	2½d. red-brown and steel blue (15.10.27)..................................	11·00	35·00
84	**17**	4d. green and violet (15.10.27)..........	18·00	16·00
81/4	*Set of 4*..................................		35·00	55·00

1926 (Feb–May). As Nos. 76/80, but on thick, opaque white chalk-surfaced "Cowan" paper.

85	2s. blue (No. F131) (C.)............................	£200	£325
	a. Trimmed opt	£600	
86	2s.6d. deep grey-brown (No. F132) (B.)............	95·00	£180
87	5s. yellow-green (No. F135) (R.) (05.26)........	£110	£180
	a. Trimmed opt	£325	
88	10s. brown-red (No. F139) (B.) (05.26)	£140	£250
	a. Trimmed opt	£350	
89	£1 rose-pink (No. F142) (B.) (05.26)	£190	£375
	a. Trimmed opt	£550	
85/9	*Set of 5*..................................	£650	£1200

1926 (Oct)–**28.** T **72** of New Zealand, overprinted with T **15**.

(a) Jones chalk-surfaced paper

90	2s. deep blue (No. 466) (R.)	10·00	40·00
	w. Wmk inverted..................................		

(b) Cowan thick, opaque chalk-surfaced paper

91	2s. light blue (No. 469) (R.) (18.6.27).............	18·00	40·00
92	3s. pale mauve (No. 470) (R.) (30.1.28)..........	16·00	50·00
90/2	*Set of 3*..................................	40·00	£120

TWO PENCE   COOK ISLANDS.
(18)   (19)

1931 (1 Mar). Surch with T **18**. P 14.

(a) No wmk

93	**11**	2d. on 1½d. black and blue (R.)...............	9·50	4·50

*(b) W **43** of New Zealand*

94	**11**	2d. on 1½d. black and blue (R.)...............	4·75	11·00

1931 (12 Nov)–**32.** Postal Fiscal stamps as Type F **6** of New Zealand. W **43**. Thick, opaque, white chalk-surfaced "Cowan" paper. P 14.

*(a) Optd with T **15***

95	2s.6d. deep brown (No. F147) (B.)....................	15·00	22·00
96	5s. green (No. F149) (R.)........................	26·00	55·00
97	10s. carmine-lake (No. F155) (B.)	38·00	£110
98	£1 pink (No. F158) (B.)........................	£120	£190

*(b) Optd with T **19** (3.32)*

98a	£3 green (No. F164) (R.)........................	£500	£900
98b	£5 indigo-blue (No. F168) (R.)........................	£250	£400

The £3 and £5 values were mainly used for fiscal purposes.

20 Capt. Cook landing

21 Capt. Cook

22 Double Maori Canoe

23 Natives working Cargo

24 Port of Avarua

25 R.M.S. *Monowai*

26 King George V

(Des L. C. Mitchell. Recess P.B.)

1932 (15 Mar–2 May). No wmk. P 13.

99	**20**	½d. black and deep green	3·50	16·00
		a. Perf 14	28·00	95·00
100	**21**	1d. black and lake..........................	9·50	4·50
		a. Centre inverted	£8500	£8500
		b. Perf compound of 13 and 14	£225	£275
		c. Perf 14	15·00	32·00
101	**22**	2d. black and brown............................	3·00	8·50
		a. Perf 14	9·00	20·00
102	**23**	2½d. black and deep blue......................	25·00	60·00
		a. Perf 14	19·00	60·00
103	**24**	4d. black and bright blue	32·00	70·00
		a. Perf 14	11·00	55·00
		b. Perf 14×13................................	30·00	£110
		c. Perf compound of 14 and 13	50·00	£120
104	**25**	6d. black and orange.......................	29·00	48·00
		a. Perf 14	4·25	15·00
105	**26**	1s. black and violet (P 14) (2.05)	23·00	23·00
99/105	*Set of 7*..................................		65·00	£160

Nos. 100b and 103c come from sheets reperforated 14 on arrival at Wellington. No. 100b comes from the first vertical column of a sheet and has 14 at left and No. 103c from the third or fourth vertical column with 13 at left or right.

Other major errors exist on this issue, but these are not listed as they originated from printer's waste which appeared on the market in 1935. They include the ½d. in vertical pair, imperforate horizontally (*price £425, unused*), and the ½d. 2d. and 2½d. with centre inverted (*prices ½d. £950, 2d. £500 and 2½d. £300, unused*).

(Recess from P.B. plates at Govt Printing Office, Wellington)

1933–36. W **43** of New Zealand (Single N Z and Star). P 14.

106	**20**	½d. black and deep green	1·25	4·50
		w. Wmk inverted..............................	—	£110
107	**21**	1d. black and scarlet (1935).................	1·50	2·00
		y. Wmk inverted and reversed.............		
108	**22**	2d. black and brown (1936)..................	1·50	50
		w. Wmk inverted..............................		
109	**23**	2½d. black and deep blue......................	1·50	2·25
110	**24**	4d. black and bright blue	1·50	50
111	**25**	6d. black and orange-yellow (1936)........	1·75	2·25
112	**26**	1s. black and violet (1936).................	22·00	40·00
106/12	*Set of 7*..................................		28·00	45·00

SILVER JUBILEE OF KING GEORGE V. 1910 – 1935.
(27)

Normal Letters

B K E N

B K E N

Narrow Letters

1935 (7 May). Silver Jubilee. Optd with T **27** (wider vertical spacing on 6d.). Colours changed. W **43** of New Zealand. P 14.

113	**21**	1d. red-brown and lake	60	1·40
		a. Narrow "K" in "KING".................	2·75	5·50
		b. Narrow "B" in "JUBILEE"..............	18·00	21·00
114	**23**	2½d. dull and deep blue (R.)..................	3·75	3·50
		a. Narrow first "E" in "GEORGE"........	3·75	6·00
115	**25**	6d. green and orange	9·00	6·00
		a. Narrow "N" in KING".................	11·00	20·00
113/15	*Set of 3*..................................		12·00	9·75

1936 (15 July)–**44.** Stamps of New Zealand optd with T **19**. W **43**. P 14.

*(a) T **72**. Cowan thick, opaque chalk-surfaced paper*

116	2s. light blue (No. 469)........................	14·00	45·00
117	3s. pale mauve (No. 470).....................	15·00	70·00

*(b) Type F **6**. Cowan thick, opaque chalk-surfaced paper*

118	2s.6d. deep brown (No. F147).....................	48·00	£110
119	5s. green (No. F149) (R.).....................	50·00	£130
120	10s. carmine-lake (No. F155).................	90·00	£250
121	£1 pink (No. F158)........................	£120	£275
118/21	*Set of 4*..................................	£250	£700

*(c) Type F **6**. Thin, hard, chalk-surfaced Wiggins Teape paper*

122	2s.6d. dull brown (No. F170) (12.40)...............	£180	£160
123	5s. green (No. F172) (R.) (10.40).........	£600	£500
123a	10s. pale carmine-lake (No. F177) (11.44)......	£150	£200
123b	£3 green (No. F183) (R.) (date?)...........	£450	£700
122/3b	*Set of 4*..................................	£1200	£1400

COOK IS'DS.
(28)

IS'DS.

Small second "S"
(R. 1/2 and R. 8/4,
first printing, and
R. 6/10, second
printing)

1937 (1 June). Coronation. Nos. 599/601 of New Zealand (inscr "12th MAY 1937") optd with T **28**.

124		1d. carmine	40	80
	a.	Small second "S"	16·00	18·00
125		2½d. Prussian blue	80	1·40
	a.	Small second "S"	27·00	30·00
126		6d. red-orange	80	60
	a.	Small second "S"	27·00	27·00
124/6	*Set of 3*		1·75	2·50

The "Small second 'S'" was corrected for the third printing.

29 King George VI

30 Native Village

31 Native Canoe

32 Tropical Landscape

(Des J. Berry (2s., 3s., and frame of 1s.). Eng B.W. Recess Govt Ptg. Office, Wellington)

1938 (2 May). W **43** of New Zealand. P 14.

127	**29**	1s. black and violet	9·00	13·00
128	**30**	2s. black and red-brown	22·00	13·00
		w. Wmk inverted		
129	**31**	3s. greenish blue and green	65·00	55·00
127/9	*Set of 3*		85·00	70·00

(Recess B.W.)

1940 (2 Sept). Surch as in T **32**. W **98** of New Zealand. P 13½×14.

130	**32**	3d. on 1½d. black and purple	75	60

Type **32** was not issued without surcharge but archival examples exist (*Price, £250, unused*).

1943–54. Postal Fiscal stamps as Type F **6** of New Zealand optd with T **19**. W **98**. Wiggins Teape chalk-surfaced paper. P 14.

131	2s.6d. dull brown (No. F193) (3.46)	£140	£140
	w. Wmk inverted (2.4.51)	48·00	48·00
132	5s. green (No. F195) (R.) (11.43)	19·00	38·00
	w. Wmk inverted (5.54)	60·00	60·00
133	10s. pale carmine-lake (No. F201) (10.48)	£110	£150
	w. Wmk inverted (10.51)	80·00	£120
134	£1 pink (No. F203) (11.47)	75·00	£130
	w. Wmk inverted (19.5.54)	£140	£180
135	£3 green (No. F208) (R.) (1946?)	£1600	£1700
	w. Wmk inverted (28.5.53)	70·00	£180
136	£5 indigo-blue (No. F211) (R.) (25.10.50)	£375	£500
	w. Wmk inverted (19.5.54)	£325	£425
131w/6w	*Set of 6*	£550	£850

The £3 and £5 were mainly used for fiscal purposes.

(Recess Govt Ptg Office, Wellington)

1944–46. W **98** of New Zealand (sideways on ½d. 1d., 1s., and 2s.). P 14.

137	**20**	½d. black and deep green (11.44)	1·75	4·00
		w. Wmk sideways inverted	6·00	9·50
138	**21**	1d. black and scarlet (3.45)	2·00	2·50
		w. Wmk sideways inverted	9·00	4·00
		x. Wmk sideways reversed		
139	**22**	2d. black and brown (2.46)	4·25	19·00
140	**23**	2½d. black and deep blue (5.45)	1·00	3·75
141	**24**	4d. black and blue (4.44)	6·00	27·00
		y. Wmk inverted and reversed	42·00	80·00
142	**25**	6d. black and orange (6.44)	4·50	4·00
143	**29**	1s. black and violet (9.44)	5·50	4·50
144	**30**	2s. black and red-brown (8.45)	38·00	60·00
145	**31**	3s. greenish blue and green (6.45)	42·00	35·00
		w. Wmk inverted	£130	
137/45	*Set of 9*		95·00	£140

The normal sideways watermark shows the star to the left of NZ *as seen from the back of the stamp.*

COOK ISLANDS
(33)

1946 (4 June). Peace. Nos. 668, 670, 674/5 of New Zealand optd with T **33** (reading up and down at sides on 2d.).

146		1d. green (Parliament House)	30	10
147		2d. purple (Royal family) (B.)	30	50
148		6d. chocolate and vermilion (Coat of arms, foundry and farm)	1·00	1·25
149		8d. black and carmine ("St. George") (B.)	60	1·25
146/9	*Set of 4*		2·00	2·75

34 Ngatangiia Channel, Rarotonga

35 Capt. Cook and map of Hervey Islands

36 Raratonga and Revd. John Williams

37 Aitutaki and palm trees

38 Rarotonga Airfield

39 Penrhyn village

40 Native hut

41 Map and Statue of Capt. Cook

42 Native hut and palms

43 *Matua* (inter-island freighter)

(Des J. Berry. Recess Waterlow)

1949 (1 Aug)–**61**. T **34/43**. W **98** of New Zealand (sideways on shilling values). P 13½×13 (horiz) or 13×13½ (vert).

150	**34**	½d. violet and brown	10	1·50
151	**35**	1d. chestnut and green	3·50	3·75
152	**36**	2d. reddish brown and scarlet	2·00	3·75
153	**37**	3d. green and ultramarine	6·00	2·00
		aw. Wmk inverted	£100	
		b. Wmk sideways (white opaque paper) (22.5.61)	7·00	3·25
154	**38**	5d. emerald-green and violet	7·50	1·50
155	**39**	6d. black and carmine	5·50	2·75
156	**40**	8d. olive-green and orange	70	3·75
		w. Wmk inverted	£150	80·00
157	**41**	1s. light blue and chocolate	4·25	4·50
158	**42**	2s. yellow-brown and carmine	7·50	13·00
		w. Wmk sideways inverted		
159	**43**	3s. light blue and bluish green	21·00	32·00
150/9	*Set of 10*		50·00	60·00

43a Queen
Elizabeth II

(Des J. Berry. Photo Harrison)

1953 (25 May). Coronation. T **43a** and similar vert design. W **98**.
P 14×14½.

160		3d. brown	1·50	85
161		6d. slate-grey	1·50	1·50

Design:—6d. Westminster Abbey.

> **IMPERFORATE STAMPS:** Imperforate examples of many Cook Islands stamps formerly in the Islands' philatelic archives, were put on sale from mid-2013. These include Nos. 160/1 and numerous issues from 1966 onwards. Such material is outside the scope of this catalogue.

1/6

(44)

1960 (1 Apr). No. 154 surch with T **44**.

162	1s.6d. on 5d. emerald-green and violet	75	1·00

45 Tiare Maori   **48** White Tern

52 Queen   **53** Island Scene
Elizabeth II

(Des J. Berry. Recess (1s.6d.), litho (others) B.W.)

1963 (4 June). T **45**, **48**, **52/3** and similar designs. W **98** of New Zealand (sideways). P 13½×13 (1d., 2d., 8d.), 13×13½ (3d., 5d., 6d., 1s.) or 13½ (others).

163		1d. emerald-green and yellow	75	65
164		2d. brown-red and yellow	30	50
165		3d. yellow, yellow-green and reddish violet...	70	65
166		5d. blue and black	8·00	2·25
167		6d. red, yellow and green	1·00	60
168		8d. black and blue	4·25	1·50
169		1s. orange-yellow and yellow-green	1·00	75
170		1s.6d. bluish violet	2·75	2·00
171		2s. bistre-brown and grey-blue	2·75	1·50
172		3s. black and yellow-green	2·00	3·00
173		5s. bistre-brown and blue	20·00	7·50
163/73		*Set* of 11	40·00	18·00

Designs: Vert (as T **45**)—2d. Fishing god; 8d. Long-tailed Tuna. Horiz (as T **48**)—3d. Frangipani; 6d. Hibiscus; 1s. Oranges. (As T **53**)—3s. Administration Centre, Mangaia; 5s. Rarotonga.

56 Eclipse and
Palm

(Des L. C. Mitchell. Litho B.W.)

1965 (31 May). Solar Eclipse Observation, Manuae Island. W **98** of New Zealand. P 13½.

174	**56**	6d. black, yellow and light blue	20	10

The Cook Islands became a self-governing territory in "free association" with New Zealand on 16 September 1965.

NIUE

Niue became a British Protectorate on 20 April 1900 and was transferred to New Zealand control on 11 June 1901. There was considerable local resentment at attempts to incorporate Niue into the Cook Islands and, in consequence, the island was recognised as a separate New Zealand dependency from 1902.

PRICES FOR STAMPS ON COVER TO 1945	
No. 1	*from* × 3
Nos. 2/5	*from* × 8
Nos. 6/7	—
Nos. 8/9	*from* × 30
Nos. 10/12	—
Nos. 13/31	*from* × 3
Nos. 32/7c	—
Nos. 38/47	*from* × 5
Nos. 48/9	—
No. 50	*from* × 15
Nos. 51/4	—
Nos. 55/61	*from* × 8
Nos. 62/8	*from* × 12
Nos. 69/71	*from* × 3
Nos. 72/4	*from* × 10
Nos. 75/8	*from* × 8
Nos. 79/88	—
Nos. 89/97	*from* × 2

NEW ZEALAND DEPENDENCY

Stamps of New Zealand overprinted

NIUE
(1)

1902 (4 Jan). Handstamped with T **1** in green or bluish green. Pirie paper. Wmk double-lined "N Z" and Star, W **38** of New Zealand. P 11.

1	**42**	1d. carmine	£300	£300

A few overprints were made with a *greenish violet* ink. These occurred only in the first vertical row and part of the second row of the first sheet overprinted owing to violet ink having been applied to the pad (*Price* £1500 *un*).

NIUE.
½ PENI.
(2)

NIUE.
TAHA PENI.
(3) 1d.

NIUE.
2½ PENI.
(4)

1902 (4 Apr). Type-set surcharges. T **2**, **3**, and **4**.

(i) Pirie paper. No wmk. P 11

2	**27**	2½d. blue (R.)	1·50	4·00
		a. No stop after "PENI"	28·00	55·00
		b. Surch double	£2500	

*(ii) Basted Mills paper. Wmk double-lined "N Z" and Star, W **38** of New Zealand*

(a) P 14

3	**23**	½d. green (R.)	5·50	7·00
		a. Spaced "U" and "E" (R. 3/3, 3/6, 8/3, 8/6)	23·00	35·00
		b. Surch inverted	£325	£600
		c. Surch double	£1200	

4	**42**	1d. carmine (B.)	50·00	55·00
		a. Spaced "U" and "E" (R. 3/3, 3/6, 8/6) ...	£190	£225
		b. No stop after "PENI" (R. 9/3)	£500	£600
		c. Varieties a. and b. on same stamp		
		(R. 8/3)	£500	£600

(b) P 11×14

5	**42**	1d. carmine (B.)	1·75	3·75
		b. Spaced "U" and "E" (R. 3/3, 3/6, 8/6) ...	14·00	26·00
		c. No stop after "PENI" (R. 9/3)	50·00	70·00
		d. Varieties b. and c. on same stamp		
		(R. 8/3)	50·00	70·00

(c) Mixed perfs

| 6 | **23** | ½d. green (R.) | £1900 | |
| 7 | **42** | 1d. carmine (B.) | £1000 | |

1902 (2 May). Type-set surcharges, T **2**, **3**. Cowan paper. Wmk single-lined "N Z" and Star, W **43** of New Zealand.

(a) P 14

8	**23**	½d. green (R.)	1·25	1·25
		a. Spaced "U" and "E" (R. 3/3, 3/6, 8/3,		
		8/6)	9·00	13·00
9	**42**	1d. carmine (B.)	60	1·00
		a. Surch double	£1800	£2000
		b. Spaced "U" and "E" (R. 3/3, 3/6, 8/6) ...	11·00	20·00
		c. No stop after "PENI" (R. 5/3, 7/3,		
		9/3, 10/3, 10/6)	9·00	17·00
		d. Varieties b. and c. on same stamp		
		(R. 8/3)	42·00	65·00
		e. "I" of "NIUE" omitted (R. 6/5 from		
		end of last ptg)	£1000	

(b) P 14×11

| 10 | **23** | ½d. green (R.) | | |

(c) Mixed perfs

11	**23**	½d. green (R.)	£1800	
12	**42**	1d. carmine (B.)	£200	£250
		a. Spaced "U" and "E" (R. 3/3, 3/6, 8/3,		
		8/6)	£600	
		b. No stop after "PENI" (R. 5/3, 7/3,		
		9/3, 10/3, 10/6)	£550	

NIUE. Tolu e Pene.

(**5**) (**6**) 3d.

Ono e Pene. Taha e Sileni.

(**7**) 6d. (**8**) 1s.

1903 (2 July). Optd with name at top, T **5**, and values at foot, T **6/8**, in blue. W **43** of New Zealand (sideways). P 11.

13	**28**	3d. yellow-brown	9·50	5·00
14	**31**	6d. rose-red	15·00	11·00
15	**34**	1s. brown-red ("Tahae" joined)	£650	
		a. Surch double, one albino	£850	
16		1s. bright red	40·00	48·00
		a. Orange-red	45·00	48·00
13/16 Set of 3			55·00	60·00

NIUE. NIUE.

½ PENI. 2½ PENI. NIUE.

(**9**) (**9a**) (**10**)

1911 (30 Nov). ½d. surch with T **9**, others optd at top as T **5** and values at foot as T **7**, **8**. W **43** of New Zealand. P 14×15 (½d.) or 14×14½ (others).

17	**51**	½d. green (C.)	50	50
18	**52**	6d. carmine (B.)	2·00	7·00
19		1s. vermilion (B.)	6·50	48·00
17/19 Set of 3			8·00	50·00

1915 (Sept). Surch with T **9a**. W **43** of New Zealand. P 14.

| 20 | **27** | 2½d. deep blue (C.) | 26·00 | 55·00 |

1917 (Aug). 1d. surch as T **3**, 3d. optd as T **5** with value as T **6**. W **43** of New Zealand.

21	**53**	1d. carmine (P 14×15) (Br.)	24·00	5·50
		a. No stop after "PENI" (R. 10/16)	£850	
22	**60**	3d. chocolate (P 14×14½) (B.)	50·00	£100
		a. No stop after "Pene" (R. 10/4)	£850	
		b. Perf 14×13½	65·00	£120
		c. Vert pair, Nos. 22/b	£180	

1917–21. Optd with T **10**. W **43** of New Zealand.

(a) P 14×15

23	**61**	½d. green (R.) (2.20)	70	2·50
24	**53**	1d. carmine (B.) (10.17)	10·00	14·00
25	**61**	1½d. slate (R.) (11.17)	1·00	2·25
26		1½d. orange-brown (R.) (2.19)	70	8·50
27		3d. chocolate (B.) (6.19)	1·60	38·00

(b) P 14×13½

28	**60**	2½d. blue (R.) (10.20)	4·50	18·00
		a. Perf 14×14½	1·25	15·00
		ab. Opt double, one albino	£500	
		b. Vert pair, Nos. 28/a	18·00	70·00

29		3d. chocolate (B.) (10.17)	3·25	2·00
		a. Perf 14×14½	1·25	1·75
		b. Vert pair, Nos. 29/a	22·00	50·00
30		6d. carmine (B.) (8.21)	10·00	24·00
		a. Perf 14×14½	4·75	24·00
		b. Vert pair, Nos. 30/a	32·00	£120
31		1s. vermilion (B.) (10.18)	16·00	38·00
		a. Perf 14×14½	5·50	27·00
		b. Vert pair, Nos. 31/a	45·00	£130
23/31a Set of 9			24·00	£120

1918–29. Postal Fiscal stamps as Type F **4** of New Zealand optd with T **10**. W **43** of New Zealand (sideways).

(i) Chalk-surfaced "De La Rue" paper

(a) P 14

| 32 | | 5s. yellow-green (R.) (7.18) | £110 | £120 |

(b) P 14½×14, comb

33		2s. deep blue (R.) (9.18)	16·00	32·00
34		2s.6d. grey-brown (B.) (2.23)	24·00	48·00
35		5s. yellow-green (R.) (10.18)	25·00	55·00
36		10s. maroon (B.) (2.23)	£140	£180
37		£1 rose-carmine (B.) (2.23)	£180	£275
33/7 Set of 5			£350	£550

(ii) Thick, opaque, white chalk-surfaced "Cowan" paper. P 14½×14

37a		5s. yellow-green (R.) (10.29)	27·00	65·00
37b		10s. brown-red (B.) (2.27)	95·00	£160
37c		£1 rose-pink (B.) (2.28)	£160	£275
37a/c Set of 3			£250	£450

11 Landing of Captain Cook

12 Landing of Captain Cook

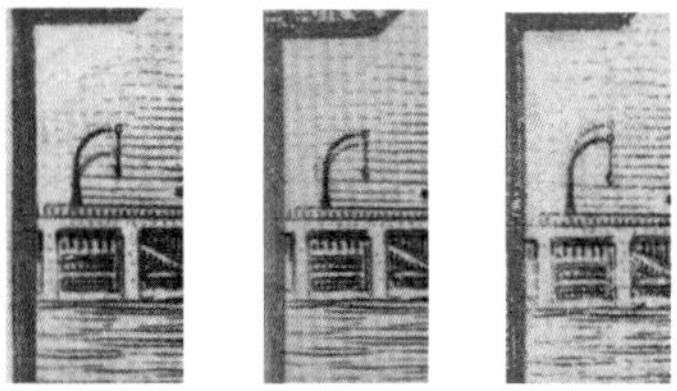

1d. R. 2/8 R. 3/6 R. 5/2

Double derrick flaws

(Des, eng and recess P.B.)

1920 (23 Aug). T **11** and similar designs. No wmk. P 14.

38		½d. black and green	3·75	4·00
39		1d. black and dull carmine	2·00	1·25
		a. Double derrick flaw (R. 2/8, 3/6 or 5/2)	7·00	7·00
40		1½d. black and red	2·75	18·00
41		3d. black and blue	1·75	15·00
42		6d. red-brown and green	5·00	18·00
43		1s. black and sepia	5·00	18·00
38/43 Set of 6			18·00	65·00

Designs: Vert—1d. Wharf at Avarua; 1½d. "Capt Cook (Dance)"; 3d. Palm tree. Horiz—6d. Huts at Arorangi; 1s. Avarua Harbour.

Examples of the 6d. with inverted centre were not supplied to the Post Office (*Price*, £850, *unused*).

1925–27. As Nos. 38/9 and new values. W **43** of New Zealand (sideways on 4d.) P 14.

44		½d. black and green (1927)	2·50	11·00
45		1d. black and deep carmine (1925)	1·75	1·00
		a. Double derrick flaw (R. 2/8, 3/6 or 5/2) ..	5·50	4·75
46		2½d. black and blue (10.27)	4·25	14·00
47		4d. black and violet (10.27)	7·00	20·00
44/7 Set of 4			14·00	42·00

Designs: Vert—2½d. Te Po, Rarotongan chief. Horiz—4d. Harbour, Rarotonga, and Mount Ikurangi.

1927–28. Admiral type of New Zealand optd as T **10**. W **43** of New Zealand. P 14.

(a) "Jones" paper (wmk inverted)

| 48 | **72** | 2s. deep blue (2.27) (R.) | 15·00 | 48·00 |

(b) "Cowan" paper

| 49 | **72** | 2s. light blue (R.) (2.28) | 18·00 | 32·00 |

1931 (1 Apr). No. 40 surch as T **18** of Cook Is.

| 50 | | 2d. on 1½d. black and red | 5·00 | 1·00 |

1931 (12 Nov). Postal Fiscal stamps as Type F **6** of New Zealand optd as T **10**. W **43** of New Zealand. Thick, opaque, chalk-surfaced "Cowan" paper. P. 14.

51	2s.6d. deep brown (B.)	4·00	11·00
52	5s. green (R.)	35·00	70·00
53	10s. carmine-lake (B.)	35·00	£110
54	£1 pink (B.)	75·00	£160
51/4	*Set of 4*	£140	£325

See also Nos. 79/82 for different type of overprint.

(Des L. C. Mitchell. Recess P.B.)

1932 (16 Mar). T **12** and similar designs inscr "NIUE" and "COOK ISLANDS". No wmk. P. 13.

55	½d. black and emerald	14·00	24·00
	a. Perf 13×14×13×13	£250	
56	1d. black and deep lake	1·00	50
57	2d. black and red-brown	7·00	4·00
	a. Perf 14×13×13×13	£140	£180
58	2½d. black and slate-blue	8·00	80·00
59	4d. black and greenish blue	14·00	65·00
	a. Perf 14	16·00	60·00
60	6d. black and orange-vermilion	2·50	2·00
61	1s. black and purple (P. 14)	3·50	5·00
55/61	*Set of 7*	45·00	£160

Designs: Vert—1d. Capt. Cook; 1s. King George V. Horiz—2d. Double Maori canoe; 2½d. Islanders working cargo; 4d. Port of Avarua; 6d. R.M.S. *Monowai*.

Examples of the 2½d. with inverted centre were not supplied to the Post Office. (*Price, £300, unused*).

Nos. 55a and 57a are mixed perforations, each having one side perforated 14 where the original perforation, 13, was inadequate.

(Recess from Perkins Bacon's plates at Govt Ptg Office, Wellington, N.Z.)

1932–36. As Nos. 55/61, but W **43** of New Zealand. P. 14.

62	½d. black and emerald	50	3·50
63	1d. black and deep lake	50	2·25
	w. Wmk inverted	50·00	
64	2d. black and yellow-brown (1.4.36)	50	1·75
	w. Wmk inverted	30·00	50·00
65	2½d. black and slate-blue	50	4·25
	w. Wmk inverted	50·00	
66	4d. black and greenish blue	1·75	4·25
	w. Wmk inverted	£160	
67	6d. black and red-orange (1.4.36)	70	75
68	1s. black and purple (1.4.36)	8·25	25·00
62/8	*Set of 7*	11·50	38·00

Imperforate proofs of No. 65 are known used on registered mail from Niue postmarked 30 August 1945 or 29 October 1945.

See also Nos. 89/97.

SILVER JUBILEE OF KING GEORGE V 1910–1935.	Normal Letters	B K E N
(13)	Narrow Letters	B K E N

1935 (7 May). Silver Jubilee. Designs as Nos. 63, 65 and 67 (colours changed) optd with T **13** (wider vertical spacing on 6d.). W **43** of New Zealand. P. 14.

69	1d. red-brown and lake	60	3·50
	a. Narrow "K" in "KING"	2·75	9·00
	b. Narrow "B" in "JUBILEE"	8·00	20·00
70	2½d. dull and deep blue (R.)	4·25	13·00
	a. Narrow first "E" in "GEORGE"	4·25	13·00
71	6d. green and orange	6·00	10·00
	a. Narrow "N" in "KING"	15·00	35·00
69/71	*Set of 3*	9·75	24·00

Examples of No. 70 imperforate horizontally are from proof sheets not issued through the Post and Telegraph Department (*Price £250 for vert pair*).

NIUE

NIUE (14) Short opt (R. 9/4)

1937 (13 May). Coronation. Nos. 599/601 of New Zealand optd with T **14**.

72	1d. carmine	30	10
	a. Short opt	15·00	
73	2½d. Prussian blue	40	1·50
	a. Short opt	17·00	
74	6d. red-orange	40	20
	a. Short opt	17·00	
72/4	*Set of 3*	1·00	1·60

15 King George VI    **16** Tropical Landscape

1938 (2 May). T **15** and similar designs inscr "NIUE COOK ISLANDS". W **43** of New Zealand. P. 14.

75	1s. black and violet	18·00	8·00
76	2s. black and red-brown	12·00	17·00
	w. Wmk inverted	£200	
77	3s. blue and yellowish green	35·00	17·00
75/7	*Set of 3*	60·00	38·00

Designs: Vert—2s. Island village. Horiz—3s. Cook Islands canoe.

1940 (2 Sept). Unissued stamp surch as in T **16**. W **98** of New Zealand. P. 13½×14.

78	3d. on 1½d. black and purple	75	40

Type **16** was not issued without surcharge but archival examples exist. (*Price, £250, unused*).

NIUE.
(17)

1941–67. Postal Fiscal stamps as Type F **6** of New Zealand with thin opt, T **17**. P. 14.

(i) Thin, hard, chalk-surfaced "Wiggins Teape" paper with vertical mesh (1941–43)

*(a) W **43** of New Zealand*

79	2s.6d. deep brown (B.) (4.41)	£110	£120
80	5s. green (R.) (4.41)	£400	£400
81	10s. pale carmine-lake (B.) (6.42)	£140	£325
82	£1 pink (B.) (2.43?)	£200	£500
79/82	*Set of 4*	£750	£1200

*(b) W **98** of New Zealand (1944–54)*

83	2s.6d. deep brown (B.) (3.45)	4·25	10·00
	w. Wmk inverted (11.51)	23·00	38·00
84	5s. green (R.) (11.44)	14·00	15·00
	w. Wmk inverted (19.5.54)	8·50	23·00
85	10s. carmine-lake (B.) (11.45)	60·00	£130
	w. Wmk inverted	75·00	£140
86	£1 pink (B.) (6.42)	65·00	75·00
83/6	*Set of 4*	£120	£200

*(ii) Unsurfaced "Wiggins Teape" paper with horizontal mesh. W **98** of New Zealand (1957–67)*

87	2s.6d. deep brown (P 14×13½) (1.11.57)	16·00	12·00
88	5s. pale yellowish green (wmk sideways) (6.67)	16·00	75·00

No. 88 came from a late printing made to fill demands from Wellington, but no supplies were sent to Niue. It exists in both line and comb perf.

1944–46. As Nos. 62/7 and 75/7, but W **98** of New Zealand (sideways on ½d., 1d., 1s. and 2s.).

89	**12**	½d. black and emerald	50	5·00
90	–	1d. black and deep lake	50	4·25
91	–	2d. black and red-brown	12·00	14·00
92	–	2½d. black and slate-blue (1946)	60	3·00
93	–	4d. black and greenish blue	4·25	1·00
		y. Wmk inverted and reversed	23·00	
94	–	6d. black and red-orange	2·25	1·40
95	**15**	1s. black and violet	1·50	1·25
96	–	2s. black and red-brown (1945)	8·50	4·00
97	–	3s. blue and yellowish green (1945)	15·00	9·00
89/97		*Set of 9*	40·00	38·00

1946 (4 June). Peace. Nos. 668, 670, 674/5 of New Zealand optd as T **17** without stop (twice, reading up and down on 2d.).

98	1d. green (Blk.)	40	10
99	2d. purple (B.)	40	10
100	6d. chocolate and vermilion (Blk.)	40	80
	a. Opt double, one albino	£550	
101	8d. black and carmine (B.)	50	80
98/101	*Set of 4*	1·50	1·60

Nos. 102/112 are vacant.

18 Map of Niue    **19** H.M.S. *Resolution*

20 Alofi landing

20a Native hut

21 Arch at Hikutavake

21a Alofi Bay

22 Spearing fish

22a Cave, Makefu

23 Bananas

24 Matapa Chasm

(Des J. Berry. Recess B.W.)

1950 (3 July). W **98** of New Zealand (sideways inverted on 1d., 2d., 3d., 4d., 6d. and 1s.). P 13½×14 (horiz) or 14×13½ (vert).

113	**18**	½d. orange and blue	20	1·75
114	**19**	1d. brown and blue-green	2·25	3·00
115	**20**	2d. black and carmine	1·25	3·00
116	**20a**	3d. blue and violet-blue	10	20
117	**21**	4d. olive-green and purple-brown	10	20
118	**21a**	6d. green and brown-orange	1·00	1·25
119	**22**	9d. orange and brown	15	1·40
120	**22a**	1s. purple and black	15	20
121	**23**	2s. brown-orange and dull green	6·00	6·00
122	**24**	3s. blue and black	5·50	5·50
113/22 *Set of 10*			15·00	20·00

1953 (25 May). Coronation. As Nos. 715 and 717 of New Zealand, but inscr "NIUE".

123	3d. brown	65	40
124	6d. slate-grey	95	40

(New Currency. 100 cents = 1 New Zealand dollar)

1c

(25)

26

1967 (10 July). Decimal currency.

*(a) No. 113/22 surch as T **25***

125	½c. on ½d.	10	10
126	1c. on 1d.	1·10	15
127	2c. on 2d.	10	10
128	2½c. on 3d.	10	10
129	3c. on 4d.	10	10
130	5c. on 6d.	10	10
131	8c. on 9d.	10	10
132	10c. on 1s.	10	10
133	20c. on 2s.	35	2·00
134	30c. on 3s.	65	1·50
125/34 *Set of 10*		2·00	3·50

*(b) Arms type of New Zealand without value, surch as in T **26***
W **98** of New Zealand (sideways). P 14

135	**26**	25c. deep yellow-brown	30	55
		a. Rough perf 11	6·00	18·00
136		50c. pale yellowish green	70	80
		a. Rough perf 11	6·00	19·00
137		$1 magenta	45	1·25
		a. Rough perf 11	7·50	13·00

138	$2 light pink	50	2·00
	a. Rough perf 11	8·50	14·00
135/8 *Set of 4*		1·75	4·25
135a/8a *Set of 4*		25·00	55·00

The 25c., $1 and $2 perf 14 exist both line and comb perforated. The 50c. is comb perforated only. The perf 11 stamps resulted from an emergency measure in the course of printing.

1967 (3 Oct). Christmas. As T **278** of New Zealand, but inscr "NIUE". W **98** (sideways) of New Zealand. P 13½×14.

139	2½c. multicoloured	10	10
	w. Wmk sideways inverted	15	30

1969 (1 Oct). Christmas. As T **301** of New Zealand, but inscr "NIUE". W **98** of New Zealand. P 13½×14½.

140	2½c. multicoloured	10	10

27 "Pua"

37 Kalahimu

(Des Mrs. K. W. Billings. Litho Enschedé)

1969 (27 Nov). T **27** and similar vert designs. Multicoloured. P 12½×13½.

141	½c. Type **27**	10	10
142	1c. "Golden Shower"	10	10
143	2c. Flamboyant	10	10
144	2½c. Frangipani	10	10
145	3c. Niue Crocus	10	10
146	5c. Hibiscus	10	10
147	8c. "Passion Fruit"	10	10
148	10c. "Kampui"	10	10
149	20c. Queen Elizabeth II (after Anthony Buckley)	35	1·75
150	30c. Tapeu Orchid	1·10	2·25
141/150 *Set of 10*		1·60	4·00

(Des G. F. Fuller. Photo Enschedé)

1970 (19 Aug). Indigenous Edible Crabs. T **37** and similar horiz designs. Multicoloured. P 13½×12½.

151	3c. Type **37**	10	10
152	5c. Kalavi	10	10
153	30c. Unga	30	25
151/3 *Set of 3*		45	40

1970 (1 Oct). Christmas. As T **314** of New Zealand, but inscr "NIUE".

154	2½c. multicoloured	10	10

38 Outrigger Canoe and Fokker F.27 Friendship Aircraft over Jungle

(Des L. C. Mitchell. Litho B.W.)

1970 (9 Dec). Opening of Niue Airport. T **38** and similar horiz designs. Multicoloured. P 13½.

155	3c. Type **38**	10	20
156	5c. *Tofua II* (cargo liner) and Fokker F.27 Friendship over harbour	15	20
157	8c. Fokker F.27 Friendship over Airport	15	30
155/7 *Set of 3*		35	65

(Des A. G. Mitchell. Litho B.W.)

1971 (23 June). Birds. T **39** and similar horiz designs. Multicoloured. P 13½.

158	5c. Type **39**	15	35
159	10c. Purple-capped Fruit Dove	40	20
160	20c. Blue-crowned Lary	60	20
158/60 *Set of 3*		1·00	70

1971 (6 Oct). Christmas. As T **325** of New Zealand, but inscr "Niue".

161	3c. multicoloured	10	10

40 Niuean Boy   **41** Octopus Lure

(Des L. C. Mitchell. Litho Harrison)

1971 (17 Nov). Niuean Portraits. T **40** and similar vert designs. Multicoloured. P 13×14.

162	4c. Type **40**	10	10
163	6c. Girl with garland	10	20
164	9c. Man	10	40
165	14c. Woman with garland	15	80
162/5 Set of 4		35	1·40

(Des A. G. Mitchell. Litho B.W.)

1972 (3 May). South Pacific Arts Festival, Fiji. T **41** and similar multicoloured designs. P 13½.

166	3c. Type **41**	10	10
167	5c. War weapons	15	15
168	10c. Sika throwing (*horiz*)	20	15
169	25c. Vivi dance (*horiz*)	30	25
166/9 Set of 4		65	55

42 Alofi Wharf

(Des A. G. Mitchell. Litho Questa)

1972 (6 Sept). 25th Anniversary of South Pacific Commission. T **42** and similar horiz designs. Multicoloured. P 14.

170	4c. Type **42**	10	10
171	5c. Medical Services	15	10
172	6c. Schoolchildren	15	10
173	18c. Dairy cattle	25	20
170/3 Set of 4		60	40

1972 (4 Oct). Christmas. As T **332** of New Zealand but inscr "NIUE".

174	3c. multicoloured	10	10

43 Silver Sweeper   **44** "Large Flower Piece" (Jan Brueghel)

(Des G. F. Fuller. Litho Harrison)

1973 (27 June). Fish. T **43** and similar horiz designs. Multicoloured. P 14×13½.

175	8c. Type **43**	25	25
176	10c. Peacock Hind ("Loi")	25	30
177	15c. Yellow-edged Lyretail ("Malau")	30	40
178	20c. Ruby Snapper ("Palu")	30	45
175/8 Set of 4		1·00	1·25

(Des and litho Enschedé)

1973 (21 Nov). Christmas. T **44** and similar vert designs showing flower studies by the artists listed. Multicoloured. P 14×13½.

179	4c. Type **44**	10	10
180	5c. Bollongier	10	10
181	10c. Ruysch	20	20
179/81 Set of 3		30	30

45 Capt. Cook and Bowsprit

(Des A. G. Mitchell. Litho Questa)

1974 (20 June). Bicentenary of Capt. Cook's Visit. T **45** and similar horiz designs each showing Cook's portrait. Multicoloured. P 13½×14.

182	2c. Type **45**	20	20
183	3c. Niue landing place	20	20
184	8c. Map of Niue	20	30
185	20c. Ensign of 1774 and Administration Building	30	65
182/5 Set of 4		80	1·25

Niue became a self-governing territory in "free association" with New Zealand on 19 October 1974.

PENRHYN ISLAND

Stamps of COOK ISLANDS were used on Penrhyn Island from late 1901 until the issue of the surcharged stamps in May 1902.

PRICES FOR STAMPS ON COVER TO 1945	
No. 1	*from × 25*
No. 3	—
Nos. 4/5	*from × 25*
Nos. 6/8	—
Nos. 9/10	*from × 50*
Nos. 11/13	—
Nos. 14/18	*from × 3*
Nos. 19/23	*from × 2*
Nos. 24/37	*from × 3*
Nos. 38/40	*from × 5*

NEW ZEALAND DEPENDENCY The island of Penrhyn, under British protection from 20 September 1888, was annexed by New Zealand on 11 June 1901.

Stamps of New Zealand overprinted or surcharged. For illustrations of New Zealand watermarks and definitive types see New Zealand.

PENRHYN ISLAND.

½ **PENI.**

(1)

PENRHYN ISLAND.

TAI PENI.

(2) 1d.

PENRHYN ISLAND.

2½ **PENI.**

(3)

1902 (5 May). T **23**, **27** and **42** surch with T **1**, **2** and **3**.

	(a) Thick, soft Pirie paper. No wmk. P 11		
1	2½d. blue (No. 260) (R.)	14·00	13·00
	a. "½" and "P" spaced (all stamps in 8th vert row)	30·00	32·00
	(b) Thin, hard Basted Mills paper. W 38 of New Zealand		
	(i) P 11		
3	1d. carmine (No. 286) (Br.)	£850	£1200
	(ii) P 14		
4	½d. green (No. 287) (R.)	1·00	14·00
	a. No stop after "ISLAND" (No. 288) (Br.)	£150	£325
5	1d. carmine (No. 288) (Br.)	3·25	28·00
	(iii) Perf compound of 11 and 14		
6	1d. carmine (No. 290) (Br.)	£1200	£1400
	(iv) Mixed perfs		
7	½d. green (No. 291) (R.)	£2250	
8	1d. carmine (No. 292) (Br.)	£2500	
	(c) Thin, hard Cowan paper. W 43 of New Zealand		
	(i) P 14		
9	½d. green (No. 302) (R.)	4·50	15·00
	a. No stop after "ISLAND" (R. 10/6)	£180	£375
10	1d. carmine (No. 303) (B.)	1·25	9·50
	a. No stop after "ISLAND" (R. 10/6)	60·00	£170
	(ii) Perf compound of 11 and 14		
11	1d. carmine (No. 305) (B.)	£15000	
	(iii) Mixed perfs		
12	½d. green (No. 306) (R.)	£2250	£2500
13	1d. carmine (No. 307) (B.)	£800	£1000

PENRHYN ISLAND. **Toru Pene.**

(**4**) (**5**) 3d.

Ono Pene. **Tahi Silingi.**

(**6**) 6d. (**7**) 1s.

1903 (28 Feb). T **28**, **31** and **34** surch with name at top, T **4**, and values at foot, T **5/7**. Thin, hard "Cowan" paper. W **43** (sideways) of New Zealand. P 11.

14	3d. yellow-brown (No. 309) (B.)	10·00	42·00
15	6d. rose-red (No. 312a) (B.)	15·00	50·00
16	1s. brown-red (No. 315) (B.)	60·00	60·00
	a. Bright red	42·00	42·00
	b. Orange-red	65·00	65·00
14/16a	Set of 3	60·00	£120

1914 (May)–**15**. T **51/2** surch with T **1** (½d.) or optd with T **4** at top and surch with T **6/7** at foot.

19	½d. yellow-green (No. 387) (C.) (5.14)	80	12·00
	a. No stop after "ISLAND"	25·00	£110
	b. No stop after "PENI" (R. 3/17)	£110	£350
	c. Vermilion opt (1.15)	80	8·00
	ca. No stop after "ISLAND"	10·00	75·00
	cb. No stop after "PENI" (R. 3/5, 3/17)	55·00	£190
22	6d. carmine (No. 393) (B.) (8.14)	23·00	75·00
23	1s. vermilion (No. 394) (B.) (8.14)	50·00	£100
19/23	Set of 3	65·00	£160

The "no stop after ISLAND" variety occurs on R. 1/4, 1/10, 1/16, 1/22, 6/4, 6/10, 6/16 and 6/22 of the carmine surcharge, No. 19, and on these positions plus R. 1/12, 1/24, 6/12 and 6/24 for the vermilion, No. 19c.

1917 (Nov)–**20**. Optd as T **4**.

(a) T **60** *(recess). W* **43** *of New Zealand. P* 14×13½

24	2½d. blue (No. 419) (R.) (10.20)	3·00	17·00
	a. Perf 14×14½	2·00	10·00
	ab. No stop after "ISLAND" (R. 10/8)	£190	£500
	b. Vert pair. Nos. 24/24a	45·00	£110
25	3d. chocolate (No. 420) (B.) (6.18)	12·00	70·00
	a. Perf 14×14½	9·50	70·00
	b. Vert pair. Nos. 25/25a	70·00	£275
26	6d. carmine (No. 425) (B.) (1.18)	8·00	26·00
	a. Perf 14×14½	5·00	21·00
	ab. No stop after "ISLAND" (R. 10/8)	£450	£900
	b. Vert pair. Nos. 26/26a	55·00	£160
27	1s. vermilion (No. 430) (B.) (12.17)	15·00	45·00
	a. Perf 14×14½	12·00	35·00
	ab. No stop after "ISLAND" (R. 10/8)	£550	£1000
	b. Vert pair. Nos. 27/27a	£100	£275
24/7	Set of 4	35·00	£140
24a/7a	Set of 4	26·00	£120

(b) T **61** *(typo). W* **43** *of New Zealand. P* 14×15

28	½d. green (No. 435) (R.) (2.20)	1·00	2·00
	a. No stop after "ISLAND" (R. 2/24)	£150	£225
	b. Narrow spacing	7·50	16·00
29	1½d. slate (No. 437) (R.)	6·50	28·00
	a. Narrow spacing	18·00	65·00
30	1½d. orange-brown (No. 438) (R.) (2.19)	60	28·00
	a. Narrow spacing	5·00	65·00
31	3d. chocolate (No. 440) (B.) (6.19)	4·00	45·00
	a. Narrow spacing	17·00	£100
28/31	Set of 4	11·00	90·00

The narrow spacing variety occurs on R. 1/5–8, 4/21–4, 7/5–8 and 9/21–4.

(Recess P.B.)

1920 (23 Aug). As T **9/14** of Cook Islands, but inscr "PENRHYN". No wmk. P 14.

32	½d. black and emerald	1·00	23·00
	a. Part imperf block of 4	£1500	
33	1d. black and deep red	1·50	15·00
	a. Double derrick flaw (R. 2/8, 3/6 or 5/2)	5·50	45·00
34	1½d. black and deep violet	6·50	19·00
35	3d. black and red	2·50	17·00
36	6d. red-brown and sepia	3·25	20·00
37	1s. black and slate-blue	10·00	26·00
32/7	Set of 6	22·00	£110

No. 32a comes from sheets on which two rows were imperforate between horizontally and the second row additionally imperforate vertically.

Examples of the ½d. and 1d. with centre inverted were not supplied to the Post Office (*Price* £1000 *each, unused*).

(Recess Govt Printing Office, Wellington)

1927–29. As T **9/10** and **16** of Cook Islands, but inscr "PENRHYN". W **43**. P 14.

38	½d. black and green (5.29)	5·50	23·00
39	1d. black and deep carmine (14.3.28)	5·50	23·00
	a. Double derrick flaw (R. 2/8, 3/6 or 5/2)	16·00	
40	2½d. red-brown and dull blue (10.27)	18·00	48·00
38/40	Set of 3	26·00	85·00

Cook Islands stamps superseded those of Penrhyn Island on 15 March 1932.

WESTERN SAMOA

PRICES FOR STAMPS ON COVER TO 1945

Nos. 1/20 are very rare used on cover.

Nos. 21/40	*from* × 20
Nos. 41/8	*from* × 100
Nos. 49/51	—
No. 52	*from* × 20
Nos. 53/6	—
Nos. 57/64	*from* × 12
Nos. 65/70	*from* × 3
Nos. 71/97	*from* × 20
Nos. 101/9	*from* × 4
Nos. 110/14	—
Nos. 115/21	*from* × 4
Nos. 122/32	—
Nos. 134/64	*from* × 4
Nos. 165/76	—
Nos. 177/214	*from* × 2

INDEPENDENT KINGDOM OF SAMOA

The first postal service in Samoa was organised by C. L. Griffiths, who had earlier run the *Fiji Times* Express post in Suva. In both instances the principal purpose of the service was the distribution of newspapers of which Griffiths was the proprietor. The first issue of the *Samoa Times* (later the *Samoa Times and South Sea Gazette*) appeared on 6 October 1877 and the newspaper continued in weekly publication until 27 August 1881.

Mail from the *Samoa Express* post to addresses overseas was routed via New South Wales, New Zealand or U.S.A. and received additional franking with stamps of the receiving country on landing.

Cancellations, inscribed "APIA SAMOA", did not arrive until March 1878 so that examples of Nos. 1/9 used before that date were cancelled in manuscript. The *Samoa Express* stamps may also be found cancelled at Fiji, Auckland and Sydney.

1

A 2nd State (Nos. 4/9)

B 3rd State (Nos. 10/19)

(Des H. H. Glover. Litho S. T. Leigh & Co, Sydney, N.S.W.)

1877 (1 Oct)–**80**.

A. 1st state: white line above "X" in "EXPRESS" not broken. P 12½

1	**1**	1d. ultramarine	£375	£275
2		3d. deep scarlet	£450	£250

3		6d. bright violet	£475	£250
		a. Pale lilac	£500	£250

B. 2nd state: white line above "X" usually broken by a spot of colour, and dot between top of "M" and "O" of "SAMOA". P 12½ (1878–79)

4	**1**	1d. ultramarine	£160	£250
5		3d. bright scarlet	£550	£650
6		6d. bright violet	£700	£700
7		1s. dull yellow	£325	£120
		b. Perf 12 (1879)	£100	£275
		c. Orange-yellow	£325	£130
8		2s. red-brown	£375	£600
		a. Chocolate	£400	£600
9		5s. green	£4000	£1300

C. 3rd state: line above "X" repaired, dot merged with upper right serif of "M" (1879)

(a) P 12½

10	**1**	1d. ultramarine	£300	£120
11		3d. vermilion	£450	£200
12		6d. lilac	£550	£140
13		2s. brown	£400	£425
		a. Chocolate	£400	£425
14		5s. green	£2250	£800
		a. Line above "X" not repaired (R. 2/3)	£3250	

(b) P 12

15	**1**	1d. blue	40·00	£700
		a. Deep blue	45·00	
		b. Ultramarine	40·00	£700
16		3d. vermilion	70·00	£750
		a. Carmine-vermilion	70·00	
17		6d. bright violet	65·00	£500
		a. Deep violet	60·00	
18		2s. deep brown	£275	
19		5s. yellow-green	£600	
		a. Deep green	£800	
		b. Line above "X" not repaired (R. 2/3)	£900	

D. 4th state: spot of colour under middle stroke of "M". P 12 (1880)

20	**1**	9d. orange-brown	80·00	£400

Originals exist imperf, but are not known used in this state.

On sheets of the 1d., 1st state, at least eight stamps have a stop after "PENNY". In the 2nd state, three stamps have the stop, and in the 3rd state, only one.

In the 1st state, all the stamps, 1d., 3d. and 6d., were in sheets of 20 (5×4) and also the 1d. in the 3rd state.

All values in the 2nd state, all values except the 1d. in the 3rd state and No. 20 were in sheets of ten (5×2).

As all sheets of all printings of the originals were imperf at the outer edges, the only stamps which can have perforations on all four sides are Nos. 1 to 3*a*, 10 and 15 to 15*b*, all other originals being imperf on one or two sides.

The perf 12 stamps, which gauge 11.8, are generally rather rough but later the machine was repaired and the 1d., 3d. and 6d. are known with clean-cut perforations.

Remainders of the 1d., unissued 2d. rose, 6d. (in sheets of 21 (7×3), 3d., 9d., 5s. (in sheets of 12 (4×3) and of the 1s. and 2s. (sheet format unknown) were found in the Samoan post office when the service closed down in 1881. The remainders are rare in complete sheets.

Reprints of all values, in sheets of 40 (8×5), were made after the originals had been withdrawn from sale. These are practically worthless.

The majority of both reprints and remainders are in the 4th state as the 9d. with the spot of colour under the middle stroke of the "M", but a few stamps (both remainders and reprints) do not show this, while on some it is very faint.

There are six known types of forgery, one of which is rather dangerous, the others being crude.

The last mail despatch organised by the proprietors of the *Samoa Express* took place on 31 August 1881, although one cover is recorded postmarked 24 September 1881.

After the withdrawal of the *Samoa Express* service it would appear that the Apia municipality appointed a postmaster to continue the overseas post. Covers are known franked with U.S.A. or New Zealand stamps in Samoa, or routed via Fiji.

In December 1886 the municipal postmaster, John Davis, was appointed Postmaster of the Kingdom of Samoa by King Malietoa. Overseas mail sent via New Zealand was subsequently accepted without the addition of New Zealand stamps, although letters to the U.S.A. continued to require such franking until August 1891.

2 Palm Trees

3 King Malietoa Laupepa

4b 7 mm   **4c** 4 mm

Description of Watermarks

(These are the same as W **12a/c** of New Zealand)

W **4a**. 6 mm between "N Z" and star; broad irregular star; comparatively wide "N"; "N Z" 11½ mm wide, with horizontal mesh.

W **4b**. 7 mm between "N Z" and star; narrower star; narrow "N"; "N Z" 10 mm wide, with vertical mesh.

W **4c**. 4 mm between "N Z" and star; narrow star; wide "N"; "N Z" 11 mm wide, with vertical mesh.

(Des A. E. Cousins (T **3**). Dies eng W. R. Bock and A. E. Cousins (T **2**) or A. E. Cousins (T **3**). Typo Govt Ptg Office, Wellington)

1886–1900.

*(i) W **4a***

(a) P 12½ (15 Oct–Nov 1886)

21	**2**	½d. purple-brown	35·00	55·00
22		1d. yellow-green	21·00	16·00
23		2d. dull orange	45·00	17·00
24		4d. blue	50·00	13·00
25		1s. rose-carmine	65·00	13·00
		a. Bisected (2½d.) (on cover)*	†	£350
26		2s.6d. reddish lilac	65·00	75·00

(b) P 12×11½ (6 July–Nov 1887)

27	**2**	½d. purple-brown	70·00	85·00
28		1d. yellow-green	£110	35·00
29		2d. yellow	95·00	£140
30		4d. blue	£275	£225
31		6d. brown-lake	50·00	20·00
32		1s. rose-carmine	—	£200
33		2s.6d. reddish lilac	£1500	

*(ii) W **4c**. P 12×11½ (9 May 1890)*

34	**2**	½d. purple-brown	80·00	42·00
35		1d. green	55·00	50·00
36		2d. brown-orange	80·00	50·00
37		4d. blue	£140	5·00
38		6d. brown-lake	£300	11·00
39		1s. rose-carmine	£350	14·00
		x. Wmk reversed	£600	£180
40		2s.6d. reddish lilac	£450	8·50

*(iii) W **4b***

(a) P 12×11½ (9 May 1890–92)

41	**2**	½d. pale purple-brown	7·50	6·50
		a. Blackish purple	8·00	6·50
42		1d. myrtle-green	38·00	2·25
		a. Green	38·00	2·25
		b. Yellow-green	38·00	2·25
43		2d. dull orange	45·00	1·75
		x. Wmk reversed	£190	£190
44	**3**	2½d. rose (22.11.92)	75·00	6·00
		a. Pale rose	75·00	6·00
45	**2**	4d. blue	£225	27·00
46		6d. brown-lake	£110	12·00
47		1s. rose-carmine	£250	6·00
48		2s.6d. slate-lilac	£325	12·00

(b) P 12½ (Mar 1891–92)

49	**2**	½d. purple-brown		
50		1d. green		
51		2d. orange-yellow	—	£1500
52	**3**	2½d. rose (7.1.92)	38·00	4·50
53	**2**	4d. blue	£4500	£1500
54		6d. brown-purple	£4500	£2500
55		1s. rose-carmine	£1200	£1500
56		2s.6d. slate-lilac	£5000	

(c) P 11 (May 1895–1900)

57	**2**	½d. purple-brown	8·00	2·75
		a. Deep purple-brown	5·00	1·75
		b. Blackish purple (1900)	3·75	35·00
58		1d. green	13·00	2·25
		a. Bluish green (1897)	12·00	2·50
		b. Deep green (1900)	4·25	26·00
		w. Wmk inverted	£750	£300
59		2d. pale yellow	45·00	45·00
		a. Orange (1896)	25·00	25·00
		b. Bright yellow (1.97)	18·00	12·00
		c. Pale ochre (10.97)	7·00	12·00
		d. Dull orange (1900)	9·00	

4a 6 mm

60	**3**	2½d. rose	6·50	10·00
		a. *Deep rose-carmine* (1900)	3·00	42·00
61	**2**	4d. blue	18·00	10·00
		a. *Deep blue* (1900)	2·75	50·00
62		6d. brown-lake	19·00	3·00
		a. *Brown-purple* (1900)	1·75	60·00
63		1s. rose	17·00	3·75
		a. *Dull rose-carmine/toned* (5.98)	5·00	38·00
		b. *Carmine* (1900)	1·50	
64		2s.6d. purple	55·00	10·00
		a. *Reddish lilac* (wmk inverted) (1897)	18·00	14·00
		b. *Deep purple/toned* (wmk reversed) (17.5.98)	4·75	9·50
		ba. *Imperf between* (vert pair)	£450	
		c. *Slate-violet*	£120	

*Following a fire on 1 April 1895 which destroyed stocks of all stamps except the 1s. value perf 12½, this was bisected diagonally and used as a 2½d. stamp for overseas letters between 24 April and May 1895, and was cancelled in blue. Fresh supplies of the 2½d. did not arrive until July 1895, although other values were available from 23 May.

Examples of the 1s. rose perforated 11, No. 63, were subsequently bisected and supplied cancelled-to-order by the post office to collectors, often with backdated cancellations. Most of these examples were bisected vertically and all were cancelled in black (*Price £7*).

The dates given relate to the earliest dates of printing in the various watermarks and perforations and not to issue dates.

The perf 11 issues (including those later surcharged or overprinted), are very unevenly perforated owing to the large size of the pins. Evenly perforated copies are extremely hard to find.

For the 2½d. black, see Nos. 81/2 and for the ½d. green and 1d. red-brown, see Nos. 88/9.

(5)   (6)   (7)

1893 (Nov–Dec). Handstamped singly, at Apia.

		(a) In two operations		
65	**5**	5d. on 4d. blue (37)	75·00	50·00
66		5d. on 4d. blue (45)	65·00	£100
67	**6**	5d. on 4d. blue (37)	£100	£110
68		5d. on 4d. blue (45)	80·00	
		(b) In three operations (Dec)		
69	**7**	5d. on 4d. blue (37) (R.)	45·00	38·00
70		5d. on 4d. blue (45) (R.)	50·00	50·00

In Types **5** and **6** the bars obliterating the original value vary in length from 13½ to 16½ mm and can occur with either the thick bar over the thin one or vice versa. Examples can be found with the bars omitted.

Double handstamps exist but we do not list them.

A surcharge as Type **7** but with stop after "d" is now considered to be a trial. It exists in black and in red. Where the "d" was applied separately its position in relation to the "5" naturally varies.

Surcharged

1½d.   **R 3d.**

(8)   (9)   (10)

The "R" in Type **10** indicates use for registration fee.

(Des and die eng A. E. Cousins. Typo New Zealand Govt Ptg Office)

1894 (26 Feb)–**1900.** W **4b** (sideways).

		(a) P 11½×12		
71	**8**	5d. dull vermilion	35·00	3·50
		a. *Dull red*	35·00	3·75
		ab. Mixed perfs 11½×12 and 12½		
		(b) P 11		
72	**8**	5d. dull red (1895)	48·00	14·00
		a. *Deep red* (1900)	6·00	23·00

No. 72 (like Nos. 71/*a*) shows wmk sideways to left (*as seen from the back of the stamp*), whereas No. 72*a* shows wmk sideways to right.

1895–1900. W **4b.**

		(i) Handstamped with T 9 or 10		
		(a) P 12×11½ (28.1.95)		
73	**2**	1½d. on 2d. dull orange (B.)	26·00	17·00
74		3d. on 2d. dull orange	55·00	22·00
		(b) P 11 (6.95)		
75	**2**	1½d. on 2d. orange (B.)	7·50	7·50
		a. *Pair, one without handstamp*	£650	
		b. *Dull yellow*	9·00	7·50
76		3d. on 2d. orange	9·50	14·00
		a. *Dull yellow*	11·00	14·00
		(ii) Handstamped as T 9 or 10. P 11 (1896)		
78	**2**	1½d. on 2d. orange-yellow (B.)	4·25	28·00

79		3d. on 2d. orange-yellow	5·50	50·00
		a. *Imperf between* (vert pair)	£700	
		b. *Pair, one without handstamp*		
		(iv) Surch typo as T 10. P 11 (7 Feb 1900)		
80	**2**	3d. on 2d. deep red-orange (G.)	2·00	£130

In No. 78 the "2" has a serif and the handstamp is in pale greenish blue instead of deep blue. In No. 79 the "R" is slightly narrower. In both instances the stamp is in a different shade.

A special printing in a distinctly different colour was made for No. 80 and the surcharge is in green.

Most of the handstamps exist double.

1896 (Aug). Printed in the wrong colour. W **4b.**

		(a) P 10×11		
81	**3**	2½d. black	3·00	3·50
		(b) P 11		
82	**3**	2½d. black	80·00	70·00
		a. *Mixed perfs 10 and 11*	£425	

Surcharged

2½d.   **PROVISIONAL GOVT.**

(11)   (12)

1898–99. W **4b.** P **11.**

		(a) Handstamped as T 11 (10.98)		
83	**2**	2½d. on 1s. dull rose-carmine/*toned*	50·00	50·00
		(b) Surch as T 11 (1899)		
84	**2**	2½d. on 1d. bluish green (R.)	75	3·00
		a. *Surch inverted*	£850	£425
85		2½d. on 1s. rose-carmine/*toned* (R.)	8·50	16·00
		a. *Surch double*	£400	
86		2½d. on 1s. dull rose-carmine/*toned* (Blk.)	13·00	13·00
		a. *Surch double*	£500	
87		2½d. on 2s.6d. deep purple/*toned* (wmk reversed)	13·00	24·00

The typographed surcharge was applied in a setting of nine, giving seven types differing in the angle and length of the fractional line, the type of stop, etc.

1899 (18 July). Colours changed. W **4b.** P **11.**

88		½d. dull blue-green	3·50	5·50
		a. *Deep green*	3·50	5·50
89		1d. deep red-brown	4·50	5·00

1899 (20 Sept)–**1900.** Provisional Government. New printings optd with T **12** (longer words and shorter letters on 5d.). W **4b.** P **11.**

90	**2**	½d. dull blue-green (R.)	3·75	5·00
		a. *Yellowish green* (1900)	4·75	10·00
91		1d. chestnut (B.)	4·50	17·00
92		2d. dull orange (R.)	2·50	12·00
		a. *Orange-yellow* (1900)	4·50	14·00
93		4d. deep dull blue (R.)	70	16·00
94	**8**	5d. dull vermilion (B.)	3·75	15·00
		a. *Red* (1900)	5·00	15·00
95	**2**	6d. brown-lake (B.)	1·50	14·00
96		1s. rose-carmine (B.)	1·50	48·00
97		2s.6d. reddish purple (R.)	4·75	30·00
90/7		Set of 8	21·00	£150

The Samoan group of islands was partitioned on 1 March 1900: Western Samoa (Upolu, Savaii, Apolima and Manono) to Germany and Eastern Samoa (Tutuila, the Manu'a Is and Rose Is) to the United States. German issues of 1900–14 will be found listed in Part 7 (*Germany*) of this catalogue, there were no U.S. issues.

The Samoan Kingdom post office run by John Davis was suspended in March 1900.

GERMAN PROTECTORATE

A German postal agency opened at Apia on 21 September 1886. Unoverprinted German stamps were used from this date; prices given below are for the most common type of quoted postmark found on each stamp with a cancellation before May 1900. Less common types and other Apia cancellations are worth more; cancellations from May 1900 are worth about 25% less than those before this date.

1886–99. Stamps of Germany cancelled with circular post-mark "APIA / KAISERL DEUTSCHE / POSTAGENTUR" or other Apia postmarks.

		(a) Nos. 38b/e (Numeral inscr "DEUTSCHE REICHS-POST")		
ZG1	**7**	2m. dull rose (4.1.89)		£12000
		a. *Mauve* (25.2.90)		£1700
		b. *Deep claret* (9.11.92)		£350
		c. *Red-lilac* (10.8.99)		£1700
		(b) Nos. 39/44 (Numeral or Eagle inscr "DEUTSCHE REICHS-POST")		
ZG2	**5**	3pf. green (1890)		£1400
ZG3		5pf. mauve (19.12.87)		£500
ZG4	**6**	10pf. carmine (14.12.86)		£250
ZG5		20pf. pale blue (17.10.86)		£225
		a. *Bright blue* (1889)		£250

ZG6		25pf. deep chestnut (1890)		—
ZG7		50pf. pale grey-olive (1886)		£160
		a. Dull olive-green (1888)		£120
		b. Bronze green (1889)		£225

(c) Nos. 46/51 (Numeral or Eagle inscr "REICHSPOST")

ZG8	**8**	3pf. brown (28.4.92)		£200
		a. Grey-brown (1892)		85·00
		b. Orange-brown (1899)		90·00
		c. Bistre-brown (1899)		90·00
ZG9		5pf. green (26.3.90)		£140
		a. Yellow-green (1891)		£140
ZG10	**9**	10pf. rose (29.3.90)		70·00
		a. Carmine (1894)		41·00
ZG11		20pf. ultramarine (24.6.90)		90·00
		a. Dull blue (1891)		70·00
ZG12		25pf. orange-yellow (14.9.92)		£650
		a. Orange (1894)		£450
ZG13		50pf. lake-brown (28.1.90)		£700
		a. Chocolate (1891)		75·00

Dates are those of earliest known use.

Nos. ZG5 and ZG7 with postmark "APIA / DEUTSCHE / POSTDAMPFSCHIFFS- / AGENTUR" are priced the same as above; this postmark on other stamps is worth more than quoted prices.

The 2m. and Nos. ZG8/13 were valid for postage until 30 September 1901.

(G **1**)

1900 (Apr). Stamps of Germany, 1889, optd with Type G **1**.

G1	**8**	3pf. grey-brown	12·50	17·00
G2		5pf. green	16·00	23·00
G3	**9**	10pf. carmine	12·50	23·00
G4		20pf. ultramarine	25·00	39·00
G5		25pf. orange	50·00	£100
G6		50pf. chocolate	50·00	£100
G1/6 *Set of 6*			£150	£275

A	B

"YACHT" KEY TYPES. Types A and B, representing the ex-Kaiser's yacht *Hohenzollern*, were in use throughout the German colonies, inscribed with the name of the particular colony for which they were issued.

Type A was printed by typography and Type B was recess-printed, both by Imperial Printing Office, Berlin.

Wmk Lozenges

Watermark. Some values listed on paper watermarked Lozenges were prepared for use and sold in Berlin, but owing to the war of 1914–18 were not issued in the colonies.

1900 (10 Dec)–**01**. No wmk.

G7	A	3pf. brown	1·40	1·50
G8		5pf. green	1·40	1·50
G9		10pf. carmine	1·40	1·50
G10		20pf. ultramarine	1·40	3·00
G11		25pf. black and red/*yellow*	1·50	16·00
G12		30pf. black and orange/*buff*	1·80	14·00
G13		40pf. black and carmine	1·80	16·00
G14		50pf. black and purple/*buff*	1·80	17·00
G15		80pf. black and carmine/*rose*	3·75	40·00
G16	B	1m. carmine (*a*) (1.01)	4·50	80·00
G17		2m. blue (*a*) (1.01)	6·25	£140
G18		3m. violet-black (*a*) (1.01)	10·50	£200
G19		5m. carmine and black (II) (*a*) (1.01)	£225	£700
G7/19 *Set of 13*			£225	£1100

The 2pf. grey in Type A is a proof.

1915–19. Wmk Lozenges.

G20	A	3pf. brown (1919)		1·40
G21		5pf. green (1919)		1·70
G22		10pf. carmine (1919)		1·70
G23	B	5m. carmine and black (II) (26×17 holes)		60·00
		a. 25×17 holes (1919)		40·00

Nos. G20/3a were only on sale in Berlin.

NEW ZEALAND OCCUPATION

The German Islands of Samoa surrendered to the New Zealand Expeditionary Force on 30 August 1914 and were administered by New Zealand until 1962.

G.R.I. G.R.I.

1 d. 1 Shillings.

(**13**) (**14**)

SETTINGS. Nos. 101/9 were surcharged by a vertical setting of ten, repeated ten times across the sheet. Nos. 110/14 were from a horizontal setting of four repeated five times in the sheet.

Nos. 101b, 102a and 104a occurred on position 6. The error was corrected during the printing of No. 102.

Nos. 101c, 102c, 104d and 105b are from position 10.

Nos. 101d, 102e and 104b are from position 1.

No. 108b is from position 9.

(Surch by *Samoanische Zeitung*, Apia)

1914 (3 Sept). German Colonial issue (ship) (no wmk) inscr "SAMOA" surch as T **13** or **14** (mark values).

101		½d. on 3pf. brown	60·00	16·00
		a. Surch double	£750	£600
		b. No fraction bar	90·00	42·00
		c. Comma after "I"	£700	£425
		d. "1" to left of "2" in "½"	85·00	40·00
102		½d. on 5pf. green	65·00	21·00
		a. No fraction bar	£140	60·00
		c. Comma after "I"	£425	£180
		d. Surch double	£750	£600
		e. "1" to left of "2" in "½"	£110	45·00
103		1d. on 10pf. carmine	£100	40·00
		a. Surch double	£800	£650
104		2½d. on 20pf. ultramarine	60·00	14·00
		a. No fraction bar	95·00	42·00
		b. "1" to left of "2" in "½"	90·00	42·00
		c. Surch inverted	£1100	£1000
		d. Comma after "I"	£350	£350
		e. Surch double	£750	£650
105		3d. on 25pf. black and red/*yellow*	80·00	40·00
		a. Surch double	£1100	£800
		b. Comma after "I"	£5000	£1100
106		4d. on 30pf. black and orange/*buff*	£130	60·00
107		5d. on 40pf. black and carmine	£130	70·00
108		6d. on 50pf. black and purple/*buff*	65·00	35·00
		a. Surch double	£1100	£1000
		b. Inverted "9" for "6"	£180	£100
109		9d. on 80pf. black and carmine/*rose*	£200	£100
110		"1 shillings" on 1m. carmine	£3250	£3500
111		"1 shilling" on 1m. carmine	£11000	£7000
112		2s. on 2m. blue	£3500	£3000
113		3s. on 3m. violet-black	£1400	£1200
		a. Surch double	£10000	£11000
114		5s. on 5m. carmine and black	£1200	£1000
		a. Surch double	£13000	£14000

No. 108b is distinguishable from 108, as the "d" and the "9" are not in a line, and the upper loop of the "9" turns downwards to the left.

UNAUTHORISED SURCHARGES. Examples of the 2d. on 20pf., 3d. on 30pf., 3d. on 40pf., 4d. on 40pf., 6d. on 80pf., 2s. on 3m. and 2s. on Marshall Islands 2m., together with a number of errors not listed above, were produced by the printer on stamps supplied by local collectors. These were not authorised by the New Zealand Military Administration.

SAMOA.

(**15**)

1914 (29 Sept)–**15**. Stamps of New Zealand. T **53**, **51**, **52** and **27**, optd as T **15**, but opt only 14 mm long on all except 2½d. Wmk "N Z" and Star, W **43** of New Zealand.

115		½d. yellow-green (R.) (P 14×15)	1·75	30
116		1d. carmine (B.) (P 14×15)	1·25	10
117		2d. mauve (R.) (P 14×14½) (10.14)	1·25	1·00
118		2½d. deep blue (R.) (P 14×15) (10.14)	1·75	1·75
		w. Wmk inverted		

119	6d. carmine (B.) (P 14×14½) (10.14)................	2·00	1·75
	a. Perf 14×13½	17·00	23·00
	b. Vert pair. Nos. 119/a (1915)	55·00	£100
120	6d. pale carmine (B.) (P 14×14½) (10.14)......	11·00	10·00
121	1s. vermilion (B.) (P 14×14½) (10.14)............	13·00	23·00
115/21 *Set of 6*................		19·00	25·00

1914–24. Postal Fiscal stamps as Type F **4** of New Zealand optd with T **15**. W **43** of New Zealand (sideways). Chalk-surfaced "De La Rue" paper.

(a) P 14 (Nov 1914–17)

122	2s. blue (R.) (9.17)	£100	£100
123	2s.6d. grey-brown (B.) (9.17)	5·50	17·00
124	5s. yellow-green (R.)	24·00	11·00
125	10s. maroon (B.)	40·00	28·00
126	£1 rose-carmine (B.)	90·00	45·00

(b) P 14½×14, comb (1917–24)

127	2s. deep blue (B.) (3.18)	8·50	5·50
128	2s.6d. grey-brown (B.) (10.24)	£425	£170
129	3s. purple (R.) (6.23)	16·00	65·00
130	5s. yellow-green (R.) (9.17)	27·00	16·00
131	10s. maroon (B.) (11.17)	85·00	48·00
132	£1 rose-carmine (B.) (3.18)	£110	70·00

We no longer list the £2 value as it is doubtful this was used for postal purposes.

See also Nos. 165/6e.

1916–19. King George V stamps of New Zealand optd as T **15**, but 14 mm long.

(a) Typo. P 14×15

134	**61**	½d. yellow-green (R.)	1·25	1·25
135		1½d. slate (R.) (1917)	50	25
136		1½d. orange-brown (R.) (1919)	30	50
137		2d. yellow (R.) (14.2.18)	2·00	25
138		3d. chocolate (B.) (1919)	4·00	22·00

(b) Recess. P 14×13½

139	**60**	2½d. blue (R.)	2·25	50
		a. Perf 14×14½	1·25	60
		b. Vert pair. Nos. 139/a	17·00	27·00
140		3d. chocolate (B.) (1917)	65	1·50
		a. Perf 14×14½	65	1·00
		b. Vert pair. Nos. 140/a	17·00	30·00
141		6d. carmine (B.) (5.5.17)	4·00	3·25
		a. Perf 14×14½	1·50	1·50
		b. Vert pair. Nos. 141/a	19·00	40·00
142		1s. vermilion (B.)	6·00	1·50
		a. Perf 14×14½	6·00	9·00
		b. Vert pair. Nos. 142/a	29·00	55·00
134/42 *Set of 9*................			16·00	26·00

LEAGUE OF NATIONS MANDATE

Administered by New Zealand.

1920 (July). Victory. Nos. 453/8 of New Zealand optd as T **15**, but 14 mm long.

143	½d. green (R.)	6·50	17·00
144	1d. carmine (B.)	3·25	22·00
145	1½d. brown-orange (R.)	2·00	12·00
146	3d. chocolate (B.)	8·00	11·00
147	6d. violet (R.)	4·50	7·50
148	1s. orange-red (B.)	13·00	11·00
143/8 *Set of 6*................		32·00	70·00

16 Native Hut

SILVER JUBILEE
OF
KING GEORGE V
1910 - 1935.
(17)

(Eng B.W. Recess-printed at Wellington, NZ)

1921 (23 Dec). W **43** of New Zealand.

(a) P 14×14½

149	**16**	½d. green	6·50	16·00
150		1d. lake	11·00	2·00
151		1½d. chestnut	1·75	22·00
152		2d. yellow	3·00	3·25
149/52 *Set of 4*................			20·00	40·00

(b) P 14×13½

153	**16**	½d. green	4·75	1·75
154		1d. lake	7·00	20
155		1½d. chestnut	22·00	14·00
156		2d. yellow	14·00	80
157		2½d. grey-blue	1·75	10·00
158		3d. sepia	1·75	6·50
159		4d. violet	1·75	3·75
160		5d. light blue	1·75	9·50
161		6d. bright carmine	1·75	8·50
162		8d. red-brown	1·75	16·00
163		9d. olive-green	2·00	30·00
164		1s. vermilion	1·75	24·00
153/64 *Set of 12*................			55·00	£110

1925–28. Postal Fiscal stamps as Type F **4** of New Zealand optd with T **15**. W **43** of New Zealand (sideways). P 14½×14.

(a) Thick, opaque, white chalk-surfaced "Cowan" paper

165	2s. blue (B.) (12.25)	£200	£225
166	2s.6d. deep grey-brown (B.) (10.28)	55·00	£110
166a	3s. mauve (R.) (9.25)	70·00	£120
166b	5s. yellow-green (R.) (11.26)	40·00	55·00
	ba. Opt at top of stamp	£2000	£2250
166c	10s. brown-red (B.) (12.25)	£200	£150
166d	£1 rose-pink (B.) (11.26)	£110	£120
165/6d *Set of 6*................		£600	£700

(b) Thin, hard, chalk-surfaced "Wiggins Teape" paper

166e	£1 rose-pink (B.) (1928)	£2750	£1200

1926–27. T **72** of New Zealand, optd with T **15**, in red.

(a) "Jones" paper

167	2s. deep blue (11.26)	5·00	18·00
	w. Wmk inverted	—	27·00
168	3s. mauve (10.26)	27·00	50·00
	w. Wmk inverted	32·00	55·00

(b) "Cowan" paper.

169	2s. light blue (10.11.27)	6·00	45·00
170	2s. pale mauve (10.11.27)	60·00	£110

1932 (Aug). Postal Fiscal stamps as Type F **6** of New Zealand optd with T **15**. W **43** of New Zealand. Thick, opaque white chalk-surfaced "Cowan" paper. P 14.

171	2s.6d. deep brown (B.)	16·00	50·00
172	5s. green (R.)	26·00	55·00
173	10s. carmine-lake (B.)	50·00	£100
174	£1 pink (B.)	75·00	£150
175	£2 bright purple (R.)	£1000	
176	£5 indigo-blue (R.)	£2500	

The £2 and £5 values were primarily for fiscal use.

1935 (7 May). Silver Jubilee. Optd with T **17**. P 14×13½.

177	**16**	1d. lake	30	30
		a. Perf 14×14½	95·00	£170
178		2½d. grey-blue	60	65
179		6d. bright carmine	2·75	5·75
177/9 *Set of 3*................			3·25	6·00

18 Samoan Girl

19 Apia

20 River scene

21 Chief and Wife

22 Canoe and house

23 R. L. Stevenson's home "Vailima"

24 Stevenson's tomb

25 Lake Lanuto'o

26 Falefa Falls

(Recess D.L.R.)

1935 (7 Aug). T **18/26**. W **43** of New Zealand ("N Z" and Star). P 14×13½ (½d., 2½d., 2s., 3s.), 14 (2d.) or 13½×14 (others).

180	½d. green	10	35
	w. Wmk inverted		
181	1d. black and carmine	10	10
	w. Wmk inverted	£100	
182	2d. black and orange	3·50	4·75
	aw. Wmk inverted		
	b. Perf 13½×14	4·00	4·25
	bw. Wmk inverted		
183	2½d. black and blue	10	10
184	4d. slate and sepia	70	15
185	6d. bright magenta	50	10
186	1s. violet and brown	30	10
187	2s. green and purple-brown	1·00	50
188	3s. blue and brown-orange	3·50	3·50
180/8	Set of 9	8·50	8·00

See also Nos. 200/3.

WESTERN SAMOA.
(27)

1935–42. Postal Fiscal stamps as Type F **6** of New Zealand optd with T **27**. W **43** of New Zealand. P 14.

(a) Thick, opaque chalk-surfaced "Cowan" paper (7.8.35)

189	2s.6d. deep brown (B.)	6·00	16·00
190	5s. green (B.)	26·00	38·00
191	10s. carmine-lake (B.)	70·00	85·00
192	£1 pink (B.)	60·00	£110
193	£2 bright purple (R.)	£160	£400
194	£5 indigo-blue (R.)	£225	£475

(b) Thin, hard chalk-surfaced "Wiggins Teape" paper (1941–42)

194a	5s. green (B.) (6.42)	£180	£225
194b	10s. pale carmine-lake (B.) (6.41)	£150	£200
194c	£2 bright purple (R.) (2.42)	£550	£1000
194d	£5 indigo-blue (R.) (2.42)	£3000	£3750

The £2 and £5 values were primarily for fiscal use. A £10 deep blue (on "Cowan" paper) was also issued, and exists with postal cancellations. See also Nos. 207/14.

28 Coastal Scene

29 Map of Western Samoa

30 Samoan dancing party

31 Robert Louis Stevenson

(Des J. Berry (1d. and 1½d.). L. C. Mitchell (2½d. and 7d.). Recess B.W.)

1939 (29 Aug). 25th Anniversary of New Zealand Control. T **28/31**. W **98** of New Zealand. P 13½×14 or 14×13½ (7d.).

195	**28**	1d. olive-green and scarlet	1·00	25
196	**29**	1½d. light blue and red-brown	1·75	75
197	**30**	2½d. red-brown and blue	3·00	1·00
198	**31**	7d. violet and slate-green	8·00	4·00
195/8		Set of 4	12·00	5·50

32 Samoan Chief

33 Apia Post Office

(Recess B.W.)

1940 (2 Sept). W **98** of New Zealand (Mult "N Z" and Star). P 14×13½.

199	**32**	3d. on 1½d. brown	75	20

T **32** was not issued without surcharge but archival examples exist (*Price*, £250 unused).

(T **33**. Des L. C. Mitchell. Recess B.W.)

1944–49. As Nos. 180, 182/3 and T **33**. W **98** of New Zealand (Mult "N Z" and Star) (sideways on 2½d.). P 14 or 13½×14 (5d.)

200	½d. green	30	21·00
202	2d. black and orange	3·50	7·50
203	2½d. black and blue (1948)	8·50	45·00
205	5d. sepia and blue (8.6.49)	2·75	1·00
200/5	Set of 4	13·50	65·00

1945–53. Postal Fiscal stamps as Type F **6** of New Zealand optd with T **27**. W **98** of New Zealand. Thin hard, chalk-surfaced "Wiggins Teape" paper. P 14.

207	2s.6d. deep brown (B.) (6.45)	20·00	35·00
	w. Wmk inverted	35·00	50·00
208	5s. green (B.) (5.45)	21·00	13·00
	w. Wmk inverted	35·00	45·00
209	10s. carmine-lake (B.) (4.46)	20·00	15·00
	w. Wmk inverted	60·00	60·00
210	£1 pink (B.) (6.48)	£140	£200
211	30s. brown (8.48)	£200	£300
212	£2 bright purple (R.) (11.47)	£200	£275
	w. Wmk inverted	£600	£750
213	£3 green (8.48)	£300	£375
214	£5 indigo-blue (R) (1946)	£425	£500
	w. Wmk inverted (5.53)	£425	£500
207/10	Set of 4	£180	£225

Values over £1 were mainly used for fiscal purposes.

WESTERN SAMOA
(34)

1946 (4 June). Peace Issue. Nos. 668, 670 and 674/5 of New Zealand optd with T **34** (reading up and down at sides on 2d.).

215	1d. green	40	15
	w. Wmk inverted	£180	
216	2d. purple (B.)	40	15
217	6d. chocolate and vermilion	80	15
218	8d. black and carmine (B.)	40	15
215/18	Set of 4	1·75	55

UNITED NATIONS TRUST TERRITORY

Administered by New Zealand.

35 Making Siapo Cloth

36 Native Houses and flags

37 Seal of Samoa

38 Malifa Falls (wrongly inscribed "Aleisa Falls")

39 Tooth-billed Pigeon

40 Bonito fishing canoe

41 Cacao harvesting

42 Thatching a Native Hut

43 Preparing Copra

44 Samoan Chieftainess

1952 (10 Mar.). T **35/44**. W **98** of New Zealand (sideways on 1s. and 3s.). P 13 (½d., 2d. and 1s.) or 13½ (others).

219	**35**	½d. claret and orange-brown	10	2·25
220	**36**	1d. olive-green and green	30	50
221	**37**	2d. carmine-red	30	10
222	**38**	3d. pale ultramarine and indigo	50	20
223	**39**	5d. brown and deep green	10·00	1·50
224	**40**	6d. pale ultramarine and rose-magenta	1·00	10
225	**41**	8d. carmine	30	30
226	**42**	1s. sepia and blue	20	10
227	**43**	2s. yellow-brown	1·00	25
228	**44**	3s. chocolate and brown-olive	3·25	2·75
219/28 *Set of 10*			15·00	7·00

1953 (25 May). Coronation. Designs as Nos. 715 and 717 of New Zealand, but inscr "WESTERN SAMOA".

229		2d. brown	1·25	15
230		6d. slate-grey	1·25	35

WESTERN

SAMOA
(45)

1955 (14 Nov). Postal Fiscal stamps as Type F **6** of New Zealand optd with T **45**. W **98** (inverted). Chalk-surfaced "Wiggins, Teape" paper. P 14.

232		5s. green (B.)	8·00	28·00
233		10s. carmine-lake (B.)	8·00	50·00
234		£1 pink (B.)	15·00	60·00
235		£2 bright purple (R.)	70·00	£160
232/5 *Set of 4*			90·00	£275

The £2 value was mainly used for fiscal purposes.

46 Native Houses and Flags

47 Seal of Samoa

48 Map of Samoa and the Mace

(Recess B.W.)

1958 (21 Mar.). Inauguration of Samoan Parliament. T **46/8**. W **98** of New Zealand (sideways). P 13½x13 (6d.) or 13½ (others).

236	**46**	4d. cerise	35	30
237	**47**	6d. deep reddish violet	35	30
238	**48**	1s. deep ultramarine	85	50
236/8 *Set of 3*			1·40	1·00

NEW ZEALAND USED ABROAD
GILBERT AND ELLICE ISLANDS

No organised postal service existed in the Gilbert and Ellice Islands before the introduction of stamp issues in January 1911. A New Zealand Postal Agency was, however, provided on Fanning Island, one of the Line Islands, primarily for the use of the staff of the Pacific Cable Board cable station which was established in 1902. The agency opened on 29 November 1902 and although Fanning Island became part of the Gilbert and Ellice Islands colony on 27 January 1916, continued to operate until replaced by a Protectorate post office on 14 February 1939. The cable station closed on 16 January 1964. Fanning Island is now known as Tabuaeran.

Z 1

The following NEW ZEALAND stamps are known postmarked on Fanning Island with Type Z **1** (in use from November 1902 until November 1936. The earliest known cover is postmarked 20 December 1902).

1882–1900 Q.V. (P 10) ½d. (*No.* 217) (P 11) ½d., 1d., 2d. (*Nos.* 236/8)
1898 Pictorials (*no wmk*) 1d., 2d., 2½d. (*Nos.* 247/8, 260)
1900 Pictorials (*W* **38**) ½d. 1½d., 2d. (*Nos.* 273, 275*b*, 276)
1901 1d. "Universal" (*W* **38**) (*Nos.* 278, 280)
1902 ½d. Mt. Cook, 1d. "Universal" (*no wmk*) (*Nos.* 294/5)
1902 ½d. Pictorial, 1d. "Universal" (*W* **43**) (*Nos.* 302*b*, 303)
1902–09 Pictorials (*W* **43**) 2d., 2½d., 3d., 5d., 6d., 8d., 9d., 1s., 2s., 5s. (*Nos.* 309, 312/7, 319/20, 322, 326, 328/9)
1907–08 Pictorials (*W* **43**) 4d. (*No.* 379)
1908 1d. "Universal" (*De La Rue paper*) 1d. (*No.* 386)
1909–12 King Edward VII (*typo*) ½d. (*No.* 387)
1909–16 King Edward VII (*recess*) 2d., 3d., 4d., 5d., 6d., 8d., 1s. (*Nos.* 388/91, 393/6, 397/8)
1909–26 1d. "Universal" (*W* **43**) 1d. (*Nos.* 405, 410)
1915–30 King George V (*recess*) 1½d., 2d. bright violet, 2½d., 3d., 4d. bright violet, 4½d., 5d., 6d., 7½d., 9d., 1s. (*Nos.* 416/17, 419/20, 422/6, 429/30)
1915–34 King George V (*typo*) ½d., 1½d. (all 3), 2d., 3d. (*Nos.* 435/40, 446, 448/b, 449/b)
1915 "WAR STAMP" opt ½d. (*No.* 452)
1920 Victory 1d., 1½d. (*Nos.* 454/5)
1922 2d. on ½d. (*No.* 459)
1923–25 Penny Postage 1d. (*No.* 460)
1926–34 Admiral design 1d. (*No.* 468)
1935–36 Pictorials ½d., 1d., 1½d., 2d., 4d., 8d., 1s. (*Nos.* 556, 557/b, 558, 559, 562, 565, 567)
1935 Silver Jubilee ½d., 1d., 6d. (*Nos.* 573/5)
1936 Anzac ½d.+½d., 1d.+1d. (*Nos.* 591/2)

Z 2

The following NEW ZEALAND stamps are known postmarked on Fanning Island with Type Z **2** (in use from 7 December 1936 to 13 February 1939):

1935–36 Pictorials (*W* **43**) 1d (*No.* 557)
1936–39 Pictorials (*W* **98**) ½d., 1d., 1½d. (*Nos.* 577/9)
1936 Chambers of Commerce Congress ½d. (*No.* 593)
1936 Health 1d.+1d. (*No.* 598)
1937 Coronation 1d., 2½d., 6d. (*Nos.* 599/601)
1938–39 King George VI ½d., 1d., 1½d. (*Nos.* 603, 605, 607)

The schooner which carried the mail from Fanning Island also called at Washington Island, another of the Line group. Problems arose, however, as the authorities insisted that mail from Washington must first pass through the Fanning Island Postal Agency before being forwarded which resulted in considerable delays. Matters were resolved by the opening of a New Zealand Postal Agency on Washington Island which operated from 1 February 1921 until the copra plantations were closed in early 1923.

The postal agency was re-established on 15 May 1924, but finally closed on 30 March 1934. Covers from this second period occur with incorrectly dated postmarks. Manuscript markings on New Zealand Nos. 578, 599/600 and 692 are unofficial and were applied during the resettlement of the island between 1937 and 1948. Washington Island is now known as Teraina.

Z 3

The following NEW ZEALAND stamps are known postmarked on Washington Island with Type Z **3**:

1909–16 King Edward VII 5d., 8d. (*Nos.* 402, 404*b*)
1915–30 King George V (*recess*) 6d., 7½d., 8d., 9d., 1s. (*Nos.* 425/7, 429/30)
1915–34 King George V (*typo*) ½d., 1½d., 2d., 3d. (*Nos.* 435, 438/9, 449)
1915 "WAR STAMP" opt ½d. (*No.* 452)
1920 Victory 1d., 1½d., 6d. (*Nos.* 454/5, 457)
1922 2d. on ½d. (*No.* 459)
1926–34 Admiral design 1d. (*No.* 468/*a*)

The above information is based on a special survey undertaken by members of the Kiribati & Tuvalu Philatelic Society and the Pacific Islands Study Circle, co-ordinated by Mr. Michael Shaw.

PITCAIRN ISLANDS

In 1920 a regular mail service was introduced. As there were no stamps available, letters were allowed free postage as long as they carried a cachet, or manuscript endorsement, indicating their origin.

The New Zealand Government withdrew the free postage concession on 12 May 1926, but after representations from the islanders, opened a postal agency on Pitcairn using New Zealand stamps cancelled with Type Z **1**. Some impressions of this postmark appear to show a double ring, but this is the result of heavy or uneven use of the handstamp. The postal agency operated from 7 June 1927 until 14 October 1940.

The Earlier New Zealand stamps are known cancelled with Type Z **1**, but these were not supplied to the postal agency and their use is considered to be contrived.

PRICES. Those quoted for Nos. Z1/72 and ZF1 are for examples showing a virtually complete strike of Type Z **1**. Due to the size of the cancellation such examples will usually be *on piece*

Z 1

Stamps of New Zealand cancelled with Type Z **1**.

1915–29. King George V (Nos. 419, 422/6, 428/31 and 446/9).

Z1	½d. green	30·00
Z2	1½d. grey-slate	65·00
Z3	1½d. orange-brown	50·00
Z4	2d. yellow	48·00
Z5	2½d. blue	85·00
Z6	3d. chocolate	90·00
Z7	4d. bright violet	85·00
Z8	4½d. deep green	£120
Z9	5d. light blue	90·00
Z10	6d. carmine	£100
Z11	7½d. red-brown	£130
Z12	8d. red-brown	£170
Z13	9d. yellowish olive	£170
Z14	1s. vermilion	£160

1923. Map of New Zealand (No. 460).

Z14*a*	1d. carmine	£100

1925. Dunedin Exhibition (No. 464).

Z14*b*	½d. yellow-green/*green*	£150
Z14*c*	1d. carmine/*rose*	£120

1926–27. King George V in Field-Marshal's or Admiral's uniform (Nos. 468/9).

Z15	1d. rose-carmine	30·00
Z16	2s. light blue	£350

1929. Anti-Tuberculosis Fund (No. 544).

Z17	1d. +1d. scarlet	£160

1931. Air (Nos. 548/9).

Z18	3d. chocolate	£300
Z19	4d. blackish purple	£350

1932. Health (No. 552).

Z21	1d. +1d. carmine	£170

1935. Pictorials (Nos. 556/8 and 560/9). W **43**.

Z22	½d. bright green	65·00
Z23	1d. scarlet	40·00
Z24	1½d. red-brown	£100
Z26	2½d. chocolate and slate	85·00
Z27	3d. brown	£100
Z28	4d. black and sepia	£130
Z29	5d. ultramarine	£150
Z30	6d. scarlet	£130
Z31	8d. chocolate	£150
Z32	9d. scarlet and black	£150
Z33	1s. deep green	£130
Z34	2s. olive-green	£350
Z35	3s. chocolate and yellow-brown	£400

1935. Silver Jubilee (Nos. 573/5).

Z36	½d. green	50·00
Z37	1d. carmine	50·00
Z38	6d. red-orange	£100

1935. Health (No. 576).

Z39	1d. +1d. scarlet	75·00

1936. Pictorials (Nos. 577/82). W **98**.

Z40	½d. bright green	50·00
Z41	1d. scarlet	17·00
Z42	1½d. red-brown	85·00
Z43	2d. orange	70·00
Z44	2½d. chocolate and slate	75·00
Z45	3d. brown	80·00

1936. 21st Anniversary of "Anzac" Landing at Gallipoli (Nos. 591/2).

Z46	½d. +½d. green	50·00
Z47	1d. +1d. scarlet	50·00

1936. Congress of British Empire Chambers of Commerce (Nos. 593/7).

Z48	½d. emerald-green	48·00
Z49	1d. scarlet	48·00
Z50	2½d. blue	65·00
Z51	4d. violet	95·00
Z52	6d. red-brown	95·00

1936. Health (No. 598).

Z53	1d. +1d. scarlet	75·00

1937. Coronation (Nos. 599/601).

Z54	1d. carmine	40·00
Z55	2½d. Prussian blue	45·00
Z56	6d. red-orange	45·00

1937. Health (No. 602).

Z57	1d. +1d. scarlet	75·00

1938. King George VI (Nos. 603, 605, 607).

Z58	½d. green	75·00
Z59	1d. scarlet	75·00
Z60	1½d. purple-brown	85·00

1939. Health (Nos. 611/12).

Z60a	1d. on ½d.+½d. green	75·00
Z60b	2d. on 1d.+1d. scarlet	75·00

1940. Centenary of British Sovereignty (Nos. 613/22, 624/5).

Z61	½d. blue-green	38·00
Z62	1d. chocolate and scarlet	42·00
Z63	1½d. light blue and mauve	50·00
Z64	2d. blue-green and chocolate	45·00
Z65	2½d. blue-green and blue	50·00
Z66	3d. purple and carmine	50·00
Z67	4d. chocolate and lake	85·00
Z68	5d. pale blue and brown	95·00
Z69	6d. emerald-green and violet	95·00
Z70	7d. black and red	£130
Z71	9d. olive-green and orange	£130
Z72	1s. sage-green and deep green	£130

POSTAL FISCAL STAMPS

1932. Arms (No. F147).

ZF1	2s.6d. deep brown	£400

Est 1856

STANLEY GIBBONS

BY APPOINTMENT TO
HER MAJESTY THE QUEEN
PHILATELISTS
STANLEY GIBBONS LTD
LONDON

The Home of Stamp Collecting since 185

1856   1896   1936   1976   2

Visit 399 Strand:

- Get advice from our experienced and knowledgeable staff
- See first hand our superb range of top quality stamps, albums and accessories
- Get insider tips on how to enhance and expand your collection
- Ask for guidance on techniques for care and storage of your stamps and covers
- View our specialist material
- All Stanley Gibbons stamps come with a lifetime guarantee of authenticity from our stamp specialist

Everything for the stamp collector.

399 Strand opening hours

• Mon-Fri 9am-5.30pm   • Sat 9:30am-5.30pm   • Sun Closed

Est 1856

STANLEY GIBBONS

Stanley Gibbons Limit
399 Strand, London, WC2R (
+44 (0)20 7557 44
www.stanleygibbons.c

STANLEY GIBBONS

Dear Catalogue User,

As a collector and Stanley Gibbons catalogue user for many years myself, I am only too aware of the need to provide you with the information you seek in an accurate, timely and easily accessible manner. Naturally, I have my own views on where changes could be made, but one thing I learned long ago is that we all have different opinions and requirements.

I would therefore be most grateful if you would complete the form overleaf and return it to me. Please contact Lorraine Holcombe (lholcombe@stanleygibbons.com) if you would like to be emailed the questionnaire.

Very many thanks for your help.

Yours sincerely,

Hugh Jefferies,
Editor.

Hugh Jefferies (Catalogue Editor)
Catalogue Questionnaire Responses
Stanley Gibbons Limited
7 Parkside, Ringwood
Hampshire BH24 3SH
United Kingdom

Questionnaire

2016 New Zealand & Dependencies

1. Level of detail

   Do you feel that the level of detail in this catalogue is:
   a. too specialised   O
   b. about right   O
   c. inadequate   O

2. Frequency of issue

   How often would you purchase a new edition of this catalogue?
   a. Annually   O
   b. Every two years   O
   c. Every three to five years   O
   d. Less frequently   O

3. Design and Quality

   How would you describe the layout and appearance of this catalogue?
   a. Excellent   O
   b. Good   O
   c. Adequate   O
   d. Poor   O

4. How important to you are the prices given in the catalogue:
   a. Important   O
   b. Quite important   O
   c. Of little interest   O
   d. Of no interest   O

5. Would you be interested in an online version of this catalogue?
   a. Yes   O
   b. No   O

6. Do you like the new format?
   a. Yes   O
   b. No   O

7. What changes would you suggest to improve the catalogue? E.g. Which other indices would you like to see included?

   ....
   ....
   ....
   ....

8. Which other Stanley Gibbons Catalogues do you buy?

   ....
   ....
   ....
   ....

9. Would you like us to let you know when the next edition of this catalogue is due to be published?
   a. Yes   O
   b. No   O

   If so please give your contact details below.

   Name: ....
   Address:..
   ....
   ....
   ....

   Email: ....
   Telephone:..

10. Which other Stanley Gibbons Catalogues are you interested in?
    a. ....
    b. ....
    c. ....

Many thanks for your comments.

Please complete and return it to: Hugh Jefferies (Catalogue Editor)
Stanley Gibbons Limited, 7 Parkside, Ringwood, Hampshire BH24 3SH, United Kingdom
or email: lholcombe@stanleygibbons.com to request a soft copy